ANATOMY AND PHYSIOLOGY OF FARM ANIMALS

ANATOMY AND PHYSIOLOGY OF FARM ANIMALS

R. D. Frandson, B.S., D.V.M., M.S.

Professor, Department of Anatomy,
College of Veterinary Medicine,
Colorado State University,
Fort Collins, Colorado

with contributions in physiology by

Elmer H. Whitten, B.S., M.Ed., Ph.D.

Professor and Head,
Department of Physiology,
and Associate Dean
for Academic Affairs,
University of Health Sciences,
Kansas City, Missouri

Third Edition

Lea & Febiger

Philadelphia

Library of Congress Cataloging in Publication Data

Frandson, R   D
   Anatomy and physiology of farm animals.

   Bibliography: p.
   Includes index.
   1. Veterinary anatomy.   2. Veterinary physiology.
I. Whitten, Elmer H.   II. Title.   [DNLM: 1. Anatomy.
Veterinary.   2. Animals, Domestic—Physiology.   SF 761 F826a]
SF761.F8   1980   636.089′2   80-25775
ISBN 0-8121-0759-4

First Edition, 1965
Reprinted, 1966, 1968, 1969, 1970, 1972

Second Edition, 1974
Reprinted, 1975, 1976, 1978, 1979

Published in Great Britain by Bailliere Tindall, London

PRINTED IN THE UNITED STATES OF AMERICA

Print Number: 6   5   4   3   2

To Z., R., S., and M.

Preface

This book was written originally as a text for students majoring in the animal sciences, 4H club members, and vocational agriculture students. Accuracy combined with simplicity and clarity of expression was my chief objective.

Since the first edition also found considerable acceptance among veterinary students and veterinary practitioners, I have attempted to make the third edition of more value to them without sacrificing the simplicity and clarity desirable in an undergraduate text. In order to conform to the terminology being used in current veterinary anatomy texts, I have used anglicized technical terms based on the Nomina Anatomica Veterinaria 1973 wherever practicable. The synonymous terminology from older texts is used parenthetically when each term is first used and both terms are included in the index.

As in the first two editions, general principles of anatomy and physiology are discussed as they apply to all animals. Important species differences are described with the most attention given to the horse and the cow. The sheep, goat, hog, and in some instances the dog are described where important differences from the horse or cow exist. When the goat is not mentioned specifically, it may be assumed that the goat is similar to the sheep. Technical terms are used throughout the book, but most terms not found in an ordinary college dictionary are defined within the text.

Where controversial subjects are treated, the generally accepted view is given in greatest detail; however, important differences from this view are also mentioned or discussed. Rather than subject the reader to an extensive discussion of divergent opinions, I have assumed responsibility for presenting what I consider to be the most logical explanation of subjects still open to question. A list of references is included for those students who wish to pursue these subjects further.

Because abbreviations may be confusing and difficult to remember, a glossary of commonly used abbreviations is included in the appendix.

Fort Collins, Colorado   *R. D. Frandson*

Acknowledgments

Acknowledgment of all sources of information and assistance in preparation of this book and its revision obviously is impossible. However, I would like to thank specifically the following colleagues and friends for their many and varied contributions.

Dr. Y. Z. Abdelbaki, Dr. T. H. Belling Jr., Miss Elsie Bergland, Mr. J. M. Bradley, Dr. H. E. Bredeck, Dr. R. W. Davis, Dr. G. P. Epling, Mr. John Foss, Dr. R. A. Kainer, Dr. Neil May, Dr. D. Will, Mr. C. Mac Leod, Mr. K. Nakamoto and Dr. H. Meyer.

Artists: Mrs. D. Dietemann, Mr. D. Giddings, Miss M. Haff, Miss R. Haff, Mrs. D. Jeffry, Mrs. W. Musslewhite, Mrs. S. Nuss, and Mrs. B. Sparks.

The many publishers who loaned illustrations and tables.

SPECIAL ACKNOWLEDGMENT

I am deeply indebted to Dr. Elmer H. Whitten for the extensive revision of all of the Physiology and Biochemistry content which represents such a large part of my book. Many entire areas have been rewritten by him, as well as hundreds of changes incorporated into the timely updating of information from the more recent literature.

Dr. Whitten received the B.S. degree with honors from a pre-medical program of study at Northeastern University, Boston, Massachusetts, where he was also elected to the scholastic honor society, THE ACADEMY, and assisted in the Department of Pharmacology at Harvard Medical School.

He received the M.Ed. degree, with emphasis in the biological sciences, from the Massachusetts State College at Bridgewater. His Ph.D. in Physiology was obtained from Colorado State University under a Graduate Research Assistantship award and a Predoctoral PHS Trainee Fellowship award in the Department of Physiology and Biophysics. He was elected to the Honor Society of Phi Kappa Phi at CSU where he also taught human physiology and assisted in experimental physiology. His research has been in the area of neonatal enteritis, published in the American Journal of Digestive Diseases, and includes an oxygenation-perfusion method for *in vitro* transport studies.

He was selected to appear in the 1972 edition of Outstanding Educators of America and in American Men and Women in Science. He is also a member of The Society of the Sigma Xi, of the American Association for the Advancement of Science, and of the New York Academy of Sciences.

Currently Dr. Whitten is Associate Dean for Academic Affairs at the University of Health Sciences, Kansas City, Missouri, where he is also Professor and Chairman of the Department of Physiology.

Contents

Chapter 1

Introduction to Anatomy and Physiology

Descriptive Terms Useful in the Study of Anatomy
Microscopic Anatomy—Animal Cells and Tissues

The General Plan of the Animal Body
Glands

The term *anatomy* has come to refer to that science which deals with the form and structure of all organisms. Literally the word means "to cut apart," and was used by early anatomists when speaking of a complete dissection of a cadaver.

In contrast to anatomy, which deals primarily with structure, *physiology* is the study of the integrated functions of the body, and the functions of all of its parts (systems, organs, tissues, cells, and cell components), including the biophysical and biochemical processes involved.

When detailed anatomy courses and detailed physiology courses are taught separately, the approach to the laboratory portion of each course is considerably different. Study in a typical *gross anatomy* laboratory is based primarily on dissection of animals. These animals usually have been preserved by embalming, and one or more parts of the vascular system have been injected with a colored material to facilitate identification of the vessels. Careful dissection coupled with close observation gives the student a concept of the shape, texture, location, and relations of those structures visible to the unaided eye that can be gained in no other way. The use of the microscope with properly prepared tissue sections on slides is equally essential for an understanding of structures that are so small they cannot be seen without optical assistance.

In the physiology laboratory the student performs experiments usually with living animals, which have been anesthetized to eliminate discomfort, to gain a better understanding of normal function of the body and the effects of changes in environment (both internal and external) on the normal animal. This includes, for example, the use of drugs, changes in temperature or altitude, surgical modifications (such as the creation of hypertension by arterial constriction), and the monitoring of changes (such as blood pressure, heart rate, breathing, electrical changes in the heart, muscle contractions, and nerve impulse velocities) with the use of electronic equipment.

The anatomists and physiologists working in research use some of the same techniques that are used in the teaching laboratory, but with considerable refinement. Both types of scientists utilize equipment and methods

1

developed in the physical sciences, particularly chemistry and physics. The anatomist applies the principles of physics to the different microscopes he uses, and applies a knowledge of chemistry in the staining of various parts of cells and tissues. The combination of chemistry and microscopic anatomy is known as *histochemistry*.

The physiologist uses many chemicals for altering the environment of the experimental animal and adapts much electronic equipment from physics and electrical engineering for monitoring responses of the animal or some part of the animal to the experimental treatment.

Although both disciplines, anatomy and physiology, commonly are pursued more or less independently, they are both facets of the total study of the animal body. A thorough knowledge of structure imparts much information about its function. However, a mere description of structure without describing function would be of little practical value. Conversely, it is impossible to gain a thorough understanding of function without a basic knowledge of the structures involved.

The science of anatomy has become so extensive that it is now divided into many specialized branches. In fact, Dorland's *Medical Dictionary* defines 30 subdivisions of anatomy. We are chiefly interested in *gross (macroscopic) anatomy*. This is the study of the form and relations (relative positions) of the structures of the body that can be seen with the unaided eye.

Comparative anatomy is a study of the structures of various species of animals, with particular emphasis on those characteristics that aid in classification.

Embryology is the study of developmental anatomy, covering the period from conception (fertilization of the egg within the female) to birth.

Another large branch of anatomy consists of the study of those tissues and cells that can be seen only with the aid of a microscope. This is known as *microscopic anatomy* and is sometimes called *histology*.

The most recent development in the study of anatomy is *ultrastructural cytology*, which deals with portions of cells and tissues as they are visualized with the aid of the electron microscope. The term "fine structure" is used frequently in reference to structures seen in electron micrographs (photographs made with the electron microscope).

Our approach to the study of anatomy will be chiefly by systems. This method of study is referred to as *systematic anatomy*. To name the study, the suffix "ology," which means "branch of knowledge or science," is added to the root word referring to the system. Table 1–1 indicates the commonly accepted systems, the name of the study of those systems, and the chief structures involved in each system.

Physiology has also become extensive in its scope, requiring subdivision and specialization into branches. Based on systems, there are now specialties in such areas as cell

Table 1–1.   Nomenclature for Systematic Anatomy

System	Name of Study	Chief Structures
Skeletal system	Osteology	Bones
Articular system	Arthrology	Joints
Muscular system	Myology	Muscles
Digestive system	Splanchnology	Stomach and intestines
Respiratory system	"	Lungs and air passages
Urinary system	"	Kidneys and bladder
Reproductive system	"	Ovaries and testes
Endocrine system	Endocrinology	Ductless glands
Nervous system	Neurology	Brain, spinal cord, nerves
Circulatory system	Angiology	Heart, vessels
Integumentary system	Dermatology	Skin
Sensory system	Esthesiology	Eye, ear

physiology, neurophysiology, gastrointestinal physiology, cardiovascular physiology, renal physiology, metabolic physiology, respiratory or pulmonary physiology, endocrine physiology, and reproductive physiology.

All of these subdivisions become the parts of such overall studies as applied physiology, comparative physiology, pathologic physiology, medical physiology, and mammalian physiology. We will be concerned with these systems and studies as they relate specifically to farm animals.

DESCRIPTIVE TERMS USEFUL IN THE STUDY OF ANATOMY

When giving geographic locations, we make use of certain arbitrary frames of reference known as meridians of latitude and longitude. However, since an animal is rarely oriented exactly with a line on the earth's surface, our frames of reference must be in relation to the animal itself and must apply regardless of the position or direction of the animal (see Figs. 1–1, 1–2). To meet these requirements, arbitrary planes

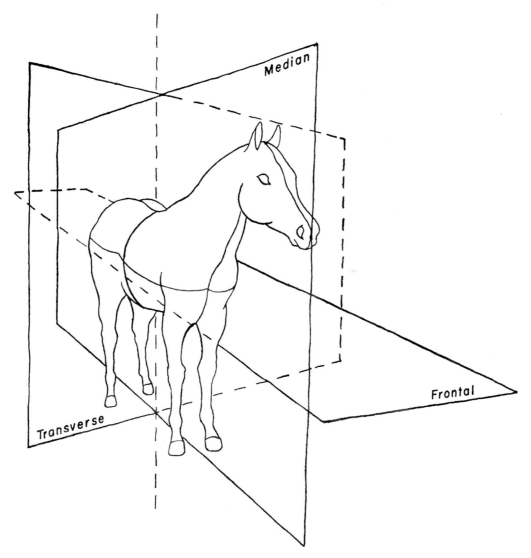

Fig. 1–1.   Imaginary planes of reference. (After Julian and Tyler, Lab. Dissection Guide for Functional Anatomy of the Domestic Animals.)

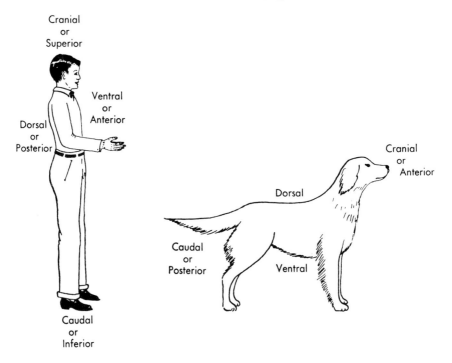

Fig. 1–2. Terminology of quadruped and human compared. (After King and Showers, Human Anatomy and Physiology, W. B. Saunders Co.)

are used as frames of reference in locating any given part of an animal body.

Cranial and *anterior* are directional terms meaning toward the head. The shoulder is cranial to the hip—it is closer to the head than is the hip.

Caudal and *posterior* mean toward the tail. The rump is caudal to the loin.

The *median plane* is an imaginary plane passing through the body craniocaudally, which divides the body into equal right and left halves. A beef carcass is split into two halves on the median plane.

A *sagittal plane* is any plane parallel to the median plane. The median plane is sometimes called the *midsagittal plane.*

A *transverse plane* is at right angles to the median plane and divides the body into cranial and caudal segments. A cross section of the body would be made on a transverse plane. The surcingle of a milker defines a transverse plane through the abdomen of a cow.

A *frontal plane* is at right angles to both the median plane and transverse planes. The frontal plane divides the body into dorsal (upper) and ventral (lower) segments. If a cow walks into a lake until the water comes above the chest, the surface of the water represents a frontal plane in relation to the cow.

In addition to the planes of reference, other descriptive terms are valuable in locating an area we wish to discuss.

Medial is an adjective meaning close to or toward the median plane. The heart is medial to the lungs: it is closer to the median plane than are the lungs. The chestnut is located on the medial side (inside) of a horse's leg; it is on the side closest to the median plane.

Lateral is the antonym of medial; it means away from the median plane. The ribs are lateral to the lungs. They are farther from the median plane.

Dorsal is a directional term meaning toward or beyond the backbone or vertebral column. The kidneys are dorsal to the intestines; they are closer to the vertebral column. *Dorsum* is the noun referring to the dorsal portion or back. A saddle is placed on the dorsum of a horse.

Ventral means away from the vertebral column or toward the mid-abdominal wall. The udder is the most ventral part of the body of a cow. It is the part of the body farthest from the vertebral column.

Deep and *internal* refer to closeness to the center of gravity or the center of an extremity. The humerus (arm bone) is deep to all other structures in the arm.

Superficial and *external* refer to proximity to the skin or surface of the body or surface of an extremity. Hair is superficial to all other structures of the body.

Proximal means relatively close to a given part, usually the vertebral column, body, or center of gravity. Proximal is generally used in reference to portions of an extremity or limb. The knee is proximal to the foot.

Distal means relatively farther from the vertebral column. The hoof is distal to the carpus or knee.

Palmar (volar) refers to the flexion or caudal surface of the forelimb distal to (below) the elbow. *Dorsal*, when used in reference to forelimbs, refers to the opposite (cranial) side.

Plantar refers to the caudal surface of the hind limb below the hock, and dorsal refers to the side directly opposite (the cranial side.).

Prone refers to a position in which the dorsal aspect or dorsum of the body or any extremity is uppermost. *Pronation* refers to the act of turning toward a prone position.

Supine refers to the position in which the ventral aspect of the body or volar or plantar aspect of an extremity is uppermost. *Supination* refers to the act of turning toward a supine position.

MICROSCOPIC ANATOMY–
ANIMAL CELLS AND TISSUES

All living things, both plants and animals, are constructed of small units called *cells*.

The simplest animals, such as the ameba, consist of a single cell that is capable of performing all functions commonly associated with life. These functions include growth (increase in size), metabolism (utilization of food), response to stimuli (such as moving toward light), contraction (shortening in one direction), and reproduction (development of new individuals of the same species).

A typical cell consists of three main parts, the *cytoplasm*, the *nucleus*, and the *cell membrane* (see Fig. 1–3). Detailed structure of the cell will be described in Chapter 2. Tissues will be discussed in the present chapter.

When the number of cells increases in animals, certain cells become specialists in one or more of the functions of the animal body. Specialized cells grouped together are called *tissues*. For example, cells that specialize in conducting impulses make up nervous tissue. Cells that specialize in holding structures together make up connective tissue.

Various tissues are associated in functional groups called *organs*. The stomach is an organ that functions in digestion of food.

A group of organs that are involved in a common enterprise make up a *system*. The stomach, liver, pancreas, and intestines are all part of the digestive system.

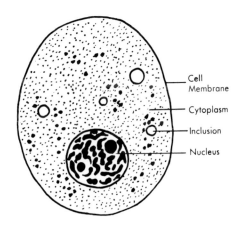

Fig. 1–3. A cell as seen with the light microscope.

Primary Types of Tissues

The primary types of tissues include: (1) *epithelial tissues*, which cover the surface of the body, line body cavities, and form the active parts of glands; (2) *connective tissues*, which support and bind other tissues together, and from which, in the case of bone marrow, the formed elements of the blood are derived; (3) *muscle tissues*, which specialize in contracting; and (4) *nervous tissues*, which conduct impulses from one part of the body to another.

EPITHELIAL TISSUES

In general the epithelial tissues are classified as *simple* (single layered) and *stratified* (many layered). Each of these types is further subdivided according to the shape of the individual cells (Fig. 1–4).

Simple epithelium includes squamous (plate-like) cells, cuboidal (cube-shaped) cells, columnar (cylindrical-shaped) cells, and pseudostratified columnar cells.

Simple squamous epithelium consists of thin, plate-like cells. They are much expanded in two directions but have little thickness. The edges are joined somewhat like mosaic tile covering a floor. A layer of simple squamous epithelium has little tensile strength and is found only as a covering layer for stronger tissues. Simple squamous epithelium is found where a smooth surface is required to reduce friction. The coverings of viscera and the linings of body cavities and blood vessels are all composed of simple squamous epithelium.

Cuboidal epithelial cells are approximately equal in all dimensions. They are found in some ducts and in passageways in the kidneys. The active tissue of many glands is composed of cuboidal cells.

Columnar epithelial cells are cylindrical in shape. They are arranged somewhat like the cells in a honeycomb or cartridges in a box. Some columnar cells have whiplike projections called cilia extending from the free extremity. The cells lining the trachea (windpipe) are of this type. The cilia wave in

such a manner as to move any foreign material in the trachea toward the mouth where it can be coughed out or swallowed.

Pseudostratified columnar epithelium is composed of columnar cells. However, they vary in length, giving the appearance of more than one layer or stratum. This type of epithelium is found in the upper respiratory tract where the lining cells are ciliated.

Stratified epithelium consists of more than one layer of epithelial cells, and includes stratified squamous, stratified columnar, and transitional epithelium.

Stratified squamous epithelium forms the outer layer of the skin and the lining of the first part of the digestive tract as far as the stomach. In ruminants, stratified squamous epithelium also lines the fore stomach (rumen, reticulum, and omasum).

Stratified squamous epithelium is the thickest and toughest of the epithelia, consisting of many layers of cells. The deepest layer, known as the stratum germinativum, contains the actively growing and multiplying cells. These cells are somewhat cuboidal in shape, but as they are pushed toward the surface, away from the food supply, they become flattened and lifeless and are constantly in the process of peeling off. This layer of dead cells becomes very thick in areas subjected to friction. Calluses are formed in this manner.

Stratified columnar epithelium is composed of more than one layer of columnar cells and is found lining part of the pharynx and salivary ducts.

Transitional epithelium forms the lining of portions of the urinary system that are subjected to stretching. These areas include the bladder and ureters. This transitional epithelium has the ability to pile up many cells thick when the bladder is relaxed, yet stretch out to a single layer when completely filled.

Glandular epithelium, which often is either cuboidal or columnar, has the ability to secrete various products. The cells may be arranged as single goblet cells, which produce mucus, or they may consist of

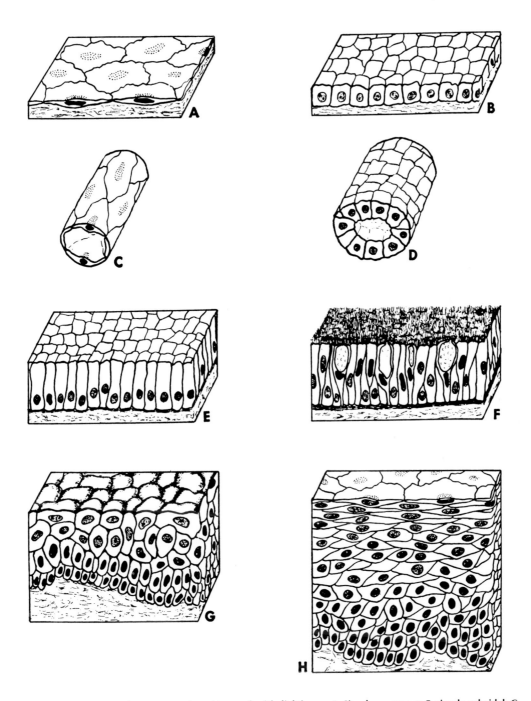

Fig. 1–4.   Diagrammatic representation of types of epithelial tissues. A, Simple squamous; B, simple cuboidal; C, simple squamous in tubular arrangement; D, simple cuboidal forming a small duct; E, simple columnar; F, pseudostratified columnar with cilia; G, transitional; H, stratified squamous (moist type). (Finerty and Cowdry, A Textbook of Histology, Lea & Febiger.)

aggregations of many cells, such as those found in most glands. Glands are described in more detail in this chapter on page 17.

CONNECTIVE TISSUES

Connective tissues, as the name implies, serve to connect other tissues. They give form and strength to many organs and often serve for protection and leverage. Connective tissues include yellow elastic tissue, collagenous (white fibrous) tissue, reticular (net-like) tissue, adipose (fat) tissue, cartilage (gristle), and bone.

Yellow elastic tissue contains kinked fibers which tend to regain their original shape after being stretched. This tissue is found in the ligamentum nuchae, a strong band that helps to support the head. Yellow elastic tissue also is found in the abdominal tunic, in the ligamenta flava of the spinal canal, in elastic arteries, and mixed with other tissues wherever elasticity is needed.

Collagenous (white fibrous) tissue is found throughout the body in various forms. Individual cells (fibroblasts) produce long fibers of collagen, which have considerable tensile strength.

In *dense regular connective tissue* (Fig. 1–5), the fibers are arranged in parallel bundles, forming cords or bands of considerable

strength. These are the *tendons,* which connect muscles to bones, and the *ligaments,* which connect bones to bones.

The fibers of *dense irregular connective tissue* are arranged in a thick mat with fibers running in all directions. The dermis of the skin, which may be tanned to make leather, consists of dense irregular connective tissue. This forms a strong covering that resists tearing and yet is flexible enough to move with the surface of the body.

Areolar connective tissue (Fig. 1–6) is found throughout the body wherever protective cushioning and flexibility are needed. For example, blood vessels are surrounded by a sheath of areolar connective tissue, which permits the vessels to move and yet protects them.

Beneath the dermis is a layer of loosely arranged areolar connective tissue fibers

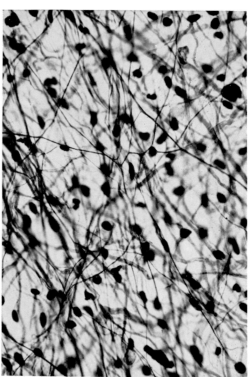

Fig. 1–6.   Areolar (loose) connective tissue. (Turtox Biological Supplies, courtesy of General Biological Supply House, Inc.)

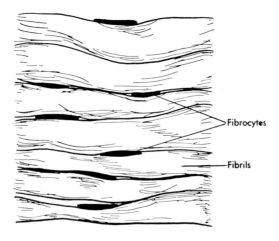

Fig. 1–5.   Diagram of dense regular connective tissue (longitudinal section of a tendon).

which attach the skin to underlying muscles. This attachment is flexible enough to permit movement of the skin. It also permits the formation of a thick layer of fat between the skin and underlying muscles. Whenever the skin is adherent to bony prominences because of a lack of areolar tissue, the skin will not move, and no layer of fat can form. This condition is seen in beef cattle that have "ties"; in this case, the skin over the back shows large dimples where fat cannot fill in because the skin is adherent to the vertebrae.

Reticular connective tissue consists of fine fibrils produced by star-shaped cells. Reticular tissue makes up the framework of lymphatic tissue, spleen, and bone marrow.

Adipose tissue (sometimes called fat) forms when connective tissue cells take up fat for storage as inclusions within the cytoplasm of the cell (Fig. 1–7). As more fat is taken up for storage, the cell eventually becomes so filled with fat that the nucleus is pushed to one side of the cell which, as a result, becomes spherical.

Cartilage is a special type of connective tissue commonly called gristle. Cartilage is firmer than fibrous tissue, yet not as hard as bone. The nature of cartilage is due to the structure of the intercellular material found between the *chondrocytes* (cartilage cells).

The three types of cartilage described are hyaline, elastic, and fibrous.

Hyaline cartilage is the glass-like covering of bones within joints. This type of cartilage forms a smooth surface that reduces friction, so that one bone easily glides over another. The actively growing areas near the ends of long bones also consist of hyaline cartilage.

Elastic cartilage consists of a mixture of cartilage substance and elastic fibers. This type of cartilage forms the basis of the external ear.

Fibrocartilage consists of a mixture of cartilage and collagenous fibers, which forms a semi-elastic cushion of great strength. The intervertebral discs found between the bodies of adjacent vertebrae are composed of fibrocartilage.

Bone is formed by bone-forming cells called *osteoblasts*. These cells produce a substance, *osteoid* tissue, which later becomes calcified to form bone. The bone may be arranged in the form of spicules (small spikes) and flat plates forming a sponge-like network called *cancellous bone* or *spongy bone*, or it may be laid down in the form of laminated cylinders *(Haversian* or *osteonal systems)* closely packed together to form compact bone (Fig. 1–8).

Cancellous bone is found in the ex-

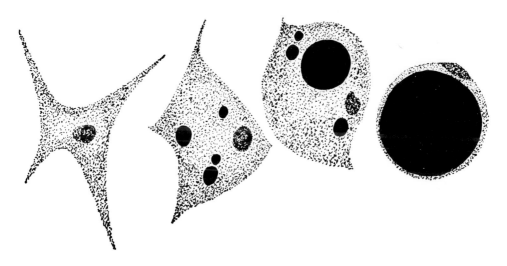

Fig. 1–7.   Typical fat cell formed by intake of fat globules. (After Ham and Leeson, Histology, J. B. Lippincott Co.)

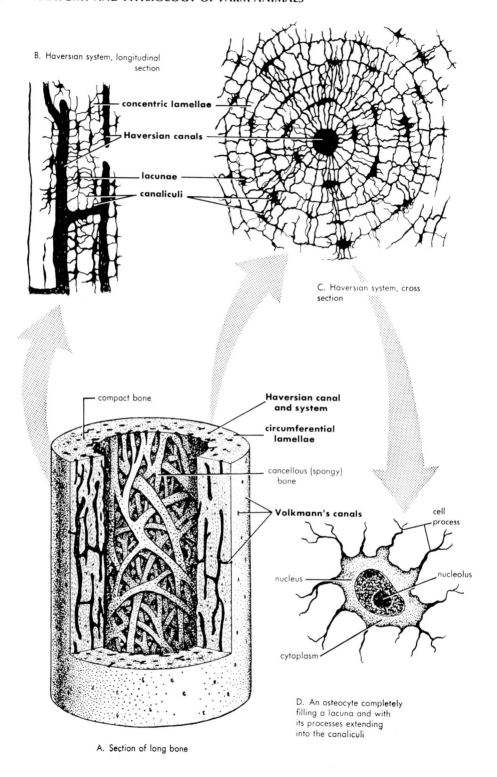

B. Haversian system, longitudinal section

concentric lamellae

Haversian canals

lacunae

canaliculi

C. Haversian system, cross section

compact bone

Haversian canal and system

circumferential lamellae

cancellous (spongy) bone

Volkmann's canals

cell process

nucleus

nucleolus

cytoplasm

D. An osteocyte completely filling a lacuna and with its processes extending into the canaliculi

A. Section of long bone

Fig. 1–8.   Bone tissue. (From Crouch, J.E.: Functional Human Anatomy. ed. 3. Philadelphia, Lea & Febiger, 1978.)

tremities of long bones where resistance to compression without excessive weight is needed. Cancellous bone is also found between two layers of compact bone as in the skull. This arrangement is called *diplöe*. The plates and spicules of bone are arranged in a manner to best resist stresses and strains imposed on the bone by weight or pull of muscles.

Compact bone, found in the shafts of long bones, consists of many laminated tubes known as *Haversian systems*. Each Haversian system consists of one canal containing vessels and nerves surrounded by circular plates of bone forming the laminated cylinder. These plates of bone are laid down in a centripetal fashion (from the periphery toward the center). After the bone is formed, the osteoblasts which became embedded

within the bone substance are called *osteocytes* (bone cells), rather than *osteoblasts* (bone-forming cells). The spaces in which the osteocytes are found are called *lacunae* (little lakes), and the spaces where the cell processes are located are called canaliculi (small canals).

In general these Haversian systems are added on the periphery of the shaft of a bone as the bone increases in diameter. Blood vessels extend from the periosteum to Haversian canals through channels called *Volkmann's canals*, which often travel at right angles to the Haversian canals.

BLOOD. Blood consists of a fluid matrix (liquid portion) called plasma, a variety of cells (Fig. 1–9), proteins, monosaccharides (simple sugars), products of fat degradation, and other circulating nutrients; plus wastes,

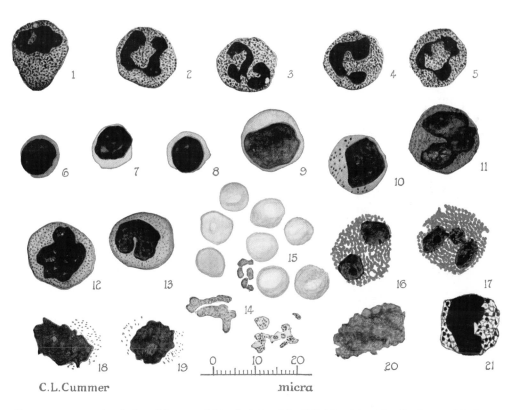

C.L.Cummer   micra

Fig. 1–9. Types of cells found in normal blood. Colored by Wright's stain. All cells drawn with the same magnification and outlined with the camera lucida for the purpose of comparing sizes. × 1150. Nos. 1 to 5, inclusive, neutrophils; 6, 7, 8, lymphocytes; 9 to 13, monocytes; 14, platelets; 15, a group of red blood cells; 16, 17, eosinophils; 18, 19, 20, "basket cells," degenerated leukocytes; 21, basophilic leukocyte. (Finerty and Cowdry's A Textbook of Histology, Lea & Febiger.)

electrolytes for acid-base balance, and chemical intermediates of cellular metabolism. It is sometimes considered to be a connective tissue because of the origin of some of its components.

Red blood cells are called *erythrocytes*. In most domestic mammals they are non-nucleated biconcave discs that contain the substance *hemoglobin*. The main function of the erythrocyte or red blood cell (RBC) is to carry hemoglobin. Hemoglobin in turn has the primary function of carrying oxygen from the lungs to all the tissues of the animal. At the tissue level, oxygen is released to the cells, while carbon dioxide, which is produced by the cells, diffuses into the blood to be carried back to the lungs where it can be eliminated during breathing.

A condition called *anemia* results from a loss of red cells, or an insufficient amount of hemoglobin synthesis, or deficiencies of folic acid or vitamin B_{12} or "intrinsic factor," or premature degradation of the red cells, or if the cells become sickled (crescent-shaped). The term *anemia* refers to a reduced concentration of *functional* red cells in the blood.

White cells (also called *leukocytes*) are one of the first lines of defense of the body against infection. They include *agranulocytes* and *granulocytes*.

Agranulocytes are of two kinds: *monocytes*, which are large, and *lymphocytes*, which usually are smaller. An excess of these cells tends to be associated with chronic types of diseases.

Granulocytes (polymorphonuclear leukocytes) are of three types and are classified according to their affinity for different stains. Granules in *neutrophils* stain indifferently, *basophils* have dark-staining granules, when stained with common blood stains, and *acidophils* (eosinophils) have red-staining granules.

Blood platelets are small, irregularly shaped particles that are associated with the clotting of the blood.

Plasma refers to the fluid part of unclotted blood. Plasma is particularly useful as a substitute for blood in transfusions because the proteins give it the same osmotic pressure as blood. Plasma, therefore, will not escape from blood vessels as readily as a salt solution will.

Serum is the supernatant yellow fluid that is expressed out when blood clots and retracts. It is plasma but without most of the clotting factors. Serum is used for prevention and treatment of diseases because it contains the antibody fractions of the blood.

MUSCLE TISSUE

The three types of muscle tissue are: striated voluntary (skeletal) muscle, smooth (involuntary, visceral, unstriated) muscle, and cardiac (involuntary striated) muscle (Fig. 1–10).

Striated muscle cells consist of long fibers which show, under the microscope, characteristic cross striations, many peripherally located nuclei, and a cell membrane called the *sarcolemma*. Each striated muscle fiber cell must have its own nerve supply in order to contract, and when stimulated, the whole fiber will contract. This is the *"all-or-none" law* of muscle contraction. However, the *force* of contraction depends on the state of the fiber at any one moment; that is, is it already fatigued, is it warmed up, is the calcium supply low, is it stretched? Striated muscle tissue plus some connective tissue makes up the flesh of meat-producing animals.

Smooth muscle cells are spindle-shaped cells that contain one centrally located nucleus per cell. They are found in the walls of the digestive tract, in the walls of blood vessels, and in the walls of urinary and reproductive organs. These cells contract more slowly than striated muscle and respond to a variety of stimuli.

Cardiac muscle is also known as *involuntary striated muscle* because it is not usually under conscious control, yet it does have cross striations. The heart is composed of a complex, branched arrangement of cardiac-muscle cells. Modified muscle cells

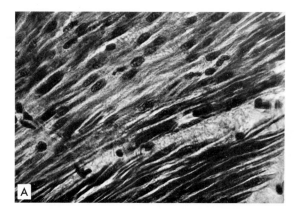

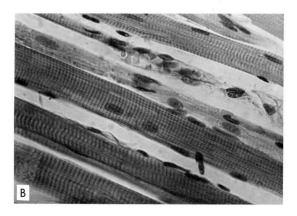

intercalated disc

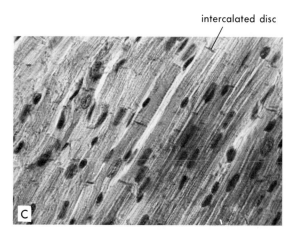

Fig. 1–10. Types of muscle tissue. *A*, Smooth muscle. *B*, Skeletal muscle. *C*, Cardiac muscle. (From Crouch, J.E.: Functional Human Anatomy. ed. 3. Philadelphia, Lea & Febiger, 1978.)

called *Purkinje's fibers* conduct impulses within the heart, much as nerve fibers do in other parts of the body, and the impulses travel throughout the heart, causing a spreading contraction wave.

NERVOUS TISSUE

The essential cell making up nervous tissue is the *neuron (nerve cell)*. This consists of a nerve cell body and two or more nerve processes (nerve fibers). The processes are called *axons* if they conduct impulses away from the cell body and *dendrites* if they conduct impulses toward the cell body (Fig. 1–11).

The cord-like structures commonly referred to as nerves may consist of thousands of nerve processes or fibers. By examining a nerve fiber either grossly or with a microscope, it is impossible to determine whether impulses were carried toward or away from the cell body. Some authorities, therefore, prefer to consider the longest process as the axon and shorter processes as dendrites.

A nerve fiber may be covered by a myelin sheath, by a neurolemma, or by both.

The special connective tissues of the nervous system proper are called *neuroglia* and are found only in the central nervous system. Outside the central nervous system, in addition to the Schwann cells, ordinary white fibrous tissue serves as the major protective covering for the nerves and bundles of nerve fibers.

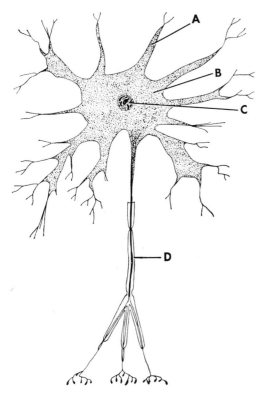

Fig. 1–11.   A typical neuron. *A,* Dendrite; *B,* Nerve cell body; *C,* Nucleus; and *D,* Axon. (After Francis, Introduction to Human Anatomy, courtesy of C. V. Mosby Co.)

THE GENERAL PLAN OF THE ANIMAL BODY

All farm animals are classified as vertebrates, and as such they have a vertebral column. The body (with the exception of a few internal organs) exhibits bilateral symmetry. This means that the right and left sides of the body are nearly identical (mirror images of each other). Similar right and left structures are called paired structures, such as a pair of gloves that are similar but not interchangeable. Most unpaired structures are located on or near the median plane, and of course, only one such structure exists in any given animal. The tongue, trachea, vertebral column, and heart are examples of unpaired structures. The ribs, limbs, eyes, and most muscles are examples of paired structures in the animal body.

A medial view of the body shows two cavities: a *dorsal cavity* containing the brain and spinal cord and a *ventral cavity* containing most of the viscera (soft structures) of the body. The ventral cavity is subdivided by the diaphragm into the thoracic cavity cranially and the abdominopelvic cavity (which includes the abdominal cavity and the pelvic cavity) caudally.

The *thoracic cavity* contains the *pericardial sac,* which surrounds the heart, and two *pleural sacs*, which surround the two lungs. These sacs are formed by *serous membranes*.

The *abdominal cavity* contains the kidneys, most of the digestive organs, and a variable amount of the internal reproductive organs in both sexes. The *pelvic cavity* contains the terminal part of the digestive system (the rectum) and all of the internal portions of the urogenital system not found in the abdominal cavity. The serous membrane that surrounds the abdominal viscera and part of the pelvic viscera is called *peritoneum*.

A transverse section through the abdominal cavity illustrates the general plan of the body as a tube (digestive tract and its derivatives) within a tube (body wall) (see Fig. 1–12). The potential space between the two tubes is the ventral body cavity, which is derived from the embryonic *celom*. Normally there are few actual air-filled spaces in the animal body except in the respiratory system and the ear. However, for the sake of

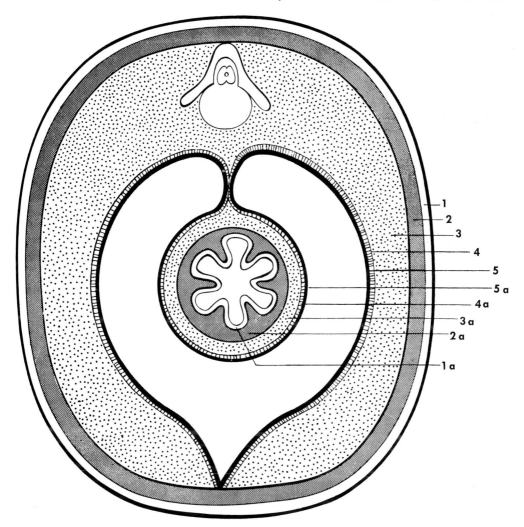

Fig. 1–12.   Cross section of the body wall and digestive tract. *1*, Skin; *2*, Fascia; *3*, Striated muscle; *4*, Retroperitoneal fascia; *5*, Parietal peritoneum; *5a*, Visceral peritoneum; *4a*, Subserous connective tissue; *3a*, Smooth muscle; *2a*, Submucous connective tissue; and *1a*, mucous membrane. (Modified from Leach, Functional Anatomy, Mammalian and Comparative, McGraw-Hill Book Co.)

clarity, many illustrations show a considerable separation between structures that, in the animal body, are actually in contact.

The layers of the body wall and the layers of the digestive tract show a remarkable similarity, although in reverse order. Layers of the body wall from without inward are the following: (1) epithelium (skin), (2) connective tissue (fascia), (3) muscle (striated), (4) connective tissue (retroperitoneal fascia), and (5) serous membrane (parietal peritoneum). The layers of the gut wall from without inward are: (1) serous membrane (visceral peritoneum), (2) connective tissue (subserous connective tissue), (3) muscle (smooth), (4) connective tissue (submucosa), and (5) epithelium (mucous membrane) (Fig. 1–12).

The serous membranes mentioned previously (pericardium, pleura, and peritoneum) are all derivatives of the lining of the celomic cavity of the embryo. Each serous membrane forms a continuous sac that is usually empty except for a small amount of serous

(watery) fluid that acts as a lubricant. In other words, no viscera are found in any of the serous sacs, although most viscera are covered by at least one layer of a serous membrane. A simple analogy is that of pushing one's fist into a partially inflated balloon. The fist is never actually within the balloon proper, but still it is surrounded by a portion of the balloon (Fig. 1–13).

That part of the serous membrane covering a viscus is called the *visceral serous membrane* (visceral pericardium, visceral pleura, and visceral peritoneum). The serous membrane lining a body cavity is called the *parietal* (wall) *serous membrane* (parietal pleura and parietal peritoneum). Parietal pericardium does not actually line a cavity but is the outer layer of the pericardial sac proper. The continuity of each serous sac is maintained by connecting layers of serous membrane that extend from the visceral layer of each serous membrane to the parietal layer of the same serous membrane. These connecting layers of serous mem-

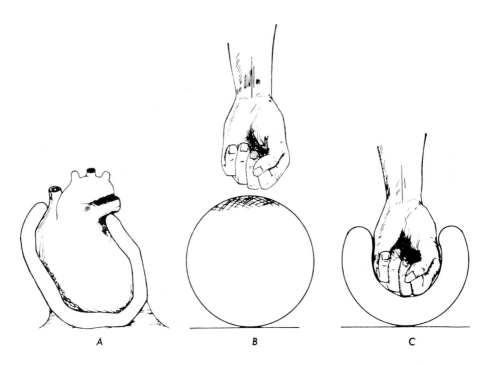

A   B   C

Fig. 1–13.   *A,* Invagination of serous membrane to form outer (parietal) and inner (visceral) layers. (Similar to a fist pushed into a balloon, *B* and *C.*) (After Kahn, Man in Structure and Function, Alfred A. Knopf, 1943.)

branes are given names based on the specific areas they connect, and they will be discussed in some detail when the systems involved are described (respiratory, circulatory, digestive, and reproductive).

GLANDS

Glandular epithelial cells are specialized for secretion or excretion. *Secretion* is the release from the gland cell of a substance that has been synthesized by the cell, and which usually affects other cells in other parts of the body. *Excretion* is the expelling of waste products that are not of use to the animal body.

Glands may be classified either as *endocrine glands* (glands without ducts, which empty their secretory products directly into the blood stream), or as *exocrine glands*

TYPES OF EXOCRINE GLANDS

If secretory portion is:

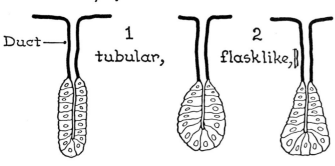
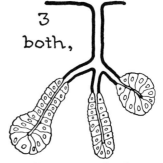

Duct— 1 tubular,   2 flasklike,   3 both,

it is a tubular exocrine gland.   it is an alveolar or acinous gland.   it is a tubulo-alveolar gland.

If duct doesn't branch: If duct branches:

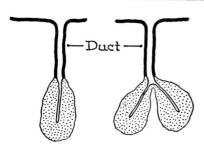
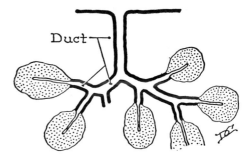

—Duct—   Duct—

it is a simple gland.   it is a compound gland.

Fig. 1–14.   Diagram showing different kinds of secretory units of exocrine glands and the difference between simple and compound glands. (Ham and Leeson, Histology, courtesy of J. B. Lippincott Co.)

(glands that empty their secretory products on an epithelial surface, usually by means of ducts).

The *endocrine glands* are an important part of the control mechanism of the body, because they produce special chemicals known as *hormones*. The endocrine glands are discussed in Chapter 32. Hormones carried to all parts of the body by the blood constitute the *humoral control* of the body. Humoral control and nervous control are the two mechanisms maintaining *homeokinesis*, also called *homeostasis* (a relatively stable but constantly changing state of the body). Humoral response to stimuli from the environment (both external and internal) is much slower and longer acting than response by way of the nervous system. The nervous system is described in some detail in Chapters 5 and 6.

The endocrine glands are considered as constituting a system, the endocrine system, and are studied under the title of endocrinology. However, exocrine glands are scattered throughout many systems, and will be discussed when the systems in which they are involved are described, such as the digestive system, the urogenital system, and the respiratory system.

According to their morphologic classification (Fig. 1–14), a gland is simple if the duct does not branch, and compound if the duct does branch. If the secretory portion forms a tube-like structure, it is called *tubular*; if the secretory portion resembles a grape or hollow ball, it is called *alveolar* or *acinar* (the terms are used interchangeably). A combination of tubular and alveolar secretory structures produces a *tubulo-alveolar* gland.

Compound glands often are subdivided into lobes, which in turn may be further subdivided into lobules. Hence the connective tissue partitions (called septa) are classified as interlobar septa if they separate lobes and as interlobular septa if they separate lobules. Similar terminology may be applied to ducts draining lobes or lobules of glands, that is, interlobar ducts and interlobular ducts, respectively.

Another classification of glands is based on the manner in which the gland cells elaborate their secretion. The most common type of gland, according to method of secretion, is the *merocrine (eccrine) gland*. Merocrine glands pass their secretory products through the cell wall without any appreciable loss of cytoplasm or noticeable damage to the *plasmalemma* (cell membrane). *Apocrine glands* lose a small amount of cytoplasm and/or cell membrane during the process of secretion. The *holocrine gland* is the least common type. After the cell is filled with secretory material, the entire holocrine gland cell is discharged to constitute the secretion.

Chapter 2

Structure of the Cell

Discovery of living cells would have been difficult, if not impossible, before the compound microscope was invented by Zacharias Jansen of Holland in 1590. Robert Hooke of England applied the term "cell" to the cavities he saw in sections of cork. Hooke published a description of cork cells in 1665, based on a study he made with his improved compound microscope. Ten years later, 1675, Marcello Malpighi published an *Anatomy of Plants*, the first systematic study of cell structure.

In 1839 Matthias Schleiden, a German botanist, and Theodor Schwann, an animal anatomist, formulated the *cell theory*, which set forth the concept that "the elementary parts of all tissues are formed of cells in an analogous, though very diversified, manner, so that it may be asserted that there is one universal principle of development for the elementary parts of organisms, however different, and that this principle is the formation of cells."

The word cell comes from the Latin "cella" meaning "a small chamber." In biology, particularly animal biology, the term cell refers more specifically to the indi-

vidual units of living structure rather than the compartments in which they may be located. There actually are no compartments as such in most tissues (with the exception of bone and cartilage), but the living units, cells, are found in groups in which individual cells are restrained mainly by adjacent cells. As early as 1772, Corti observed the jelly-like material in the cell that later was called protoplasm.

MICROSCOPIC STUDY OF THE CELL

Most cells range in diameter from about 10 to 100 μ (micra); cells that are multiplying range from about 20 to 30 μ in diameter.* (1 μ = 1/1000 mm [millimeter], and there are about 25 mm in 1 inch; 1 μ = 1/25,000 inch.) (See Table 2–1.) Sizes of cells vary considerably from one type of cell to another, but with the exception of yolks of birds' eggs (which are considered single cells), the dis-

*In the International System of Units, it is recommended that the term micron (μ) be replaced by the term micrometer (μm), and the angstrom (Å) be converted to the measurements of nanometer or picometer (1 Å = 0.1 nm = 100 pm).

Table 2–1.   Measurements

Since 1 Å, as stated below, equals about 1,250,000,000 of an inch, 75 Å equals about 3/10,000,000 of an inch. The diameter of a hydrogen atom is 1 Å.

1 meter	= 100 centimeters (cm)	1 micron	= 0.001 mm	1 angstrom	= 0.1 mμ
	1,000 millimeters (mm)		1,000 mμ		about 1/250,000,000
	39.37 inches		10,000 Å		inch
			about 1/25,000 inch		
1 millimeter	= 0.001 meter	1 millimicron	= 0.001 μ	1 inch	= approximately
	1,000 microns (μ)		10 Å		2.5 cm
	1,000,000 millimicrons (mμ)		about 1/25,000,000		25 mm
	10,000,000 angstroms (Å)		inch		25,000 μ
	about 1/25 inch				25,000,000 mμ
					250,000,000 Å

From Anthony, C. P.: Textbook of Anatomy and Physiology. ed. 9. St. Louis, C. V. Mosby Co., 1975.

tance from the interior of the cell to some portion of the cell membrane (surface of the cell) is seldom over 50 μ. For efficient functioning, all parts of the protoplasm must be relatively close to a source of nutrition and route of waste excretion. This automatically limits the size of cells, because too large a cell could not transport nutrients to the center of the cell or eliminate waste products from the center of the cell.

Generally, cells grow to a certain size and then either divide or never grow any further until they die (as is the usual case for nerve cells of the central nervous system and red blood cells). How large a cell grows before it divides correlates well with the amount of DNA in the nucleus and the amount of protein being synthesized.

A large surface area in comparison to the volume results from small cell size (see Fig. 2–1). This relationship is also an important factor in efficient cell functioning.

The cell membrane (plasma membrane) is thin—70 to 100 Å in thickness. 1 Å (angstrom) = 1/10,000,000 mm, which is about the diameter of a hydrogen atom.* Regardless of its composition, a membrane of this dimension (100 Å thick) can have little tensile strength; this is another reason why cells must be small. As an analogy, a ton of grain could be handled reasonably well if it were placed in small paper sacks, but it would be completely unmovable if placed in one large sack made of paper the same thickness.

The uniformly small size of cells and the much smaller sizes of structures within the cell have made effective study of cells difficult. As noted earlier, the existence of cells was not confirmed before the microscope was invented. Details of the actual structure of the various parts of cells have not been known with any degree of certainty until the development and use of the electron microscope. The study of gross anatomy goes back in history several centuries, but an understanding of the finer structure of the animal body had to wait for technologic developments.

Light Microscopy

Some cells are located in tissues that are thin enough to be illuminated from one side and observed with a microscope from the opposite side. This is true of the web of the foot of the frog, the mesentery attaching to the intestine, and a few other tissues. In these instances living cells can be observed directly, and this technique is useful for the study of blood circulation. Specific cells may also be taken from a living animal and grown on artificial medium by a technique called *tissue culture*. These cells may then be studied in the living state, even at rather high magnifications.

Except for the foregoing situations, cells usually are studied after undergoing more or less manipulation, so that what is actually seen with the microscope bears little re-

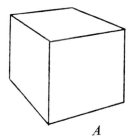 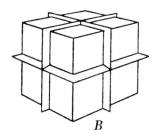 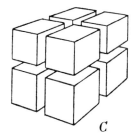

A   B   C

Fig. 2–1.   Relationship of surface area and volume. *A*, Cube 1 cm (centimeter) on a side has a volume of 1 cc (cubic centimeter) and area of 6 cm^2 (square centimeters). *B*, Three complete cuts produces eight small cubes. *C*, Eight small cubes have a total volume of 1 cc but total surface area of 12 cm^2.

semblance to the living cell. A typical treatment of tissue before it can be examined with a light microscope includes:

1. Fixation with some agent, such as formalin, that will coagulate the protein and prevent further changes in the tissue, such as autolysis and bacterial action.

2. Embedding the tissue in a material that will permit cutting very thin sections. Paraffin and nitrocellulose are commonly used for this purpose. Since most embedding media are not water-soluble, the fixed tissue must be dehydrated and then infiltrated with some material such as xylene, which is miscible with the embedding medium.

3. Sectioning the tissue into very thin slices (generally between 2 and 20 μ in thickness), so that the sections may be placed on a glass slide. An instrument called a microtome is used for this purpose. It consists of a sharp knife blade and a mechanism for moving the tissue past the blade and then advancing it a definite distance after each cutting.

4. Staining the section so that different cells or different parts of cells can be differentiated according to color. *Hematoxylin* and *eosin* are stains commonly used together, and this treatment is designated by "H & E stain." The hematoxylin tends to stain acid portions of a cell dark blue or purple (these are called basophilic areas), and the eosin tends to stain the basic portions of a cell pink to red (these are called acidophilic areas). Much may be learned by applying a variety of stains to a tissue to determine how different portions react with various chemicals. This type of study is known as *histochemistry*.

5. The last step, of course, is the actual examination of the stained section of tissue on the slide by means of a microscope and light transmitted through the section.

This approach to the study of the animal body has been standard for many years and will continue to be of great use regardless of newer developments. However, some factors should be kept in mind when studying sections or photographs of sections.

The relationship of the tissue sections to the actual tissue is about the same as that of a sack of potato chips to a growing potato. Both the sections and the potato chips have been processed so that actual resemblance to the original structure is practically nil. Both are seen in two dimensions, length and width, with thickness being of little importance as far as visualization is concerned.

A technique known as *wax plate reconstruction* is sometimes used to visualize microscopic structures in three dimensions. By this method the structures seen on a slide are magnified and projected onto a wax plate, and the unwanted portions are then cut away. This process is repeated with the next section that was cut from the block of tissue, and corresponding areas of this wax plate are matched with the preceding wax plate. After many repetitions, a reconstruction has been produced that resembles the original tissue, except that it is much larger and consists of wax rather than tissue. This is a time-consuming and meticulous technique, but the results are gratifying because it is almost the only way to gain a good, three-dimensional concept of microscopic structures.

The light microscope can magnify objects to a maximum of about 1500 times the original size. This is known as the magnification, or power, of the microscope. Resolving power refers to the property of showing two objects as separate structures. The light microscope can resolve (separate) two structures that are as close as approximately 0.2 μ (i.e., about 2000 Å). This resolving power depends greatly on the wavelength of the light used to observe the tissue and the numerical aperture of the objective lens of the microscope. For example, an oil immersion objective having a 1.4 numerical aperture has a resolving power of 0.185 μ when used with a violet light of about 4000 Å-wavelength (the shortest in the visible spectrum).

Another development in light microscopy is the *phase contrast microscope*, which can be used with unstained and/or living cells, because it depends on differences in refraction of various parts of a cell for image formation.

Electron Microscopy

Electron microscopes do not use visible light for the delineation of structures as in the light microscope, but instead use a beam of electrons focused by electromagnetic lenses. The electron beam may be passed through a thin specimen in the transmission electron microscope, or reflected from the surface of an object and studied with the scanning electron microscope.

SCANNING ELECTRON MICROSCOPE (SEM). The scanning electron microscope is a versatile instrument with a magnification range from $15 \times$ (diameters) to $100,000 \times$, and with a resolution in the vicinity of 100 Å. Depth of field with the scanning electron microscope is much greater than with any light microscope. The images, however, are only black and white with the electron microscope. (For an example of scanning electron micrographs, see Fig. 15–2.)

Preparation of specimens for observation with the scanning electron microscope is relatively simple. Biologic material of a nonmetallic nature generally is dehydrated and then coated with a thin layer of metallic gold before it is placed in the scanning electron microscope.

TRANSMISSION ELECTRON MICROSCOPE. The transmission electron microscope is capable of much higher magnification (as much as $300,000 \times$) with an effective resolution of less than 5 Å. By the use of photographic enlargement and projection techniques, the magnifications can exceed 1,000,000 and still show good detail (Fig. 2–2). (Transmission electron micrographs are shown in Fig. 2–6.) Because so much more detail can be seen in a small area, tissue preparation for transmission electron microscopy is much more exacting and time-consuming than for light microscopy.

The best means of fixation involves the applying of a fixative (*osmium tetroxide* is commonly used) to living tissue, either directly to the surface or by perfusion of the fixative into blood vessels of an anesthetized animal. If this type of fixation is impracticable, a biopsy specimen may be removed and fixed, or a piece of tissue may be removed

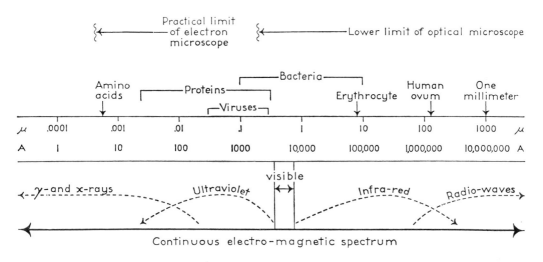

Fig. 2–2.   Comparison of sizes of amino acids, proteins, and living units with wavelengths of different kinds of radiation. (Bloom and Fawcett, A Textbook of Histology, courtesy of W. B. Saunders Co.)

immediately following slaughter. In either case, the time from the living state to immersion in the fixative should not exceed two minutes, and the size of tissue should not exceed 1 mm on a side.

Osmium tetroxide acts both as a fixative and as a stain. Other heavy metals including lead may be used as so-called stains. The term "stain" may be used somewhat loosely, because the areas where the metals concentrate inhibit the passage of electrons, giving an electron-dense appearance that shows up as a dark area in the final photographic print.

After fixation, the tissue is dehydrated and infiltrated with plastic and then embedded in plastic for sectioning. The sections are cut extremely thin (less than 300 Å in thickness), placed on a grid, and examined with the electron microscope.

The picture of the typical cell viewed with the electron microscope still shows most of the structures described by light microscopists, but in much greater detail.

The classic separation of the cell into presumed living *organelles* and nonliving *metaplastic inclusions* has become somewhat blurred by findings with the electron microscope and the discovery that genetic information is carried from cell to cell and organism to organism only through DNA (deoxyribonucleic acid). Although the mechanisms of life are becoming clearer, the definition of life is more difficult.

GENERAL ANATOMY OF THE CELL

The typical cell seen in light microscopy consists of a nucleus and cytoplasm surrounded by the plasma membrane. The nucleus contains a nucleolus and *chromatin material*, which forms into *chromosomes* during cell division, and it is surrounded by a nuclear membrane called the *nuclear envelope*. The cytoplasm contains a number of different structures, including the *endoplasmic reticulum*, *Golgi apparatus*,

mitochondria, and inclusions that can be demonstrated by special preparation and staining techniques.

Separation of Cellular Constituents

The structure and function of cell organelles can be determined to some extent by separating the various cellular constituents, analyzing them chemically, and determining what biochemical reactions they can perform. First, an appropriate sample of cells is homogenized (finely ground) and then subjected to centrifugation (rapid spinning) at different speeds to separate the homogenate into different fractions. The heaviest structures, the nuclei, settle out first, then the mitochondria, and finally the microsomes, which are fragments of rough endoplasmic reticulum (see Fig. 2–3).

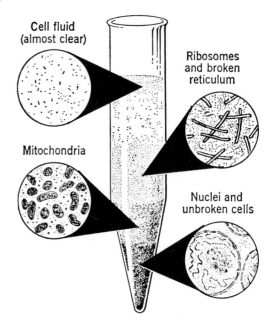

Fig. 2–3. The separation of cell structures by centrifugation. The cell fractions are shown in successive layers. Ordinarily, extra fluid would be added before the cells are centrifuged, with the result that the top layer would be disproportionately larger than that shown as cell fluid here. (Amer. Inst. Biological Sciences, courtesy of Harcourt, Brace and World.)

Intercellular Contact

All vertebrates develop from subdivision of a single cell, the fertilized egg. Unicellular animals also develop by subdivision of a single parent cell. When the parent cell of a unicellular animal divides, the resulting daughter cells each go their own separate way, but the daughter cells of the fertilized ovum of a multicellular animal for some reason stay together and eventually differentiate into cells making up different tissues. The question of what holds these cells together and why they differentiate is still largely unanswered, although some incorrect ideas have been dispelled with the use of the electron microscope. Light microscopists described such things as intercellular bridges and intercellular cement, which cannot be visualized with the electron microscope. Generally the plasma membranes of adjacent cells appear to be separated by a rather constant space of about 200 Å. Although it is difficult to prove that no cement exists between these plasma membranes, it is equally difficult to identify the nature of a cementing substance if it does exist, perhaps because of the pretreatment of the cells during preparation for viewing by electron microscopy. The *desmosomes (macula adherens)* seen in electron micrographs were once called intercellular bridges. However, desmosomes appear to be simply localized thickenings of adjacent plasma membranes with tiny fibrils *(tonofibrils)* radiating from the thickening into the cytoplasm of the respective cell, with no other continuity between cells.

Zona occludens, called *terminal bars* in light microscopy, resemble desmosomes when seen in cross section. They are ribbon-like thickenings of the plasma membrane just below the free surface of columnar cells. Each terminal bar passes completely around the periphery of the cell at the same level as the terminal bars of adjacent cells. In light microscopy the terminal bars were described as cementing substance.

Interdigitation of adjacent plasma membranes no doubt helps keep some cells together. This consists of fingerlike projections from one cell that fit appropriate invaginations of adjacent cells.

The Plasma Membrane

The structure of the plasma membrane, as well as the structure of other membranes within the cell, has not been established with certainty. Since there is no available technique for directly observing the molecular arrangements of the membrane, what we purport to know has been inferred from indirect evidence.

According to the Danielli-Davson model, the plasma membrane consists of three layers as seen in electron micrographs. It is proposed that both the outermost and the innermost layers are composed of protein, while the middle layer of the "sandwich" is a bimolecular layer of primarily phospholipids. These phospholipids apparently are arranged with their polar (hydrophilic) ends facing the protein layers, while their nonpolar (hydrophobic) ends face each other in the center of the membrane.

Modifications of this Danielli-Davson model have been proposed that suggest that protein may exist throughout the membrane or within the lipid bilayer. Various protein shapes and conformations may move and change as part of a dynamic, ever-changing system. (See Figs. 2–4, 2–5.)

The presence of *pores* (small holes) in the plasma membrane has been both postulated and denied, since no conclusive evidence has yet been presented to prove their existence. Invaginations of the cell membrane (called *caveoli*) are sometimes seen in close proximity to small membrane-bound vesicles (called *pinocytotic vesicles*).

Modifications of the plasma membrane occur largely on the free surface of cells (a surface not adjacent to any other cells). These modifications usually increase the cell surface and presumably function in absorption or secretion. The *striated border (brush*

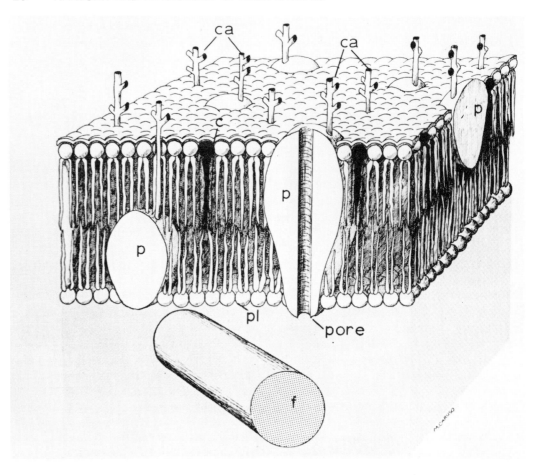

Fig. 2–4. The appearance of the plasma membrane structure. The bimolecular leaflet contains phospholipids *(pl)*, cholesterol *(c)*, and proteins *(p)*. Carbohydrate moieties *(ca)* extend from the external surface, some attached to protein and some to lipid. Some proteins (perhaps most) span the bilayer. Some are thought to form aqueous channels (pores) and some are involved with facilitated transport of certain ions or metabolites. Cytoplasmic filaments *(f)* may be closely associated with the membrane, and some microtubules (not illustrated) terminate near the membrane as well. The membrane bilayer exhibits fluidity, permitting integral proteins to move laterally, thus changing the sites of surface active areas, aqueous channels, and membrane interactions with microfilaments and microtubules. (From Copenhaver, W. M., et al.: Bailey's Textbook of Histology. ed. 7. © 1978, The Williams & Wilkins Co., Baltimore.)

border) seen in light microscopy appears in electron micrographs to consist of remarkably uniform fingerlike projections of a constant height and width, at least for a given cell type. Less regular projections, called *stereocilia*, are irregular branched extensions of the cell cytoplasm that are not motile. Microvilli are somewhat similar to stereocilia, except that they are smaller and unbranched.

Motile cilia (kinocilia) are complex, elongated, fingerlike projections from cell surfaces found in areas where material is moved past the surface, as in the lining of the trachea and the lining of the uterine tubes. Each cilium is associated with a basal body that resembles a *centriole* normally seen in the cytoplasm of all cells. From the basal body, nine pairs of peripheral tubules and one central pair of tubules extend into and throughout most of the length of the related cilium. These tubules are parallel with the

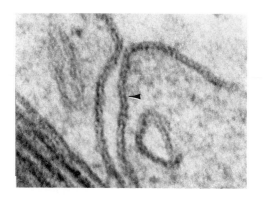

Fig. 2–5. Electron micrograph of the infolded trilaminar plasma membrane (arrow) of a lemmocyte. × 327,680. (From Dellmann, H. D., and Brown, E. M.: Textbook of Veterinary Histology. Philadelphia, Lea & Febiger, 1976.)

long axis of the cilium and are presumed to produce movement of the cilium, since they contain contractile protein.

Nucleus

The *nucleus* contains the genetic material of the cell: chromatin in the nondividing cell, and chromosomes in the dividing cell. The nuclei of somatic cells contain the information necessary for determining the form and structure of new cells, and the nuclei of sex cells contain the information necessary to determine the characteristics of a new individual. The appearance of chromosomes during cell division has been worked out well with techniques of light microscopy. O. L. Miller Jr., by the use of transmission electron microscopy, has demonstrated RNA actively transcribing from the DNA of genes in chromosomes. (See Fig. 2–6.)

The *nuclear envelope*, which surrounds the cell nucleus, is comprised of two distinct membranes separated by a space of about 200 Å. The outer membrane is believed to be continuous with the endoplasmic reticulum. Pores (small gaps or interruptions) in the nuclear envelope have been seen, described, and photographed as discrete holes in the *annuli* of fenestrations. Annuli are small depressions where the inner and outer membranes of the nuclear envelope come together, eliminating the space between them. These pores permit continuity between the protoplasm of the nucleus (nucleoplasm) and the cytoplasm outside the nucleus, allowing exchange of fluid and fluid substances.

The *nucleoli* in the nucleus consist largely of clustered RNA *(ribonucleic acid)* granules, and these show up as electron-dense structures. The DNA in the nucleus appears much less dense in electron micrographs. Fine filaments may also be seen scattered throughout the nucleus.

Cytoplasm

Organelles in the cytoplasm outside the nucleus include the endoplasmic reticulum (either smooth-surfaced or rough-surfaced), mitochondria, Golgi apparatus, centrioles, free ribosomes, various types of vesicles (including multivesicular bodies, microbodies, droplets), lysosomes, and peroxisomes.

Endoplasmic Reticulum. The endoplasmic reticulum consists of a system of tubes or flattened sacs located in the cytoplasm of practically all cells. The outer nuclear membrane often shows continuity with the endoplasmic reticulum, and the plasma membrane has been occasionally described as joining the endoplasmic reticulum. Some authorities, however, do not believe that the plasma membrane is ever continuous with the endoplasmic reticulum.

Occasionally dilations occur in the endoplasmic reticulum. These dilations are called *cisternae*, and presumably may contain products of secretion. Some endoplasmic reticulum is covered with small round bodies on the outer surface called *ribosomes*. This type is called *rough endoplasmic reticulum* (also *alpha cytomembrane* and *ergastoplasm*).

Smooth endoplasmic reticulum (also called *beta cytomembrane*) has no ribosomes on the surface of the membrane. The smooth endoplasmic reticulum is related to

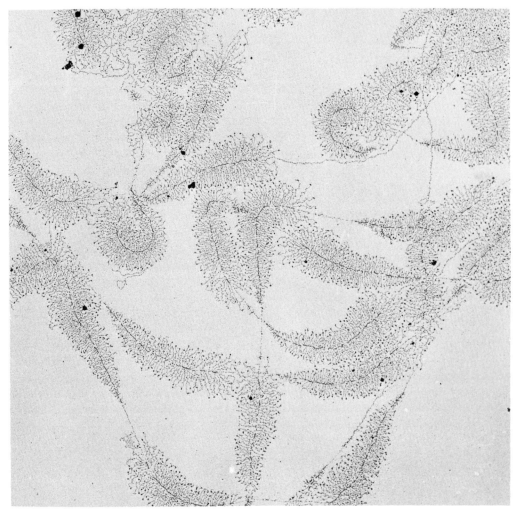

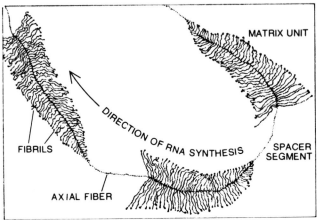

the Golgi apparatus and appears to be continuous with it.

Mitochondria. Mitochondria are usually oval structures found in the cytoplasm of cells. They range in size from spheres 0.2 μ in diameter to elongated structures 8 μ long. On section, each mitochondrion shows an outer enclosing membrane and an inner folded membrane. The inner membrane is thrown into inward projecting folds called *cristae*. Knob-like projections attached to the cristae have also been described. Mitochondria contain the enzymes associated with oxidation in the citric acid cycle and the concurrent storage of energy by means of the change of ADP to ATP (see Chapter 23). Cells undergoing active metabolism have large numbers of mitochondria in the cytoplasm.

Golgi Apparatus. The Golgi apparatus usually appears as a series of flattened membranous sacs near the nucleus. The electron microscope has definitely proven that the Golgi apparatus is not an artifact of fixation or staining, as some believed from the evidence of light microscopy. Golgi membranes closely resemble smooth-surfaced endoplasmic reticulum, and the two may be associated or even continuous.

Other Components of the Cell. Microsomes are pieces of rough-surfaced endoplasmic reticulum (having ribosomes attached) that have been torn from their natural state by homogenizing the cell. They can be separated by ultracentrifugation from other parts of homogenized (ground) cells, being somewhat lighter than the mitochondria and nuclei.

The granules seen on the surface of various membranes in the cell and also seen as clumps of granules or as individual granules are called *ribosomes*. These consist mostly of RNA. If the granules are unattached, they are called *free ribosomes*.

Less constant structures are the various types of membrane-bound vesicles that may contain stored material such as lipid or glycogen, secretory material, or enzymes as in the lysosomes.

The relative quantities of the different cell constituents seem to vary with the specialization and function of different types of cells. Some of these differences will be pointed out when specific tissues are discussed in subsequent chapters.

Fig. 2–6.   Active genes for ribosomal RNA are arrayed within an unwound nucleolar core that was stained with tungstic acid and enlarged 26,000 diameters in the electron micrograph, elements of which are interpreted in the simplified drawing (below). One sees a long axial fiber in the form of a collapsed circle, with a series of arrowhead-shaped "matrix units" along it. Each unit is composed of a set of fine lateral fibrils of graded lengths. By staining and enzyme testing the axial fiber is identified as a complex of DNA and protein, the fibrils as complexes of RNA and protein. The segment of DNA within each matrix unit is a gene for ribosomal RNA; each fibril is a protein-complexed ribosomal-RNA precursor molecule that was being transcribed from the gene in the living oocyte. The stretches of the fiber between matrix units are inactive "spacer" segments the function of which is not yet known. (From The Visualization of Genes in Action, O. L. Miller, Jr. Copyright ©, 1973 by Scientific American, Inc. All rights reserved.)

Chapter *3*

Physiology of the Cell

Physiology of the cell is a broad field encompassing all cellular functions. It involves the physical and chemical changes that occur in the normal functioning of the cell. This cellular physiology includes application of most laws of physics and chemistry as they pertain to living cells. The findings of cellular physiologists must be interpreted in the light of structures identified with various techniques, including the use of the electron microscope, the phase-contrast microscope, the ordinary light microscope, x-ray diffraction, histochemistry, isotope studies, and others. As De Robertis et al., 1975, state, "the concepts of *form* and *function* fuse into inseparable unity."

PROPERTIES OF LIFE

It is difficult if not impossible to give a satisfactory definition of life. However, the cell is the functional unit of all animal life. It is the basic unit that makes up all tissues, organs, and systems, which in turn make up the total animal. Therefore, the properties of the cell are equated with those of life. These properties include growth, reproduction, absorption, metabolism, excretion, secretion, irritability, conductivity, and contractility. The last two, however, are not properties universal to all cells. They are primarily characteristic of nerve and muscle cells, respectively.

Growth refers to increase in size, usually by increase in the amount of protoplasm. Increase in size of a cell or organ beyond normal is called *hypertrophy*. A decrease in size from normal is called *atrophy*. Failure of a tissue or organ to develop is called *aplasia*, while incomplete development or defective development of a tissue or organ is called *hypoplasia*.

30

Reproduction of a cell or of an organism implies the ability to produce more cells or more organisms that are essentially the same as the original. Increase in size of a structure because of increased number of cells is called *hyperplasia*.

Absorption refers to the process of taking dissolved materials into the substance of the cell. This can be a passive process dependent on the forces of diffusion and osmosis, or it can be an active process requiring the expenditure of energy from ATP, or it may occur by electrochemical ionic forces and affinities that require no direct expenditure of energy. All three can be occurring at the same time across the same membrane.

Two other means of getting extracellular materials into the cell are *phagocytosis* and *pinocytosis* (Fig. 3–1). If the material is engulfed by an ameboid-like action of the cell, the process is called phagocytosis, and cells with this ability are called *phagocytes*. The cell flows around the material until it is com-

pletely surrounded and thereby engulfed. This ability is characteristic of some white blood cells (WBC), which engulf large particulate matter, tissue debris, degenerated red blood cells (RBC), or bacteria.

Pinocytosis is the process by which cells can take in fluid and molecules too large to be carried across the plasma membrane by active transport, particularly small proteins. The substance first becomes adsorbed to (in physical contact with) the plasma membrane. This changes the surface tension and electrical properties of the membrane, causing it to invaginate into the cell and taking in with it the substance and some extracellular fluid. The invagination forms a membrane-bound pocket or tear-drop-like *pinocytotic vesicle* which blebs off, and the plasma membrane closes over the invagination. The vesicle, which is now within the cytoplasm, contains extracellular particles and fluid which are finally released into the cytoplasm proper when its membrane is digested away

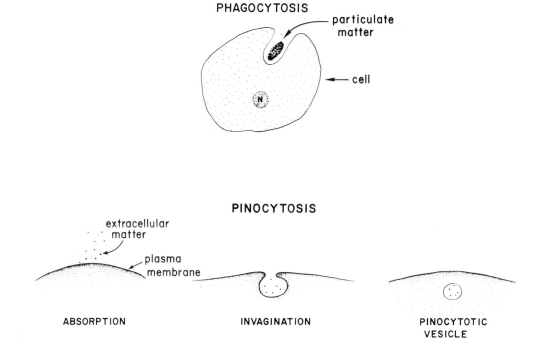

Fig. 3–1. Phagocytosis and pinocytosis.

by lysosomes (packets of enzymes in the cytoplasm). Pinocytosis has been observed in a number of mammalian cells, particularly those equipped with microvilli, as in the epithelial cells lining the intestinal tract and renal proximal tubules.

Metabolism (internal respiration) refers to the utilization of nutrients by the cell, consisting essentially of oxidation of carbon compounds to carbon dioxide and water, with the release of energy. This is not like burning but is a slow, controlled, stepwise process that is discussed in Chapter 23. Oxidation not only includes the addition of oxygen, but also refers to the removal of hydrogen or the removal of electrons. Metabolism refers to the sum total of the biochemical reactions occurring in each cell, and therefore, in the entire animal. Those reactions that build and maintain the body through energy formation are called *anabolic*, and those reactions that release energy by the breakdown of substances are called *catabolic*.

Excretion and *secretion* at the cellular level refer to loss of material from the cell. If waste products are lost, the process is called excretion; if useful products are released, the process is called secretion. Both active and passive excretion and secretion occur. To function efficiently, all parts of the cell protoplasm must be reasonably close to the plasma membrane for absorption of nutrients, excretion of wastes, and secretion of synthesized products. These restraints, therefore, tend to limit the optimal size of cells.

The secretion of products synthesized by the cell into the extracellular fluid (ECF) that bathes the cells, occurs by a process called *exocytosis, emiocytosis,* or *reverse pinocytosis*. This is essentially the opposite of pinocytosis. Membrane-bound (surrounded) vesicles containing secretory substances that have been "packaged" by the Golgi apparatus migrate in the cytoplasm to the plasma membrane. Here they become adsorbed to the membrane, causing the membrane at those points to rupture, releasing the contents of the vesicles into the extracellular fluid space. This expulsion of vesicular contents is also a means of excreting some metabolic waste products from the cell.

Irritability (also called excitability) consists of the property of being able to react to a stimulus. The reaction to a stimulus must necessarily consist of one of the other properties of protoplasm, such as conduction or contraction.

Conductivity is the property of transmitting an impulse from one point in the cell to another. Nerve cells and muscle cells are specialized for the functions of conductivity and irritability.

Contractility is the property of shortening in one direction. Muscle cells are specialized for contractions, although some other cells and cell organelles also contain contractile protein and exhibit limited movement (e.g., cilia).

CHEMICAL COMPOSITION OF THE CELL

Chemical composition of various parts of the cell plays an important role in cellular function. The approximate composition of protoplasm by percentage of constituent is: water, 85; protein, 10; lipid, 2; inorganic matter, 1.5; and other substances including carbohydrates, 1.5. Of equal or greater importance is the arrangement of molecules, particularly the proteins, nucleic acids, lipids, and their precursors.

Water

Water is by far the largest constituent of protoplasm and certainly one of the most important. The amorphous portion of the cell, the protoplasm proper, is largely a colloidal solution in water. Water also acts as a solvent for inorganic substances and enters into many reactions that occur in the cell.

Water occurs in the cell as *free water*, which is available for use in metabolism, and as *bound water*, which is adsorbed to the surface of protein and other molecules. The water of the tissues and body fluids is mostly free water, capable of passing in and out of cells and between the cardiovascular system and the tissues.

The water content of the animal body as a whole ranges from 55 to 67% of body weight. About 40% of the water (by weight) lies within the body cells and is called *intracellular fluid*. Another 15% by weight is called *interstitial fluid* and includes: the water between the cells (bathing the cells), the lymph in the lymph vessels, the cerebrospinal fluid (CSF), the fluid in the joints, the fluid in the eyes (intraocular fluid), and the serous fluid in the visceral spaces (i.e., pericardial, pleural, and peritoneal spaces).

About 5% of the body water by weight is in the blood plasma. The plasma and the interstitial fluid are referred to as the extracellular fluid (ECF), meaning all fluid outside of the cells, which therefore amounts to about 20% of the body weight. Of course, the total weight or volume of water varies from one animal to another according to size.

Water is lost each day from the body mostly in the urine, but also in the feces, from the lungs during breathing or panting, by evaporation from the skin, and by sweating. The animal is aware of urination and defecation. However, loss from the lungs and evaporation from the skin is called *insensible water loss*, because the animal is unaware of it.

Water losses must be replenished if the animal is to remain in water balance and not become dehydrated. This water replacement is obtained mostly by drinking water, but also comes from the water contained in feed and from *metabolic water*. Metabolic water is the water generated in all the cells of the body by mitochondria during the formation of energy (ATP) from food nutrients.

Water is important as a solvent for all water-soluble substances in the body. It transports nutrients to the cells and waste products and secretory products from the cells by way of the cardiovascular system.

Water enters into many biochemical reactions in the body.

The physical properties of water are important in temperature regulation. Its property of high *specific heat* allows appreciable raising of the body temperature. The high *heat conductivity* of water enables effective transfer of heat from the body core to the skin surface and *evaporation* allows heat loss for cooling the body surface.

The quantity of water taken in varies considerably with the environment to which the animal or organism is adapted. The time required for a complete turnover of the amount of water equal to the body weight varies with the species. De Robertis et al., 1960, give this time for the ameba as 7 days; man, 4 weeks; camel, 3 months; tortoise, 1 year; and some cacti, 29 years.

Proteins

After water, proteins comprise the next largest constituent of protoplasm. Proteins and related substances are involved in many functions of protoplasm and the cell. The large size of many protein molecules makes them an important factor in maintaining osmotic pressure within the cell, so that the water content of the cell remains at a relatively constant level. Some proteins serve as structural elements, as in hair, wool, horns, hooves, and as the collagen of connective tissue. All enzymes, which catalyze chemical reactions in cells, are proteins. Protein makes up many of the hormones. Protein permits muscle contraction, since the muscle filaments are contractile proteins. Proteins are carriers of some substances in the blood and maintain the potential osmotic pressure of the blood. Immunity depends on proteins as antibodies. All cell membranes are partly protein, and proteins are associated with the genes involved in the transmission of genetic information from cell to cell and from generation to generation.

Proteins are large macromolecules made up of polymers of amino acids linked together by *peptide bonds*, forming polypeptide chains. Each protein molecule consists of one or more of these polypeptide chains.

Proteins can be classified as *structural proteins* or as *reactive proteins*. Structural proteins include the following fibrous proteins: *collagens*, which are the major proteins of connective tissue, and which represent about 30% of the total protein content of the animal body; *elastins*, which are present in elastic tissues in the ligamentum nuchae, the abdominal tunic, and some arteries; and *keratins*, which are the proteins of wool, hair, horns, and hoofs.

Reactive proteins include enzymes, protein hormones, globulins of blood and muscle, *histones* and *protamines* associated with nucleic acids, contractile proteins, and those proteins that are conjugated with nonamino substances. Conjugated proteins include *nucleoproteins* (proteins combined with nucleic acids), *mucoproteins* and *glycoproteins* (proteins combined with carbohydrate), and *lipoproteins* (proteins combined with lipids).

Within each protein subgroup, differences often occur from one animal species to another in the sequence of the amino acids of the polypeptide chains. For example, the serum albumin in the blood of horses is different from that in the blood of cattle and sheep. In cattle, the protein hormone insulin is slightly different from that in swine. Proteins and the amino acids that form them are discussed in more detail in later chapters.

Lipids

Although lipids (fatty substances) account for a relatively small percentage of protoplasm, they are important in forming a part of the plasma membrane and other membranous constituents of the cell. In addition, lipids are found in some vitamins and in some hormones and, of course, provide a convenient way to store energy in the form of body fat.

Triglycerides are the lipids that store energy in adipose tissue of the animal.

Prostaglandins are a group of hormones that are 20-carbon atom unsaturated fatty acids derived from other lipids. They are present in varying concentrations in different tissues throughout the body.

Waxes are also a class of lipids. The waxes synthesized in the animal occur mostly in the epithelial cells of the skin. Here the waxes form a protective coating on the skin or hair as a water-repellent and as a barrier against bacteria. Lanolin is wool fat and cerumen is ear wax.

Vitamins A, D, E, and K contain lipids. *Phospholipids* make up a considerable portion of cell membranes. *Cholesterol* is a lipid that is a constituent of all animal cells and is present in the blood and the bile. *Steroids* (such as bile acids and sex hormones) are derived from lipids. It is readily appreciated that lipids are important in the homeokinesis of the healthy animal. Lipids are described in greater detail in the chapters on foods, absorption, and metabolism.

Carbohydrates

Carbohydrates make up less than 1% of most cells. Relatively little carbohydrate is found in protoplasm, even though carbohydrate forms a major part of the food of most animals.

Energy can be stored more efficiently as fat than as carbohydrate in the animal body because most of both the carbon and hydrogen of fats can be oxidized, but the hydrogen and oxygen of carbohydrates are in the same proportion as in water, so in effect only the carbon is available for oxidation. However, carbohydrates in the cells have a high rate of turnover and utilization as energy for the ongoing metabolism of the cells. The simple sugar, glucose, is converted to energy in the cells. Glucose can also be polymerized to form glycogen as a storage form of potential energy. Glycogen is stored mainly in liver cells. In plants, the carbohydrates not only serve for storage of energy, but also are of structural importance. Several sugars are found in combination with proteins to form much of the ground substance (noncellular portion) of connective tissues and some of the special fluids of the body, such as synovial fluids and the liquids of the eye.

The sugar deoxyribose is found in combination with a base (purine or pyrimidine) and a phosphate, forming *DNA (deoxyribonucleic acid)* which is the carrier of all genetic information from generation to generation and from cell to cell, and is believed to be ultimately in control of all functions of the cell. DNA is found almost exclusively in the nucleus of the cell. A related substance, *RNA (ribonucleic acid),* includes the sugar ribose combined with a base and a phosphate. RNA is intimately associated with synthesis of all cell proteins.

Inorganic Substances

Inorganic substances in protoplasm may exist as ionizable salts such as NaCl, or they may be combined with proteins, lipids, or carbohydrates. Iodine is an essential part of the hormone *thyroxine;* iron is necessary in *hemoglobin;* and phosphorus, joined with *adenosine* to form *ADP (adenosine diphosphate)* or *ATP (adenosine triphosphate),* is vital for energy relationships in almost all living matter.

Inorganic salts and their ions aid in maintaining a constant pH and help to regulate osmotic pressure. The electrolytes are especially essential to nerve and muscle function.

An electrolyte is any molecular substance that, in solution, will dissociate into its electrically charged components, called *ions.* For example, this occurs when NaCl (sodium chloride) in solution dissociates into Na^+ and Cl^- ions. The solution can then carry an electric charge and current.

Of all the atoms or elements found in protoplasm, over 99% comprise the elements hydrogen, carbon, oxygen, and nitrogen. In addition to these and the iodine, iron, and phosphorus already mentioned, protoplasm also contains calcium, chlorine, potassium, sulfur, sodium, magnesium, copper, manganese, zinc, cobalt, chromium, selenium, molybdenum, fluorine, silicone, tin, and vanadium. Of the 24 different elements found in the body cells, 20 represent less than 1% of the total in living tissue.

The major ions found within cells in order of abundance, expressed in milliequivalents per liter of fluid (mEq/L), are: potassium (K^+), 140 mEq/L; phosphate ($HPO_4^=$), 75 mEq/L, magnesium (Mg^{++}), 60 mEq/L; sodium (Na^+), 10 mEq/L; bicarbonate (HCO_3^-), 10 mEq/L; and chloride (Cl^-), 4 mEq/L.

A *milliequivalent* is 1/1000 of an equivalent. The equivalent weight is the weight in grams that will displace or react with one gram-atomic weight of hydrogen ($H^+ = 1.008$ gm). So one equivalent has the same reactive power equivalent to H^+. The weight of one equivalent of an element is equal to its atomic weight divided by its *valence* (the number of positive or negative charges). Therefore, 23 gm of Na^+ ($23 \div 1$) has the same number of positive charges available for reaction as does 20 gm of Ca^{++} ($40 \div 2$). Also, 35.5 gm of Cl^- ($35.5 \div 1$) has as many charges available as 23 gm of Na^+ and 20 gm of Ca^{++}. So they represent equal equivalents.

The practical importance of this concept is that laboratory reports and records of measurements of fluid electrolyte and ion concentrations are often expressed as mEq/L. Another way of expressing measurements is in mg%, which is the same thing as milligrams per 100 milliliters (mg/100 ml). Measurements may also be expressed as mg/dl, where dl means deciliter, which equals 100 ml or 1/10 of a liter. A liter is 1000 ml or 1.06 quarts.

PHYSICAL FORM OF CELLULAR COMPONENTS

Of equal, if not greater, importance than what materials are found in the cell is the physical form of these substances. With the exception of the *organelles* (the actual formed structures within the cell), the *cytoplasm* (protoplasm exclusive of the nucleus) is largely a colloidal solution. *Colloidal solutions* contain particles that are larger than molecules of *crystalloids*, such as sugar or salt in a true solution, yet the colloidal particles are small enough to have a relatively large surface area. Undoubtedly the configuration of the surfaces of these particles plays an important part in the living activities of protoplasm. Crystalloids readily pass through living membranes and can be crystallized out of solution. Examples of crystalloids are glucose, salts, urea, uric acid, and creatinine.

Colloidal particles may range in diameter from 1 to 500 mμ, although size is not the only characteristic that differentiates colloids from crystalloids. Colloids scatter light in the so-called *Tyndall effect,* as seen when a narrow beam of light passes through dusty air in a room. Crystalloids ordinarily have very little light-scattering effect. Colloidal particles do not pass through a semipermeable membrane such as sausage casing, but crystalloids pass through freely. This differential movement of different sized particles depends on the permeability of the membrane to each particle. The process of separating colloids and crystalloids in this manner is called *dialysis.*

The small molecular size of crystalloids in solution prevents them from having any appreciable surface activity. Colloids, on the other hand, present a definite interface (surface) at the junction of the colloidal particle and the dispersing medium (water).

Colloidal particles diffuse in solution much more slowly than crystalloids, and the viscosity of a colloidal solution is much greater than that of a crystalloid solution. In some colloidal solutions, the particles form such strong bonds (attachment) to each other that the solution becomes practically a solid. This state is known as a *gel* (such as gelatin or *Jell-O* when set); it may be contrasted with the *sol* form, which is liquid.

The relation of the colloidal particles to the dispersing medium is called *lyophilic* (solvent-loving) if there is an attraction between the particles and the solvent. This type of colloidal solution has no tendency to settle out by forming larger clumps (Fig. 3–2).

If there is no attraction between the colloidal particles and the solvent, the solution is called *lyophobic* (solvent-hating) and is unstable because the particles tend to clump and settle out. The same tendency occurs in emulsions such as oil in water. The oil droplets tend to coalesce and form larger and larger globules until two separate layers are formed. The emulsion can be stabilized if the oil droplets are surrounded by a film of protein. The water-soluble portions of the protein, including the hydroxyl and amino radicals, dissolve in the water, while the methyl and phenyl radicals dissolve in the oil. These oil droplets surrounded by a protein stabilizer repel each other because the water-soluble portion of the protein tends to ionize, producing surfaces with similar charges. Soaps have a similar effect in emulsifying oil, because the fatty-acid portion is soluble in the fat, and the sodium or other metallic ion is soluble in the water.

The presence of proteins in the form of colloidal particles explains many of the phenomena observed in living cells. These colloidal proteins may be either globular

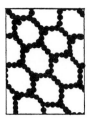

SOL   GEL   PRECIPITATION

Fig. 3–2. Colloidal states. In the fluid *sol* state the particles bounce about freely. In the *gel* state the particles probably form a continuous network, rendering the system jelly-like. When colloidal particles clump together into larger masses, they "settle out" by gravity, or precipitate. (Carlson, Johnson, and Cavert, The Machinery of the Body, courtesy of University of Chicago Press.)

(spherical) in form or of a fibrous (elongated) form. Many structures within cells as well as structures extruded from cells may be simply aggregations of one or both forms of protein colloids. When we speak of cell water, however, it should be considered that some water is possibly in a semi-crystalline form in the cell. Such a physical form of the cell "solvent" would have effects on cell chemistry different from those occurring in the liquid state.

TRANSPORT ACROSS MEMBRANES

The plasma membrane is a major factor in controlling *homeokinesis* (homeostasis) within the cell. This is the phenomenon of attempting to maintain a relatively constant internal environment through ongoing dynamic exchanges, as is true for the entire animal body. Conventionally the term *homeostasis* has been used for this phenomenon, but since the cells and the body are never in a static condition, the more meaningful term homeokinesis is preferable. Homeokinesis implies a constant state of dynamic change or kinesis while maintaining function within normal ranges of variation. (The term homeokinesis also refers to a stage of mitosis in which equal amounts of chromatin go to each daughter nucleus of the dividing cell.)

The plasma membrane and the membranes of intracellular organelles have an important place in determining what enters and leaves the cell or its organelles. Our very life and that of animals depend on this capability of controlling what enters and leaves the cells. It is therefore important to understand and appreciate the processes involved in membrane transport before discussing the functions of the animal's organs and systems.

The processes by which transport into and out of cells occurs are: diffusion, facilitated diffusion, osmosis, active transport, pinocytosis, and phagocytosis. (Pinocytosis and phagocytosis were described at the beginning of this chapter.)

Diffusion and Facilitated Diffusion

Diffusion is a *passive* mechanism. It is simply the distribution of a substance in a solvent (usually water) so that it becomes equally concentrated throughout the medium. Diffusion occurs because all molecules and ions have *kinetic energy*. They collide with each other and bounce away, to become so dispersed in the solvent that an equal concentration appears throughout. Diffusion occurs in fluid systems and across membranes that permit the passage of both the solute particles and the solvent. It proceeds from the region of greater concentration of particles to the region of lower concentration, so the net diffusion is said to occur "down" its *concentration gradient*.

Only a few substances, such as O_2, CO_2, and alcohol, are capable of diffusion across plasma membranes by kinetic energy alone. The molecules must be both water soluble and lipid soluble to diffuse across the membrane. Certain drugs have this property of membrane solubility, such as anesthetics including barbiturates. Cell membranes are *selectively permeable* (also called *differentially permeable*). That is, they permit some substances to pass through the membrane more readily than others, and some not at all. The *rate of net diffusion* across membranes depends on: (1) the permeability of the membrane to the specific molecules or ions, (2) the concentration difference on the two sides of the membrane, (3) the difference in electrical charges, and (4) the kinetic energy, or pressure difference, on the two sides of the membrane.

Facilitated diffusion is the same as simple or free diffusion in that it operates "down" the concentration and electrochemical gradients passively. However, facilitated diffusion involves a *carrier system* in the membrane to assist the crossing, but does not require the energy of ATP, as occurs in *active transport*.

Sugars, especially glucose, basically depend on facilitated diffusion to enter the cells, joining with a carrier substance upon reaching the lipid bilayer of the membrane. The carrier apparently is protein, and the glucose-carrier complex crosses the membrane "down" the glucose concentration gradient to the inside of the cell membrane. Here the carrier releases the glucose to enter the cell while the carrier remains in the membrane for more transport. Other substances besides glucose, such as amino acids, also depend on facilitated diffusion to cross cell membranes. Diffusion and facillitated diffusion are illustrated in Figure 3–3.

In addition to concentration differences, the speed at which facilitated diffusion occurs also depends on the amount of carrier substance available in the membrane. In the case of glucose the speed of entry is greatly increased by the hormone *insulin*, which is secreted by the pancreas. The major role of insulin is to facilitate the entry of glucose into the cells, where it can be used for producing energy.

Osmosis

Osmosis refers to the movement of water (solvent) across the cell membranes. Since the membranes are selectively permeable,

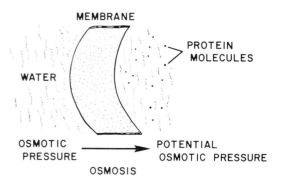

Fig. 3–4.   Osmosis in relation to a plasma membrane.

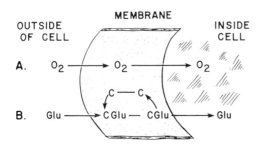

A. Free diffusion of O_2
B. Facilitated diffusion of Glucose
    Glu = glucose   c = carrier

Fig. 3–3.   Examples of free diffusion and facilitated diffusion across a plasma membrane.

some solute substances in the body and cell fluids (proteins, for example) cannot cross the membrane. Therefore, in order to have a pressure equilibrium on both sides of the membrane, water must move across to make up for the concentration differences of those substances that cannot cross. If a cell, for example, has a higher concentration of solutes than the interstitial fluid bathing the cell, then water will move into the cell from the interstitial fluid until the pressure is again equalized on both sides of the membrane. As the water moves in, the volume in the cell increases, which in turn increases its pressure. This is called *osmotic pressure* because it is due to the movement of water by osmosis. This phenomenon exerts a driving force from the solution on the less concentrated solute side of the membrane to the solution on the more concentrated solute side of the membrane (Fig. 3–4).

The force of *osmotic pressure* can be measured by enclosing the concentrated solution in a container whose walls are formed at least in part by a semipermeable membrane and surrounded by distilled water. This container is closed except for its connection to a vertical tube into which the fluid rises as water molecules pass through the pores of the membrane into the concentrated solution. The height the fluid rises in the tube is a measure of the osmotic pressure of the solution within the container. The fluid will continue to rise until the hydrostatic pressure of

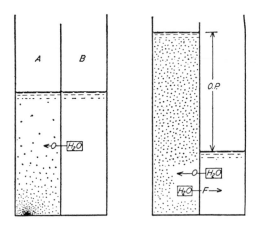

Fig. 3-5. Osmosis. A membrane impermeable to sugar prevents the dissolving sugar molecules from diffusing into chamber *B*. Water migrates from *B* to *A*, and equilibrium is established (right) when the osmotic flow of water (O) is equalized by the filtration of water (F) in the opposite direction. Distance O.P. is measure of osmotic pressure. (Carlson, Johnson, and Cavert, The Machinery of the Body, courtesy of University of Chicago Press.)

the column of fluid is equal to the osmotic pressure of the solution (Fig. 3-5). This type of measuring device is called an *osmometer*, and the tube may be connected to a mercury manometer (tube of mercury) to obtain a standard pressure.

Osmotic pressure is an important mechanism in maintaining homeokinesis or homeostasis (the relatively constant state of protoplasm) by determining to a large extent whether water will enter the cell or leave the cell. If the concentration of solutions on

each side of a membrane is the same, as seen with cells in blood, the bathing fluid is said to be *isotonic (isosmotic)* in relation to the cells. This means that the osmotic pressure is the same on both sides of the membrane. A 0.85 per cent solution of sodium chloride is considered to be *isotonic* with mammalian red blood cells and for this reason is called *physiologic saline solution (abbreviated PSS)*. Physiologic saline solution can be used to moisten exposed tissues, such as open wounds, without causing damage to the cells.

If the bathing fluid has a lower osmotic pressure than the cells, it is said to be *hypotonic* and water will tend to cross the membrane and enter the cells. In the case of red blood cells in hypotonic plasma, the water entering the cells can cause them to swell and finally burst, a condition called *hemolysis* of the red cells (see Fig. 3-6).

Red blood cells in a *hypertonic* plasma (more concentrated than the cell cytoplasm) will lose water to the plasma and become wrinkled. The wrinkling of red blood cells is called *crenation*. In relation to mammalian cells, a solution less concentrated than 0.85 per cent sodium chloride is said to be hypotonic; one more concentrated than 0.85 per sent sodium chloride is said to be hypertonic; and of course a 0.85 per cent sodium chloride solution is isotonic.

Osmosis is a means of compensating for differences in solute concentrations on the

Fig. 3-6. Osmotic effects upon red blood cells, showing swelling of the cells and hemolysis when they are placed in weak salt solutions, and shrinking when they are placed in strong salt solutions. Dots represent salt particles. Hemoglobin is shown in black. (Carlson, Johnson, and Cavert, The Machinery of the Body, courtesy of University of Chicago Press.)

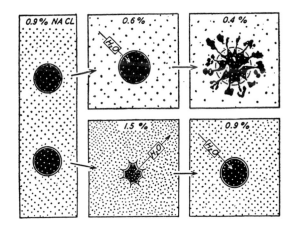

two sides of the cell membrane. The water osmotically moves from the side of least solute (particle) concentration to the side of greatest solute concentration, thereby diluting the concentrated side so that its solute pressure will equal that on the other side.

While osmotic pressure refers to the pressure exerted by the water itself, it is created by the fact that certain substances, such as proteins, cannot cross the membrane. Therefore, these nondiffusible solute substances exert a *potential osmotic pressure* that causes water to move by osmosis to the side of the membrane where the solute concentration is greatest.

The potential osmotic pressure is determined by the number of solute particles— the more solute particles in a volume of fluid, the greater the potential osmotic pressure. The number of particles is determined by the *molar concentration* of the solution and by the number of ions formed if the solute is an electrolyte. Molar concentration is equal to the grams of solute in one liter of solution divided by the molecular weight of the solute. If the solute molecules are not ionizable (not an electrolyte), then the potential osmotic pressure is directly proportional to the molar concentration. However, in the case of electrolytes, we have to multiply the number of ions formed per molecule by the molar concentration to calculate the potential osmotic pressure. For example, glucose is a nonelectrolyte, with one particle per molecule, but NaCl is an electrolyte, giving two particles (Na^+ and Cl^-) per molecule. So the number of particles of solute per liter of solution determines the potential osmotic pressure. It follows then that if the two solutions on each side of a membrane have the same osmolarity, they will have the same number of particles available to act osmotically.

These concepts of osmosis, osmotic pressure, and potential osmotic pressure become important in the treatment of the animal when such problems exist as edema, hypotension, dehydration, blood loss from hemorrhage, inflammation from infection, intravenous treatment of milk fever, and diarrhea. Furthermore, they are important principles in normal functions of the animal, such as the homeokinesis of blood and lymph flow, the excretion of wastes in the urine by the kidneys, the activity of muscles, the digestion and absorption of food, and other functions, as will be discussed in subsequent chapters.

Hydrostatic pressure may also drive appropriate materials across a selectively permeable membrane. This is illustrated by the fact that an increase in blood pressure will increase the amount of fluid entering the kidney nephrons from the blood plasma. (This process is explained in Chapter 22.)

The passage of electrolytes across a selectively permeable membrane is influenced by the electric charges of the ions on each side of the membrane. If all ions could pass freely through the membrane, an ionic equilibrium would be reached when the same number of positive and negative charges were found on each side of the membrane. But this does not occur in the living animal. The semipermeable membrane, however, is completely passive to water, in that it simply acts as a mechanical filter under net hydrostatic pressure or osmotic gradients.

Active Transport

Although the plasma membrane can function as a passive filter, it must do much more than that to account for the variety of materials that pass across it, and the variable speeds of such transport. Further, molecules of various substances can move across the plasma membrane (either into or out of the cell) "against" osmotic pressure, against hydrostatic pressure, against concentration gradients, and against an electrochemical gradient. The term "against" as used here means that the substance is moving in the direction opposite to that which would occur in diffusion. Therefore, it is also said to be traveling in an "uphill gradient." This movement across the plasma membrane requires work, utilizing the energy produced by the cell, and is called *active transport*.

The fact that sodium usually is found in greater concentration outside the cell and potassium is found in greater concentration inside the cell suggests some form of active transport, at least of the sodium ions. This mechanism has been called the *"sodium pump."* It is extremely important in nerve, muscle, and hormone functions of the animal, as will be discussed later.

Some substances are actively absorbed by cells, and others are actively secreted. This implies that transport is associated with the metabolism of the cell, because metabolic poisons and other injuries to the cell can destroy such transport and frequently increase the permeability of the plasma membrane to many substances. However, such injuries to the cell's normal function also cause transport changes by changing or damaging physical relationships within the cell and its membranes.

The physical and chemical makeup of the plasma membrane and the electrical activity of its components contribute much to the process of active transport. Current predominant evidence is that a *carrier system* is involved in active transport. A carrier complex is formed between the material to be transported across the membrane and a membrane carrier molecule by action of an enzyme. Energy is required for enzyme linking of the material to the carrier, it is believed, as well as during the ultimate separation of the carrier from the transported material at the other side of the membrane. This energy is derived from ATP in the presence of magnesium ions (Mg^{++}), both of which are present in the membrane along with the enzyme ATPase, which brings about the release of energy from ATP.

The maintenance of cellular ionic concentrations may also depend on the relative affinities that different ions and charged molecules have for complexing with one another, requiring no ion pumps. In that case, the membrane would act like a semiconductor junction (an interface between two dissimilar materials).

CYTOPLASMIC ORGANELLES

The Golgi Apparatus

The Golgi complex *(Golgi apparatus)* varies in size and location in cells of different tissues (Fig. 3–7). It functions as the site of the final stages of synthesis of secretory products of the cell, and "packages" these products by surrounding them with a membrane for either temporary storage in the cell or for transport to the plasma membrane where exocytosis occurs, releasing the products into the extracellular fluid as a form of secretion. Mucopolysaccharides may be formed in the Golgi apparatus, and glycoproteins are terminally synthesized in the Golgi apparatus as combinations of carbohydrates and proteins, which have been transported to the Golgi apparatus by the smooth and rough endoplasmic reticulum.

The Endoplasmic Reticulum and Ribosomes

The endoplasmic reticulum (ER) is a membranous network found throughout the cytoplasm of the cell (Fig. 3–7). It was first described in the endoplasm (the cytoplasm deepest in the cell), giving rise to the name endoplasmic reticulum. Although still called the endoplasmic reticulum, it has been observed in all parts of the cytoplasm and may be continuous with the outer nuclear membrane. The endoplasmic reticulum is in the form of tubules and sheets, with occasional enlarged sacs or vesicles called *cisternae*.

The fact that ribosomes are found associated with some endoplasmic reticulum, like beads along the reticular membrane, has given it the name of *rough endoplasmic reticulum*, as opposed to the smooth type, which has no ribosomes associated with it. The rough endoplasmic reticulum (rough ER) is involved with protein synthesis by virtue of its ribosomal activity, and the more rough ER found in a cell, the greater the

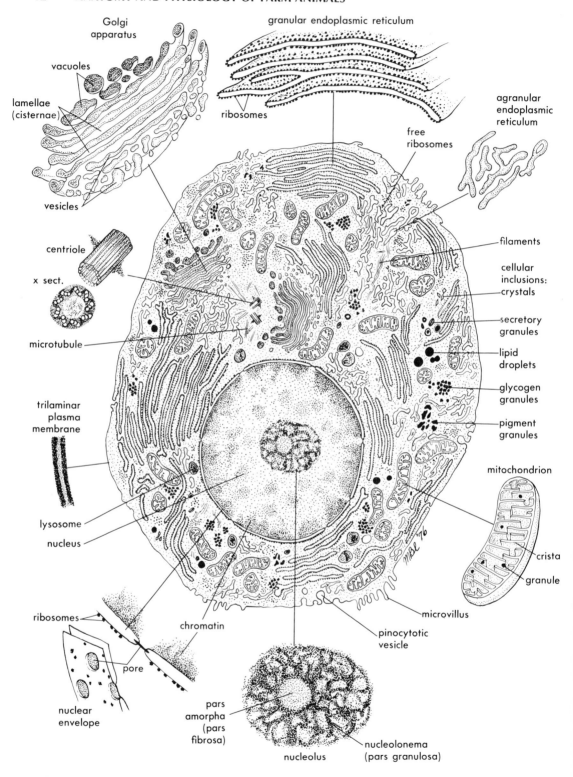

Golgi apparatus

vacuoles

lamellae (cisternae)

ribosomes

vesicles

granular endoplasmic reticulum

free ribosomes

agranular endoplasmic reticulum

centriole

x sect.

microtubule

trilaminar plasma membrane

lysosome

nucleus

filaments

cellular inclusions: crystals

secretory granules

lipid droplets

glycogen granules

pigment granules

mitochondrion

crista

granule

microvillus

pinocytotic vesicle

ribosomes

chromatin

pore

nuclear envelope

pars amorpha (pars fibrosa)

nucleolus

nucleolonema (pars granulosa)

Fig. 3–7.   Schematic drawing of a cell as seen in electron micrographs. (From Crouch, J.E.: Functional Human Anatomy. ed. 3. Philadelphia, Lea & Febiger, 1978.)

amount of proteins (including enzymes) the cell is capable of synthesizing. It has been suggested that the protein products are then carried away from the site of synthesis by the channels in the endoplasmic reticulum.

Smooth-surfaced endoplasmic reticulum may be involved in the synthesis and transport of glycogen, lipids and steroids. In muscle cells, the ER may act as a medium for the conduction of impulses and the transport of calcium ions essential for bringing about a contraction of the muscle.

Ribosomes are small spherical organelles which are either attached to rough endoplasmic reticulum or are free in the cytoplasm (Fig. 3–7). Each ribosome is composed of two round subunits, one larger than the other. Ribosomes consist of about two thirds RNA (ribonucleic acid) and one third protein. They help to synthesize protein. The ribosomes of the rough ER synthesize proteins for secretion from the cell, whereas the free ribosomes produce structural proteins and enzymes (which are proteins) for metabolic use by the cell itself. The *free ribosomes* appear in groups or clusters called *polyribosomes* or *polysomes*. Because of the composition of ribosomes, they are sometimes referred to as ribonucleoprotein granules (RNP).

Mitochondria

Mitochondria have a specific gravity that is next to that of nuclei, as shown by sedimentation or centrifuging a cellular homogenate. The double membrane of the mitochondrion, with the *cristae* projecting into the interior, gives a large amount of surface for attachment of enzymes (Fig. 3–7). Studies of fragmented mitochondria indicate that all the enzymes associated with oxidation of nutrients to carbon dioxide, ATP, and water are found in the mitochondria. Thus, all of the enzymes and coenzymes involved in the *tricarboxylic acid cycle* (also called the *Krebs cycle* or *citric acid cycle*) are largely localized in the mitochondria.

Oxidation during the tricarboxylic acid cycle releases carbon dioxide and hydrogen atom pairs (H_2). The H_2 then furnishes its electrons to the *mitochondrial electron transport* system to drive a series of reduction reactions, culminating in the formation of water and storage of the energy produced in the form of ATP (adenosine triphosphate). The ATP is formed by the oxidative phosphorylation of ADP (adenosine diphosphate), which adds one inorganic phosphate molecule to ADP, thereby creating the higher-energy compound ATP. The energy incorporated into ATP then becomes available for any cellular activity that requires energy, such as protein synthesis, muscle contraction, and active transport. Energy is released in reconversion of ATP to ADP and inorganic phosphate. Most of these processes requiring energy are located outside of the mitochondria, although some synthesis occurs within the mitochondria.

Since the mitochondria produce the energy for the cell, it follows that the more mitochondria present in a cell, the more active is the cell. Mitochondria contain their own DNA and RNA for the purpose of reproducing themselves. They also carry on partial synthesis of proteins and lipids and have their own ribosomes.

Lysosomes

Lysosomes are larger than ribosomes but smaller than mitochondria. They range in diameter from 0.25 to 0.75 μ. Lysosomes apparently originate from the endoplasmic reticulum and the Golgi apparatus. They are membrane-bound packages of digestive (hydrolytic) enzymes (Fig. 3–7). Many of the enzymes have been identified, and the most prominent one seems to be acid phosphatase, which is released when a cell is injured for the apparent purpose of digesting the debris. Lysosomes of dying cells rupture, releasing their enzymes in order to lyse (destroy) the useless cell. Hence they may take part in the normal turnover of body cells as the cells complete their life cycle.

Vesicles of engulfed material from phagocytosis and pinocytosis appear to fuse with the membrane of the lysosomes, thereby bringing about the enzymatic digestion of the membrane and some of the contents of the vesicle. The enzymes apparently act either within the lysosome or are released into the cytoplasm. The only mammalian cells that are known not to contain lysosomes are the red blood cells.

The lysosome enzymes can degrade proteins, carbohydrates, and nucleic acids, and so the lysosome is considered to be the digestive organ of the cell. White blood cells, which act as scavenger cells by phagocytizing bacteria, dead tissue, and broken cell debris, contain a lot of lysosomes.

When cells contain inactive lysosomes, disease can follow. An example is Pompe's disease, in which glycogen cannot be digested by the lysosomes. On the other hand, changes caused by sunburn occur when lysosomes in the skin cells are ruptured by the ultraviolet light of the sun.

Other Structures

Peroxisomes are smaller than lysosomes and in some cells are more numerous than lysosomes. Peroxisomes contain *oxidase* enzymes responsible for producing H_2O_2 (hydrogen peroxide), and about 40% of their enzyme content is *catalase*, the enzyme that degrades hydrogen peroxide.

Microtubules are tiny rod-like tubes that are scattered throughout the cytoplasm in most cells (Fig. 3–7). They apparently serve as skeletal elements to give some structural form to the cell. However, microtubules are also involved as spindle fibers in cell division and as contractile elements in cilia, the fibrils that produce ciliary motion. They may also serve to assist transport of molecules within some cells, such as the axons of neurons (nerve cells).

Microfilaments are rod-like organelles that are thinner than microtubules (Fig. 3–7). They also are associated with contraction and with providing structural integrity, such as helping to keep microvilli extended on the border of epithelial cells to provide optimal absorption of food products from the small intestine. Microfilaments may also assist in the movement of fibroblasts in the heart, in the contraction of all muscle cells, in the growth of axons, and in the retraction of blood clots.

The *centriole* is a short cylinder that looks like the basal body of a cilium and consists of 9 paired filaments arranged in a circle (Fig. 3–7). The centriole is located near the nucleus in all cells and generally it is paired—two centrioles comprising what is called the *centrosome*. The centrosome functions in cell division, forming the two poles of the spindle from which the asters radiate.

NUCLEUS

Experiments have shown that the functional activity and the continued life of the cell depend on the presence and functional integrity of a nucleus. A cell from which the nucleus has been removed (enucleated) gradually ceases its activity, atrophies, and finally dies. However, if the nucleus is replaced with a nucleus from a cell of the same species prior to irreversible atrophy, function of the cell can be restored. The only cells in higher animals that do not have nuclei are mature red blood cells. This lack of a nucleus is associated with their short life-span of only 120 days.

Fig. 3–8. Molecular constituents of RNA and DNA (deoxyribonucleic acid) are five bases, two sugars and phosphoric acid. The union of a base, a sugar and phosphoric acid yields a nucleotide *(lower right)*. RNA is a giant molecule built up of nucleotides containing ribose sugar and any one of four bases: adenine, uracil, guanine, or cytosine. DNA consists of nucleotides containing deoxyribose and the same four bases except that thymine replaces uracil. Adenylic acid at lower right is an RNA nucleotide; if a particular oxygen atom is removed (arrow), it becomes deoxyadenylic acid and a building block for DNA. (From Stevens, C. F.: The Neuron. Sci. Am., *241*:54, 1979.)

BASES

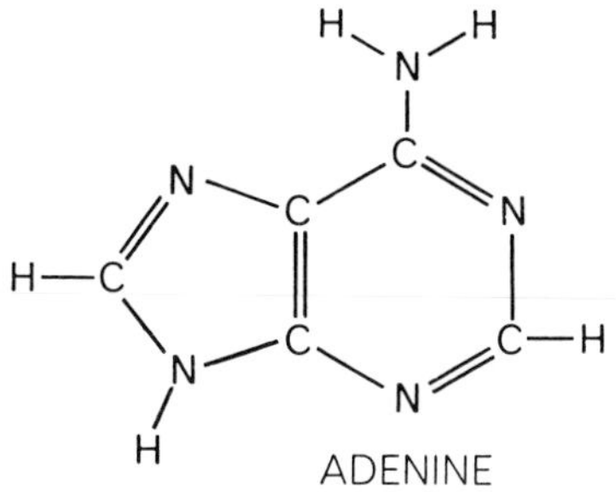

ADENINE

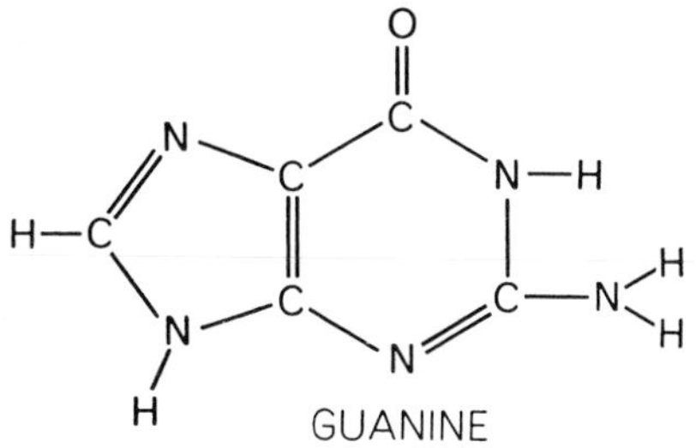

GUANINE

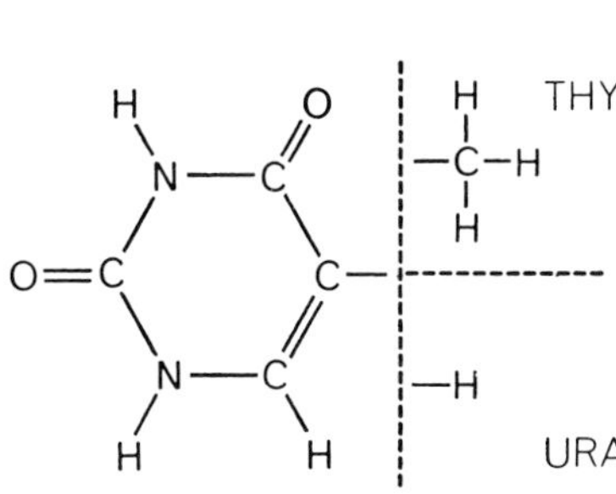

THYMINE

URACIL

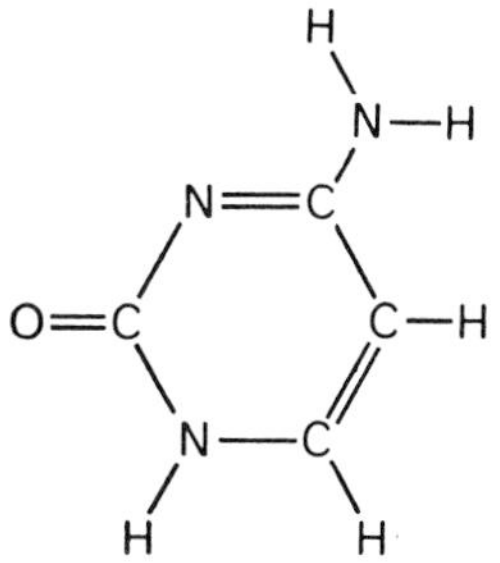

CYTOSINE

SUGARS

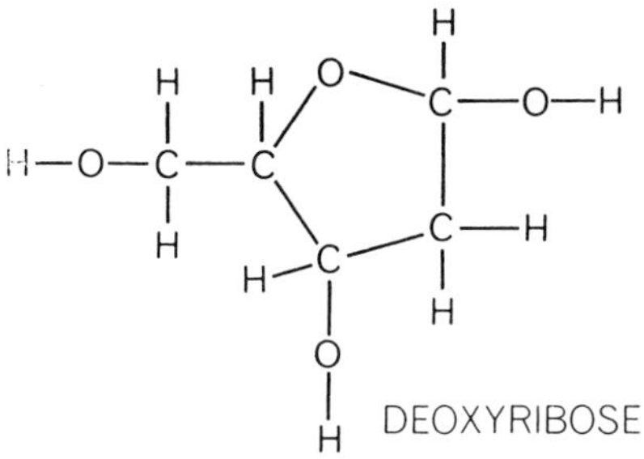

DEOXYRIBOSE

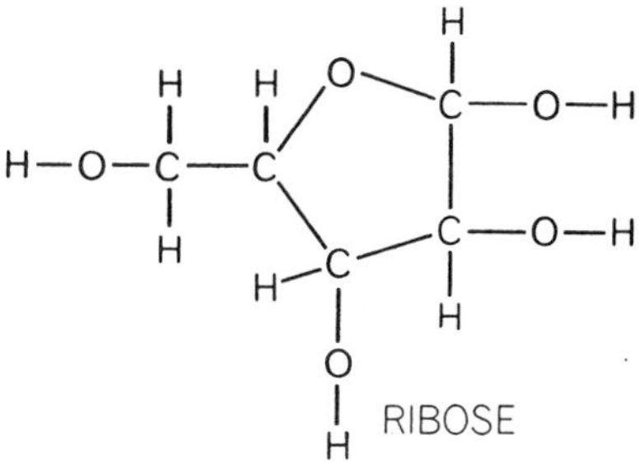

RIBOSE

PHOSPHORIC ACID

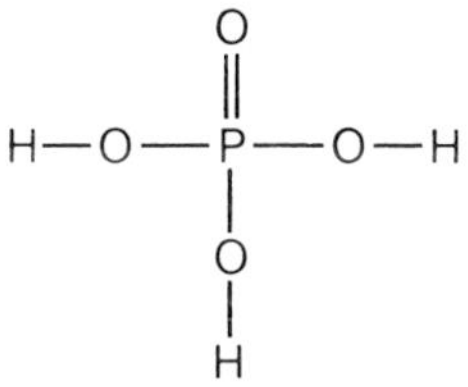

NUCLEOTIDE
(ADENYLIC ACID)

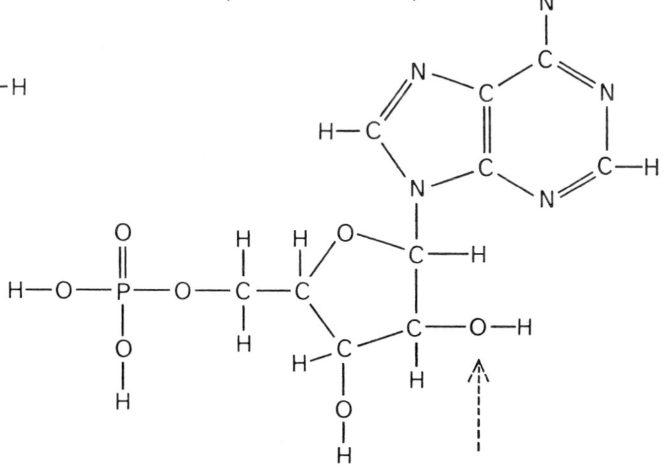

The primary functions of the nucleus are: (1) to regulate or control protein synthesis in the cell, thereby regulating the biochemical activities of the cell, and (2) to ensure the passage of genetic material (the chromosomes and their component genes) to subsequent generations of cells and/or organisms, resulting from division of the cell after replication of the DNA.

Constituents of the nucleus can be identified by chemical analysis, and the location of many of them can be determined by histochemical methods, in which specific substances are stained and their location observed in tissue sections.

The nuclei of all cells contain DNA (deoxyribonucleic acid), RNA (ribonucleic acid), proteins, lipids, and inorganic compounds. Most of the RNA in the nucleus is located in the nucleolus, and there also may be a small amount of DNA in the nucleolus. Some proteins, including enzymes, are also present in the nucleolus. It is presumed that the nucleolus functions in some synthesis of RNA as well as RNA storage.

DNA (Deoxyribonucleic Acid)
and RNA (Ribonucleic Acid)

DNA is what comprises the essence of the genes and the chromosomes. Chromosomes are composed of chains or sequences of DNA covered with protein coats in the form of protamines and histones. It is believed that the protein coat covering the DNA is protective or inhibitory, requiring specific enzymes for its breakdown whenever RNA is to be formed from any part of the DNA template. Since chromosomes are complexed with proteins in this way, they are sometimes referred to as *deoxyribonucleoprotein*.

DNA and RNA both consist of many small units *(monomers)* joined to form long chains. Each monomer, called a *nucleotide*, is made up of a phosphate, a sugar, and either a *purine* or *pyrimidine* base. The sugar in RNA is ribose, but the sugar in DNA is called deoxyribose because it lacks

one oxygen atom that is present in ribose (Fig. 3–8).

The two purines, *adenine* and *guanine*, and the pyrimidine *cytosine* are found as bases in both DNA and RNA. However, the pyrimidine *thymine* occurs only in DNA, and the pyrimidine *uracil* occurs only in RNA.

The structure of DNA was determined by Watson and Crick to be a double helix something like a spiral stair or twisted metal ladder. The rails consist of two long chains of sugar-phosphate molecules, and the rungs are made up of paired bases that hold the two parts of the double helix together. Adenine is always paired with thymine, and guanine is always paired with cytosine. The two strands are joined together by hydrogen bonds between the bases (Fig. 3–9).

All genetic information carried by the chromosomes from one generation of cells to the next is coded by the specific sequence of purine and pyrimidine bases in a DNA molecule. This sequential arrangement of bases and its control of heredity, both on the cellular level and the species level, has been referred to as the *genetic code* and also as the language of life. Eventually the code is interpreted by the cell largely as specific proteins, particularly enzymes.

The two strands of the DNA double helix are not identical but are complementary. In other words, wherever adenine appears on one strand, thymine will be in the same position on the opposite strand, and wherever guanine is located on one strand, cytosine is found in the same position on the opposite strand. Replication of DNA results by splitting the double helices at the point of junction of complementary bases. Each separated strand then serves as a template or model for the formation of its complementary strand, thus resulting in two double DNA helices which are replicas of the original DNA double helix (Fig. 3–10).

As stated earlier, the DNA of the nucleus is essential for the continued production of enzymes and other proteins by the cell. This involves a series of steps, the first of which is enzyme-mediated, transcribing small parts of the DNA in essentially the same manner as DNA replication, except confined to small areas of the double helix. This process is called *transcription*, and the products are called *ribosomal RNA*, *messenger RNA* and *transfer RNA*, which are then either stored in the nucleolus or leave the nucleus and enter the cell cytoplasm.

The messenger RNA (mRNA) joins the ribosomes on the rough endoplasmic reticulum after it leaves the nucleus. There is at least one transfer RNA (tRNA) for each of the approximately 20 different amino acids in the cell. These specific tRNA unite with the specific amino acids in the cytoplasm through the aid of energy from ATP. Then, as the mRNA moves across a series of ribosomes, it codes for a specific sequence of amino acids which are donated by the tRNA amino-acyl complexes. This phase is called *translation* and results in the production of a specific protein from a series of specific amino acids laid down in the right order and linked together by peptide bonds (Fig. 3–11).

It appears that the same general principles of information-transfer apply regardless of whether the cell is producing proteins for use outside the cell or for additional and reparative purposes and enzyme needs within the cell. These same principles also seem to apply to all living things, from viruses up through the hierarchy of plants, lower animals, vertebrates, and man.

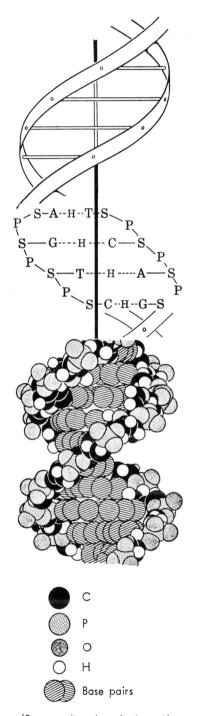

C
P
O
H
Base pairs

(*See opposite column for legend.*)

Fig. 3–9. The helix of DNA, with three different ways of representing the molecular arrangement. *Top*, general picture of the double helix, with the phosphate-sugar combinations making up the outside spirals and the base pairs the cross-bars; *middle*, a somewhat more detailed representation: phosphate *P*, sugar *S*, adenine *A*, thymine *T*, guanine *g*, cystosine *C*, and hydrogen *H*; *bottom*, detailed structure showing how the space is filled with atoms; carbon C, oxygen O, hydrogen H, phosphorus P, and the base pairs. (Carl P. Swanson, The Cell, courtesy of Prentice-Hall, Inc.)

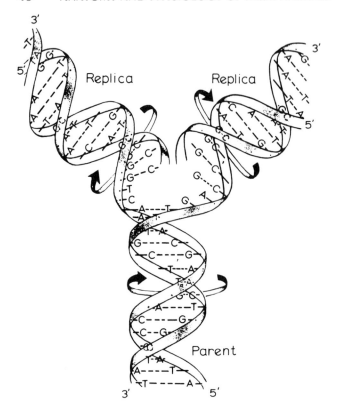

Fig. 3–10. Semiconservative replication of DNA. (From Bell, G. H., et al.: Textbook of Physiology and Biochemistry. 8th ed. Baltimore, The Williams & Wilkins Co., 1979.)

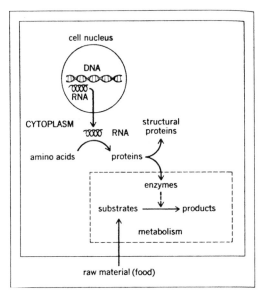

Fig. 3–11. The relations between metabolism, the synthesis of protein enzymes, and the transfer of the information required for protein synthesis from the DNA molecules in the nucleus to the site of protein synthesis in the cytoplasm by RNA molecules. (From Vander et al.: Human Physiology, Copyright © 1979, McGraw-Hill Book Company. Used with permission.)

Viruses consist essentially of DNA or RNA and a protein coat. They depend on a host cell in which to complete a life cycle and to multiply. Upon entering (infecting) a cell, the virus leaves its protein coat behind while the DNA or RNA is passed into the cell. Ultimately its mRNA is substituted into the protein and nucleic acid mechanism of the host cell, which is then induced to manufacture viral DNA or RNA and protein for the production of many new viruses.

In a dividing somatic cell, the quantity of DNA is doubled in late interphase or early prophase in preparation for doubling the number of chromosomes. Considerable RNA leaves the nucleus at this time and enters the cytoplasm, increasing the RNA content of the cytoplasm appreciably. During starvation of a cell, the amounts of RNA and protein may decrease, but the DNA remains constant. The RNA content of the cell closely reflects the metabolic activity of the cell. As cellular activity increases, the quantity of RNA increases.

Cell Division

The nucleus has been accepted as an important part of the cell for a long time. Its functions in cell division and transmission of genetic characteristics are well known. The nucleus also indirectly controls the cytoplasmic functions of the cell, including the metabolism and structure of the cell.

Mitosis

Mitosis, the division of somatic cells, has been well described for many years. The period between active cell divisions is called the *interphase* and may vary from a matter of minutes in actively proliferating tissue to practically a permanent condition in cells that no longer divide, such as neurons in mature tissues.

The nuclear changes in a mitotic cycle include the following arbitrarily selected divisions (even though it is normally a continuous, uninterrupted process): prophase, metaphase, anaphase, and telophase (Fig. 3–12).

The stimulus initiating cell division is not definitely known, although several factors

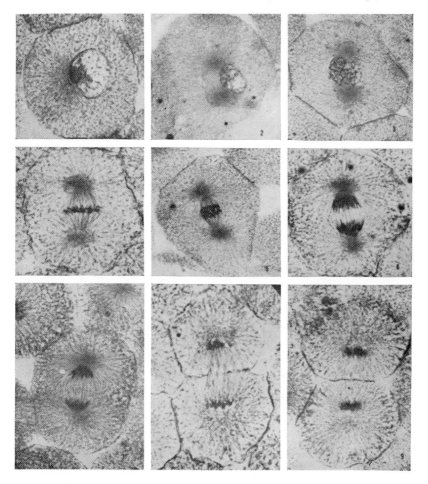

Fig. 3–12.   States of mitosis in cells of the Whitefish blastula: *1*, Interphase, with cell center adjacent to nucleus; *2*, early prophase showing development of astral centers; *3*, late prophase, with astral centers at opposite ends of the cell; *4*, metaphase; *5*, early anaphase; *6*, late anaphase; *7*, early telophase; *8*, mid-telophase, showing cleavage furrow; *9*, telophase-interphase following separation of daughter cells. (Courtesy of Mr. Philip G. Coleman, Michigan State University.)

have been suggested, including absolute cell size, disproportionate size of nucleus and cytoplasm, and doubling of quantity of genetic material in the nucleus. Exceptions can be found to each of these factors to question that any one of them is the only stimulus for cell division. Nevertheless, cells in the animal body die and are sloughed off by the millions every day. These cells must be replaced if normal life is to continue, and the replacement cells must contain exact replicas of the chromosomes of the original parent cell if the cell's function is to be the same. Replication, or "duplication," of the chromosomes and their genes (DNA sequences that make up the chromosomes) must occur in the cell before division or reproduction of a cell can occur, so that the same genetic characteristics can be passed along to the daughter cells when *mitosis* occurs.

Interphase. DNA replication occurs during interphase, the part of the *cell cycle* that includes all of the time during which the cell is not undergoing mitosis.

DNA replication involves first the uncoiling and separation of the two DNA strands of each of the chromosomes in the nucleus. Then *new* complementary strands form along each of the two separated strands. Each separated strand serves as a template for a new strand. The components of the new strands come from the "pool" of deoxyribose, phosphate ions, and purine and pyrimidine bases normally found in the cell nucleoplasm. The result is that each of the two original strands of each chromosome is now paired with a *new* complementary strand, forming two spiral helix chromosomes wherever there was one before.

Prophase. During *prophase* there is an increase in refractivity (bending of light), turgidity, and surface tension of the cell. The cytoplasm tends to become more viscous, and the nucleus tends to become less viscous. The chromosomal material, *chromatid*, becomes visible as a twisted filamentous mass of threads in the nucleo-

plasm. (The term "mitosis" comes from the Greek mitos, meaning thread.)

Also during prophase the nuclear envelope and the nucleolus begin to break down and disappear as such, and the two centrioles move to opposite poles of the cell. Microtubules become organized and arranged in a fan-shape, radiating outward from the centrioles to the *equator* at the center of the cell. This formation of *asters* makes up the *mitotic spindle*.

Metaphase. Metaphase is the period when the nuclear envelope and nucleolus totally disappear as such. The chromatids then move and line up across the cell's equator in the middle of the spindle. The spindle microtubules then attach to the centromere region of the chromatids.

Anaphase. Anaphase is the stage in which each centromere divides, separating the two chromatids, which are then properly called chromosomes again. Now the cell contains twice as many chromosomes as it had originally. Half of the chromosomes then begin to be pulled toward each centriole at respective poles of the spindle.

Telophase. Telophase begins when one half of the chromosomes have been drawn by the microtubules to each pole of the cell. A nuclear envelope then forms around each set of daughter chromosomes and a nucleolus appears in each new nucleus. The spindle tubules disappear and the chromosomes begin unwinding to look more like filaments than like condensed chromosomes. They lose their visible identity as chromosomes and are called *chromatin* or chromatin material throughout the interphase period.

Division of the cell itself then occurs, forming two daughter cells. The division of the cytoplasm is called *cytokinesis*. It starts with an invagination of the plasma membrane around the equator of the cell and ends by pinching off the two halves with a nucleus in each half (daughter cell). Each centriole also is replicated, and each daughter cell becomes a duplicate of the parent cell. Mitosis is now complete.

DNA and RNA

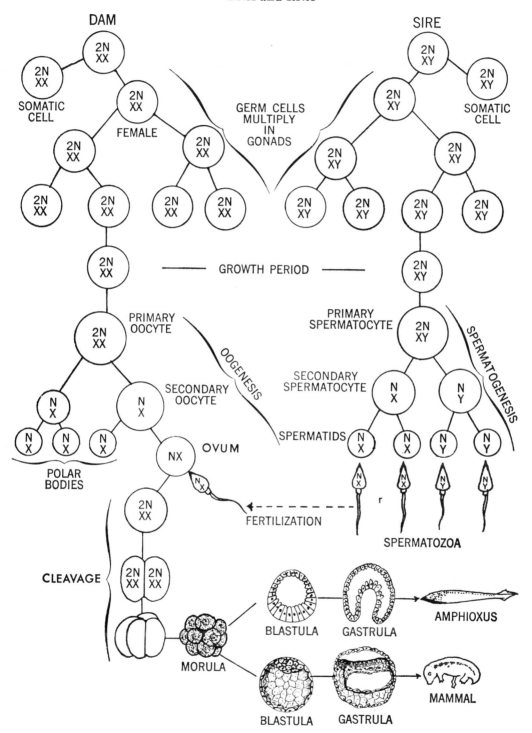

Fig. 3–13.   Diagram illustrating gametogenesis (oogenesis in the dam and spermatogenesis in the sire), cleavage, and development of the embryo in amphioxus and in a mammal. (After Alexander, Biology, Barnes and Noble.)

Meiosis

Meiosis *(reduction division)* differs from mitosis in a number of ways. It occurs during *gametogenesis,* the formation of ova (eggs) in the female and spermatozoa in the male (see Fig. 3–13). Since fertilization produces a doubling of the number of chromosomes in the fertilized ovum (an equal number is contributed by the male and by the female), there must be a mechanism to reduce the somatic, or diploid, number of chromosomes before fertilization takes place. Otherwise, chromosome numbers would increase geometrically, a constant number of chromosomes in a species could not be maintained, and reproduction would cease after a few generations because of the massive numbers of chromosomes produced.

Meiosis not only reduces the somatic (diploid) number of chromosomes by one-half to the haploid number, it also increases the genetic variability of the offspring by a process called "crossing over." Homologous chromosomes in the primary sex cells pair up during prophase of meiosis. Homologous chromosomes are similar chromosomes, one contributed by the female and one by the male. These paired homologous chromosomes may then cross over and exchange similar areas, such as one end, the middle portion, or both ends, resulting in two new chromosomes, each of which is different from either parent chromosome.

Crossing over is then followed by meiotic division I and meiotic division II. During both meiotic divisions (I and II) the cell goes through an interphase, prophase, metaphase, anaphase, and telophase just as occurs in mitosis, except that crossing over between chromatids occurs beforehand, changing the genetic makeup of the chromosomes. Then, in the anaphase of division I, the chromatids do not separate before moving to each pole as they did in mitosis. Therefore, when the cell divides in telophase, each daughter cell will have half as many chromosomes (n) as the parent cell (2n).

Meiotic division II, which follows, simply duplicates the two daughter cells to form four cells, much as occurs in mitosis. However, each chromatid separates into two chromosomes, one of which migrates to each pole to maintain the haploid number (n) in each new sex cell, the *gamete*. The male gametes are called spermatozoa or sperm cells, while female gametes are called ova or egg cells. When fertilization takes place, the union of an ovum and a spermatozoan restores the original 2n diploid number of chromosomes, from which the offspring is formed as an embryo, then a fetus, and finally a newborn animal (neonate).

Embryology

Embryology is the study of the early prenatal development of an animal. It begins with the fertilization of the ovum by a spermatozoon to form a zygote, which in turn becomes a morula, a blastula, a gastrula, and then an embryo. Strictly speaking, the period of the embryo terminates when the various organs and organ systems are formed. The embryo then becomes a fetus that more or less resembles an adult of the same species. In cattle the embryo becomes a fetus approximately at the end of the second month of gestation. The fetus becomes a newborn animal at parturition (birth).

The ovum contains a large amount of nutritional material (yolk) that provides energy for the early stages of cell division. The ovum and spermatozoon each contribute one-half of the chromosomes to the newly formed zygote (see Fig. 3–11).

EMBRYOLOGY OF AMPHIOXUS

The embryology of amphioxus, a primitive chordate, is studied because of its simplicity. In amphioxus, the first mitotic divisions, known as cleavage, increase the number of cells (blastomeres) with little if any increase in actual volume, because cleavage occurs so rapidly that there is not enough time for the customary growth of daughter cells before a new division occurs. However, the nuclei of the daughter cells are of normal size and contain a full complement of chromosomes. The mass of small cells resulting from cleavage has a lobulated appearance resembling a mulberry; hence the name "*morula*" given to this stage (Fig. 4–1).

The morula then becomes a hollowed sphere, the *blastula*. One pole (end) of the blastula is called the *animal pole*. The animal pole consists of cells that contain little yolk material and eventually form the *ectoderm*, the outer germ layer. The opposite end of the blastula is called the *vegetal pole*. It consists of cells with a much higher yolk content than the cells of the animal pole. These vegetal pole cells will form the *endoderm*, the inner germ layer.

Because the yolk material in the vegetal pole cells inhibits mitosis, the cells of the animal pole multiply much more rapidly. These rapidly multiplying animal pole cells soon overlap the vegetal pole cells and produce a double-layered invaginated ball called a *gastrula*.

The two layers of the gastrula grow into close apposition, effacing the cavity of the blastula. The new cavity formed by the invagination is called the *archenteron (primitive gut)*, which eventually forms the lumen of the digestive and respiratory systems. The archenteron opens to the exterior by way of the blastopore.

The embryo in this gastrula stage elongates and begins to differentiate in a number of ways.

A series of paired outpouchings on each side of the dorsal junction of endoderm and ectoderm form the *somites* (segments) which eventually give rise to most of the body wall. These mesodermal (middle skin) structures appear to originate from the dorsal endoderm. The cavities coalesce to form the *celom* (body cavity), bounded by outer and inner layers of *mesoderm*. The outer layer of mesoderm fuses with the ectoderm to form the *somatopleure* (body wall), and the inner layer fuses with the endoderm to form the *splanchnopleure* (gut wall). At the same time, the dorsal plate of ectoderm evaginates longitudinally to form first a groove, then a tube *(neural tube)*, which is the forerunner of the nervous system. Concurrently the roof of the archenteron forms the *notochord*, the basis of the skeleton.

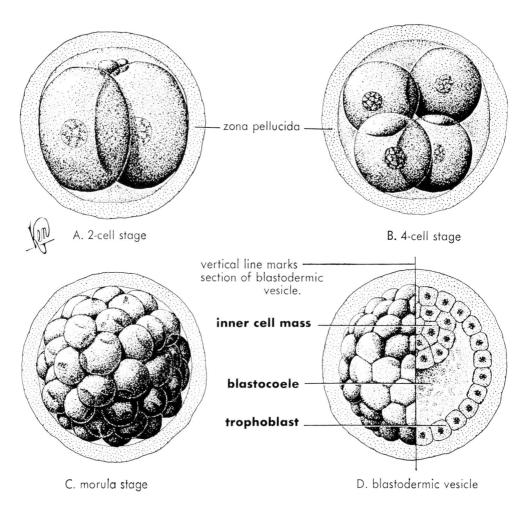

A. 2-cell stage

zona pellucida

B. 4-cell stage

vertical line marks
section of blastodermic
vesicle.

inner cell mass

blastocoele

trophoblast

C. morula stage

D. blastodermic vesicle

Fig. 4–1.   Diagrams of human embryos from cleavage to blastodermic vesicle (blastocyst). (From Crouch, J.E.: Functional Human Anatomy. ed. 3. Philadelphia, Lea & Febiger, 1978.)

MAMMALIAN EMBRYOLOGY

When the mammalian morula reaches the uterus, the morula becomes a *blastula* (or blastocyst) consisting of many cells, each termed a blastomere. The blastula is a hollow ball consisting of a layer of cells, the trophoblast, which surrounds the blastocele, a cavity into which the inner cell mass protrudes (from the trophoblast). The inner cell mass eventually forms the body of the embryo. In this process three germ layers are produced.

The *ectoderm* (outer skin) develops from the outer cells of the inner cell mass and is continuous with the trophoblast. The *endoderm* (inner skin) grows into the blastocele just deep to the trophoblast to form the *archenteron* or primitive gut. The *mesoderm* (middle skin) grows between the ectoderm and the endoderm and splits into two layers forming a cavity, the celom, between the two layers.

The outer layer of the mesoderm and the adjacent ectoderm make up the *somatopleure,* which forms part of the body wall and also enters into the formation of the fetal membranes. The inner layer of the mesoderm and the endoderm form the *splanchnopleure,* which forms the wall of the gut (Fig. 4–2).

The dorsal surface of the embryonic disc (the forerunner of the embryo) develops an elongated thickening called the *primitive streak,* and a rod-shaped mass, the *notochord.* Mesodermal cells on each side of the notochord form the segmentally arranged somites, which in turn develop into vertebrae and muscles. Other areas of

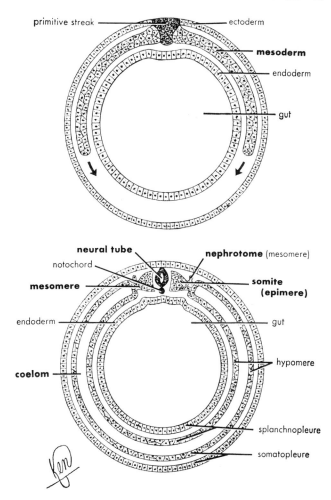

Fig. 4–2. Diagrammatic representation to show spread and differentiation of the mesoderm. The hypomere includes an inner splanchnic mesoderm and an outer somatic mesoderm. The splanchnic mesoderm and endoderm form the splachnopleure. The somatic endoderm and ectoderm form the somatopleure. (Modified from Arey. Crouch, J.E.: Functional Human Anatomy. ed. 3. Philadelphia, Lea & Febiger, 1978.)

Table 4–1.   The Germ-Layer Origin of Tissues

Ectoderm	Mesoderm (including mesenchyme)	Endoderm
1. Epidermis, including: cutaneous glands, hair, nails, lens	1. Muscle (all types)	Epithelium of:
	2. Connective tissue, cartilage, bone, notochord	1. Pharynx, including: root of tongue, auditory tube,
2. Epithelium of: sense organs, nasal cavity, sinuses, mouth, including: oral glands, enamel. anal canal	3. Blood, bone marrow	tonsils; thyroid, parathyroids; thymus
	4. Lymphoid tissue	2. Larynx, trachea, lungs
	Epithelium of:	3. Digestive tube, including associated glands
	5. Blood vessels, lymphatics	
	6. Body cavities	4. Bladder
3. Nervous tissue, including: hypophysis, chromaffin tissue	7. Kidney, ureter	5. Vagina (all?), vestibule
	8. Gonads, genital ducts	6. Urethra, including associated glands
	9. Suprarenal cortex	
	10. Joint cavities	

(From Arey, Developmental Anatomy, courtesy of W. B. Saunders Co.)

mesoderm produce urogenital organs and blood vascular organs.

The ectoderm above the notochord forms a groove that becomes the neural tube, which eventually forms the central nervous system. The epidermis of the skin is also derived from the ectoderm.

As these changes are occurring, the trophoblast becomes elongated and attached to the lining of the uterus, where it absorbs nutrients from the uterine glands. The actual fetal membranes develop later.

Differentiation of the relatively indifferent cells of each of the three germ layers to form specialized tissue cells is called *histogenesis*. Much is known about when and where various tissues and organs develop, but little is known about why these changes take place. It has been established that the *DNA (deoxyribonucleic acid)* of the nucleus

in the form of chromosomes contains the information that influences development of all the various parts of the animal. During embryonic and fetal life, the cells differentiate into specific tissue cells, which in turn form organs and systems. Thus the embryo becomes a fetus and finally a *neonate* (newborn animal).

In general, the ectoderm forms the outer epithelium and nervous system, the endoderm forms the lungs and gut epithelium and its derivatives, and the mesoderm forms muscles, connective tissues, blood, and most of the urogenital system (organs associated with the urinary system and reproductive system).

The subject of embryology is covered in greater detail in standard textbooks on embryology. This subject is also called developmental anatomy.

Chapter 5

Anatomy of the Nervous System

The nervous system of early multicellular forms such as the hydra consists of a fine network of individual nerve cells without any brain or special coordinating center. As organisms become more complex, the specialization of nerve cells increases, with some cells (sensory, or afferent) conducting stimuli from the surface to the central portion of the organism, where each contacts another neuron (motor, or efferent). This neuron, in turn, is responsible for relaying the impulse from the central region to the effector cells, producing the required action.

The next step is the development of an integrative mechanism, or central nervous system, to coordinate activities according to the stimuli received by the sensory neurons. This coordination is produced largely by neurons interposed between afferent and efferent neurons which are called *intercalated neurons, internuncial neurons, association neurons, connector neurons,* or simply *interneurons.* Much of the central nervous system (brain and spinal cord) of higher animals consists of interneurons, which connect neurons from various levels or segments and integrate their activity.

ORGANIZATION

Each neuron consists of a *cyton* or *soma* (nerve cell body) and one or more nerve processes. The nerve processes are called *dendrites* (or *dendrons*) if they conduct impulses toward the cell bodies; they are called *axons* (also axis-cylinder processes, neuraxons, or neurites) if they conduct impulses away from the cell bodies.

The junction of the axon of one neuron with another neuron is called a *synapse.* The synapse is the point of contact between neurons that are functionally related. This contact may be between the axon of one neuron and the cell body of another neuron, or between the axon of one neuron and a dendrite of another neuron. Of course, any given neuron may synapse with axons or dendrites of many other neurons through branching of its terminal ends.

The many classifications and subdivisions

57

of the nervous system will seem considerably less formidable if one remembers that they are all arbitrary names for geographic or physiologic groupings of nerve cells and/or nerve processes.

Groups of nerve cell bodies within the brain or spinal cord are generally called *nuclei*, while groups of nerve cell bodies outside the brain and spinal cord are usually called *ganglia*. This type of nucleus should not be confused with the central body of a cell, which is also called a nucleus. Similarly, bundles of nerve processes within the brain or spinal cord are frequently called *tracts,* or *fasciculi*, while bundles of processes outside the central nervous system are called *nerves*.

For descriptive purposes the entire nervous system can be divided into two parts:

(1) the central nervous system, which includes the brain and spinal cord, and (2) the peripheral nervous system, which consists of cranial nerves and spinal nerves going to somatic (body) structures, and the autonomic nervous system, going to visceral structures (Fig. 5–1). Some autonomic neurons travel with certain cranial and spinal nerves enroute to visceral structures.

The following classification is an arbitrary division of the nervous system of mammals that groups various portions for convenience of description. Remember that the nervous system is an integrated unit, and that any separation into parts is a man-made invention.

Central nervous system (CNS)

    Brain—enclosed in cranial part of skull

    Spinal cord—enclosed in vertebral canal

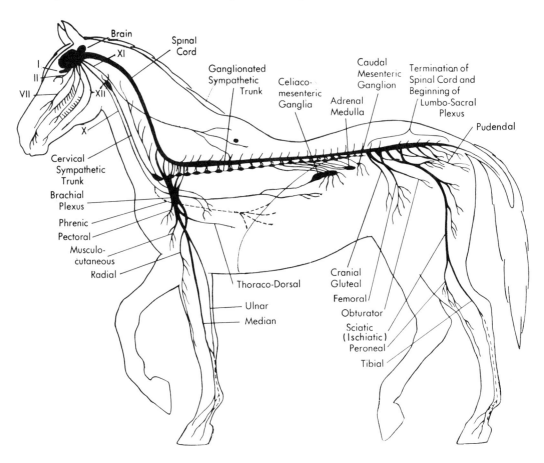

Fig. 5–1.   Nervous system of the horse.

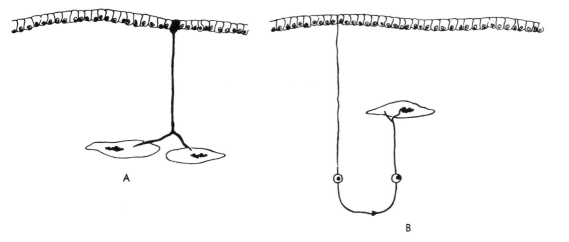

Fig. 5–2. Early stages in evolution of nervous tissue. *A*, Modified ectodermal cell extends from surface to muscle cells. *B*, Chain of two modified ectodermal cells (neurons) extending from surface to muscle cell. (After Ham, Histology, J. B. Lippincott Co.)

Peripheral nervous system (PNS)
    Cranial nerves—emerge through cranial foramina of skull
    Spinal nerves—emerge through intervertebral foramina
    Autonomic nervous system (ANS)
        Sympathetic nervous system—thoracolumbar portion
        Parasympathetic nervous system—cranio-sacral portion
    Figure 5–2 shows early stages in the evolution of nervous tissue.

HISTOLOGY

Nervous tissue consists not only of neurons but also of supporting tissue. In the central nervous system (brain and spinal cord), the supporting tissue is called *neuroglia*, while most of the supporting tissue of the peripheral nervous system is ordinary white fibrous connective tissue.

Structure of the Neuron. The neuron consists of the nerve cell body (cyton) and all of its processes. The cell body consists of a relatively large mass of cytoplasm, a nucleus, and one or more nucleoli. The cytoplasm is sometimes called *neuroplasm*. Among the important parts of the cytoplasm are the organelles, which include *mitochondria, fibrils, Golgi network,* and a *centrosome*.

The most common inclusions seen in nerve cell cytoplasm are the *Nissl bodies,* or *tigroid bodies,* which are dark-staining granules of rough endoplasmic reticulum. The term "tigroid bodies" comes from the striped appearance they impart to some cells. Other inclusions found in the cytoplasm include fat and pigments. A yellow-brown *lipochrome* pigment and black *melanin* pigment are commonly present.

Neurons may be classified according to the number of nerve processes. *Unipolar neurons* have one process, *bipolar neurons* have one dendrite and one axon, and *multipolar neurons* have a number of dendrites but usually only one axon. Dendrites are short protoplasmic processes that branch repeatedly. The cytoplasm of the cell body extends into the dendrites and axon. The axon arises from a conical mound of cytoplasm, the *axon hillock.* (See Fig. 5–3.) Although only one axon leaves the cell body, it frequently gives off right-angle collateral branches along its course, which end in more or less profuse terminal arborizations, or *telodendria,* as does the main axon.

In a motor nerve, each terminal branch supplies a single muscle fiber. The entire

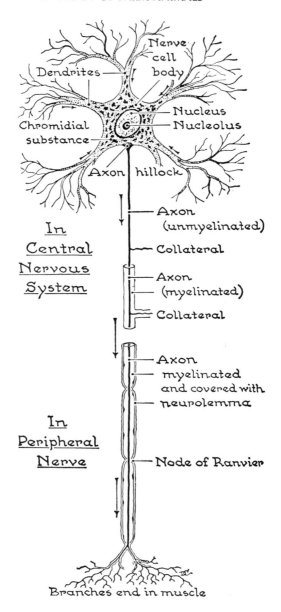

Fig. 5–3.   Diagram of a multipolar neuron. (Ham and Lesson, Histology, 4th ed., courtesy of J. B. Lippincott Co.)

unit, motor nerve plus all muscle fibers it supplies, is termed a *motor unit*.

Nerve fibers may be myelinated or unmyelinated. Myelinated fibers are surrounded by a white sheath of fatty material. Studies with the electron microscope have shown that the myelin sheath actually consists of many layers of cell membrane of a *Schwann cell (lemmocyte)* wrapped around the nerve fiber in such a manner that in cross section the myelin sheath resembles a slice of jelly roll. The nerve fibers that were described as lacking both myelin sheath and neurolemma when observed with light microscopy have been found to be invaginated into the cell membrane of a Schwann cell, so that all nerve fibers are covered by at least one layer of cell membrane. Several unmyelinated fibers may be invaginated into separate areas of the same Schwann cell (see Fig. 5–4).

EMBRYOLOGY

Whether the development of the nervous system is considered from the standpoint of developmental anatomy of the individual or from the evolutionary development of the race, the steps are similar.

The early embryo first shows a thickening of ectodermal cells on the dorsum just anterior to the *primitive streak*. The primitive streak is one of the first areas of cellular differentiation, and it indicates the longitudinal axis of the embryo. This thickening, the *neural plate*, grows faster along the lateral margins than in the center, thus forming the *neural groove*. Next, the edges of the groove come into apposition dorsally to form the *neural tube*. The entire central nervous system is formed from the neural tube. The lumen of the neural tube persists in the adult

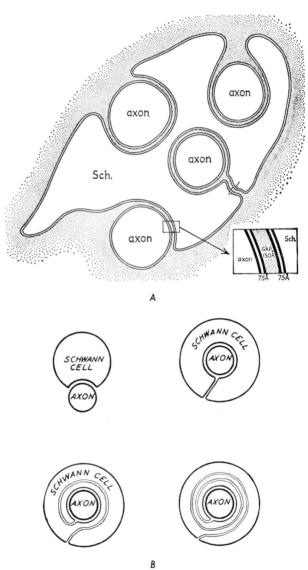

Fig. 5–4. *A*, Diagram of non-myelinated fibers in relation to a neurilemma cell. (Causey, G., The Cell of Schwann, Edinburgh, Livingstone.)

B, Diagram to illustrate the process of myelinization of axons as outlined by Geren and Schmitt, 1957. (Finerty and Cowdry, A Textbook of Histology, 5th ed., Lea & Febiger.)

as the *central canal* of the spinal cord and as the two *lateral ventricles,* the *third ventricle* and the *fourth ventricle* of the brain.

Neural crest cells lateral to the neural tube eventually form sensory ganglia and some of the sympathetic ganglia.

Although the rostral (cranial) end of the embryonic brain develops earliest and is the largest, closure of this portion is slower than the more caudal parts, which will form the cranial part of the spinal cord.

In this early period the segmental nature of the organism is indicated by the development of *somites* in the *mesoderm.* These serially arranged paired thickenings on each side of the neural tube eventually form voluntary muscles, vertebrae, and skin.

Development of the spinal cord continues by increasing the thickness of the wall of the neural tube and decreasing the size of the lumen. Three concentric layers make up the neural tube: an inner ependymal layer, a middle mantle layer, and a superficial marginal layer.

The thin *ependymal layer* of cells forms the lining of the central canal of the spinal cord and of the ventricles of the brain.

The *mantle layer,* which becomes the gray matter of the spinal cord, is arranged in a longitudinal column extending the entire length of the spinal cord. In cross section this column has an H, or butterfly, shape and consists largely of nerve cell bodies, which give it the gray appearance. The dorsal branches of the H, or dorsal wings of the butterfly are called the dorsal horns; the ventral branches are called ventral horns. The dorsal horns receive processes of the afferent (sensory) nerves which enter the spinal cord. The ventral horns contain the cells of origin of the motor neurons.

The *marginal layer,* which is most superficial, consists of longitudinal nerve processes that make up the white matter of the spinal cord. The white color comes from the myelin sheaths, fatty material surrounding the nerve fibers. These fibers are grouped into more or less functional units, the dorsal, lateral, and ventral columns of white matter which are separated by the dorsal and ventral horns of gray matter.

The dorsal root ganglia are derived from the neural crest cells. Nerve cells in these ganglia give rise to some fibers that grow toward the dorsal horn of the spinal cord, and other fibers that enter the spinal nerve as sensory, or afferent, fibers. The portion of these fibers that extends from the spinal nerve to the spinal cord is known as the dorsal root of the spinal nerve.

The ventral root of the spinal nerve consists largely of fibers that grow from the nerve cells located in the ventral horn of the spinal cord. The dorsal and ventral roots unite close to the intervertebral foramen to form the spinal nerve.

Development of the brain begins before the spinal cord develops and continues at a rapid pace throughout embryonic and fetal life, and into the neonatal period. The first gross subdivisions of the brain form the so-called three-vesicle stage. These subdivisions are the *prosencephalon,* or *forebrain; mesencephalon,* or *midbrain;* and *rhombencephalon,* or *hindbrain.*

The prosencephalon is widened by the presence of optic vesicles, which are the forerunners of the eyes. At this stage the neural tube is not completely closed, leaving a cranial opening called the *anterior neuropore* and a caudal opening called the *sinus rhomboidalis.*

In the five-vesicle stage of development, the prosencephalon further subdivides to form the *telencephalon* and the *diencephalon;* the mesencephalon does not subdivide; and the rhombencephalon divides into the *metencephalon* and the *myelencephalon.*

THE CENTRAL NERVOUS SYSTEM

Some appreciation of the complexity of the central nervous system (brain and spinal cord) can be gained by comparing the evolution of the nervous system with the development of electronic control mechanisms, such as those used to guide missiles and rockets. From the first simple mechanical adding machine, man has developed complex electronic brains with innumerable circuits, switches, and relays. However, the most sophisticated electronic apparatus is bulky, crude, and nonversatile when compared with the mammalian nervous system. All man-made devices are limited in the types of information they can receive and process. The central nervous system, on the other hand, not only receives but interprets and evaluates such diverse information as changes in light waves, sound waves, temperature, gravitation, pressure, and chemicals. While a 2½-inch cable such as the transatlantic telephone cable contains 2100 pairs of wires, the pituitary stalk of the human brain, which is less than ½ inch in diameter, contains approximately 50,000 individual nerve fibers.

Brain

The gross subdivisions of the adult brain include the cerebrum, the cerebellum, and the brain stem (Fig. 5–5).

Telencephalon. The telencephalon includes the *cerebral cortex,* the *corpora striata,* and the *rhinencephalon.* The telencephalon encloses the cavities of the lateral ventricles, the *interventricular foramina of Monro,* and the rostral portion of the third ventricle (Figs. 5–6, 5–7).

The surface area of the *cerebrum* is increased greatly by numerous foldings to form convex ridges, called *gyri,* which are convolutions separated by furrows called *fissures* or *sulci.* In man and some animals, the cortical areas have been extensively mapped to localize specific sensory and motor functions. Division of the cerebrum into lobes is indicated in Figures 5–8 and 5–9; Figures 5–10 and 5–11 show a ventral

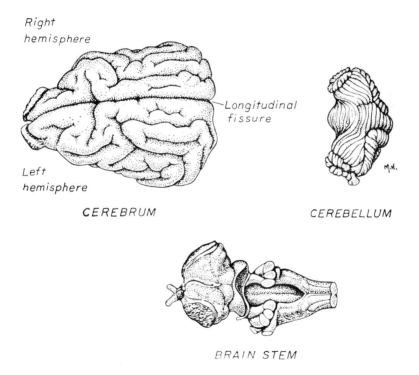

Fig. 5–5. Gross subdivisions of the brain. (Meyer, in Miller, Christensen, and Evans, Anatomy of the Dog, courtesy of W.B. Saunders Co.)

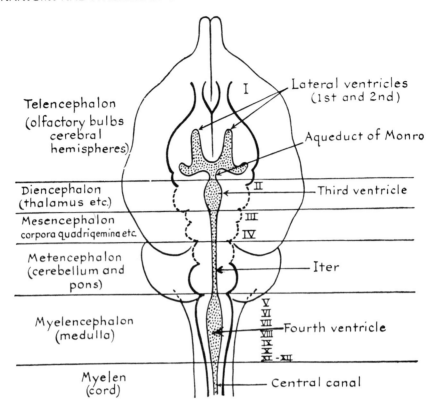

Fig. 5–6. General plan of the mammalian brain. (Iter is cerebral aqueduct.) (Leach, Functional Anatomy, Mammalian and Comparative, courtesy of McGraw-Hill Book Co.)

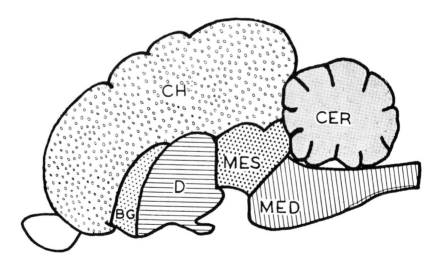

Fig. 5–7. Schematic median section of the dog brain. CH, Cerebral hemisphere; BG, Basal ganglion; D, Diencephalon; MES, Mesencephalon; CER, Cerebellum; MED, Medulla oblongata. (McGrath, Neurologic Examination of the Dog, Lea & Febiger.)

view of the brain and a sagittal section respectively.

The highest types of mental activities, such as voluntary muscle control, interpretation of sensations, and reasoning, involve the cells of the cerebral cortex, thus leading to the use of the term "gray matter" as synonymous with mental ability.

The *corpus striatum* of each cerebral hemisphere consists of a mixture of white and gray matter, thus giving a striated appearance, as the name implies. The gray matter of the corpus striatum is represented by a number of nuclear masses sometimes called the *basal nuclei*, or *basal ganglia*, even though the term "ganglion" usually

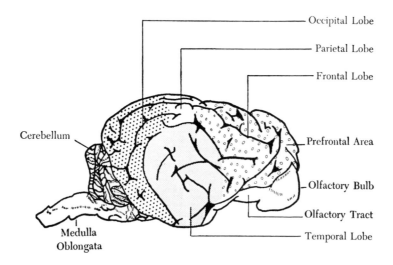

Fig. 5–8.   Diagrammatic lateral view of dog's brain. (McGrath, Neurologic Examination of the Dog, Lea & Febiger.)

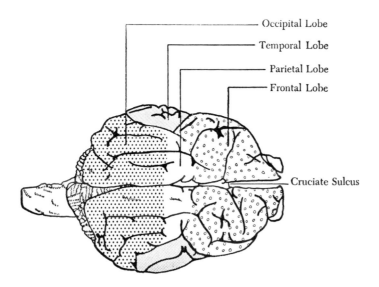

Fig. 5–9.   Diagrammatic dorsal view of dog's brain. (McGrath, Neurologic Examination of the Dog, Lea & Febiger.)

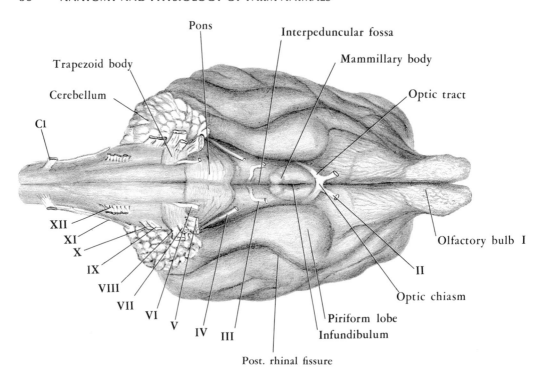

Pons
Interpeduncular fossa
Mammillary body
Trapezoid body
Optic tract
Cerebellum
C1
XII
XI
X
IX
VIII
VII
VI
V
IV   III
Olfactory bulb I
II
Optic chiasm
Piriform lobe
Infundibulum
Post. rhinal fissure

Fig. 5–10.   Ventral view of the dog brain and cranial nerves (Roman Numerals). (Jenkins, T.W.: Functional Mammalian Neuroanatomy. ed. 2, Philadelphia, Lea & Febiger, 1978.)

refers to an accumulation of cell bodies outside the central nervous system. The white matter of the corpus striatum consists, to a large extent, of projection fibers that connect the cerebral cortex with other parts of the central nervous system and indirectly with the peripheral nervous system.

The *rhinencephalon* is, from the evolutionary standpoint, one of the oldest parts of the cerebrum. It is associated primarily with the sense of smell and is therefore sometimes called the *olfactory brain*.

Diencephalon. The diencephalon is the part of the prosencephalon located next to the midbrain. The *thalamus,* the *epithalamus,* the *hypothalamus,* and most of the third ventricle are included in the diencephalon.

The *thalamus* is essentially a relay center for nerve fibers, connecting the cerebral hemispheres with the brain stem and spinal cord. The *epithalamus* includes the *habenu-*

lar nuclei (associated with smell), white matter tracts, and the *pineal body,* which is sometimes considered to be an endocrine organ.

The *hypothalamus* includes the *pituitary gland* (one of the most important endocrine glands) and the structures closely associated with it. These structures include the *tuber cinereum,* which attaches the stalk of the pituitary gland to the brain; the *optic chiasm,* or crossing of the optic nerves just cranial to the pituitary gland; and the *mammillary bodies,* located immediately caudal to the pituitary gland.

Mesencephalon. The *mesencephalon,* or *midbrain,* is that portion of the brain that does not subdivide during the development from the embryo to the adult. As the name implies, the midbrain is located between the prosencephalon cranially and the rhombencephalon caudally. The two *cerebral peduncles* and four *quadrigeminal bodies*

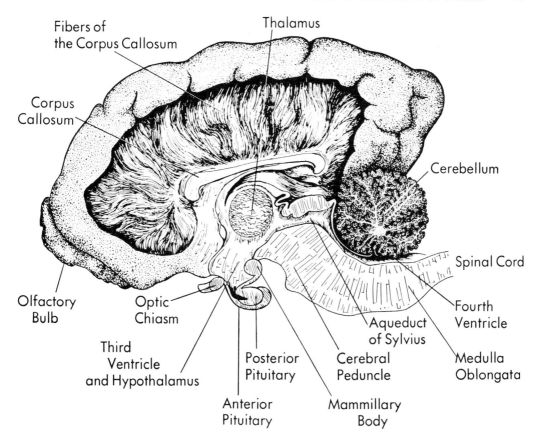

Fibers of the Corpus Callosum

Thalamus

Corpus Callosum

Cerebellum

Olfactory Bulb

Optic Chiasm

Spinal Cord

Fourth Ventricle

Third Ventricle and Hypothalamus

Posterior Pituitary

Cerebral Peduncle

Aqueduct of Sylvius

Medulla Oblongata

Anterior Pituitary

Mammillary Body

Fig. 5–11. Sagittal section of the brain partially excavated. (After Meyer in Miller, Christensen, and Evans, Anatomy of the Dog, courtesy of W. B. Saunders Co.)

are the largest structures of the mesencephalon, or midbrain.

The *cerebral peduncles*, also called *crura cerebri*, are essentially the continuation of the right and left halves of the spinal cord and brain stem into the respective cerebral hemispheres. They contain fiber tracts and nuclei.

The *quadrigeminal bodies (corpora quadrigemina)* consist of a right and a left anterior (cranial or superior) colliculus, and a right and left posterior (caudal or inferior) colliculus. The antierior colliculi are associated with vision; the posterior are associated with hearing.

Rhombencephalon. The *rhombencephalon*, or *hindbrain*, is subdivided into the *metencephalon;* the *myelencephalon,* or

medulla oblongata (frequently referred to as the medulla); and the fourth ventricle.

The *metencephalon* includes the *cerebellum* and the *pons*. The cerebellum consists of two lateral hemispheres and a median ridge called the *vermis*, because of its resemblance to a worm. The surface of the cerebellum consists of many laminae called *folia*. When cut on the median line, the cerebellum gives the appearance of foliage, thus leading to the ancient term "arbor vitae" or "tree of life," for this view of the cerebellum. In the cerebellum the white matter is chiefly centrally located and the gray matter peripherally located, as they are in the cerebrum.

The pons is located ventral to the cerebellum and appears to form a bridge of fibers from one hemisphere of the cerebellum to the other. Many other fiber tracts and nuclei make up the remainder of the pons.

The *fourth ventricle* is located ventral to the cerebellum and dorsal to the pons and brain stem.

The *myelencephalon* forms the medulla oblongata. It is the cranial continuation of the spinal cord, from which it is arbitrarily separated at the foramen magnum, the largest foramen in the skull. The fourth ventricle covers much of the dorsal surface of the brain stem, giving it somewhat the appearance of the spinal cord before the neural groove was completely closed.

Besides containing many fiber tracts from the spinal cord, the brain stem is the site of nuclei for *cranial nerves,* including those termed *V, VI, VII, IX, X, XI,* and *XII.* It also contains reflex centers for the control of respiration and circulation.

Ventricles. The ventricles of the brain are derivatives of the embryonic neural canal. Right and left *lateral ventricles* are located within the respective cerebral hemispheres. They connect with the *third ventricle* by way of the interventricular foramina of Monro. Most of the third ventricle is surrounded by the diencephalon. A portion of the third ventricle projects into the infundibulum (the stalk) of the pituitary gland. The third ventricle connects with the fourth ventricle by way of the *aqueduct of Sylvius,* also called the *cerebral aqueduct.*

The *fourth ventricle,* located between the cerebellum above and pons and medulla below, communicates with the *subarachnoid space* through the *foramina* of *Magendie* and *Luschka.* Each of the four *choroid plexuses* of the ventricles (one plexus for each ventricle) consists of a network of blood capillaries that protrudes into the lumen of the ventricle. Each plexus is covered intimately by a layer of ependymal cells derived from the lining membrane of the ventricles.

Cerebrospinal fluid is found in the ventricles of the brain, where it is formed by the choroid plexuses, and in the subarachnoid space surrounding the brain and spinal cord. The cerebrospinal fluid is a combination of transudate, which passively crosses the capillary vessel wall, and an active secretion by the ependymal cells.

The route of passage of cerebrospinal fluid is from the two lateral ventricles through the interventricular foramina into the third ventricle, then by way of the cerebral aqueduct into the fourth ventricle, and finally through the foramina of Luschka and Magendie into the subarachnoid space, where it surrounds both the brain and spinal cord. Any obstruction in this route may cause extensive damage to the brain.

Hydrocephalus, or water on the brain, frequently results from obstruction of the interventricular foramina. If this occurs in the embryo or fetus, the cerebrum may become extremely thin due to the pressure of the fluid, which cannot escape from the lateral ventricles. In extreme cases the fetal cranium may become so enlarged that normal parturition is difficult or impossible.

Meninges

The coverings of the brain and spinal cord, called *meninges,* include, from without inward, the *dura mater,* the *arachnoidea,* and the *pia mater* (Figs. 5–12, 5–13).

The *dura mater* is a tough fibrous covering of the central nervous system. In the cranial cavity the dura mater blends intimately with the inner periosteum of the cranial bones. It also forms the *falx cerebri,* a median sickle-shaped fold which partially separates the cerebral hemispheres, and another fold of dura mater, called the *tentorium cerebelli,* which runs transversely between the cerebellum and the cerebrum. The dura mater contains channels filled with blood, called the sinuses of the dura mater. These sinuses are essentially veins that carry blood from the brain back toward the heart.

The spinal dura mater surrounds the spinal cord. It is separated from the periosteum

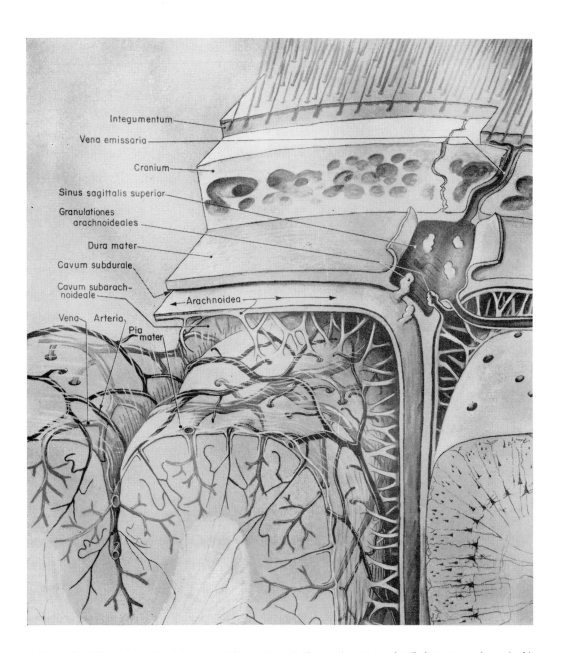

Fig. 5–12.   Three-dimensional diagram of the meninges in the cranium. Some detailed structures shown in this diagram are not mentioned in the text. (Elias and Pauly, Human Microanatomy, 2nd ed., courtesy of Da Vinci Publishing Co.)

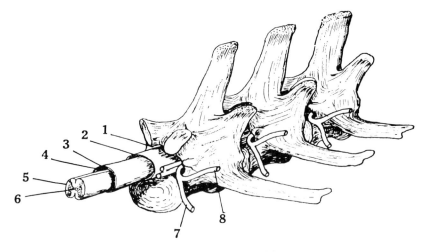

MENINGES AND SPINAL CORD

1. Epidural space
2. Dura mater
3. Arachnoidea
4. Subarachnoid space

5. Pia mater
6. Gray matter of spinal cord
7. Spinal nerve—ventral branch
8. Spinal nerve—dorsal branch

Fig. 5–13.   Three-dimensional diagram of the spinal cord and its meninges. (Foust and Getty, Atlas and Dissection Guide for the Study of the Anatomy of Domestic Animals, courtesy of the Iowa State College Press.)

of the vertebral canal by a fat-filled space, the *epidural space*.

The next deeper membrane is the *arachnoidea*. It is assumed to resemble a spider web, hence the name arachnoid, after arachnid—the spider. The outer layer is practically fused to the dura mater, so the subdural space is almost nonexistent. Spiderweb-like projections extend from the outer layer of the arachnoidea inward to the pia mater. The space between the arachnoidea and pia mater is known as the subarachnoid space and contains cerebrospinal fluid. The cerebrospinal fluid formed in the ventricles of the brain acts as a protective cushion for the brain and spinal cord.

The *pia mater* is the deepest of the meninges. It is a delicate membrane that closely invests the brain and spinal cord. The pia mater forms a sheath around the blood vessels and follows them into the substance of the brain, forming the so-called pial barrier, which inhibits movement of certain chemicals between the cerebral blood flow and the nervous tissue of the brain.

Spinal Cord

The spinal cord is the caudal continuation of the medulla oblongata. Segmentation is more distinct in the spinal cord, with each segment giving rise to a pair of spinal nerves. The spinal cord receives sensory, afferent, fibers by way of the dorsal roots of the spinal nerves and gives off the efferent, motor, fibers to the ventral roots of the spinal nerves.

The central gray matter of the spinal cord consists primarily of nerve cell bodies and their processes.

Tracts of the Spinal Cord. The peripheral white matter can be roughly divided into three columns on each lateral half of the cord: a dorsal white column, a lateral white column, and a ventral white column.

The *dorsal white columns* contain afferent tracts (Fig. 5–14), which convey impulses or stimuli from joints, tendons, muscles, and bones. These are called proprioceptive functions because they give a sense of position of limbs or other body parts without the use of vision. The chief *tracts* in each dorsal white

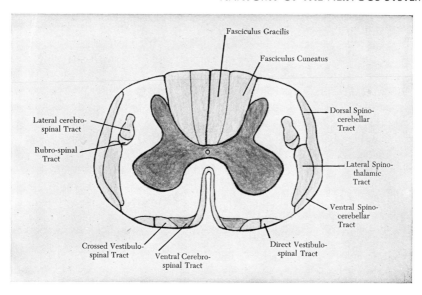

Fig. 5–14. Diagrammatic view of spinal cord in cross section to indicate location of gray and white matter. Note location of major fiber tracts. (McGrath, Neurologic Examination of the Dog, Lea & Febiger.)

column are the *fasciculus gracilis* and the *fasciculus cuneatus.*

The *fasciculus gracilis*, the more medial tract, is formed from dorsal root fibers of the lower thoracic, lumbar, sacral, and caudal nerves. These fibers end in the *nucleus gracilis* in the medulla.

The *fasciculus cuneatus*, lateral to the fasciculus gracilis, is found only in the cervical region, since it receives fibers only from dorsal roots of upper thoracic and cervical nerves. The fibers end in the *nucleus cuneatus*, also located in the medulla.

Many tracts are named according to the structures they connect. The lateral white columns contain the following tracts: *dorsal* and *ventral spinocerebellar, rubrospinal, lateral spinothalamic,* and *lateral cortico-spinal.*

The dorsal spinocerebellar tract conducts proprioceptive impulses from the spinal cord to the cerebellum to aid coordination of movements.

The rubrospinal tract connects the red nucleus in the midbrain with motor cells in the ventral gray horn of the spinal cord on the opposite side. The red nucleus receives impulses from the cerebellum. Thus the spinocerebellar tract, the cerebellum, and the rubrospinal tracts are important in reflex control of movements, particularly those of locomotion.

The lateral spinothalamic tract conducts impulses relating to pain and temperature. It receives fibers from the dorsal gray horn of the opposite side, travels up the spinal cord, and terminates in the thalamus.

The lateral corticospinal tract carries voluntary motor impulses from the motor area of the cerebral cortex to cells in the ventral gray horn of the spinal cord. These fibers pass by way of the internal capsule, cerebral peduncle, pons, and medulla to the spinal cord. A majority of the fibers cross to the opposite side in the medulla.

Important tracts in the ventral white columns include the *direct vestibulospinal tract*, the *crossed vestibulospinal tract*, and the *ventral corticospinal (cerebrospinal) tract.*

The direct vestibulospinal tract extends from the *lateral vestibular nucleus* to motor nuclei of the spinal cord. It transmits impulses which maintain the tone of the extensor muscles.

The crossed vestibulospinal tract extends

from the *descending vestibular nucleus* to motor centers of the opposite side of the spinal cord. It conducts impulses that inhibit, or decrease, tone in extensor muscles.

The ventral corticospinal tract connects the motor area of the cerebral cortex with motor cells in the ventral gray horns on the same side and opposite sides of the spinal cord. The impulses are associated with voluntary motor activity.

PERIPHERAL NERVOUS SYSTEM

The *peripheral nervous system* provides a means of communication from the environment (both external and internal), where stimuli are received by receptor organs, to the central nervous system, and from the central nervous system to the proper effector organs in the body, muscles, or glands.

By definition, the peripheral nervous system includes all nervous structures outside the brain and spinal cord. Of course this is an arbitrary division simply for convenience of description. This classification of the peripheral nervous system includes peripheral ganglia and spinal nerves, cranial nerves, and autonomic nerves.

Spinal Nerves

Somatic Components. With the exception of cervical nerves and caudal nerves, a pair of spinal nerves (one right and one left) emerges behind the vertebra of the same serial number and name (Fig. 5–15). For example, the first pair of thoracic nerves emerges through the intervertebral foramina located between the first and second thoracic vertebrae; the last pair of thoracic nerves emerges through the intervertebral foramina between the last thoracic and first lumbar vertebrae, and the second pair of lumbar nerves emerges through the foramina between the second and third lumbar vertebrae. Thus there are the same number of pairs of thoracic, lumbar, and sacral nerves as there are similar vertebrae.

The first pair of cervical nerves emerges through the foramina in the first cervical vertebra, and the second pair between the first and the second cervical vertebrae. Therefore, there are eight pairs of cervical nerves although only seven cervical vertebrae.

Usually there are fewer pairs of caudal (coccygeal) nerves than there are caudal vertebrae. The terminal part of the spinal cord, meninges, and nerves is called the *cauda equina* (horse's tail).

A typical spinal nerve may be compared to a tree because it has roots, the nerve proper, and various branches (see Figs. 5–16 and 5–17).

The *dorsal root* enters the dorsal portion of the spinal cord. It carries only afferent (sensory) impulses from the periphery of the animal toward the spinal cord. The nerve cell bodies of these afferent neurons are located in the *dorsal root ganglion*, a swelling on the dorsal root close to the point where the dorsal and ventral roots join to form the spinal nerve proper. These sensory neurons are classified as *pseudo-unipolar neurons*.

The *ventral root* emerges from the ventral portion of the spinal cord. It carries efferent (or motor) impulses from the spinal cord to striated muscle fibers. The nerve cell bodies of these *somatic motor nerves* (derived from ventral roots) are located in the ventral horn of the spinal cord.

Near the intervertebral foramen, the dorsal root, which is sensory, meets the ventral root, which is motor, to form the main part of the spinal nerve. The spinal nerve proper thus contains both sensory and motor fibers, so it is classified as a mixed nerve.

Almost as soon as the spinal nerve emerges from the vertebral canal through the intervertebral foramen, it divides into a dorsal branch and a ventral branch. Both of these branches are mixed nerves, because each contains both sensory and motor fibers.

In general, the dorsal branches of spinal nerves supply structures that are dorsal to the transverse processes of the vertebrae. The ventral branches supply structures ven-

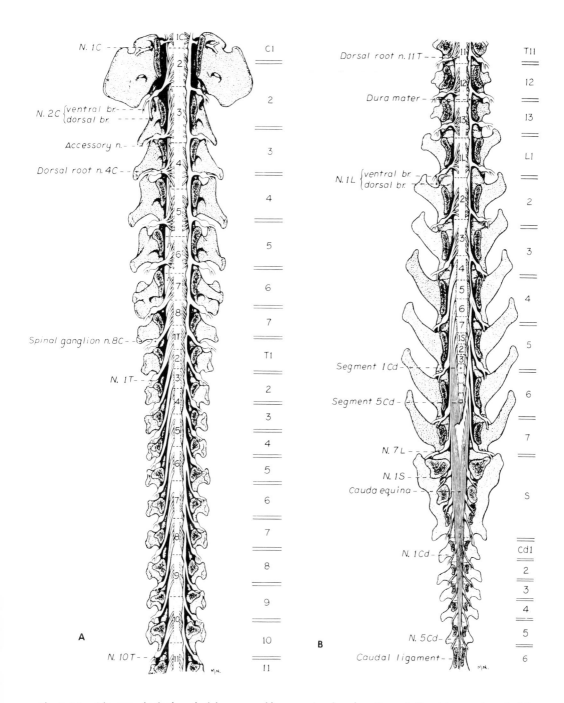

Fig. 5–15. Diagram of spinal cord of dog exposed by removing dorsal portions of all vertebrae and most of the dura mater except on the extreme right side of the spinal cord. *A,* Spinal cord from 1st cervical nerve to 11th thoracic nerve. *B,* Spinal cord from 11th thoracic nerve to 5th caudal nerve.

C = Cervical; T = thoracic; L = lumbar; S = sacral; Cd = caudal.

Numbers on spinal cord indicate origin of spinal nerve of same number. Numbers to right of each drawing indicate vertebra number at that level. (McClure in Miller, Christensen, and Evans, Anatomy of the Dog, courtesy of W.B. Saunders Co.)

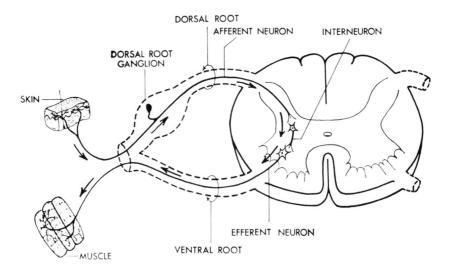

Fig. 5–16.   Diagrammatic cross-section of the spinal cord. (Kitchell in Miller, Christensen, and Evans, Anatomy of the Dog; courtesy of W. B. Saunders Co.)

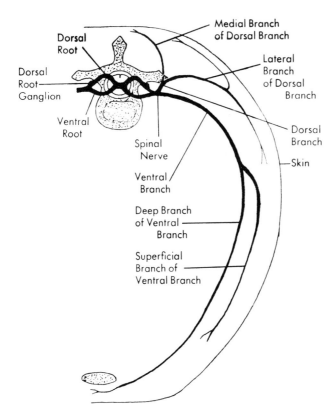

Fig. 5–17.   Diagram of a typical spinal nerve.

tral to the transverse processes and most structures of the forelimbs and hindlimbs.

The spinal nerves tend to supply sensory and motor fibers to the region of the body in the area where they emerge from the spinal cord. The appendages, however, are supplied with sensory and motor fibers by braidlike arrangements of nerves known as *plexuses*.

Brachial Plexus. Each forelimb is supplied by a *brachial plexus*, which is a network of nerves derived from the last three or four cervical and first one or two thoracic nerves (Figs. 5–18, 5–19A). The spinal cord shows a considerable increase in size in this region, known as the *cervical enlargement*.

Derivation of the Brachial Plexus

Horse: Last 3 cervical and first 2 thoracic nerves
Cow: Last 3 cervical and first thoracic nerves
Sheep: Last 3 cervical and first thoracic nerves
Pig: Last 3 cervical and first thoracic nerves
Dog: Last 3 cervical and first 2 thoracic nerves

The brachial plexus gives rise to specific named nerves that innervate the muscles of the forelimb and also supply sensation to the same general regions of the skin. Table 5–1 lists the nerves derived from the brachial plexus and the region and muscles supplied by each.

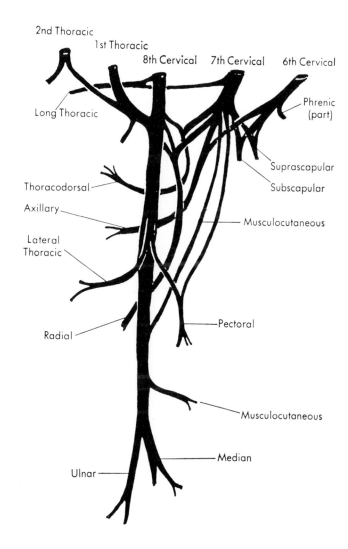

Fig. 5–18. Diagram of brachial plexus of cow showing names of nerves involved. (After McLeod, Bovine Anatomy, 2nd ed., Burgess Pub. Co.)

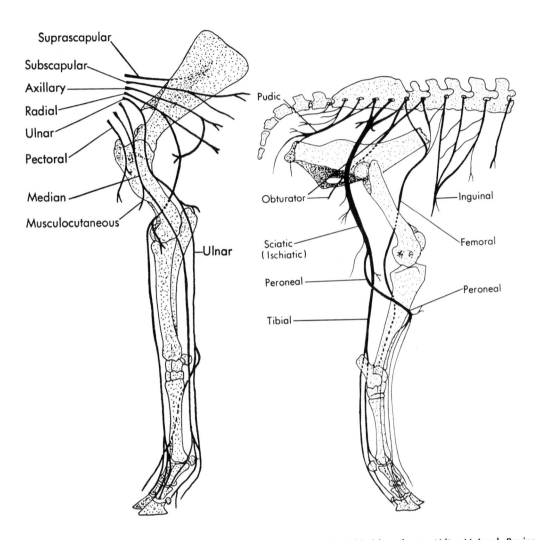

Suprascapular

Subscapular

Axillary

Radial

Ulnar

Pectoral

Median

Musculocutaneous

Ulnar

Pudic

Obturator

Sciatic
(Ischiatic)

Peroneal

Tibial

Inguinal

Femoral

Peroneal

Fig. 5–19. *A*, Nerve supply of front leg of cow. *B*, Nerve supply of hind leg of cow. (After McLeod, *Bovine Anatomy*, 2nd ed., Burgess Pub. Co.)

Table 5–1. Nerves of Brachial Plexus

Nerve	Region	Muscles Supplied
Pectoral	Shoulder	Superficial and deep pectorals
Suprascapular	Shoulder	Supraspinatus Infraspinatus
Subscapular	Shoulder	Subscapularis
Long thoracic	Shoulder	Serratus ventralis
Axillary	Shoulder	Teres major Teres minor Deltoid Brachiocephalicus
Thoracodorsal	Shoulder	Latissimus dorsi
Lateral thoracic	Shoulder	Cutaneous trunci
Musculocutaneous	Arm	Biceps brachii Coracobrachialis Brachialis
Median	Forearm	Flexor carpi radialis Superficial digital flexor Deep digital flexor (part) Pronator teres (if present) Pronator quadratus (if present)
Ulnar	Forearm	Flexor carpi ulnaris Deep digital flexor (part)
	Digit	Many intrinsic muscles of digit (if present)
Radial	Arm	Triceps, medial, lateral, long heads (also accessory in dog) Anconeus
	Forearm	Brachioradialis (if present) Extensor carpi radialis Common digital extensor Lateral digital extensor Extensor carpi ulnaris (ulnaris lateralis) Abductor pollicis longus (abductor digiti I or extensor carpi obliquis) Supinator (if present)

Lumbosacral Plexus. The right and the left *lumbosacral plexuses* supply nerves to the respective hindlimb as the corresponding brachial plexuses do to the corresponding front limb (Fig. 5–19B). The lumbosacral plexuses are made up of the ventral branches of the last few lumbar and first one or two sacral nerves:

Derivation of the Lumbosacral Plexus

Horse: Last 3 lumbar and first 2 sacral nerves
Cow: Last 3 lumbar and first 2 sacral nerves
Sheep: Last 3 lumbar and first 2 sacral nerves
Pig: Last 3 lumbar and first sacral nerves
Dog: Last 5 lumbar and first sacral nerves

The nerves derived from the lumbosacral plexus are listed in Table 5–2.

Cranial Nerves

The 12 pairs of cranial nerves in general resemble ordinary spinal nerves with the exception that they have no dorsal or ventral roots and emerge through various foramina of the skull rather than through intervertebral foramina, as do the spinal nerves. Another difference is that some cranial nerves are strictly sensory (afferent) and

Table 5–2.   Nerves of Lumbosacral Plexus

Nerve	Region	Muscles Supplied
Cranial gluteal	Rump	Middle gluteus Deep gluteus Tensor fasciae latae

Caudal gluteal	Rump	Superficial gluteus
		    Part of middle gluteus, semitendinosus,
		    and biceps femoris in horse

Femoral	Thigh	Sartorius
		Quadriceps femoris
		    Rectus femoris
		    Vastus lateralis
		    Vastus medialis
		    Vastus intermedius
		Psoas major and iliacus

Obturator	Thigh	Adductor Gracilis Pectineus External obturator
Sciatic (Ischiatic)	Thigh	Semitendinosus Semimembranosus Biceps femoris Internal obturator Gemellus Quadratus femoris
Tibial	Leg	Gastrocnemius Superficial digital flexor Deep digital flexor Popliteus Tibialis caudalis
Peroneal	Leg	Tibialis cranialis Long digital extensor Lateral digital extensor Peroneus tertius Peroneus longus (if present) Peroneus brevis (if present)

some are strictly motor (efferent), while spinal nerves are all mixed (containing both sensory and motor fibers). Some cranial nerves, however, are also mixed.

Cranial nerves are known by number (usually indicated by Roman numeral) and by name. The sequence of numbers is approximately in the order the nerves appear to be derived from the brain, from rostral to caudal (Fig. 5–20).

Table 5–3 summarizes the general relationships of the cranial nerves.

Autonomic Nervous System

The autonomic nervous system is the part of the peripheral nervous system that inner-vates smooth muscle, cardiac muscle, and glands (Fig. 5–21). In other words, the autonomic nervous system is associated with visceral structures, while the remainder of the peripheral nervous system is associated with somatic structures. Using this breakdown, we find four types of nerves in the peripheral nervous system.

Visceral efferent fibers and visceral afferent fibers make up the autonomic portion, while somatic afferent (sensory) fibers and somatic efferent (motor) fibers form the remainder of the peripheral nervous system.

Some authorities disagree with such a simple concept of the peripheral nervous system. They believe that the term "somatic" should be limited to nerves supplying

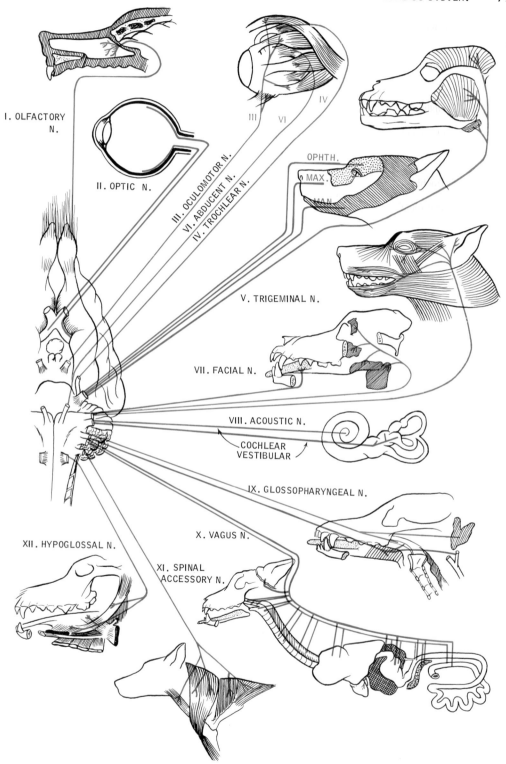

I. OLFACTORY
    N.

II. OPTIC N.

III. OCULOMOTOR N.

VI. ABDUCENT N.

IV. TROCHLEAR N.

III

IV

VI

OPHTH.

MAX.

MAN.

V. TRIGEMINAL N.

VII. FACIAL N.

VIII. ACOUSTIC N.

COCHLEAR
VESTIBULAR

IX. GLOSSOPHARYNGEAL N.

X. VAGUS N.

XII. HYPOGLOSSAL N.

XI. SPINAL
ACCESSORY N.

Fig. 5–20.   The origin and major distribution of the cranial nerves in the dog. Green indicates afferent fibers; red indicates efferent fibers. (From Hoerlein, 1965, by permission of W. B. Saunders Company.)

Table 5–3. Cranial Nerves

No.	Name	Type	Distribution
I	Olfactory	Sensory	Nasal mucous membrane (sense of smell)
II	Optic	Sensory	Retina of eye (sight)
III	Oculomotor	Motor	Most muscles of eye Parasympathetic to ciliary muscle and circular muscle of iris
IV	Trochlear	Motor	Dorsal oblique muscle of eye
V	Trigeminal	Mixed	Sensory—to eye and face Motor—to muscles of mastication
VI	Abducens	Motor	Retractor and lateral rectus muscles of eye
VII	Facial	Mixed	Sensory—region of ear and taste to cranial ⅔ of tongue Motor—to muscles of facial expression Parasympathetic to mandibular and sublingual salivary glands
VIII	Vestibulocochlear	Sensory	Cochlea (hearing) and Semicircular canals (equilibrium)
IX	Glossopharyngeal	Mixed	Sensory—to pharynx and taste to caudal ⅓ of tongue Motor—to muscle of pharynx Parasympathetic to parotid salivary glands
X	Vagus	Mixed	Sensory—to pharynx and larynx Motor—to muscles of larynx Parasympathetic to visceral structures in the thorax and abdomen
XI	Spinal Accessory	Motor	Motor—to muscles of shoulder and neck
XII	Hypoglossal	Motor	Motor—to muscles of tongue

structures definitely known to be derived from somites.

Sympathetic Nervous System. The sympathetic portion of the autonomic nervous system is also called the *thoracolumbar* portion because the sympathetic outflow is mainly from thoracic and lumbar spinal nerves (Fig. 5–22). The cells of origin of the visceral efferent fibers of the sympathetic nerves are located in the lateral gray column of the thoracic and lumbar segments of the spinal cord. The lateral gray column is located dorsolateral to the ventral gray horn of

the spinal cord, where the cell bodies of the somatic motor nerves are located. Unlike the somatic efferent nerves, which have no cell bodies or synapses outside the central nervous system, the sympathetic nerves synapse with *secondary neurons* (postganglionic neurons) located in sympathetic ganglia relatively close to the spinal column.

In the thoracic, lumbar, and sacral regions, sympathetic ganglia, called *vertebral* (or *paravertebral*) *ganglia*, are located close to each intervertebral space, with a ganglion on each side of each vertebra. In addition to

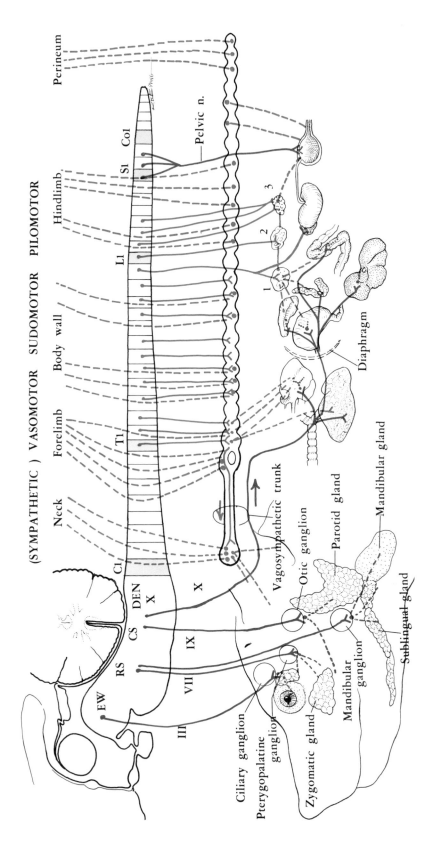

Fig. 5–21. Diagram illustrating the general organization of the autonomic nervous system. Sympathetic neurons are red, parasympathetic neurons blue. Solid lines represent presynaptic (preganglionic) neurons; broken lines, postsynaptic (postganglionic) neurons. *EW*, Edinger-Westphal nucleus; *RS*, rostral salivatory nucleus; *CS*, caudal salivatory nucleus; *DEN X*, dorsal efferent nucleus of *X*; *C1*, cervical 1 level; *T1*, thoracic 1 level; *L1*, lumbar 1 level; *S1*, sacral 1 level; *Co1*, coccygeal 1 level; *III*, oculomotor nerve; *VII*, facial nerve; *IX*, glossopharyngeal nerve; *X*, vagus nerve; *1*, celiac ganglion; *2*, cranial mesenteric ganglion; *3*, caudal mesenteric ganglion. (Jenkins, T.W.: Functional Mammalian Neuroanatomy. ed. 2. Philadelphia, Lea & Febiger, 1978.)

81

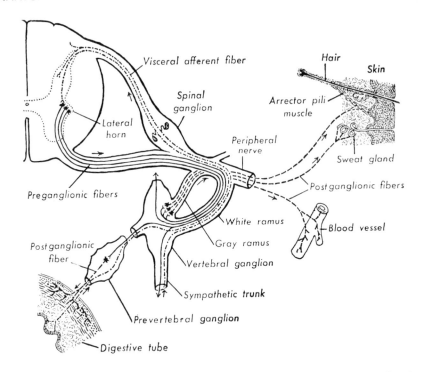

Fig. 5–22. Diagram showing relation of sympathetic, visceral efferent neurons to thoracic spinal cord, sympathetic trunk and visceral structures. Pregnanglionic fibers are shown in solid lines, postganglionic fibers in broken lines, and visceral afferent fibers in dot-and-dash lines. The direction of a conduction is indicated by arrows. (Bailey's Textbook of Histology, 12th ed. The Williams & Wilkins Co.)

these vertebral ganglia located on the bodies of the vertebrae, other specially named paired sympathetic ganglia are located ventral to the vertebral column, which are called *prevertebral* (or *collateral*) *ganglia.* These include the *celiac ganglia, cranial mesenteric ganglia,* and *caudal mesenteric ganglia.* The *cranial* and *caudal cervical ganglia* are sometimes considered to be vertebral rather than prevertebral ganglia. The sympathetic ganglia contain nerve cell bodies outside the central nervous system and are also the location of synapses between preganglionic sympathetic fibers and postganglionic sympathetic fibers. The preganglionic sympathetic fibers are myelinated fibers, extending from sympathetic neurons in the lateral gray column of the spinal cord to a sympathetic vertebral or prevertebral ganglion by way of the ventral roots of the thoracic and lumbar spinal nerves, the spinal

nerves proper, and the ventral branches of the spinal nerves. Although each preganglionic fiber will synapse with one or more sympathetic postganglionic neurons in a ganglion, the fiber does not necessarily synapse in the first ganglion it encounters, but may continue over a considerable distance to another vertebral ganglion, or it may synapse in a prevertebral ganglion.

The cell bodies of postganglionic neurons *(secondary neurons)* are located in vertebral or prevertebral sympathetic ganglia. The processes of these secondary neurons are unmyelinated fibers called postganglionic fibers. They travel directly to the organ or structure being supplied with sympathetic fibers, usually by way of the vessels that supply blood to the structure. Thus preganglionic sympathetic fibers travel from thoracic and lumbar parts of the spinal cord to sympathetic ganglia. Postganglionic sympathetic fibers travel from sympathetic ganglia to an organ.

One exception to this general arrangement is the so-called *gray rami*, which return from each sympathetic vertebral ganglion to the spinal nerve of the same serial number, to be distributed with the branchings of the spinal nerve to the skin, including peripheral blood vessels, sweat glands, and *pilomotor* fibers (smooth muscle cells in the skin that raise the hairs during fright, anger, or cold weather). Another exception is the preganglionic sympathetic nerve fibers that go all the way to the adrenal medulla *without* synapsing in a ganglion, but rather synapse on the *chromaffin cells* of the medulla to effect secretion of *catecholamines*.

The many interconnections between various levels of ganglia (by both preganglionic fibers and postganglionic sympathetic fibers) form paired nerve trunks which pass along each side of the vertebral column from the region of the head as far back as the caudal end of the sacrum. The main paired trunk, the *ganglionated sympathetic trunk* of each side, receives *white rami communicantes* from the ventral branches of the thoracic and lumbar spinal nerves. These white rami are simply that portion of the myelinated preganglionic fibers extending from the ventral branch of a thoracic or lumbar spinal nerve to the vertebral ganglion of the same serial number. They parallel the gray rami, which are unmyelinated postganglionic fibers returning from the sympathetic vertebral ganglion to the spinal nerve of the same serial number.

Thus the white rami communicantes, which enter the ganglionated sympathetic trunk in the thoracic and lumbar regions, constitute the entire efferent connection of the sympathetic system with the central nervous system. In other words, the entire outflow to the sympathetic system is from thoracic and lumbar segments of the spinal cord. The rest of the sympathetic nervous system consists of nerve trunks and ganglia associated with visceral structures of the body. The *greater* and *lesser splanchnic*

nerves carry sympathetic fibers to the abdominal viscera by way of ganglia and plexuses, such as *celiac, cranial mesenteric,* and *caudal mesenteric plexuses.*

The head receives sympathetic fibers by way of the *cervical sympathetic trunk* on each side of the neck, which extends from the caudal cervical ganglion to the cranial cervical ganglion. The caudal cervical ganglion is located under cover of the first rib close to the ganglionated sympathetic trunk (to which it connects) in the region of the first thoracic vertebra. Fibers from the ganglionated sympathetic trunk pass to thoracic organs (heart and lungs) by way of the caudal cervical ganglion and the first few thoracic ganglia. Other fibers pass up the neck through the cervical sympathetic trunk to the cranial cervical ganglion, and thence to smooth muscle and glands of the head by way of the *carotid plexus,* which follows branches of the carotid artery.

Parasympathetic Nervous System. The parasympathetic portion of the autonomic nervous system is made up of cranial and sacral portions. Fibers of the cranial portion are distributed to visceral structures by way of four cranial nerves: the *oculomotor, facial, glossopharyngeal,* and *vagus.* The first three nerves mentioned above supply parasympathetic fibers to smooth muscle and glands in the region of the head, the same structures supplied by the carotid plexus of the sympathetic system.

The vagus nerve, one of the longest in the body, supplies parasympathetic fibers to the heart and lungs in the thorax and to nearly all abdominal viscera.

The last part of the digestive tract and most of the urogenital system are supplied with parasympathetic fibers from the *sacral portion* of the parasympathetic nervous system.

A comparison of the sympathetic and parasympathetic nervous systems shows the following anatomical differences:

The sympathetic system is derived from thoracic and lumbar segments of the spinal cord; preganglionic fibers are relatively short, while postganglionic fibers extending from sympathetic ganglia to the organs supplied are relatively long.

The parasympathetic system is derived from cranial and sacral portions of the nervous system. The parasympathetic ganglia are located within or close to the organs supplied. Thus the preganglionic fibers are relatively long and the postganglionic fibers are short.

Chapter 6

Physiology of the Nervous System

Irritability and conductivity are two properties associated with life that a single-celled organism such as the ameba possesses. In order to adjust to changes in the external environment, the single cell must be receptive to stimuli such as changes of light, temperature, osmotic pressure, pH, and touch. In other words, it must be irritable. Not only are the stimuli received, but they must be transmitted electrochemically along the membrane to the portion of the cell that will take appropriate action. This transmission represents conductivity.

As organisms evolved into more complex forms, these two activities were performed by specialized cells that were the forerunners of nerve cells, called neurons. These cells had to have contact both with the surface of the animal, where changes in environment are most noticeable, and with deeper (effector) cells, such as muscle cells or gland cells, which specialize in either contraction or secretion. Certain epithelial cells at first produced elongated processes to facilitate this type of nervous activity. Thus, the nervous system of higher animals logically originated from the ectoderm, or external layer of the animal (Fig. 5–2).

Perception of changes in external environment (everything associated with the animal but external to it) and changes of internal environment (the entire internal makeup of the animal), as well as the ability to adapt to these changes, basically depends upon the proper functioning of the individual neurons or nerve cells that constitute the nervous system of an animal.

PHYSIOLOGY OF THE NERVE IMPULSE

It is convenient to compare the nervous system to various electrical systems such as a telephone exchange, with wires represented by nerve fibers. While such an analogy is useful, there are many areas in which the comparison is not valid.

In most electrical systems, the electric current is supplied by an outside device, such as a generator or battery, and the wires passively conduct the current. The efficiency of the system, therefore, depends to a large extent on the ability of the wire to conduct the current. The similar ability of a nerve fiber to conduct electricity passively is limited. The major difference between a wire and a nerve fiber lies in the ability of the nerve fiber to propagate actively an impulse throughout its length without diminution or decrement. This is possible because of the energy that is available from metabolism within the nerve and the special membrane properties of the nerve fiber, which produce the *resting potential* of the plasma membrane of the nerve cell and its processes.

Resting Potential. This resting potential of the membrane is the electrical difference between the negative charges inside the membrane next to the axoplasm (protoplasm of the nerve) and the positive charges outside the membrane next to the extracellular fluid surrounding the nerve and its processes. The resting potential is produced by differences in ions and their charges on the inside and outside of the plasma membrane. There is a small excess of positive ions (cations) outside the plasma membrane of a resting (polarized) nerve cell, and a small excess of negative ions (anions) inside the plasma membrane.

This unequal distribution of charges produces a measurable voltage difference across the membrane, the *membrane potential*, which is found on the membranes of all cells. The membrane potential varies from cell to cell (from -10 mv to -100 mv), but in most nerve and muscle cells it is about -85 millivolts (-85 mv). This means that the inside of the membrane is 85 mv more negative than the outside. (See Fig. 6–1.)

The plasma membrane in the resting condition (electrically polarized) is almost impermeable to Na^+ ions (and, of course, to protein, which tends to be negative), but it is very permeable to both K^+ and Cl^- ions.

Sodium ions (Na^+) are actively transported to the outside, building up the positive charges outside and leaving the inside negative. Even though some of these sodium ions tend to "leak" down their chemical and concentration gradients to the inside of the membrane, the active transport "sodium pump" continually pumps them back out to keep the resting membrane polarized.

The negative Cl^- ions move freely through the plasma membrane to accompany the Na^+ ions transported outside the membrane by the sodium pump. K^+ ions also readily pass through the plasma membrane, but into the cytoplasm, to help electrically balance the negative protein charges inside the plasma membrane of the nerve cell. Some K^+ ions are also actively transported through the plasma membrane into the cell by the potassium pump.

The excess negative and positive charges tend to attract each other, so they line up on each side of the membrane, creating an electrical potential across the membrane just like any charged electrical capacitor.

The pumping of Na^+ depends on adenosine triphosphate (ATP) to supply energy, plus a carrier system in the membrane, for the "uphill" chemical and electrical gradient transport of Na^+ ions. In the process, a relatively high potassium (K^+) ion concentration is created inside the cell. A membrane enzyme, *adenosine triphosphatase* (ATPase), hydrolyzes (degrades with water) the ATP to ADP *(adenosine diphosphate)*, providing the energy needed for transport. Hence, the active transport complex is referred to as the *Na-K-ATPase system*.

The Na^+ and Cl^- ions outside the cell tend to balance the "potential osmotic pressure" of the nondiffusible intracellular organic substances, especially the proteins, which are negatively charged. The net result is that there is in the extracellular fluid bathing the cells a concentration of 140 mEq/L of Na^+, 103 mEq/L of Cl^-, and 5 mEq/L of K^+. On the inside of the cell, however, there is only 10 mEq/L of Na^+, 4 mEq/L of Cl^-, but 140 mEq/L of K^+. This ionic imbalance of the resting membrane potential is maintained by the Na-K-ATPase system; there is no net gain or loss, or net flux (movement), of ions on either side of the resting membrane. In fact, when we also consider the negatively charged ions (anions) on the inside of the cell (phosphates, sulfates, amino acids) and the nondiffusible, negatively charged proteins in the cell, we find that *each side* of the cell membrane is in equilibrium—the concentra-

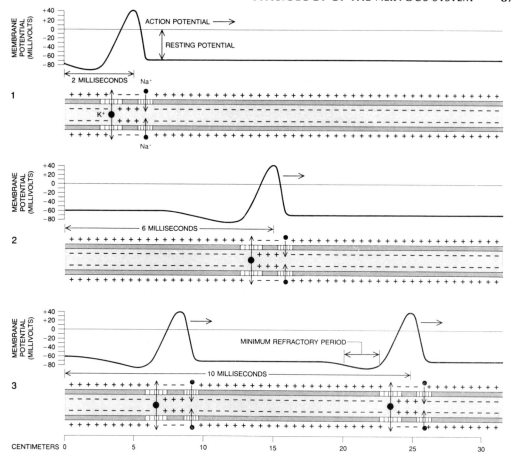

Fig. 6–1. Propagation of nerve impulse along the axon coincides with a localized inflow of sodium ions *(Na+)* followed by an outflow of potassium ions *(K+)* through channels that are "gated," or controlled, by voltage changes across the axon membrane. The electrical event that sends a nerve impulse traveling down the axon normally originates in the cell body. The impulse begins with a slight depolarization, or reduction in the negative potential, across the membrane of the axon where it leaves the cell body. The slight voltage shift opens some of the sodium channels, shifting the voltage still further. The inflow of sodium ions accelerates until the inner surface of the membrane is locally positive. The voltage reversal closes the sodium channel and opens the potassium channel. The outflow of potassium ions quickly restores the negative potential. The voltage reversal, known as the action potential, propagates itself down the axon *(1, 2)*. After a brief refractory period, a second impulse can follow *(3)*. The impulse-propagation speed is that measured in the giant axon of the squid. (From Scientific American, 241:60, Sept., 1979.)

tion of anions equals that of the cations on the same side.

Action Potentials. The nerve fiber is capable of converting mechanical and chemical stimuli to electrical energy (Fig. 6–2).

A *stimulus* is any change in the environment of a nerve which, if large enough, will depolarize the resting potential, and cause the nerve to produce an *action potential* (a *nerve impulse*). This impulse is essentially a

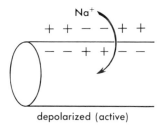

Fig. 6–2. Action potential. (From Crouch, J. E.: Functional Human Anatomy. ed. 3. Philadelphia, Lea & Febiger, 1978.)

wave of electrical change moving along the membrane of the nerve fiber.

Stimuli can be physical, chemical, or electrical in nature. In fact, any change in the environment, either internal or external, can serve as a stimulus. If the stimulus is barely strong enough to initiate an action potential and therefore an impulse in a nerve, it is called a *threshold stimulus*. In the living animal most stimuli are physical or chemical in nature and include gravity, pressure, temperature, light (for vision), chemical composition of the body fluids or of the air (for smell), and osmotic pressure. With the exception of an electric fence, electric prod, or electric eel, electrical stimuli are rare outside of the experimental laboratory. However, because of the ease of controlling strength, duration, and frequency of electrical stimuli, they are the most commonly used stimuli for experimental work in the study of nerve response to stimuli and transmission of impulses.

Only nerve cells and muscle cells can have their membrane permeabilities to Na^+ and K^+ altered enough to cause a *rapid* change in the membrane potential, thereby producing an *action potential*. The action potential provides the means of transmitting an impulse along the membrane and therefore the means of rapid communication and response throughout the body. Nerve cells are discussed here, and the few differences that apply to muscle cells will be covered in Chapter 12.

An action potential results from a reversal of polarity on the plasma membrane created by an adequate stimulus, a stimulus capable of significantly increasing the membrane permeability to Na^+.

Depolarization and Repolarization. When a stimulus is just strong enough to initiate an action potential, it is called a *threshold stimulus*. The resultant action potential consists of a depolarization of the membrane followed by repolarization back to the resting potential. An action potential is seen on an oscilloscope as a spikelike deflection that lasts about 1 millisecond (1

msec or 1/1000 of a second) on a specific part of a nerve membrane.

Depolarization involves a rapid increase in the membrane's permeability to Na^+. This allows Na^+ ions to rush across the membrane into the cell and thereby create a positive state inside the cell. The Na^+ ion influx therefore reverses the internal polarity of the membrane from its resting state and the inside becomes relatively more positive. (See Fig. 6–1.) Starting at a resting potential of −85 mv for a nerve cell, the stimulus overcomes the polarizing ability of the Na-K-ATPase system and produces a rapid change to about +50 mv, which is the *voltage plateau* for Na^+ influx.

Repolarization begins after Na^+ influx essentially stops at its plateau. Then the permeability to K^+ increases and K^+ ions move from the inside to the outside of the membrane until this mechanism also becomes inactivated. There is a slight "overshoot," however, in the initial repolarizing, going to about −88 mv. During the recovery phase, the Na-K-ATPase system utilizes the metabolic energy of ATP of the nerve cell to actively transport the Na^+ out of the cell to the extracellular fluid and to transport the K^+ into the cell.

While Na^+ is rushing into the cell, the nerve cell is unable to produce another action potential regardless of how strong a stimulus is applied. This time period is called the *absolute refractory period*. The time when K^+ is moving out of the cell is called the *relative refractory period* because another action potential can be produced, but only by a second stimulus stronger than a threshold stimulus. This is because the outward current flow due to K^+ tends to decrease the effect of any inward Na^+ current.

Conductance. The whole process of producing an action potential, depolarization, and repolarization depends on changes in membrane *conductance* to Na^+ and K^+. Conductance is a property of the cell membrane that is equivalent to the *permeability* of the membrane to any ion. Therefore, conductance is the reciprocal of resistance $\left(C = \dfrac{1}{R}\right)$. So, as conductance for an ion increases, the resistance to its passage decreases. Changes in the net flux of Na^+ and K^+ ions account for the electrical events of the action potential.

The Nerve Impulse. The localized production of an action potential would have little use unless it was propagated along the axon of the neuronal membrane to serve as a means of communication between two points. This propagation of the action potential is called the *nerve impulse.*

The nerve impulse is essentially a wave of electrical change moving along the membrane of the nerve fiber. This depolarization wave travels as a self-perpetuating reaction which, along an unmyelinated nerve fiber, is analogous to burning a trail of gunpowder or igniting a fuse. The action potential itself acts as the stimulus that depolarizes the adjacent membrane down to the threshold level by the electrotonic spread of current. This current excites the adjacent parts of the membrane, thereby producing another electrical stimulus and an action potential. This, in turn, acts to stimulate the next membrane region, and so on, as it proceeds along the nerve fiber as a wave of continuous current flow.

Propagation normally proceeds orthodromically (in one direction) because the membrane behind it is hyperpolarized from the high outflow of K^+. Furthermore, it proceeds without reduction in size of the potential because the magnitude of the action potential depends on the ionic concentration gradients of the membrane, not on the strength of the stimulus. This transmission of the depolarization process (propagation) is called the *impulse* (Fig. 6–1). It applies to both nerve and muscle membranes.

Conduction Velocities. For any one nerve fiber, the speed of conduction of the impulse remains constant—it does not increase nor decrease as it moves away from the site of stimulation. However, *different* nerve fibers vary in their speed of conduction, because of differences in current flow related to the cross-sectional area of the axon. Large-diameter fibers propagate action potentials (impulses) at higher velocities than do small-diameter fibers, because large fibers have less internal resistance to the flow of current.

Large unmyelinated fibers, 20 μ in diameter, approach conduction velocities of 250 miles per hour (130 m/sec). At this rate an impulse could travel 6 feet in about 15 milliseconds (msec). The smallest unmyelinated fibers of the body, about 0.5 μ in diameter, conduct at only about 20 inches per second (½ m/sec). The rate of conduction is directly proportional to the size of the nerve fiber.

Myelinated nerve fibers conduct impulses more rapidly than unmyelinated nerve fibers, because of the insulating qualities of the Schwann cells surrounding the fiber. This Schwann cell membrane contains the lipid *sphingomyelin,* which is a good insulator against ionic flow. Each Schwann cell covers about a 1-mm distance along the fiber, and the junction between two Schwann cells is called the *node of Ranvier.* No myelin is present at these nodes, so the membrane is highly permeable. At these junction points without myelin, the axon plasma membrane (axolemma) is directly bathed by the extracellular fluid. The ionic current flow can cross the membrane only at these nodes; it cannot cross the insulated regions. Therefore the circuits of current must flow from node to node. Since this is analogous to "jumping" from one node to the next, it is given the name *saltatory conduction* (from saltare—to jump) (Fig. 6–3). The current actually flows through the axoplasm on the inside and the extracellular fluid (ECF) on the outside.

Neuronal Synapse. A synapse is a specialized junction between two neurons, or between a neuron ending and a muscle cell or a gland cell (Fig. 6–4). At the synapse the electrical activity in the *presynaptic neuron* chemically links and influences the electrical excitability of the *postsynaptic neuron*

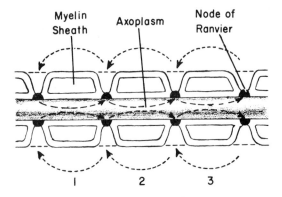

Fig. 6–3. Saltatory conduction along a myelinated axon. (From Guyton, A. C.: Textbook of Medical Physiology. ed. 5. Philadelphia, W. B. Saunders, 1976.)

(or muscle or gland). Presynaptic neurons conduct impulses toward the synapse, while postsynaptic neurons conduct impulses away from the synapse. The postsynaptic neuron's excitability is either increased, in the case of an *excitatory* (type I) *synapse*, or decreased, at an *inhibitory* (type II) *synapse*.

Synapses operate in only one direction—from the presynaptic neuron, which conducts the impulse of the action potential to its terminal swelling (called the *synaptic knob*, *bulb*, or *bouton*) to the postsynaptic neuron. This one-direction conduction is called *orthodromic conduction*.

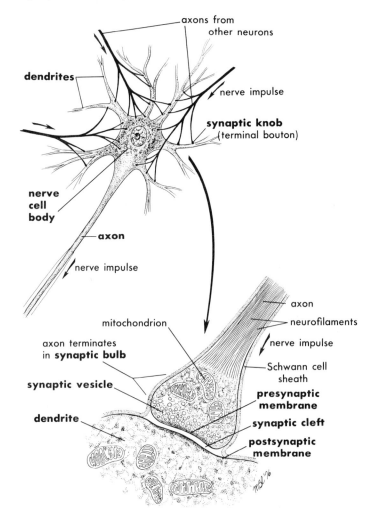

Fig. 6–4. Functional anatomy of a synapse. (From Crouch, J. E.: Functional Human Anatomy. ed. 3. Philadelphia, Lea & Febiger, 1978.)

Vesicles in the synaptic knob of the axon on the presynaptic side contain transmitter substance. There are also many mitochondria in the knob, but only a few along the length of the axon. The transmitter substance is synthesized in the knob and packaged in the vesicles. The mitochondria produce the ATP energy for the synthesis.

Transmission at the synapses is accomplished by the release of a specific transmitter substance from the presynaptic terminal bulb (synaptic knob) into the *synaptic cleft*, the space between the terminal knob and the membrane of the postsynaptic neuron. The width of this cleft averages 200 Å [20 nanometers (nm) or one millionth of an inch]. The transmitter substance diffuses across the cleft to the area on the postsynaptic neuron that lies directly under the synaptic knob, which is called the *subsynaptic membrane*. Here the chemical transmitter substance changes the membrane permeability (conductance) and may cause a new electrical depolarization postsynaptically.

When an impulse travels along the presynaptic axon to the terminal ending, it in turn depolarizes the membrane of the synaptic knob, Ca^{++} enters from the extracellular fluid, and some of the vesicles line up on the presynaptic membrane and expel their contents of transmitter substance molecules into the synaptic cleft by exocytosis.

Type I synapses are usually axodendritic (axon to dendrite), excitatory, and have round vesicles in the knob. If the transmitter substance is excitatory, it produces a partial, subthreshold depolarization on the postsynaptic neuronal membrane. This is called an *excitatory postsynaptic potential,* abbreviated EPSP. It is not strong enough to produce an action potential by itself, but it *facilitates* bringing the postsynaptic membrane closer to its threshold potential for firing by allowing Na^+ to enter. The EPSP is *passively* propagated (versus active propagation in the case of an action potential), and so it will gradually die-out unless summated (reinforced) by the addition of enough other EPSPs to produce an action potential on the postsynaptic neuron. The EPSP is therefore a subthreshold potential. Excitatory transmitter substances found in the nervous system are acetylcholine, norepinephrine, dopamine, and serotonin (5-hydroxytryptamine). Other possible excitatory transmitters are glutamic acid, histamine, and prostaglandins.

Type II synapses are usually axosomatic (axon to cell body), inhibitory, and have oblong vesicles. If the transmitter substance is inhibitory, it will lessen the likelihood that an action potential will be produced on the postsynaptic neuron. This is because it increases the postsynaptic membrane permeability to K^+ and Cl^-, but not to Na^+. The K^+ flows out, the Cl^- in, thus hyperpolarizing the membrane because of the increased inside negativity. This is called an *inhibitory postsynaptic potential*, abbreviated IPSP. Special interneurons located in the spinal cord, called *Golgi bottle neurons*, produce such IPSPs postsynaptically. Inhibitory transmitters may be *glycine* and *gamma-aminobutyric acid* (GABA).

With hundreds of neuron synaptic knobs terminating on a single postsynaptic neuron, there will be many EPSPs and IPSPs produced at any one time. Since they are passively propagated, the effects of these nearly simultaneous EPSPs and IPSPs will blend together. This is the principle of *synaptic integration*. If the number of EPSPs predominate, then there will be a generalized depolarization of the membrane (excitation) toward a resultant action potential firing the neuron. If IPSPs predominate, then there will be hyperpolarization, inhibiting an action potential from being produced. Thus, the degree of postsynaptic excitation depends on the algebraic sum of all the effective EPSPs and IPSPs produced on the postsynaptic neuron at any one moment.

Factors Affecting Transmission. The synapse is the weakest link in the nervous system neuron chain; it is here that many changes affect the transmission of impulses. Many drugs, for example, act at the synapse. These include morphine, strychnine, carbamylcholine, and tranquilizers. However, the excitability of neurons can also be affected. For example, when the animal is in a state of *alkalosis* (increased pH of the body fluids), neuron excitability increases. Alkalosis may be seen following vomiting, when stomach acid is lost, and the animal shakes all over from the increased excitability of the nerve fibers. Conversely, a state of *acidosis* decreases the excitability of the neurons, as occurs in the lethargy produced by prolonged diarrhea (scours). Also, since the entire nervous system is critically dependent on a constant oxygen supply, any hypoxia (decreased O_2) that the animal is exposed to will decrease the excitability of neurons. Hypoxia may occur from overwork and general fatigue until the oxygen debt is recovered.

Nerves and striated muscle fibers act according to the *all or none law*. In other words, any stimulus above the threshold will trigger an action potential and an impulse, but a change below threshold level will not. Further, the impulses conducted over a given nerve fiber are of the same magnitude and character, regardless of the stimulus that initiates them. Of course, the frequency of impulses can change. If an action potential fires, the impulse will be propagated over the given nerve fiber without any decrease in its magnitude and character, regardless of the stimulus that initiated it. The action potentials are all alike in any one nerve fiber—they only differ from nerve fiber to nerve fiber in magnitude and duration. Also, there is no such thing as an inhibitory action potential; instead, the inhibitory or excitatory *effects* of action potentials are achieved only at the synapse by means of the transmitter substance.

Convergence refers to the fact that a number of axonal endings synapse on a single postsynaptic cell and its dendrites. Thus convergence of stimuli, as from the eye, ear, and skin, can cause a strong motor response (Fig. 6–5).

Divergence is the opposite situation—each axon usually subdivides at its distal end into many branches that separate and terminate on many different neurons. This allows the activity in one neuron to influence the excitability of several other neurons (Fig. 6–5).

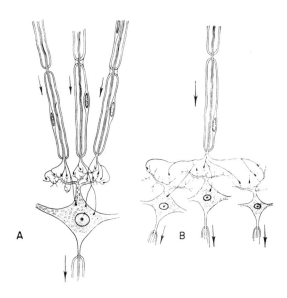

Fig. 6–5. Convergence and divergence. *A*, Three axons are in synaptic connection with a single nerve cell body; this effect is called convergence. *B*, A single axon makes synaptic connection with three nerve cell bodies; this spreading effect is called divergence. (After Grollman, The Human Body, The Macmillan Co.)

REFLEXES

A reflex action is an automatic, or unconscious, response of an effector organ (muscle or gland) to an appropriate stimulus. This action includes a chain of at least two neurons, making up a *reflex arc*. The two essential neurons in a reflex arc include an afferent, sensory, or receptor neuron, and an efferent, motor, or effector neuron. Usually one or more connector neurons (interneurons) are interposed between the receptor neurons and the effector neurons.

Although reflexes may involve various parts of the brain and the autonomic nervous system, the simplest reflex is the spinal reflex. A typical *spinal reflex* is the stretch reflex, illustrated by tapping the patellar ligament to cause the knee, or stifle, to extend—the so-called *knee jerk*. In this reflex action, proprioceptor neurons related to the quadriceps muscle fibers are stimulated by the sudden stretching of the muscle caused by striking the ligament at the front of the stifle. This impulse is carried to the spinal cord by way of the dorsal root of the appropriate spinal nerve. The impulse is then transmitted directly to the applicable motor neurons in the ventral gray horn of the spinal cord. The impulse then travels to the muscle fibers of the quadriceps femoris muscle of the thigh (in this case the same muscle in which the reflex originated), causing it to contract. This type of *stretch reflex* is also known as a *postural reflex* because it aids in maintaining a standing position. If the stifle suddenly flexes, this action stretches the quadriceps muscle, which initiates the reflex that causes the quadriceps to contract, thus extending the stifle to support the weight of the animal. The same reflex occurs in man when the area just below the knee is struck (Fig. 6–6).

The fact that reflex action does not require conscious control may be demonstrated with an animal such as a frog, in which the brain has been separated from the spinal cord by cutting the cord. An animal with the spinal cord severed is called a *spinal animal,* because all activities caudal to the point of the operation must be due only to action of the spinal cord, since there is no connection with the brain.

The frog is particularly useful for demonstrating spinal reflexes because the period of spinal shock (resulting from the severing operation) in which reflex activity is absent and the animal is completely limp lasts for only a few minutes. The period of spinal shock in mammals lasts several hours or more.

After recovery from spinal shock, the animal will flex (withdraw) a leg upon stimulation such as pinching the toe, applying a weak acid, or applying an electric shock (Fig. 6–7). Interconnection from one side of the spinal cord to the other and from one level (cervical, thoracic, lumbar) to another can be demonstrated by using stronger stimuli and restraining the stimulated ex-

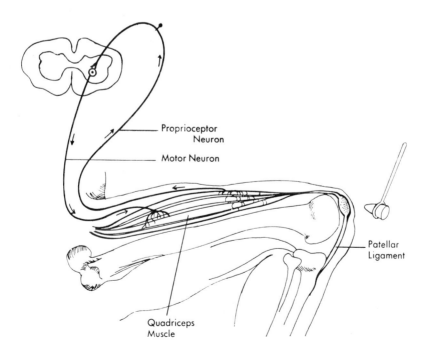

Proprioceptor
Neuron

Motor Neuron

Patellar
Ligament

Quadriceps
Muscle

Fig. 6–6. Diagram of stretch reflex.

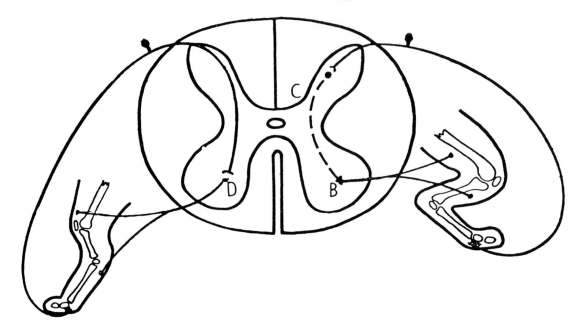

Fig. 6–7. Simple spinal reflexes.
Left: Extensor thrust. Light pressure on the sole activates a two-neuron arc, resulting in extension and support of the body. A similar effect is produced if a muscle is slightly stretched by flexion of the joint—the stretch reflex.
Right: Flexor reflex. Noxious stimulus of the limb activates a three-neuron arc resulting in sharp flexion and withdrawal from the stimulus; at the same time, the opposite limb is extended to provide compensating support.
A two-neuron extensor reflex has little facility for spread and may be classified as intrasegmental or local. The flexor reflex, with its extra rank of neurons, can spread widely to affect the motor neurons for many muscles and is intersegmental. (Elliot, Textbook of Neuroanatomy, courtesy of J. B. Lippincott Co.)

tremities. If the stimulated leg is prevented from flexing upon stimulation, the opposite leg will flex, thus showing the presence of connections from one side of the spinal cord to the opposite side. If both hind legs are restrained from flexing upon strong stimulation, the front legs will flex; or if a strong stimulus is applied to the ventral aspect of the body, all four legs will flex, thus showing connections between various levels of the spinal cord.

Reflexes may be of a somatic nature as the one first described, in which the effector organ consists of striated muscle. Reflexes of importance to the regulation of visceral functions are mediated by the autonomic nervous system. In these, effector organs are either smooth muscle, cardiac muscle, or glands.

The classic example of a visceral reflex is the production of gastric secretions by a dog when he is shown food. Both salivary and gastric glands secrete in preparation for ingestion of the food. Some of the most famous work on reflexes was performed by Pavlov, who found he could condition a dog to salivate upon the ringing of a bell, if the bell had been rung at the time food was offered to the dog for a number of times. This is the well-known example of a conditioned reflex, in which one stimulus is substituted for another to produce the same response.

Reflex centers are located throughout the central nervous system. Those associated with the spinal cord are the simplest and may involve only one side of the cord, both sides, or different levels of the cord, as illustrated by reactions of a spinal animal.

More complex reflexes are mediated through reflex centers found in the brain. The medulla oblongata contains reflex centers for control of heart action, vessel size, respiration, swallowing, vomiting, coughing, and sneezing.

The cerebellum contains most of the reflex centers associated with locomotion and posture. Many of these reflexes are inborn, as shown by a newborn foal running after its mother. However, they are subject to considerable modification during learning processes. For example, the complicated movements of a well-trained gaited horse are largely reflex in nature but have been modified considerably by training. This is true of most skilled physical activities, whether of man or animals.

The hypothalamus of the diencephalon contains reflex centers associated with temperature regulation and water balance. They control such functions as shivering, vasomotor activity in peripheral vessels, sweating, and urine excretion, as well as erection of hairs and feathers.

The cerebrum may be involved in such reflexes as the pupillary reflex, in which light striking the retina causes constriction of the pupil, and a general startle reaction to loud noises or frightening objects.

Either the absence or the exaggeration of reflexes indicates some abnormality of the reflex pathway. Reflexes are used extensively in human medicine and to a lesser degree in veterinary medicine in diagnosis of pathologic conditions. Reflex activity decreases under the influence of anesthetics. The presence or absence of specific reflexes is of considerable value in determining the depth of anesthesia in an animal.

In the dog, spinal reflexes include flexor reflex, in which the limb is withdrawn when the footpad or toe is pinched; knee jerk, in which extension of the knee results from tapping the patellar ligament; extensor thrust reflex, in which extension of the limb occurs when the foot is pushed toward the body as would occur in normal body support; and spinal visceral reflexes, which control micturition and defecation.

Attitudinal and postural reactions include the tonic neck reflexes, in which passively extending the neck (raising the head) increases the tone of extensor muscles of the forelimbs and decreases the tone of extensor muscles of the hind limbs. This could be a partial explanation for the value of raising a horse's head to prevent kicking. Conversely, when a horse gets his head down, he is much more likely to kick or buck. Tonic eye reflexes keep the eyes looking in the original direction when the head is moved.

The extensor postural thrust enables the limbs to support the weight of the body without conscious thought on the part of the animal. Righting, placing, and hopping reactions are associated with regaining a normal standing position following some imposed deviation in position on the animal's body or limbs.

Reflexes associated with the cranial nerves include the corneal reflex, in which the eyelids close in response to stimulation of the cornea of the eye, the pupillary reflex, in which the size of the pupil varies with light intensity, the pharyngeal reflexes, for swallowing or vomiting, and auditory reflexes, in which the animal turns its head toward a sound.

PHYSIOLOGY OF THE AUTONOMIC NERVOUS SYSTEM

The major role of the autonomic nervous system (ANS) is to maintain a relatively stable internal body environment; that is, to maintain a state of homeokinesis (homeostasis). It does so by regulating the activity of cardiac muscle, smooth muscle, and glands. The distribution of its nerves, therefore, is widespread throughout the body, innervating all the viscera.

Since the autonomic nervous system functions to maintain internal homeokinesis, it controls functions that are normally carried on below the level of consciousness. However, emotional reactions and stimuli to the lower brain centers from the cerebal cortex during the animal's activities will also affect the ANS.

Activation of the autonomic nervous system can occur either by cerebrocortical input or by sensory input to the hypothalamus. The *hypothalamus* acts as the major integrator of the ANS. It receives stimuli from sensory receptors all over the body. In turn, the hypothalamus then influences the quantity of signals transmitted down the brain stem and spinal cord. A posterior part of the hypothalamus integrates information mostly for the sympathetic division of the ANS output, and an anterior part of the hypothalamus integrates information mostly for the parasympathetic division output. More simplified integration also occurs at the brain stem level and at the spinal cord level, where simple visceral reflexes operate from the viscera to the spinal cord or brain stem and back to the viscera.

The output of the ANS is by way of those portions of spinal nerves and cranial nerves that are anatomically subdivided into the preganglionic neurons and postganglionic neurons described earlier. Each preganglionic axon branches, and can therefore synapse, with as many as ten postganglionic neurons in a ganglion, thereby resulting in a more diffuse response by the visceral effectors.

Most organs of the body receive both sympathetic and parasympathetic innervation. In general, the effect of sympathetic stimulation is opposite that of parasympathetic stimulation of a given organ. Thus the two systems act in a reciprocal fashion. Both are needed for adequate control, and paralysis of either one has essentially the same effect as excessive stimulation of the opposite. For example, blocking the parasympathetic nerve supply to the eye with atropine paralyzes the circular smooth muscle fibers of the iris, which constrict the pupil. This permits the radial smooth muscle fibers, which are supplied by sympathetic nerves, to dilate the pupil.

It is impossible to state conclusively that one system stimulates and the other depresses unless a specific organ or function is being discussed. A more accurate generalization is the concept of "fight or flight" activity produced by the sympathetic system, as opposed to the quiet relaxed vegetative type of activity favored by the parasympathetic system (see Table 6–1).

The *"fight or flight"* mechanism can be visualized by imagining what changes would favor muscular activity either fighting or running away. Factors favorable to this type of activity, which result from sympathetic stimulation, include: increased heart rate,

Table 6–1.   Actions of Autonomic Stimulation

Organ	Sympathetic Portion Causes	Parasympathetic Portion Causes
Sweat glands	Secretion	No effect
Salivary glands	Mucous secretion	Serous secretion
Digestive glands	Inhibition of secretion	Secretion
Muscles of hair follicles	Contraction (erection of hair)	No effect
Muscles of digestive tract	Inhibition of peristalsis	Peristalsis
	Contraction of sphincters	Relaxation of sphincters
Muscles of bronchi	Relaxation (dilation of bronchi)	Contraction (constriction of bronchi)
Muscles of bladder	Contraction of sphincter (relaxation of wall)	Relaxation of sphincter (contraction of wall—urination)
Muscles of uterus	Contraction	Inhibition of contraction
Muscles of blood vessels	Vasoconstriction (vasodilation in skeletal muscle and coronary arteries)	Vasodilation
Muscles of eye		
Iris	Contraction of radial muscles (dilation of pupil)	Contraction of circular muscles (constriction of pupil)
Ciliary muscle	Relaxation (accommodation for distant vision)	Contraction (accommodation for near vision)

higher blood pressure, dilation of the bronchi, dilation of the pupil, and decreased activity of the digestive tract.

Parasympathetic stimulation produces the opposite actions, including: slower heart rate, lower blood pressure, constriction of the bronchi and pupil, and increased activity of the digestive tract.

From the anatomic and functional viewpoints, the autonomic nervous system can be divided rather definitely into sympathetic and parasympathetic portions. However, when the type of chemical released at the nerve endings is considered, the two autonomic divisions and the somatic nervous system show a considerable amount of overlapping.

In general, the parasympathetic fibers release *acetylcholine* at postganglionic nerve endings, as well as at synapses between preganglionic and postganglionic neurons. Acetylcholine is also released (1) from the preganglionic neurons at synapses in sympathetic ganglia, (2) at motor end plates at the junction of somatic motor nerve endings and striated muscle fibers, and (3) by postganglionic sympathetic fibers at eccrine skin sweat glands, some of the blood vessels supplying skeletal muscle, and the uterus. All fibers that release acetylcholine are said to be *cholinergic*. The enzyme AChE, *acetylcholinesterase* degrades some of the acetylcholine that is released into the *synaptic cleft* during chemical transmission of the nerve impulse. The *choline* liberated by the action of AChE is resorbed by the nerve ending. Some acetylcholine, however, diffuses out of the cleft into the surrounding fluids, where it is degraded by *serum cholinesterase*.

Most postganglionic sympathetic fibers release the substance *norepinephrine* (also called noradrenalin), which is similar to *epinephrine* (adrenaline) produced by the medullary portion of the adrenal glands. In fact, the medulla of the adrenal gland resembles a sympathetic ganglion because it contains similar nerve cells and receives a number of sympathetic fibers, and the action

of epinephrine closely resembles the effect of sympathetic stimulation. Fibers that produce norepinephrine are called *adrenergic* because they are stimulated by the secretion commonly known as adrenaline, which is another name for epinephrine. (Adrenergic also refers to the adrenal glands, which secrete both catecholamines—epinephrine and norepinephrine.) The norepinephrine released from adrenergic nerve terminals is partly degraded by methylation by action of the enzyme catechol O-methyl transferase. However, most norepinephrine is actively resorbed by the nerve ending, where any excess is then oxidized in the mitochondria by the enzyme monoamine oxidase (MAO).

The receptive nerve endings of visceral afferent nerves are located in most of the structures supplied by autonomic nerves. The afferent nerves travel with the postganglionic and preganglionic autonomic nerves through the plexuses and ganglia but do not synapse until they reach the central nervous system. The cell bodies of these visceral afferent nerves are located in the dorsal root ganglia, and their processes reach the spinal cord by way of the dorsal root of the spinal nerve, just as somatic afferent nerves do. Most of the impulses carried by visceral afferent fibers never reach conscious level, but they form the afferent side of many autonomic reflexes that control such functions as blood pressure, heart rate, and activity of the digestive and urogenital systems.

In man, and presumably in animals, most visceral sensations are rather ill-defined and poorly localized. Stimuli that can cause pain in viscera include: stretching or distention, strong contractions, loss of blood supply, and chemical substances.

Referred pain is a condition in which visceral stimuli are interpreted as coming from a somatic body area. This phenomenon is described in Chapter 7.

Adrenal Catecholamines. Stimulation of the sympathetic division of the autonomic nervous system (ANS) produces widespread effects in the whole animal body, not just discrete responses from specific organs. This is due not only to divergence in the ganglia, but also to the fact that the adrenal medullae respond by secreting the catecholamines, epinephrine and norepinephrine, directly into the vascular system, where they circulate in the blood throughout the body. This wide circulation permits diffuse effects to occur, which last at least ten times as long (e.g., several minutes) as the effects from direct release of norepinephrine from a nerve ending (seconds). The catecholamine secretion from the adrenal medullae is a mixture of 75% epinephrine and 25% norepinephrine.

Secretion from the adrenal medullae occurs to some degree whenever the sympathetic division of the ANS is stimulated. However, its most noticeable effects occur in situations of emergency, such as when the animal is afraid, anxious, under stress, fatigued, cold, hemorrhaging from a wound, or in shock. In all such cases, secretion of the adrenal catecholamines produces widespread reactions, because the adrenal medullary catecholamines emptied into the blood can stimulate many parts of the body other than the relatively few body cells directly innervated by sympathetic nerve fibers.

The adrenal catecholamines support and magnify the effects of sympathetic axons that directly innervate visceral organs. Once in the blood, epinephrine and norepinephrine from the adrenal medullae remain active until they diffuse into tissues and exert their effects on the cells. They remain highly active for about 30 seconds before they begin to be degraded by the tissue enzyme, catechol-O-methyl transferase; this degradation occurs mostly in the liver.

Most of the postganglionic autonomic neurons innervating the organs simply spread out through the organs and touch the cells as they pass by. Along these branches are bead-like enlargements called *varicosities*. Here the vesicles of transmitter substance (acetylcholine or norepinephrine) are located, along with many mitochondria

that supply the energy from ATP needed to synthesize the transmitter substance. When an action potential is transmitted as an impulse along these fibers, it depolarizes the membrane, Ca^{++} ions enter, and the transmitter is released by exocytosis. The transmitter substance then acts on the cell membranes of the organ to bring about a response.

Inactive metabolites of norepinephrine can be measured in the animal's urine as *metanephrine, normetanephrine,* and *vanillyl-mandelic-acid* (VMA).

ANESTHETICS

Chemicals or drugs that inhibit or completely block passage of nerve impulses are called anesthetics. *Local anesthetics* are used in restricted areas of the peripheral nervous system, as in blocking a horse's leg for firing or blocking the nerves to the horn of a cow for dehorning.

General anesthetics affect the central nervous system and cause unconsciousness if used in sufficient quantities. An excess of anesthetic agent can cause death by depressing vital reflex centers in the brain.

Sedatives and *hypnotics* reduce nerve irritability and tend to induce sleep.

GENERAL PATHOLOGY OF THE NERVOUS SYSTEM

Injury to the cell body and injury to nerve processes are the two general types of damage that may occur in the nervous system.

The first, if serious enough to cause death of the cell, is irreparable, as occurs in paralytic poliomyelitis in man and some nervous forms of distemper in dogs. Since the adult animal and essentially the newborn animal already have all the neurons that can be formed, death of any nerve cells may be serious because nerve cells cannot be replaced.

Injury to nerve processes, most common in peripheral nerves, may or may not be permanent. It can vary from as transient a condition as a limb's going to sleep due to pressure on a nerve trunk, through crushing of a nerve, as sometimes occurs during difficult parturition, to actual cutting of a nerve by barbed wire, a mower, or some other means.

Frequently nerves recover spontaneously in a relatively short time following damage from light pressure or crushing. However, when a nerve is cut, the distal portion undergoes a process known as *Wallerian degeneration*, in which the axon becomes fragmented, the myelin sheath breaks down, and the neurolemma may undergo some changes.

Retrograde degeneration refers to somewhat similar changes that sometimes affect the proximal segment of a cut nerve and may eventually involve the cell body, causing its death.

If the cell body and proximal segment remain healthy, then regrowth of the nerve process may occur, particularly if the neurolemma or myelin sheath of the distal segment is brought into close proximity to the cut end of the proximal segment. The healthy proximal end will sprout new nerve fiber endings, and there is a chance that one or more will find their way into some of the peripheral Schwann cell sheaths. If it does, then each fiber will grow down the sheath at a rate of 1 to 3 mm per day. The new nerve fiber will be less functional than it was originally, its diameter will be lesser, and the transmission of impulses will be slower, but function may be restored to the effector organ innervated. *Neuromas* (nerve tumors) can form on the end of a severed nerve by the intermeshing of all the new sprouts, thus forming a tumor. When such neuromas form on the proximal ends of severed sensory nerves, they may produce *phantom sensations*. These are sensations produced from nerve fiber endings that normally would be farther away, giving the feeling that the whole nerve still exists. The best example occurs in humans following an amputation of a limb, when the sensations give the feeling that the limb is still there.

Peripheral nerve injuries result in loss of sensation or muscle activity or both in the specific area supplied by the particular nerve or nerves involved.

Central nervous system damage may be caused by many different factors, such as trauma (injury), tumors, infections, or toxins (poisons). Usually the symptoms of damage to the central nervous system are much more general than those of peripheral nerve injuries. These symptoms may range from partial or complete paralysis, as is often seen in spinal cord lesions, to spasms or convulsions that result from uncontrolled muscular contraction. Because most fiber tracts from one side of the brain cross to the opposite side of the spinal cord, a lesion on one side of the brain will result in impaired functioning of the opposite side of the body. Vision, hearing, and cutaneous sensations, as well as motor activity, may be impaired by disorders of the central nervous system.

Chapter 7

Sense Organs

Sensations are highly subjective responses of the brain to various stimuli. It is impossible to know *exactly* what an animal (or another person, for that matter) sees, feels, hears, or smells. We infer what sensations an animal may experience by observing its reaction to various stimuli, the results of various experiments, and by imagining what we might feel in similar situations.

The amount of pain an animal feels in various situations is particularly difficult to determine by simply observing the actions or reactions of an animal. People and presumably animals can exhibit movements and even vocalizations when undergoing or recovering from general anesthesia, with no memory of any pain having been involved. Many movements may be entirely reflex without even reaching the level of consciousness. On the other hand, a person or animal under the influence of a curare-like drug (similar to arrow poison) is conscious of everything, including painful stimuli, but is unable to react because of paralysis of all voluntary muscles at the motor end-plate (junction of motor nerve and voluntary striated muscle fibers).

The sensation of pain is often much greater if the pain is anticipated. For example, many people have been unaware of a cut from a sharp knife or a saw until they saw or felt blood running from the wound.

Sensations generally are the result of afferent impulses from stimuli that eventually reach a conscious level in the cerebral cortex. However, some afferent impulses function in *somatic reflexes,* without ever reaching the level of consciousness. This can be illustrated by producing reflex activity in decerebrate (spinal) animals.

Special senses include smell, sight, taste, hearing, and equilibrium. Organic sensations include, among others, hunger, thirst, the sensation of bladder fullness, and sexual sensations. Other sensations not classified above include touch, pressure, cold, heat, pain, proprioception, and visceral sensations. Figure 7–1 shows various nerve endings concerned with cutaneous and deep sensibility.

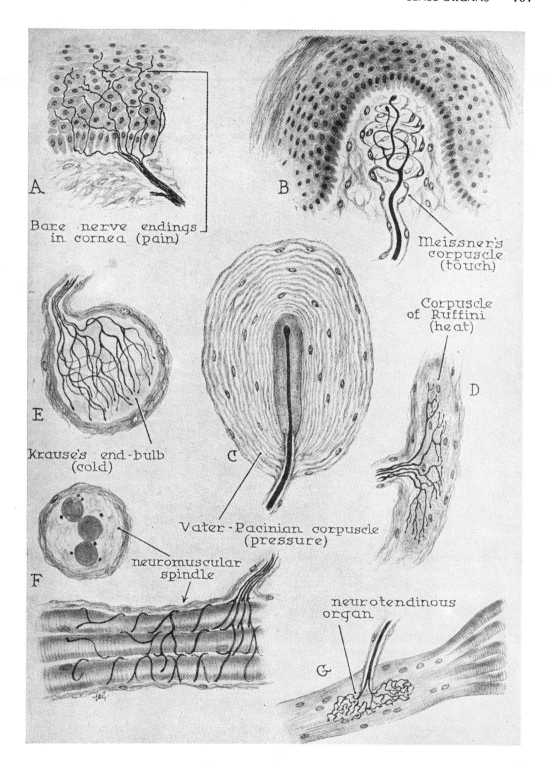

Fig. 7–1.   Diagrams of the various types of nerve endings concerned in cutaneous and deep sensibility. (Ham and Leeson, Histology, courtesy of J.B. Lippincott Co.)

The sensation of touch is believed to be received by specialized nerve endings known as *Meissner's corpuscles,* by those known as *Merkel's disks,* and by naked nerve endings near hair follicles.

Meissner's corpuscles are located just deep to the epidermis in connective tissue papillae of the dermis. Merkel's disks are found in sensitive epithelium such as the tongue, where each disk is attached to a modified epithelial cell. Naked nerve endings surround hair follicles, particularly those of tactile hairs, such as are found in the muzzles of many animals.

Deep pressure sensation is produced by stimulation of receptors called *Vater-Pacinian corpuscles,* which are located in subcutaneous connective tissue, in connective tissue around joints, in the external genitalia of both males and females, and in relation to both serous membranes and mucous membranes. These corpuscles resemble an onion, with many concentric layers of connective tissue surrounding the expanded termination of the nerve.

The difference between touch receptors and deep pressure receptors may account for the fact that a horse often resents a light touch that tickles but stands for a moderately heavy slap without objection.

Special receptors for heat, termed *corpuscles of Ruffini,* and receptors for cold, termed *Krause end-bulbs* are believed to exist mainly in connective tissue of several areas of the body.

SENSORY RECEPTOR MECHANISMS AND TYPES

In considering the neural mechanisms of sensation, we are dealing with a mechanism called *sensory transduction;* that is, how the terminal ends of peripheral nerve fibers, often acting in concert with non-neuronal cells that surround them (see Fig. 7–1), convert impinging energy (stimuli) into local excitation at the nerve ending, and how this in turn elicits trains of afferent nerve impulses. This mechanism of peripheral encoding determines what information the nervous system receives about the quality, location, intensity, and patterns of stimuli that produce sensations.

Communication along neural processes over distances greater than 1 mm can occur only by the propagation of action potentials. Therefore, all information about the environment must be transduced (translated) into action potentials, regardless of whether it is presented in the form of sound energy, chemical energy, thermal energy, light energy, or mechanical energy (touch, pressure, stretch).

Doctrine of Specific Nerve Energies. The receptors that convert or transduce all this information to electrochemical energy are specialized peripheral endings of afferent neurons. Some of these nerve endings are intimately connected with, or encapsulated by, non-neuronal cells, as in *Meissner's corpuscles, Pacinian corpuscles, Merkel's disks,* and *Krause's end-bulbs,* in which case they form sense organs.

In each case, the receptors are specific; that is, they respond more readily (at a lower threshold) to one form of energy than to any other form. Therefore, the receptors are exquisitely sensitive to their specific energy form. This is called the *doctrine of specific nerve endings*—the unique sensitivity of nerve receptors to one form of energy. For example, no matter how much light is shined into an ear, the animal never hears it or sees it because the ear only transmits sound energy. However, almost any sensation can be painful if excessive stimuli are received.

Receptor Graded Responses. When a receptor is stimulated, the extent of nerve-ending depolarization increases with increased *intensity* of the stimulus and with the *rate of change* in application of the stimulus—how fast the stimulus is applied. For example, if the weight of a saddle is thrown onto the back of a horse all at once, the magnitude of the depolarization of the skin pressure receptors will be much greater than if the saddle is gently lowered onto the back; the point is that all sensory receptors are subject to *graded responses*—they do not act simply as an all-or-none action potential.

Generator (Receptor) Potentials. The response of all sensory receptors produces a localized *generator potential* at the nerve terminal. A generator potential is the amount of voltage produced by the change in the resting potential of a nerve fiber (receptor), due to a stimulus that causes a localized change in membrane permeability and a *local* flow of current. If it is great enough to depolarize the membrane of the afferent neuron to threshold, then an action potential is initiated and propagated along the neuron. The sensation that is felt depends on where the transmitted signal ends in the central nervous system.

The *amplitude* (size) of the generator potential can be increased by (1) summation, in which a second generator potential is added before the first has died away; (2) increased frequency of stimuli, and (3) greater intensity of the stimulus. This increased amplitude of the generator potential results in an increased frequency of firing of action potentials.

Adaptation (accommodation) of sensory receptors results in a reduced amplitude of generator potentials in the presence of a constant stimulus, with a consequent reduction in the frequency of firing of action potentials.

Phasic or *rate receptors* adapt quickly to extinction (cease to produce action potentials for the specific modality). These include pressure receptors (Pacinian corpuscles) which, for example, allow one to wear a wristwatch without being conscious of its presence. Receptors for the sense of smell in man also adapt quickly and completely, so that one soon becomes unaware of a constant, unpleasant odor. However, this may not be completely true of all animals, as trained tracking dogs apparently can follow a specific scent for miles over a period of hours.

Tonic receptors adapt slowly, if at all, and may continue to fire action potentials for hours. Stimuli for pain, sight, and sound continue to be perceived with no apparent decrease in intensity over long periods of time.

PAIN

Pain is received by naked terminal branches of sensory neurons. These branches intermingle in many areas of the skin and connective tissues, as well as in the cornea of the eye and other areas of the body. These nerve endings respond to all intense stimuli, including chemical, thermal, electrical, and mechanical stimuli. Generator potentials are produced by the chemical results of these stimuli.

The sensation of pain is a natural protective means of alerting the body to prevent further damage to body tissues. Therefore, the pain receptors warn the animal of harmful injurious stimuli. The pain receptors are often called *nociceptors*, from the Latin word *noceo*, meaning "to injure." So, when the "pain reaction threshold" is exceeded, the animal will withdraw reflexly from the painful stimulus to prevent further damage. On the other hand, if the pain modality is blocked by a drug or by cutting a sensory nerve, considerable tissue damage can result since the animal no longer feels the pain and does not withdraw from the injurious stimulus.

The *reaction threshold* for pain (when the animal withdraws from the stimulus causing it) apparently varies from species to species, and from animal to animal within the same species. Animals that tend to be high-strung and more excitable are less able to endure pain. Animals that are more complacent and easy-going react less intensely to the same painful stimulus. The threshold at which reaction occurs can be raised by drugs, thereby decreasing the sensitivity to pain. Examples of such drugs are the tranquilizers and narcotic analgesics. Any means of diverting the animal's concentration or attention, such as a twitch on the lip during minor surgery, will also reduce pain perception.

Although specific pain tracts in the spinal cord have been identified, the exact mechanism of pain transmission is still not known, and basically three theories have been postulated to attempt to explain it. One is based simply on the *intensity* of the stimulus. This corresponds with the frequency of the impulses transmitted over the nerve fibers and the number of fibers transmitting at one time. Another is based on the *pattern* of fibers firing, each fiber responding to a specific spectrum of nociceptor stimuli. The third, and most accepted, theory is that *specific receptors* respond only to stimuli of specific intensities. Therefore, specialized nociceptors are said to exist, which modifies the pattern theory.

The *gate control theory* of pain postulates that stimulation of large, fast fibers (which are mechanoreceptors, not pain fibers) will normally inhibit the transmission of signals over the pain fibers in the spinal cord. So, if large, fast, nonpain fiber activity predominates, it is said to "close the pain gates." Further, when the pain signals exceed the large-fiber mechanoreceptor signals, then the gates are "open" and pain is sensed by the brain.

Nerve endings for pain are essentially chemoreceptors. The most recent evidence suggests that a pain stimulus produces cell injury, which allows the release of proteolytic enzymes from the cell. These enzymes then act on gamma globulins to split off polypeptides, including bradykinin. Tissue ischemia (interruption of blood flow) also causes pain, probably as a result of hypoxia produced in the tissue. This causes lactic acid to accumulate, which by itself, or by causing the release of proteolytic enzymes, chemically stimulates the pain nerve fiber endings.

PROPRIOCEPTION

Proprioception, also called *muscle sense*, indicates the relative positions of various parts of the body without having to use the eyes. This sense of position is important in physical activities such as walking, running, fighting, and grazing.

Proprioception is subdivided into so-called conscious proprioception, which reaches the cerebral cortex of the brain, where it may or may not be consciously perceived, and unconscious proprioception, which goes to the cerebellum for use in integrating the motor activities of the animal.

Nerve endings for muscle sense are arranged around some modified (intrafusal) muscle fibers as *neuromuscular spindles* (Fig. 7–2), or at the junction of muscles and tendons as *neurotendinous organs* (Golgi tendon organs). The muscle spindles are the primary source of input for the *stretch reflex*, which causes a stretched muscle to contract, as seen in the patellar reflex (described in Chapter 6), and in *postural reflexes,* which help the animal to maintain a standing position. The Golgi tendon organs, on the other hand, supply information to interneurons in the spinal cord, which inhibit contractions of the muscles when the tendon is stretched excessively.

The muscle spindles are oriented parallel to the surrounding muscle fibers and are attached in such a manner that stretching of the muscle and its voluntary striated fibers (extrafusal fibers) also stretches *intrafusal* (within the spindle) modified striated muscle fibers (Fig. 7–2).

Intrafusal fibers are of two types: "nuclear bag" fibers, which are dilated in the middle, and "nuclear chain" fibers, which are of uniform diameter. Both types of fibers receive primary afferent nerve fibers (type A, group 1A), which surround the middle of each intrafusal fiber as annulospiral primary nerve endings. Smaller secondary afferent nerves (type A, group II) originate away from the middle on both types of intrafusal fibers.

When a muscle is stretched (and consequently the muscle spindles are also stretched), the primary afferent nerves respond to the length of the intrafusal fibers and the speed at which they are stretched, while the secondary afferent nerves respond only to the length of the stretched intrafusal fibers. These afferent neurons carry impulses to the spinal cord by way of the dorsal root of the spinal nerve. They synapse directly with motor neurons (type A α) that innervate the regular voluntary muscle fibers (extrafusal fibers) of the stretched muscle. The stretch reflex is called a monosynaptic reflex because only one synapse is involved between the afferent

nerves from the muscle spindles and the motor nerves to the voluntary muscle fibers. There are no interneurons interposed between the afferent and efferent neurons.

The intrafusal muscle fibers also receive motor nerve fibers called type A γ fibers, which cause contraction of the ends of the intrafusal muscle fibers, which in turn stretches the centers of the intrafusal fibers and stimulates the primary and secondary

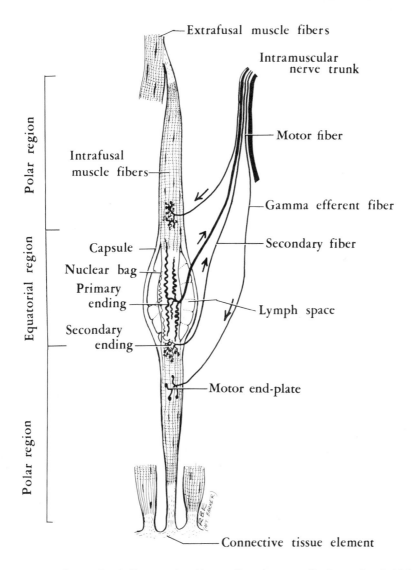

Fig. 7–2. Diagram of a muscle spindle. Note that this complicated nerve ending is associated with both sensory and motor neurons. The extrafusal muscle fibers are those in which the spindle is located (see text for details of structure and function). (After Barker, 1948, from Jenkins, T.W.: Functional Mammalian Anatomy. ed. 2. Philadelphia, Lea & Febiger, 1978.)

afferent receptors. Of course, impulses carried by afferent fibers from the intrafusal muscle fibers reach the spinal cord, where they stimulate the motor neurons to cause the voluntary muscle fibers (extrafusal) to contract again, shortening the total muscle.

This arrangement of afferent and efferent neurons of the intrafusal muscle fibers with the efferent motor neurons to the regular extrafusal muscle fibers is called the gamma loop. The gamma loop forms a feedback mechanism that can be compared to power-assisted steering in a car, in which a slight pressure on the steering wheel is translated into powerful turning (steering) of the front wheels. The gamma loop functions in smooth voluntary control of muscles and in maintaining muscle tone by receiving impulses from higher centers of the brain.

MYELINATION AND SPINAL TRACTS OF PERIPHERAL SENSORY NERVES

In general, proprioceptive fibers are heavily myelinated, touch fibers have medium myelination, and pain fibers are relatively unmyelinated. The cell bodies of peripheral sensory nerves are located in the dorsal root ganglia of spinal nerves and in comparable ganglia of certain cranial nerves.

There is a tendency for nerve fibers carrying impulses of each sensory modality (touch, pain, heat, cold) to be grouped in specific tracts of the spinal cord. For example, light touch impulses are carried in the lateral spinothalamic tract. Each impulse carried by a peripheral sensory nerve may have one or more of several possible destinations. It may function only in the afferent side of a reflex arc, such as proprioceptive impulses in normal walking. It may reach a conscious level *(cerebral cortex)* without being involved in reflex actions, as in minor temperature and pressure changes. An impulse may also result in both reflex action and conscious perception; for instance, in touching a hot object, the finger is withdrawn automatically (reflexly) and pain is also felt.

VISCERAL SENSATIONS

Visceral sensations involve structures within the body cavities. During surgical procedures in animals under local anesthesia, visceral organs may be handled, burned, cut, or crushed without causing apparent pain, as long as the body wall is not involved and no traction is applied to the peritoneum. Painful stimuli to visceral organs include lack of blood supply, sudden distention, sudden contraction, and chemical irritation. Smooth muscle spasm in tubular viscera, with its resulting ischemia, is often manifested as rhythmic *cramps*. For example, this occurs in contraction of the uterus during parturition (delivery of the foal or calf), in blockage of the ureter, in enteritis (inflammation of the intestine), or colic due to excess gas production. These pain impulses are carried largely by visceral afferent fibers accompanying or within the sympathetic nerves. However, the afferent limbs of vital visceral reflexes are found in parasympathetic nerves. These reflexes include cardiac reflexes, aortic reflexes, *Hering-Breuer reflexes*, and reflexes for micturition.

So-called organic sensations such as hunger, thirst, sexual sensations, and sensation of bladder fullness are carried by visceral afferent nerves. These organic sensations indicate a need and tend to lead to activity that satisfies the need.

Referred Pain. In man, and presumably in animals, most visceral sensations are rather ill-defined and poorly localized. True visceral pain is often referred either to other places on the body surface or to deep tissues other than the site of origin. This seems to be due to the convergence of afferent fibers synapsing in the spinal cord in the same nerve tracts that receive impulses from the body surface and from the muscle and joint proprioceptor pain fibers. This allows the signal to be interpreted by the brain as sensation coming from areas of the body other than the site of origin.

Referred pain, while well established in man, is largely a subjective phenomenon, and therefore its existence in animals is difficult to establish. An example might be the high degree of sensitivity in the region of the sternum that some cows exhibit when suffering from traumatic gastritis caused by a wire or nail perforating the wall of the fore stomach.

TASTE

Taste buds, the end-organs for the sense of taste, consist of fusiform gustatory cells intermingled with sustentacular (supporting) cells arranged in somewhat barrel-shaped groups. Hair-like processes of the gustatory cells project through a pore at the superficial portion of the taste bud (Fig. 7–3). Nerve fibers terminate around the gustatory cells.

Circumvallate and *fungiform papillae* of the tongue contain the most taste buds, although some are also found on the palate, pharynx, and larynx. The sensation of taste is supplied to the anterior two-thirds of the tongue by the *chorda tympani* branch of the facial nerve, which accompanies the *lingual branch* of the *trigeminal nerve*. The posterior one-third of the tongue receives taste by way of the lingual branch of the *glossopharyngeal nerve*. Other sensations (heat, cold, touch, pain) to the tongue are supplied by the lingual branch of the trigeminal nerve. Probably the taste buds located on areas other than the tongue are supplied by the *vagus nerve*.

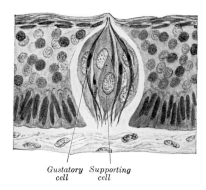

Gustatory *Supporting*
cell   *cell*

Fig. 7–3. Taste bud. (From Goss, C.M.: Gray's Anatomy of the Human Body. ed. 29. Philadelphia, Lea & Febiger, 1973.)

In man, the four specific taste modalities include sweet, salt, bitter, and sour (acid). Other taste sensations involve mixtures of these basic tastes or combinations of tastes and smell. The base of the tongue is sensitive to bitter taste, the lateral sides of the tongue respond primarily to sour stimuli but also to salt, and the tip of the tongue is sensitive to all four modalities but is more sensitive to sweet and salt.

Taste appears to be an important factor in the ability of an animal to select food containing elements or factors in which the animal is deficient. For example, vitamin-deficient rats will select foods high in the particular vitamin they need. Rats with the adrenal glands removed prefer saline solutions to pure water to replace the salt that has been lost. If the parathyroid glands are removed, the rats prefer solutions containing calcium. This ability to correct dietary deficiencies is lost if the sensory nerves for taste are cut. The taste buds are chemo-receptors for the obvious reason that they are stimulated by chemicals.

SMELL

The *olfactory system* is associated with the sense of smell. The sense of smell is mediated by the *olfactory (I cranial)* nerve. Olfactory nerve cells are scattered among columnar supporting cells throughout the olfactory mucous membrane in the dorso-caudal part of the nasal cavity.

The nucleus of each olfactory cell is located near the basement membrane of the mucous membrane. A peripheral process extends between supporting cells to the surface, where it bears a tuft of several fine hair-like projections, which are the actual receptors for the sense of smell. Since these processes normally are covered by moist mucus, the material to be smelled probably must go into solution before it can reach the sensory cells. However, some authorities believe that very fine particles of some substances may be perceived without actually dissolving.

The central process of each olfactory

nerve cell passes through a foramen in the *cribriform plate* of the *ethmoid bone* to the olfactory bulb of the brain, where it synapses with cells whose central processes make up the olfactory tract of the brain. Some nerve fibers in each olfactory tract cross to the opposite side of the brain by way of the anterior commissure. The remainder of the nerve fibers pass caudally to various areas of the brain. The presence of many connections and interconnections has been postulated, but there is little general agreement about terminations of the olfactory tract, even though the rhinencephalon *(olfactory cortex)* is one of the oldest parts of the brain.

Development of the olfactory system varies considerably from one species to another. The sense of smell is well developed in the dog, but poorly developed in man. Conclusive experiments in this field are difficult to design, and attempts to transfer conclusions from man to animals and animals to man are particularly hazardous.

HEARING AND BALANCE

The ear can be divided into three main parts: the external ear, the middle ear, and the inner ear. The external ear extends from the exterior as far as the tympanic membrane. The middle ear extends from the tympanic membrane into the air-filled excavation within the *petrous temporal bone*. The inner ear is also excavated in the petrous temporal bone but is filled with fluid.

The basis of the external ear consists of three cartilages (Fig. 7–4). The *conchal cartilage* is the largest of the three. It is a seashell-shaped cartilage that funnels sound waves into the ear canal. The *scutiform cartilage* is a shield-shaped cartilage that acts as a *sesamoid bone* for some of the ear muscles. The third cartilage is the *annular cartilage*, which is shaped like a tube and connects the conchal cartilage with the external osseous auditory canal.

The conchal cartilage is an elastic cartilage that is somewhat funnel-shaped. It is lined on the inside with relatively hairless skin. On the outside it is protected with a layer of skin which, in most animals, is covered with a generous amount of hair.

The external ear can be pointed in any desired direction, particularly in the horse. The ear can be rotated on a longitudinal axis and it can be tilted forward, tilted backward, and tilted laterally. The mobility of the ear is

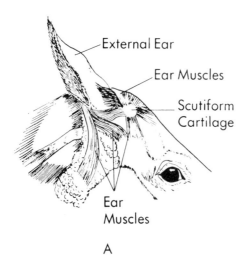

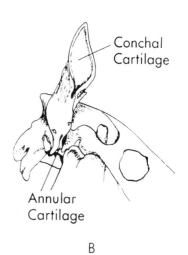

Fig. 7–4. The external ear. (After Ellenberger, An Atlas of Animal Anatomy for Artists, courtesy of Dover Publications, Inc.)

of value in localizing and picking up sounds. The funnel-shaped cartilage concentrates sound waves and directs them toward the tympanic membrane.

The scutiform cartilage is located on the superficial surface of the temporal muscle and attaches to the extrinsic ear muscles. Some muscles attach directly to the conchal cartilage and some attach indirectly by way of the scutiform cartilage. The extrinsic muscles of the ear are supplied by the *facial (VII cranial)* nerve. The external ear receives sensation from the trigeminal (V cranial), facial (VII cranial), and vagus (X cranial) nerves.

The middle ear is a cavity in the petrous temporal bone that communicates with the pharynx by way of the eustachian tube (auditory tube) (Fig. 7–5). The middle ear is separated from the external ear by the tympanic membrane, and from the inner ear by the membranes that close the oval window and the round window.

The three *auditory ossicles* are found in the middle ear. From without inward they are the *malleus* (hammer), *incus* (anvil), and *stapes* (stirrup). These ossicles provide a mechanical linkage from the tympanic membrane to the membrane closing the oval window. There are also two striated muscles within the middle ear, the *tensor tympani muscle* and the *stapedius muscle*. The tensor tympani muscle originates on the upper wall of the eustachian tube and inserts on the malleus. It receives its nerve supply from the mandibular division of the trigeminal nerve. The stapedius muscle inserts on the stapes and is supplied by the facial nerve. These two small muscles function in dampening excessively loud noises and may also function to increase the acuity of hearing.

The inner ear is likewise an excavation, known as the *osseous labyrinth*, within the petrous temporal bone. Within the osseous labyrinth is a completely closed connective tissue structure almost co-extensive with it, but somewhat smaller, called the *membranous labyrinth*, which contains *endolymph* and does not communicate with any other cavity. Between the osseous labyrinth and

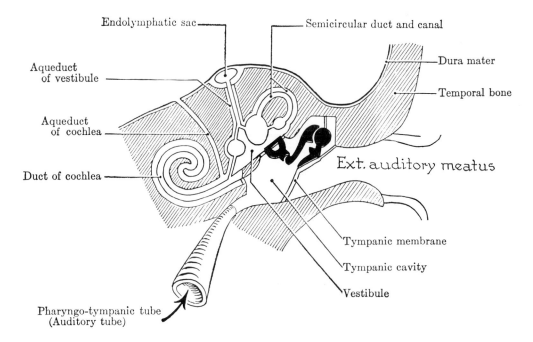

Fig. 7–5. A diagram of the parts of the ear. (Pharyngo-tympanic tube is also called auditory tube or Eustachian tube.) (Grant, An Atlas of Anatomy, courtesy of The Williams & Wilkins Co.)

the membranous labyrinth is a fluid, the *perilymph*. The perilymph is continuous with the cerebrospinal fluid by way of a small canal called the *aqueduct of cochlea*.

The inner ear may also be divided into two parts according to function. The *cochlear portion* receives the cochlear branch of the *vestibulocochlear (VIII cranial) nerve*. This portion is sensory for sound. The *vestibular part* functions mainly for the mediation of balance and is supplied by the vestibular branch of the VIII cranial nerve. The vestibular portion of the inner ear is housed in the parts of the osseous labyrinth known as the vestibule and the three semicircular canals. Each semicircular canal both leaves and returns to the vestibule. The three semicircular canals are arranged so that each is in a different plane: one approximately horizontal, one approximately frontal, and one approximately sagittal (see Fig. 7–6).

The membranous labyrinth also includes three semicircular canals, one in each of the osseous semicircular canals. Two membranous sacs, the *utricle* and *saccule*, also are part of the membranous labyrinth and are located within the vestibule. Both ends of each semicircular canal open into the utricle. The utricle also communicates with the saccule through the *endolymphatic duct*. The saccule, in turn, communicates with the *membranous cochlea*.

The Mechanisms of Balance

Neuroepithelial areas specialized for reception of stimuli relating to balance and movement are found in the vestibular part of the membranous labyrinth. They are made up of sustentacular (supporting) cells intermingled with hair cells. The hair cells have nonmotile cilia on the free surface, and each cell is related to nonmyelinated nerve endings of the vestibular part of the vestibulocochlear (VIII or auditory) nerve.

The sensitive areas of the saccule and ut-

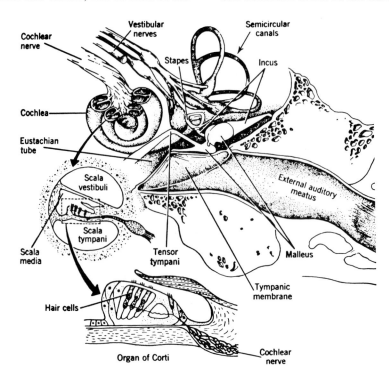

Fig. 7–6. The general anatomy of the external, middle, and internal ears. (Reproduced by permission from Torrey, Morphogenesis of the Vertebrates, John Wiley.)

ricle, known as *maculae acusticae*, are associated with static equilibrium (position of the head in space). The surface of each macula (one in the saccule and one in the utricle) is covered with a gelatinous membrane, the *otolithic membrane*, which contains many crystals of calcium carbonate called otoliths. Stimulation of the hair cells of the maculae is due to the effect of gravity on the otolithic membranes.

One end of each semicircular canal is expanded to form the ampulla. Within each ampulla is a receptor organ, the *crista*, which consists of a ridge of neuroepithelium at right angles to the plane of the respective semicircular canal. The crista resembles a macula of the saccule or utricle, except that it is surmounted by a tall, rounded mass called the *cupula* instead of being covered by an otolithic membrane, as found in the macula. Between the sustentacular cells of the crista are the hair cells, around which terminate naked endings of the vestibulocochlear nerve (vestibular part). The cristae reflect changes in movement (kinetic sense) because of displacement of the cupula over the cilia of the hair cells. This displacement results from pressure changes of the endolymph within the semicircular canals due to sudden movements of the head in or near the plane of the affected semicircular canal.

Impulses carried by the vestibular part of the vestibulocochlear nerve are responsible for reflex movements of the eyes, head, and other parts of the body and also may produce vertigo (dizziness), as seen in motion sickness. Of course, the sense of position and equilibrium is due largely to these impulses.

In order for an animal to maintain equilibrium of its total body and parts, there is a continuous stream of sensory inputs to the central nervous system and motor outputs from it, so that orientation in space is perceived and maintained. The sensory inputs originate primarily from the proprioceptors, the vestibular apparatus, and vision. They form what is called the *equilibration triad*, which is a highly integrated complex.

The macula of the utricle provides sensory inputs to the brain regarding the position of the head (Fig. 7–7). The relatively heavy weight of the $CaCO_3$ otoliths resting on the hairs in the gelatinous mass produce the stimulus to the hair cells as the head moves. The weight of this otoconial layer

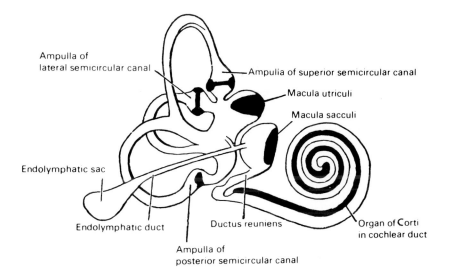

Fig. 7–7.   Outline of cavities of the left membranous labyrinth viewed from the medial aspect. Receptor regions of the neuroepithelium are sketched in black. (From Copenhaver, W. M., et al.: Bailey's Textbook of Hisology. ed. 17. Baltimore, Williams & Wilkins, 1978.)

shifts in the direction of the tilt of the head, and therefore bends the hairs in that direction. Further, the hair cells are oriented in different directions in the maculae, and so different groups of hair cells respond to different spatial tilts of the head. The resulting nerve fiber impulses are transmitted to the nuclei in the brain stem and to the cerebellum.

The semicircular canals only sense the *beginning* of head rotation and the *stopping* of rotation; thus they sense the *rate-of-change* of head rotation, which is called *angular acceleration*. As the head starts to rotate, the endolymph tends to retain its original position in the canals because of inertia. The attached bodies of the hair cells turn with the canals. The hairs, however, are pulled against the relatively stationary endolymph, which bends the hairs opposite to the direction of head rotation. Then, as the initial inertia is overcome, the hairs slowly return to their resting position. This is why they are stimulated only during changes in rate of motion, because once endolymph flow equals rotation rate, there is no shearing force to bend the hairs within the cupula. When the canal rotation stops, the hairs bend in the direction of the continued endolymph flow.

The shearing force bending the hairs on the receptor cells is related to the frequency of action potentials in the afferent nerve. In the resting position there is a tonic discharge of impulses. The rate of firing speeds up when the hairs are bent directionally, at a rate depending on the shearing force of acceleration. Upon stopping rotation, the hairs bend in the opposite direction, slowing down the frequency of action potentials or stopping them in the afferent nerve. Thus, the mechanical event of directional hair displacement causes either depolarization or hyperpolarization of the nerve endings.

Physiology of Hearing

The cochlear portion of the osseous labyrinth resembles a short, broad metal screw (made of bone) surrounded by a loose-fitting congruent female screw (also made of bone). This produces in effect a spiral tube hollowed out of the petrous temporal bone. The inner male screwlike portion is called the *modiolus*, and it transmits the cochlear portion of the vestibulocochlear nerve to the *organ of Corti* within the membranous labyrinth. The membranous labyrinth extends from the bony thread (the spiral lamina) of the modiolus across the lumen of the osseous labyrinth to the connective tissue lining the outer wall of the osseous labyrinth. Thus the cavity of the osseous labyrinth, which contains the perilymph, is completely divided into two spiral tubes by the membranous labyrinth. However, at the apex of the spiral the *scala vestibuli* communicates with *scala tympani* through a small opening, the *helicotrema*. The upper tube (assuming the base is horizontal and the apex is above the base) is the scala vestibuli, which opens into the vestibule, so that the perilymph in both cavities (cochlear and vestibular) is continuous. The lower tube, the scala tympani, opens into the area of the round window.

The aqueduct of cochlea is a small duct through which perilymph from the cochlea communicates with cerebrospinal fluid in the *subarachnoid space*. A small tube, the *endolymphatic duct*, leads from the saccule to the *endolymphatic sac* just inside the *dura mater*. The endolymphatic sac and duct act as a safety valve for the endolymph in case excess pressure is applied to the membranous labyrinth. The membranous labyrinth of the cochlea contains a channel, the *scala media* (cochlear duct), which parallels the scala vestibuli and scala tympani by spiraling around between them. It is continuous with the saccule and contains endolymph.

The spiral organ of Corti is the portion of the cochlea that is sensitive to sound. It contains neuroepithelial tissue somewhat similar to that in the vestibular portion of the inner ear. Columnar supporting cells and sensitive hair cells are surrounded by naked

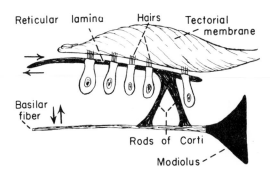

Reticular lamina   Hairs   Tectorial
                                 membrane

Basilar
fiber

Rods of Corti

Modiolus

Fig. 7–8.   Stimulation of the hair cells by the to-and-fro movement of the hairs in the tectorial membrane. (From Guyton, A.C.: Textbook of Medical Physiology. ed. 5. Philadelphia, W.B. Saunders, 1976.)

endings of nerve cells located in the *spiral ganglion*, which is in the modiolus next to the *osseous spiral lamina*. The cilia of the hair cells are overlaid by a thin jelly-like membrane, the *tectorial membrane* (Fig. 7–8).

Axons of nerve cells in the spiral ganglion pass to the cochlear nuclei of the brain stem by way of the cochlear branch of the vestibulocochlear nerve. The dendrites of these nerves are disposed around the hair cells of the organ of Corti. Impulses pass from the *cochlear nuclei* to the *medial geniculate body*, and then to the auditory centers of the cerebral cortex.

Sound waves striking the tympanic membrane are transferred mechanically by the ossicles to the membrane of the oval win-

dow. Pressure (either positive or negative) on this membrane is transmitted to the perilymph of the vestibule and throughout all the perilymph and endolymph of the osseous and membranous labyrinths.

In the cochlea, the route of transmission of the shock wave is from the perilymph of the vestibule to the scala vestibuli, then to the cochlear duct and organ of Corti, and finally to the scala tympani and the round window. The pressure waves in the fluid bend the hair cells, which initiate an impulse in the appropriate nerve fibers so that the brain finally interprets the end result as sound (Fig. 7–9).

Sounds of high frequency appear to stimulate the neuroepithelial cells at the base of the cochlea, and low-frequency sound waves stimulate the neuroepithelial cells at the apex.

Sound energy is transmitted through air as a disturbance of molecules. In a vacuum, there are no molecules of air and hence no sound. The disturbance of air molecules produces *sound waves*. These waves consist of alternating regions of *compression* of the molecules, where pressure is therefore high, and regions of *rarefaction*, where the molecules are farther apart and the pressure is therefore lower. Sound waves, then, are transmitters of energy.

The frequency of the vibration of the sound source is correlated with the *pitch*— the faster the vibration, the higher the pitch.

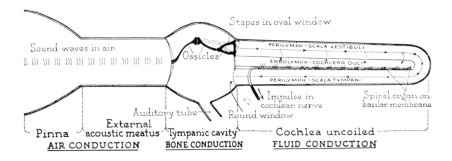

Fig. 7–9.   Diagram of sound transmission from the air to impulse in cochlear nerve. Dotted lines indicate the position of the ossicles and various membranes after inward displacement of the tympanic membrane. (King and Showers, Human Anatomy and Physiology, courtesy of W.B. Saunders Co.)

The range of frequencies that can be heard varies considerably from species to species, and even within a given species of animal. This fact is used as a basis for the "silent" dog whistles, which are pitched high enough so that they are above the range of the human ear but can be heard by dogs. It is well known that the bat uses very high frequency sounds in a type of sonar to guide its flight in the dark.

Loudness is correlated with the *amplitude* of the sound wave. The amplitude is the difference between the pressure of the air molecules in a zone of compression and a zone of rarefaction. The greater the amplitude, the louder the sound. The ear is capable of discriminating changes in loudness (wave amplitude) over a wide range. For convenience, loudness is expressed in terms of the logarithm of the actual amplitude. The energy scale is based on the *decibel unit* (db), which is a unit of sound pressure. A ten-fold increase in intensity is one *bel*, and 1/10 of a bel is a decibel. The human range of hearing is 0 to 140 db. Above the 140 decibel level, the loudness produces pain.

Another characteristic of hearing is the ability to differentiate sounds according to the quality or *timbre* of the sound. This quality varies with the degree of *purity* of the sound wave. A pure wave is sinusoidal in nature, whereas complex waves have overtones (harmonic vibrations) added.

The animal localizes the direction from which a sound is coming primarily by the time-lag between the arrival of the sound into the two ears, and secondarily, by the difference in the intensities heard by the two ears, since the sound is louder on the side closest to the sound source.

The first event in normal hearing is the entrance of the air pressure waves down the external auditory canal of the ear to the tympanic membrane, causing it to vibrate. The amount of vibration is a function of the force and velocity with which the air molecules strike the membrane, and so it is related to what will be perceived as loudness. The tympanic membrane is highly sensitive to the force of the air molecules, and it stops vibrating almost immediately when the sound waves stop.

The middle ear is an air-filled space that is kept at atmospheric pressure by the periodic opening of the auditory (Eustachian) tube during chewing, swallowing, and yawning. This tube connects the middle ear with the pharynx. The auditory ossicles, in the middle ear, mechanically transmit the sound energy vibrations from the tympanic membrane to the membrane of the oval window of the cochlea in the inner ear.

If the amplitude of the sound (loudness) increases to a level that could damage the delicate organ of Corti or the basilar membrane, an *attenuation reflex* is triggered to lessen the sound transmission to the oval window. The attenuation reflex causes contraction of the stapedius muscle (which inserts on the neck of the stapes) and the tensor tympani muscle (inserting on the manubrium of the malleus).

The vibration of the footplate of the stapes on the oval window sets up corresponding movements in the perilymph of the scala vestibuli as a fluid pressure wave. Since fluid is incompressible, any movement of the oval window membrane must be compensated by an opposite movement of the membrane covering the round window.

The energy of the fluid pressure wave originating at the oval window passes in two directions, as shown in Figure 7–9. Some wave energy passes along the basilar membrane to the apex of the cochlea, where the perilymph of the scala vestibuli is continuous with the perilymph of the scala tympani by way of the helicotrema. The fluid wave then passes back through the scala tympani, to be dissipated at the round window by bulging it outward into the middle ear. However, most of the pressure waves cause the basilar membrane to deflect into the scala tympani, which dissipates the energy in a "short-cut" manner to the round window.

Although the vestibular membrane separates the perilymph of the scala vestibuli from the endolymph of the cochlear duct, the membrane is so thin that it offers virtually no resistance to the transfer of fluid vibrations from the scala vestibuli to the scala media (cochlear duct). Therefore, the two chambers are considered as one when we talk about fluid vibration waves.

The deflection of the basilar membrane is possible because of the elastic tension of the membrane. It consists of about 20,000 *basilar fibers* that project outward from the modiolus of the cochlea, much like a piano keyboard, except that there are 20,000 "keys." The elastic tension also contributes to the initial pressure wave being transmitted as a *traveling wave* along the basilar membrane, which is comparable to the movement of a pressure wave down an artery.

The basilar membrane decreases in rigidity as it increases in *width* progressively from the base of the cochlea to the apex. The basilar fibers projecting outward also get progressively longer from the base to the apex. This difference in width and compliance or tension of the membrane, plus the total mass of the fluid set in motion by the vibrating fibers, produces a different frequency *resonance* at each point along the membrane. A high-frequency resonance occurs in the region at the base of the cochlea, where the basilar fibers are shorter and thicker and the membrane is relatively stiff (i.e., less compliant). At the other end, at the apex, the resonance is low-frequency because the fibers are long and thin, the membrane is relatively wider and more compliant, and a greater mass of fluid is set in motion.

With such progressive changes occurring all along the basilar membrane, each part of it has a *natural resonant frequency* that corresponds to a particular sound frequency, which causes the membrane to vibrate more readily at that point. This vibration dissipates much of the wave energy at that point (transferring it to the scala tympani), so the traveling wave essentially ends there. This is referred to as the *place principle* for the de-

termination of the pitch of the sound. Hence, high-frequency sound waves travel only a short distance along the basilar membrane, whereas low frequency waves may travel all the way to the apex. Therefore, just as the tympanic membrane functions as a resonator to reproduce vibrations from the sound source, so does the basilar membrane resonate to transmit the waves through fluid.

The fluid vibrations must be sensed and transduced into nerve fiber action potentials to transmit impulses to the brain for hearing. This transduction is accomplished by the organ of Corti, which lies on the surface of the basilar membrane. More specifically, it is the *hair cells* of the organ of Corti that are the actual sensory receptors. The hair cells help to produce the generator potentials that can produce action potentials on the network of nerve fiber endings terminating on the hair cells, from which they are transmitted to the *spiral ganglion of Corti* and into the cochlear nerve.

Since the hairs that project from the top of the hair cells are embedded in the rather elastic but gelatinous tectorial membrane, the back-and-forth movements of the fluid tend to shear and bend the hairs as that portion of the basilar membrane moves. This shearing and bending of the hairs changes the membrane potential of the hair cells, either depolarizing or hyperpolarizing the membrane, depending on the direction of the bend.

Transduction of the loudness of the sound by the organ of Corti is accomplished by temporal and spatial summation. As the amplitude of the vibration of the basilar membrane increases with increased sound fluid waves, there is a corresponding increase in the frequency of firing of action potentials in the nerve ending, resulting in *temporal summation*. Increased amplitudes of the fluid waves (louder sound) will also increase the number of hair cells responding to the sound, because more of the basilar membrane will vibrate, thus increasing loudness by *spatial summation*, with a greater total signal going to the brain over more nerve fibers.

The spatial orientation along the basilar membrane and organ of Corti for different sound frequencies is maintained during transmission of the signal over the nerve and nerve tracts to the brain. That is, the nerve fibers on one side of the nerve and tract transmit signals of frequencies that are different from the nerve fibers of the other side of the nerve and tract. This occurs all the way to the brain cortex as a pattern of frequency orientation or localization.

If an animal is subjected to prolonged stimulation by a sound of high frequency, degenerative changes occur in the basal portion of the organ of Corti. If the sound is of low frequency, the damage appears near the apex of the organ of Corti. Also, injury to the apical portion of the organ of Corti results in deafness to low tones, and injury to the basal portion causes deafness to high-pitched tones.

Deafness, the inability to hear, as well as impaired hearing may result from involvement of any link in the chain of structures from the air in the external ear, through the tympanic membrane, the auditory ossicles, the structures of the inner ear, to and including the cochlear branch of the vestibulocochlear nerve and its central connections.

Deafness may be either of two types: *conduction deafness* or *nerve deafness*. Conduction deafness is impaired transmission in the middle ear, usually due to fibrosis or ankylosis (the stapes becomes ankylosed to the oval window by bony overgrowth). Nerve deafness is due to damage or degeneration of the vestibulocochlear nerve or central nervous system pathways.

Causes include a variety of factors, such as toxins from disease organisms, injuries, drugs, obstructions, and genetic factors. Most of these factors may also involve the vestibular part of the inner ear, resulting in dizziness, nausea, or loss of equilibrium.

SIGHT

The eye consists of two segments of two spheres (Figs. 7–10, 7–11). The larger segment of the larger sphere is posterior and appears externally as the *sclera* or "white of the eye." The smaller segment of the smaller sphere is the *cornea*, which is the transparent anterior portion of the eye.

The main part of the eyeball consists of the sclera superficially. The next layer is the *vascular tunic* and includes the choroid, ciliary body, and iris. This layer contains vessels, nerves, and much elastic tissue. The deepest layer is the *nervous tunic* called the *retina*. It is the origin of the optic nerve and contains the *rods* and *cones*, which are receptive to light stimuli. These stimuli re-

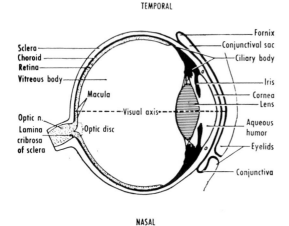

Fig. 7–10. Horizontal section of eyeball. Note the three tunics and the visual axis. (Gardner, Gray and O'Rahilly, Anatomy, courtesy of W.B. Saunders Co.)

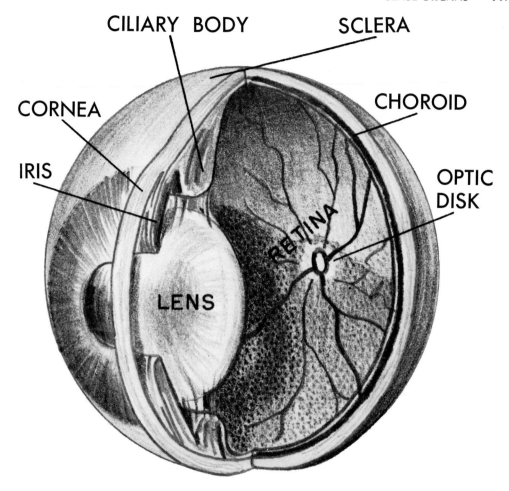

CILIARY BODY   SCLERA

CORNEA

CHOROID

IRIS

OPTIC
DISK

RETINA

LENS

Fig. 7-11. The eye with section removed. (From Magrane, W.G.: Canine Ophthalmology. ed. 3. Philadelphia, Lea & Febiger, 1977.)

ceived on the retina are transmitted by way of the optic nerve to the brain, where they are interpreted as visual images.

The interior of the posterior part of the eye is filled with a gelatinous material, the *vitreous humor* (also called the vitreous body). At the front of the vitreous humor is located the lens, a biconvex structure. Surrounding the periphery of the lens is the *ciliary body* (Fig. 7–12). The ciliary body includes the *ciliary processes,* which attach the choroid to the lens, and the ciliary muscle, which extends from the choroid to the attachment of the iris at the corneoscleral junction.

Focusing the lens is a process called *ac-*

commodation. It is accomplished by means of contraction or relaxation of the *ciliary muscle,* which is a smooth muscle that completely circumscribes the lens, attaching to the corneoscleral junction and to the choroid. Since the choroid is elastic, its tension normally pulls on the ciliary processes, which in turn stretch the lens of the eye, making it flatter or less convex. This is accommodation for distant vision, or focusing the lens for greater distance. If focusing is necessary for close vision, the ciliary muscle contracts, stretching the choroid and relaxing the ciliary processes, thus permitting the lens to become more biconvex. The ciliary

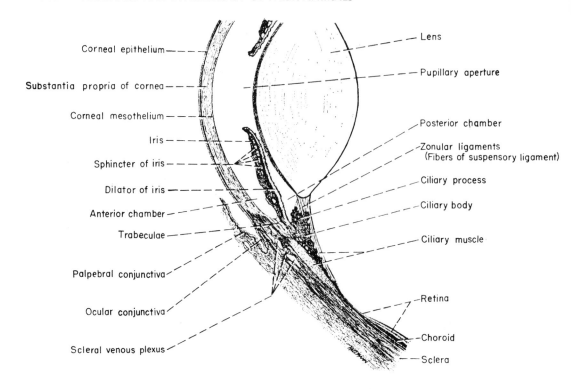

Corneal epithelium

Substantia propria of cornea

Corneal mesothelium

Iris

Sphincter of iris

Dilator of iris

Anterior chamber

Trabeculae

Palpebral conjunctiva

Ocular conjunctiva

Scleral venous plexus

Lens

Pupillary aperture

Posterior chamber

Zonular ligaments
(Fibers of suspensory ligament)

Ciliary process

Ciliary body

Ciliary muscle

Retina

Choroid

Sclera

Fig. 7–12. Longitudinal section of anterior part of eye showing attachments of cornea, iris, and lens. (Getty, The Sense Organs, in Miller, Christensen, Evans, Anatomy of the Dog, courtesy of W.B. Saunders Co.)

muscle is supplied by parasympathetic fibers of the oculomotor (III cranial) nerve.

The *iris* is the pigmented structure of the eye that forms a "curtain" to control the amount of light entering the eye. The *pupil* of the eye is an opening approximately in the center of the iris. The size of the pupil is determined by two sets of smooth muscles. One set of muscles of the iris consists of circular fibers that circumscribe the pupil to form a sphincter. The *circular fibers* (sphincter pupillae) are supplied by the *parasympathetic* portion of the *oculomotor nerve*. These circular fibers decrease the size of the pupil when reflexly stimulated by an increased amount of light. The other set of fibers, the *radial fibers*, is supplied by the sympathetic nerves from the *cranial cervical ganglion* of the *cervical sympathetic trunk* by way of the *carotid plexus*. The pupil

of the eye is reflexly dilated whenever the level of light is decreased. A solution of *atropine* instilled into the eye paralyzes the parasympathetic nerve fibers which supply the constrictor muscles of the iris, thus permitting the sympathetic nerve input to dominate and produce dilation of the pupil of the eye by contraction of the radial muscle fibers.

The portion of the eye between the cornea and the lens is incompletely divided into two parts by the iris. That portion between the cornea and the iris is known as the *anterior chamber*, and that portion between the iris and the lens is known as the *posterior chamber* of the eye. The fluid within these two chambers is called the *aqueous humor*. It normally communicates freely from one chamber to the other through the pupil of the iris.

Physiology of Sight

For an animal to "see" anything in the visual field of the eyes, light must pass into the eye and form an image on the retina. This stimulates the rods and cones (the sensory receptors) resulting in impulses being transmitted to the visual cortex of the brain.

As the light rays pass from air into the eye, they are *refracted* (bent) and slowed when they enter *obliquely*. Those light rays that enter *perpendicular* to the eye, as occurs in its center, undergo no refraction, but the velocity is slowed. The degree of bending of the non-perpendicular rays depends on the angle of incidence that the light waves strike the eye, and depends on the "index of refraction" of each part of the eye. That is, each of the media through which the light waves pass causes a different degree of bending. Most of the refraction occurs as the light passes through the cornea, because there is a greater difference between the index of refraction of air with that of the cornea interface than there is between the other refractive media of the eye. Also, the more convex the surface is, the greater will be the bending. Refraction also occurs as the light rays pass through the anterior surface of the lens from the aqueous humor, and again at the rear surface of the lens as the rays pass into the less dense vitreous humor. And so the cornea, aqueous humor, lens, and vitreous humor all bend the entering light rays in an amount and direction that depends on their respective density and curvature.

The normal *relaxed* eye is referred to as being *emmetropic*. That is, normal refraction bends the light rays just enough to bring them to a sharp focus on the retina when the light is coming from an object 20 feet or more away. At 20 feet and beyond, light rays are almost parallel. When the object is closer than 20 feet, the entering light rays are diverging, and so *accommodation* occurs to bring the image into focus on the retina. This is accomplished by changing the shape of the lens. The change in shape is accomplished by parasympathetic stimulation, causing the ciliary muscles to contract and to pull the choroid toward the lens. This *decreases* the tension on the suspensory ligaments, which allows the lens to assume a more spherical shape, increasing its curvature and allowing sharp focus of close objects by greater bending of the light rays. In accommodating for distant vision, the ciliary muscle fibers relax and tension is *increased* on the suspensory ligaments. This ability to accommodate decreases with increasing age, due to the fact that the lens becomes less elastic and therefore cannot increase its curvature as much for close vision. This condition is called *presbyopia*—farsightedness.

The image formed on the retina is upside down (inverted) as a result of the light rays crossing as they pass through the eye. The retina is the "nervous tunic" of the eye. It has a blind spot, the optic disk, where the optic nerve enters the eye. There are no photoreceptors at the optic disk—no rods or cones.

The light must pass through several layers of the retina to reach the rod and cone photoreceptors, which are close to the choroid and sclera (Fig. 7–13). The only layer beyond the photoreceptors is a layer of pigmented cells, which absorbs the light that is not absorbed by the photoreceptors and prevents the light from scattering. Once the photoreceptors are stimulated, the impulses generated then travel back out through the retinal cell layers (toward the vitreous humor), and finally into the optic nerve by appropriate synapses. In the process of retinal transmission, at least five functional cell types in the various layers of the retina can influence the reception and transmission of nervous impulses: the receptor cells (rods and cones), bipolar cells, ganglion cells, horizontal cells, and amacrine cells (Fig. 7–13).

The rods are more sensitive to light than the cones and they are found throughout the retina. They are functionally most important for visual perception when the light is of low

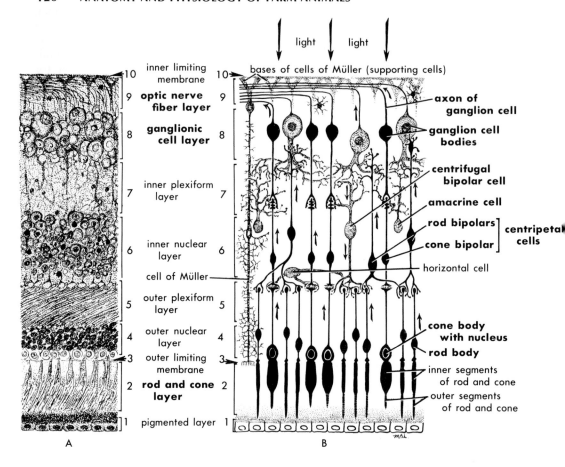

Fig. 7–13. Layers of the adult human retina. *A*, Retina stained routinely and highly magnified. *B*, Schematic presentation of retina to show types of nerve cells and their relationships. Large arrows at top indicate light coming to retina; small arrows show the direction of passage of nerve impulses. Note that the light must penetrate most of the retina to reach the light-sensitive rods and cones. The impulses then pass inward to the retina surface and to the optic nerve. (From Crouch, J.E.,*Functional Human Anatomy*, ed. 3. Philadelphia, Lea & Febiger, 1978.)

intensity, as at dusk and after dark. The cones are not as sensitive to light as the rods, and they are functionally most important when the light intensity is high, as in daylight. The cones are also responsible for color vision in animals that have such discrimination.

The photochemistry that occurs in the outer segments of the rods and cones is important in explaining how light energy is translated into nerve impulses by changing the membrane potential of these receptor cells (Fig. 7–14). The rods and cones contain pigments that undergo chemical changes in the presence of light; these are called photo-

chemicals. The only difference between the photochemicals of the rods and those of the cones is the *opsins* of the pigment. (The opsins are the protein fraction of the chemical.) In the rods, this is *rhodopsin,* and in the cones there are three types of *photopsins,* which differ from rhodopsin only in their response or sensitivity to various wavelengths of light; otherwise, they are the same as rhodopsin.

Rhodopsin (also called *visual purple)* is a combination of *scotopsin* (a protein) and the carotenoid pigment called *cis-retinene.* In the presence of light, the rhodopsin absorbs the light and begins to decompose, changing

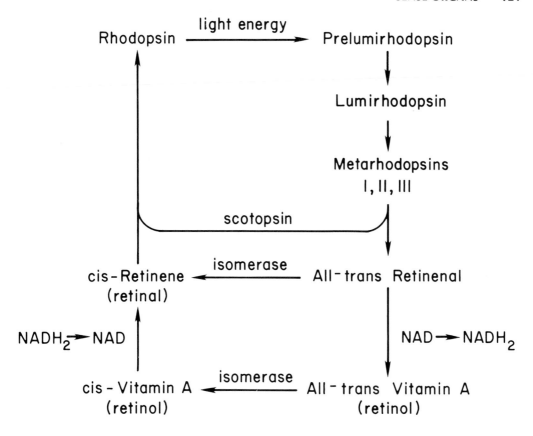

Fig. 7–14. Relationship of Vitamin A to rhodopsin.

the cis-retinene to the all-*trans* form of ret-inene. This occurs through intermediate steps of forming *lumirhodopsin* and *metarhodopsins*, from which the scotopsin then splits off from the trans-retinene. This process acts as the stimulus to generate potential changes of the rod membranes, which result in impulses transmitted to the brain.

The all-trans retinene is then converted back to cis-retinene by an isomerase enzyme. Then the cis-retinene recombines with the scotopsin to form rhodopsin again, thereby replenishing the photochemical. The retinene is synthesized from vitamin A, as illustrated in Figure 7–14, and the rhodopsin is synthesized in the relative absence of light.

The eyes are capable of adapting to high levels of light intensity and to low levels of illumination. *Light adaptation* occurs when the animal is exposed to bright light, such as coming out of a dark barn into bright sunlight. This causes the photochemicals of the rods and cones to be reduced to opsins and retinene, decreasing the amount of photochemical present, which reduces the sensitivity of the eye to light. At the same time, the diameter of the pupil of the eye is decreased by parasympathetic reflex constriction of the circular muscle in the iris. This decreases the amount of light entering the eye.

Dark adaptation, on the other hand, occurs when the animal moves from a well-lighted environment into a dark place, or more gradually as the evening darkness occurs. The retinene and opsins of the rods and cones, and the vitamin A present, are converted into the photopsins. This replenishment of the photochemicals enables the eyes to detect very low levels of light intensity. Within 20 minutes after entering darkness, the sensitivity of the photoreceptors can increase by about 5,000 times and 45 minutes after entering darkness, by about 25,000 times.

The cones adapt much faster than the rods—in fact, within a few minutes—but the cones do not have the sensitivity of the rods. The sensitivity of the rods greatly increases in dark adaptation, mostly due to the fact that so many rod neurons converge through the retinal layers onto one ganglion cell. This allows summation of their inputs to the ganglion cells to produce a larger signal to the optic nerve. Cones have very little convergence. Of course, also occurring in the process of dark adaptation is dilation of the pupil of each eye. This is a reflex reaction due to sympathetic stimulation of the dilator muscles of the pupil in the iris, which increases the diameter of the pupils to enhance the reception of light on the retina through the pupil opening.

Eye Muscles. A group of extrinsic muscles holds the eyeball in the orbit against a pad of *retro-ocular fat* (Figs. 7–15, 7–16). These muscles include the *dorsal (superior) rectus* and *ventral (inferior) rectus* muscles, which rotate the eyeball around a horizontal axis extending from the medial canthus (corner) of the eye to the lateral canthus of the eye. The *lateral (external) rectus* and *medial (internal) rectus* muscles rotate the eyeball around a vertical axis.

There are two oblique muscles. The *dorsal (superior) oblique* muscle originates with the other ocular muscles near the apex of the orbit, passes forward around a pulley of cartilage, the *trochlea,* on the medial wall of the orbit, and inserts on the sclera at the dorsum of the eye. This muscle rotates the top of the eye medially. The *ventral (inferior) oblique* muscle originates in the ventral part of the medial side of the orbit and inserts on the ventral part of the sclera. It rotates the ventral part of the eye medially. Thus, the two oblique muscles rotate the eye around a horizontal axis extending from the anterior to the posterior poles of the eye.

A series of muscles alternates with the rectus muscles just deep to them, inserting on the sclera a little posterior to the insertion of the recti. These deeper muscles, not present in man, are called collectively the *retractor oculi* muscles.

Another group of muscles associated with the eye are the muscles of the eyelid. These include the *levator palpebrae superioris proprius,* which originates near the apex of the orbit and inserts into the tissue of the eyelid between the conjunctiva and the skin of the upper eyelid. It serves as one of the major muscles to raise the upper eyelid. Cir-

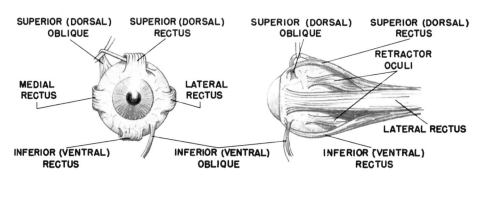

FRONT VIEW   LATERAL VIEW

Fig. 7–15.   The extrinsic muscles. (From Magrane, W.G.: Canine Ophthalmology. ed. 3. Philadelphia, Lea & Febiger, 1977.)

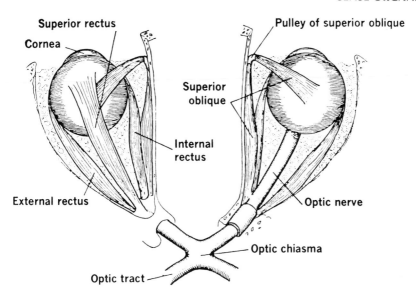

Fig. 7–16.   Diagram showing the eyeballs from above. On the right the superior rectus has been removed to show the insertion of the superior oblique behind the equator of the eyeball. (From W. D. Zoethout, Introduction to Human Physiology, St. Louis, The C. V. Mosby Co.)

cular muscle fibers in the eyelid are known as the *orbicularis oculi* muscle. These muscle fibers serve as a sphincter to close the eyelids. The *retractor of the lateral canthus, corrugator supercilii,* and *malaris* muscles also affect the upper and lower eyelids.

The muscles of the eyelid and the eyebrow, with the exception of the levator palpebrae superioris proprius, can be considered muscles of facial expression, and they are supplied by the *facial nerve.* The dorsal oblique muscle passes around a trochlea. Its nerve supply is the *trochlear (IV cranial) nerve.*

The lateral rectus muscle causes the eye to rotate laterally (abduct). It is supplied by the *abducens (VI cranial) nerve* along with the retractor oculi muscle. All the other muscles of the eye are supplied by the *oculomotor (III cranial) nerve.* These muscles include the dorsal rectus, medial rectus, ventral rectus, ventral oblique, and levator palpebrae superioris proprius muscle.

Sensation to the eye and associated structures, with the exception of the sensation of vision, is supplied completely by branches of the *trigeminal (V cranial) nerve.*

The Conjunctiva. The membrane lining the eyelids and covering the eyeball is known as the conjunctiva. The portion that lines the eyelids is the *palpebral conjunctiva,* and that covering the eyeball is the *bulbar conjunctiva.* Both parts of the membrane contain blood vessels, except for the portion that forms the superficial layer of the cornea, which contains no blood vessels. The conjunctiva is of considerable value in examining animals because the blood vessels are close to the surface in this particular area. The color of the blood and general condition of the vascular system can be discovered by examining the conjunctiva. Conditions such as *jaundice* and *conjunctivitis* can be seen, particularly when the upper and lower eyelids are everted.

The Lacrimal Apparatus. The lacrimal apparatus includes the *lacrimal gland,* ducts of the lacrimal gland leading into the *conjunctival sac,* and a means of withdrawing the tears (lacrimal secretion) from the surface of the eye (Fig. 7–17). The lacrimal gland, located within the orbit dorsal to the eyeball, empties the lacrimal secretion (tears) into the space between the palpebral

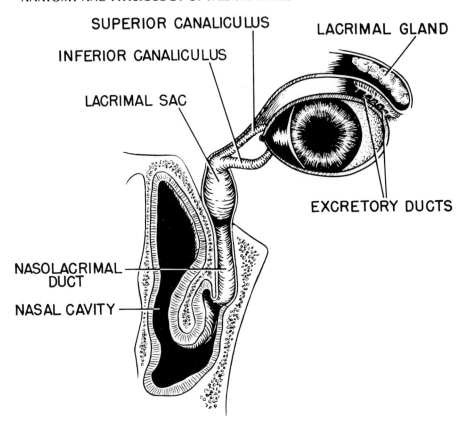

SUPERIOR CANALICULUS

INFERIOR CANALICULUS

LACRIMAL GLAND

LACRIMAL SAC

EXCRETORY DUCTS

NASOLACRIMAL DUCT

NASAL CAVITY

Fig. 7–17.   The lacrimal production and drainage system of the dog. (From Magrane, W.G.: Canine Ophthalmology. ed. 3. Philadelphia, Lea & Febiger, 1977.)

conjunctiva and bulbar conjunctiva. The ducts from the lacrimal gland enter the dorsal fornix at the junction of the conjunctiva of the upper eyelid and the bulbar conjunctiva. This secretion washes out foreign particles that may get into the eye and also lubricates the eyelid in relation to the eyeball; a moist cornea is necessary for proper refraction of light.

The fluid passes from the eye by way of two *puncta lacrimalia* (small openings, one in the upper lid near the medial canthus and one in the lower lid near the medial canthus). Leading from each punctum lacrimale is a small duct that goes to the *lacrimal sac*, located in a fossa of the orbit in the *lacrimal bone*. From the lacrimal sac is a duct leading into the nasal cavity, passing along the wall of the maxilla in the *osseous nasolacrimal*

canal and emptying into the lower part of the nasal cavity. In the horse, the nasolacrimal duct opens on the floor of the nasal cavity close to the junction of skin and mucous membrane. Obstruction of any of the excretory portions of the lacimal apparatus may result in tears overflowing the margin of the eyelids.

The Eyelids. The eyelids consist of an upper and a lower fold of skin lined with mucous membrane, the conjunctiva. The margin of each lid has a number of sebaceous glands, the *meibomian glands,* which produce a waxy substance that helps prevent tears from overflowing onto the face.

In domestic animals a plate of cartilage is located along the medial side of the eyeball. It is partially covered by conjunctiva and

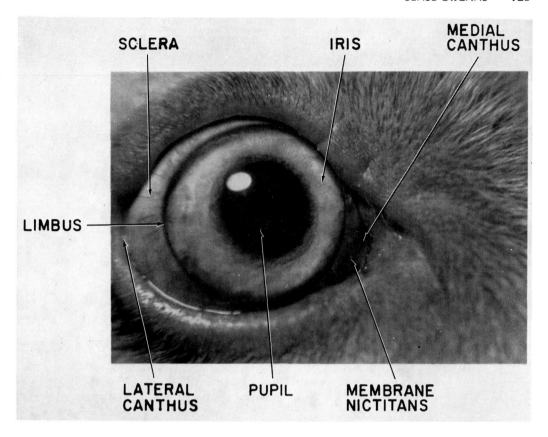

SCLERA   IRIS   MEDIAL CANTHUS

LIMBUS

LATERAL CANTHUS   PUPIL   MEMBRANE NICTITANS

Fig. 7–18.   The external eye. (From Magrane, W.G.: Canine Ophthalmology. ed. 3. Philadelphia, Lea & Febiger, 1977.)

Table 7–1.   Physiologic Classification of Nerve Fibers

Type*	Group†	Fiber diameter (μ)	Conduction velocity m/sec	Fibers
Aα	IA	12–22	72–120	Afferents from primary endings of muscle spindle.
Aα	IB	12–22	72–120	Afferents from Golgi tendon organs.
Aα		12–22	72–120	*Efferent* motor fibers to extrafusal skeletal muscle fibers.
Aβ	II	6–12	36–72	Afferents from secondary endings of muscle spindle. Afferents from skin touch and pressure receptors.
Aγ		4–8	12–48	*Efferent* motor fibers to intrafusal muscle fibers.
Aδ	III	1–6	6–24	Afferents from touch, pain, and temperature receptors (myelinated).
B		1–3	3–15	Preganglionic myelinated autonomic fibers.
C	IV	0.1–1.0	0.5–2	Unmyelinated afferents from touch, pain, and temperature receptors.
C				Postganglionic unmyelinated autonomic fibers.

*Only Type C (IV) fibers are unmyelinated.

†Roman numeral classification (groups) applies only to *sensory* fibers (afferents); it is based on fiber size and origin.

partially embedded in the retro-ocular fat. This cartilage is the basis of the third eyelid, sometimes called the *nictitating membrane (membrana nictitans)* (Fig. 7–18). It is a remnant of the complete third eyelid of lower animal forms, including the chicken. No muscles attach to the third eyelid, so its movement is entirely passive. The third eyelid is extruded whenever the extrinsic muscles of the eye contract, putting additional pressure on the retro-ocular fat. Protrusion of the third eyelid is a prominent symptom of conditions in which all striated muscles of the body contract, such as in *strychnine poisoning* and *tetanus* (lockjaw).

Chapter 8

The Skeletal System

The study of the bones that collectively make up the skeleton or framework of the body is called *osteology*.

The skeleton of a living animal is made up of bones that are themselves living structures (Fig. 8–1). They have blood vessels, lymphatic vessels, and nerves; they are subject to disease, repair themselves, and adjust to changes in stress.

About one-third of the weight of bone consists of an organic framework of fibrous tissue and cells. This organic matter mainly consists of collagen and polysaccharides called glycosaminoglycans, which contain chondroitin sulfate. They give resilience and toughness to bones. The remaining two-thirds of the weight of bone consists of an inorganic component (largely calcium and phosphorus salts) deposited within the organic framework. These salts give hardness and rigidity to bones and make them resist the passage of x-rays. If the inorganic salts are removed by soaking a bone in dilute acid, the resulting decalcified bone will retain its original form but will be flexible enough to be tied in a knot. On the other hand, if the organic matter is removed by charring in a furnace so that only the inorganic salts remain, the bone will be brittle and break unless handled with extreme care.

TERMINOLOGY

Certain terms routinely used in reference to bones, particularly long bones, include the following:

Compact (dense or *cortical) bone* refers to the hard layer of bone that covers most bones and forms almost the entire shaft of long bones.

Cancellous (spongy) bone is composed of plates *(spicules)* arranged to form a porous network. The spaces are usually filled with bone marrow.

Cortex denotes the compact bone that forms the shaft of a long bone.

Medullary cavity (marrow cavity) is the space surrounded by the cortex of a long bone. In young animals it is filled with *red bone marrow*, which gradually changes to fatty *yellow marrow* in old animals.

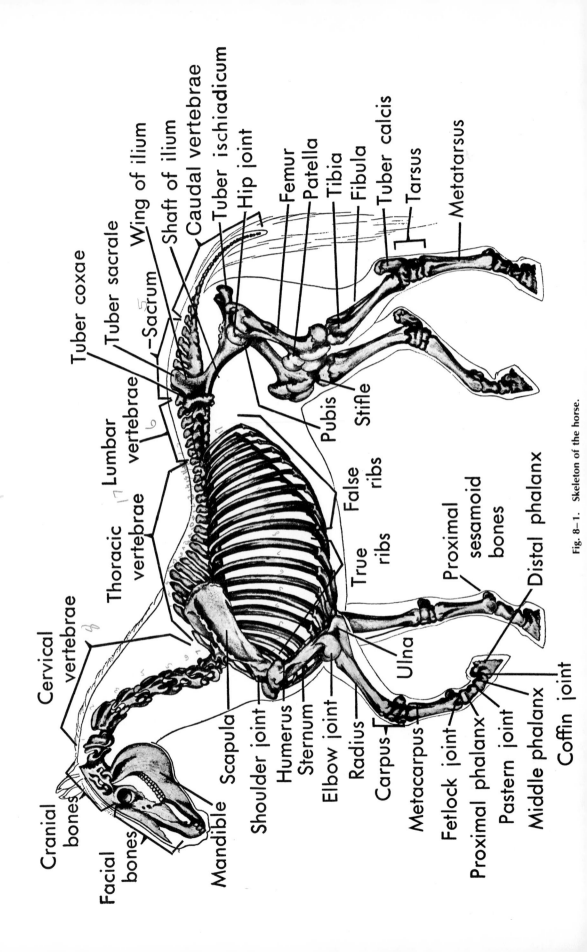

Fig. 8–1. Skeleton of the horse.

Cranial bones

Facial bones

Cervical vertebrae

Tuber coxae

Tuber sacrale

Wing of ilium

Shaft of ilium

Caudal vertebrae

Tuber ischiadicum

Hip joint

Femur

Patella

Tibia

Fibula

Tuber calcis

Tarsus

Metatarsus

Sacrum

Thoracic vertebrae

Lumbar vertebrae

Pubis

Stifle

True ribs

False ribs

Proximal sesamoid bones

Distal phalanx

Mandible

Scapula

Shoulder joint

Humerus

Sternum

Elbow joint

Radius

Ulna

Carpus

Metacarpus

Fetlock joint

Proximal phalanx

Pastern joint

Middle phalanx

Coffin joint

Epiphysis refers to either extremity of a long bone. The end closest to the body is the proximal epiphysis, and the end farthest from the body is the distal epiphysis.

Diaphysis is the cylindrical shaft of a long bone situated between the two epiphyses.

Epiphyseal cartilage or *disk (physis)* is a layer of *hyaline cartilage* that separates the diaphysis and epiphysis within the *metaphysis* of an immature bone. This is the only area in which a bone can increase in length.

Articular cartilage is a thin layer of hyaline cartilage that covers the articular surface of a bone.

Periosteum is a fibrous membrane that covers the surface of a bone, except where articular cartilage is located. It is responsible for increases in the diameter of bones and it functions in the healing of fractures.

Endosteum is a fibrous membrane that lines the marrow cavity and *osteonal (Haversian) canals* of a bone.

Many of the projections from bones and depressions in bones have general names that depend to some extent on their size and function. Both projections and depressions may be articular or nonarticular. If they are articular, they form an integral part of a joint and are covered with articular cartilage. Nonarticular projections and depressions are located outside of joints. Many of them provide areas for attachment of muscle tendons or of ligaments.

Articular projections include the following:

A *head* is a spherical articular projection, such as the head of the femur.

A *condyle (condylus)* is a more or less cylindrical articular mass, such as the condyles on the distal end of the humerus.

A *trochlea* is a pulley-like articular mass, as found at the distal end of the femur, on which the patella slides.

A *facet* is a relatively flat articular surface, as found between adjacent carpal bones.

Nonarticular projections include the following:

A *process* is a general term for a bony projection, such as the spinous process or transverse process of a vertebra.

A *tuberosity (tuber, tuberus)* is a relatively large nonarticular projection, such as the major (lateral) tuberosity on the proximal end of the humerus.

A *tubercle (tuberculum)* is a smaller projection. Tubercle and tuberosity are sometimes used interchangeably.

A *spine (spina)* may be a pointed projection, such as the spine at the proximal end of the tibia, or it may refer to a ridge, such as the spine of the scapula. (Spine is sometimes used as a synonym for the vertebral column.)

A *crest* is a term for a sharp ridge.

A *neck* is a cylindrical part of a bone to which a head is attached. For example, the neck of the femur is located between the head of the femur and the rest of the proximal end of the femur.

A *line (linea)* is a small ridge or mark on a bone, often caused by the pull of a muscle. The gluteal lines on the ilium are caused by pull of the gluteal muscles.

Articular depressions include the following:

A *glenoid cavity* (cavity glenoidalis) is a shallow articular concavity (depression), as is found on the articular surface of the scapula.

A *cotyloid cavity* is a deep articular concavity, such as the *acetabulum* of the hip joint.

A *notch* may be an articular indentation, such as the semilunar notch of the ulna, which articulates with the condyles of the humerus, or it may be a nonarticular indentation in the margin of a bone.

Nonarticular depressions include the following:

A *fossa* is a large, nonarticular depression, such as the atlantal fossa located ventral to the wing of the atlas.

A *fovea* is a small nonarticular depression, such as the fovea capitis on the head of the femur.

A *foramen* is a circumscribed hole in a

bone. The foramen magnum at the base of the skull through which the spinal cord passes is an example of a foramen.

A *canal* is a tunnel through one or more bones, such as the vertebral canal, through which the spinal cord passes along the length of the vertebral column.

CLASSIFICATION OF BONES ACCORDING TO GROSS APPEARANCE

Any bone may be classified in one of the following groups: long, short, flat, sesamoid, pneumatic, or irregular.

Long bones are greater in one dimension than any other. Each consists of a relatively cylindrical shaft (diaphysis) and two extremities called epiphyses with a *metaphysis* between each epiphysis and the diaphysis. A long bone grows in length only at the epiphyseal cartilage, which is located within the metaphysis at the junctions of the diaphysis and each epiphysis (Fig. 8–2). Long bones function chiefly as levers and aid in support, locomotion, and prehension. The best examples of long bones are found in the extremities and include: *pectoral limb*, humerus, radius, ulna, metacarpals, phalanges; *pelvic limb*, femur, tibia, fibula, metatarsals, and phalanges.

Short bones are somewhat cuboid, or approximately equal in all dimensions. There is no marrow cavity, but the interior is composed of spongy substance filled with marrow spaces. The exterior is formed by a thin layer of compact substance.

Short bones function in absorbing concussion, and they are found in complex joints such as the carpus (knee) and tarsus (hock), where a variety of movements as well as absorption of shock are desired.

Flat bones are relatively thin and expanded in two dimensions. They consist of two plates of compact substance, lamina externa and lamina interna, separated by spongy material called *diploë*.

Flat bones function chiefly for protection of vital organs such as the brain, the heart and lungs, and the pelvic viscera, but many provide large areas for attachment of muscles. The scapulae and pelvic bones have large areas for muscle attachment.

Sesamoid bones resemble a sesame seed and are developed along the course of tendons to reduce friction or change the course of tendons. They may also change the angle of pull of muscles and thus give a greater mechanical advantage. The patella (knee cap) is the largest sesamoid bone in the body.

Pneumatic bones contain air spaces or sinuses that communicate with the exterior. The frontal bones and maxillary bones of the skull are examples of this type of bone.

Irregular bones are unpaired bones located on the median plane and include the vertebrae and some of the unpaired bones of the skull. These bones do not fit very well into any other classification and serve for protection, support, and muscle attachment.

FUNCTIONS OF BONES

The functions of bones include providing protection, giving rigidity and form to the body, acting as levers, storing minerals, and providing a site for blood formation.

Protection of vital organs is one of the important functions of bones. The central nervous system is protected by the skull and vertebral column; the heart and lungs, by the rib cage; and internal parts of the urogenital system, by the pelvis.

Animals without a skeleton of some type have little or no regular form. The skeleton gives a basis for the external structure and appearance of most animals as we know them.

In the vertebrates, locomotion, defense, offense, grasping, and other activities of this type depend largely upon the action of muscles that attach to levers. Almost without exception, these levers are made of bone and are integral parts of the skeleton.

The entire skeleton serves as a dynamic storage area for minerals, particularly calcium and phosphorus. These minerals are

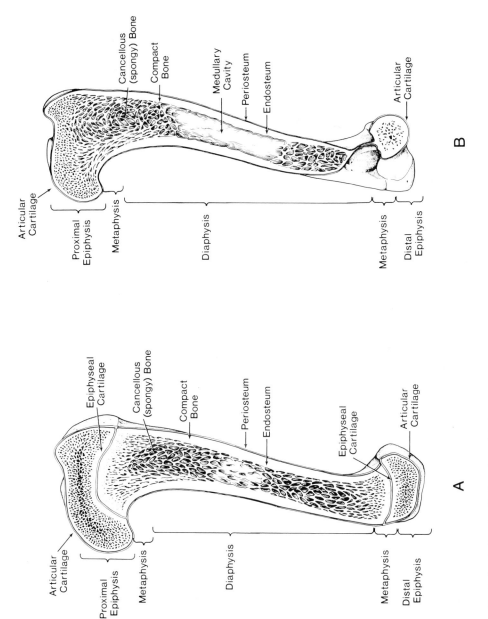

Fig. 8–2. *A,* **Longitudinal section of the humerus of a young dog.** *B,* **A longitudinal section of the humerus of a mature dog.**

deposited and withdrawn as needed in the ongoing homeokinetic process.

Blood formation is not strictly a function of bone proper, but of the marrow found within the marrow cavity of long bones and within the spongy substance of all young bones.

AXIAL SKELETON

The axial skeleton includes practically all bones except those of the limbs or appendages. The bones comprising the axial skeleton are either on the midline, such as vertebrae and skull, or are attached to midline bones, as are the ribs. Table 8–1 indicates the bones of the axial skeleton by regions.

Skull

That part of the skeleton which forms the basis of the head is called the skull. It functions in protection of the brain, supports many of the sense organs, and forms passages for the beginning of the digestive and respiratory systems.

Table 8–1.   Bones of the Axial Skeleton

Skull	Vertebrae
Cranial bones	cervical
occipital	thoracic
parietal	lumbar
interparietal	sacral
temporal	caudal
frontal	
ethmoid	Ribs
sphenoid	true—join sternum by costal
	cartilages
Facial bones	false—not directly connected
pterygoid	with sternum
lacrimal	floating—last 1 or 2 pair con-
nasal	nected only with vertebrae
palatine	
conchae	Sternum
(turbinates)	Manubrium
maxilla	body
incisive	xiphoid process
(premaxilla)	
zygomatic	
(malar)	
vomer	
mandible	
hyoid	

The skull consists of (1) a cranial part, which surrounds the brain and (2) the remainder, which is the facial part (Figs. 8–3, 8–4). Much of the observable species difference, as far as the head is concerned, depends on variations in the facial part of the skull.

The *cranium* is formed largely from the membrane type of bones, which consists of an inner and outer plate of dense bone separararated by a layer of *diploë* (spongy bone).

The caudal (posterior) and dorsal walls of the cranium are formed by the *occipital, parietal, interparietal,* and *frontal* bones. The *horn cores* develop on the frontal bones in animals that have horns.

Laterally and ventrally the walls are formed by the *temporal bones,* which contain the middle and inner ears, and the *sphenoid bone,* which supports the brain and pituitary gland.

Rostrally (anteriorly), the *ethmoid bone* presents numerous openings for passage of the olfactory nerves associated with the sense of smell.

The *facial* portion can be divided into orbital, nasal, and oral regions.

Orbit means "track," and refers to the bony socket that protects the eye during life. The orbit is surrounded by portions of the *frontal, lacrimal,* and *zygomatic* (malar) bones.

The nasal and oral portions of the skull may be long, as in the horse, or relatively short, as in man. Dogs show a great range in length of these portions, as may be seen by comparing the Boston terrier with the greyhound.

The air passages through the nasal part of the skull are bounded dorsally by the *nasal bones,* laterally by the *maxillae* and *premaxillae,* and ventrally by the *palatine processes* of the maxillae, premaxillae, and *palatine* bones. The nasal passages are separated longitudinally by the *vomer bone* and a cartilaginous septum. Scroll-like *conchae (turbinate bones)* are attached to the lateral walls of the nasal cavity and project into the

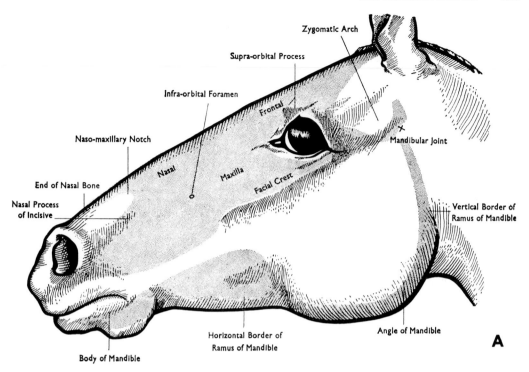

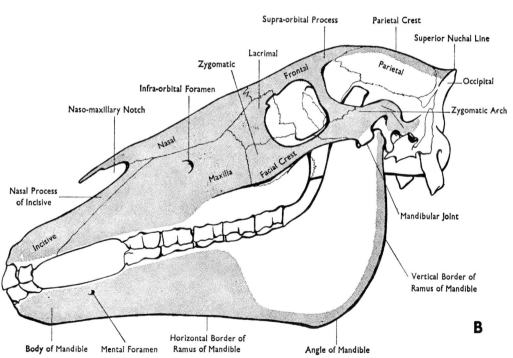

Fig. 8–3. *A,* Head of horse, side view. The shaded parts are those that can be identified in the living animal, though it should be noted that the parietal crest is not always so conspicuous anteriorly as in this specimen. With regard to the mandible, the borders only are subcutaneous. *B,* Skull of horse, side view. (Taylor, Regional and Applied Anatomy of the Domestic Animals, courtesy of J. B. Lippincott Co.)

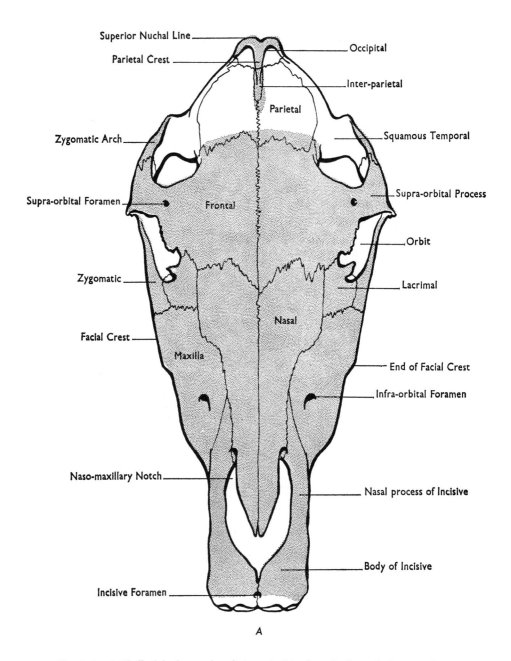

Fig. 8–4. *A*, Skull of the horse, dorsal view. (Incisive bone is also called premaxilla.)

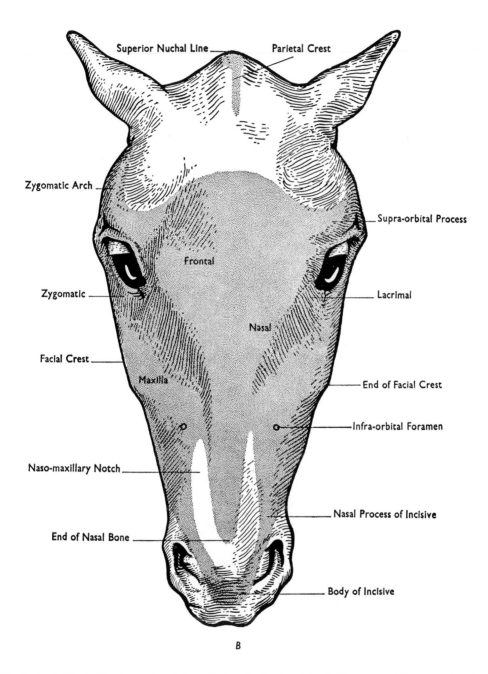

Fig. 8–4. *B,* Head of the horse, dorsal view. (Taylor, Regional and Applied Anatomy of the Domestic Animals, courtesy of J. B. Lippincott Co.)

nasal passages. These conchae serve as a basis for the end organs of the sense of smell and also give support to many blood vessels that help warm the inspired air.

Communicating with the *nasal cavity* are excavations, known as *sinuses*, within some of the bones. The bones that may contain these sinuses include the frontal, maxillary, nasal, sphenoid, and palatine bones. The frontal sinus in cattle may be exposed by dehorning mature animals (Fig. 8–5).

The *oral (mouth)* portion is roofed by the maxillae and premaxillae, which contain teeth, and by the palatine bone.

Ventrolaterally, the *mandible* completes the oral portion. The mandible pivots on a part of the temporal bone just in front of the opening of the ear. The mandible contains all the lower teeth and gives attachment to some of the muscles associated with chewing and swallowing.

Vertebral Column

The vertebral column is composed of median, unpaired, irregular bones called vertebrae (see Fig. 8–6). The following letters are used to designate the respective regions:

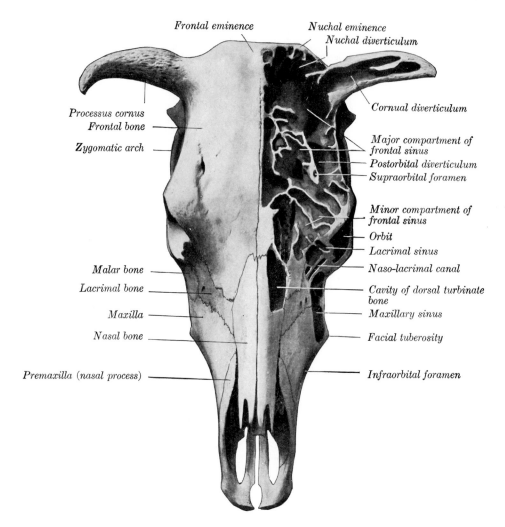

Fig. 8–5.   Skull of the cow, dorsal view; sinuses opened. (Sisson and Grossman, The Anatomy of the Domestic Animals, courtesy of W. B. Saunders Co.)

C: Cervical vertebrae—neck region
T: Thoracic or dorsal—chest region
L: Lumbar—loin region
S: Sacral—in region of pelvis—fused or false
       vertebrae
LS: Fused lumbar and sacral
Cd: Caudal (Coccygeal)—located in tail

A *vertebral formula* for a given species consists of the letter symbol for each region followed by the number of vertebrae in that region in the given species. Vertebral formulas of common animals and man include:

Horse: C 77 T 18 L 6 S 5 Cd 15–20
Cow: C 7 T 13 L 6 S 5 Cd 18–20
Sheep: C 7 T 13 L 6–7 S 4 Cd 16–18
Goat: C 7 T 13 L 7 S 4 Cd 12
Hog: C 7 T 14–15 L 6–7 S 4 Cd 20–23
Dog: C 7 T 13 L 7 S 3 Cd 20–23
Chicken: C 14 T 7 LS 14 Cd 6
Man: C 7 T 12 L 5 S 5 Cd 4

The parts of a typical vertebra include the body, the arch, and the processes.

The *body* (corpus) is a cylindrical mass forming the ventral aspect of the vertebra.

Dorsally, the *arch* completes the *vertebral foramen*, which contains the spinal cord.

Cranial and caudal *articular processes* form joints with adjacent vertebrae.

Spinous processes project dorsally to form the spine.

Transverse processes project laterally from the arch.

The *intervertebral foramina* are formed laterally between vertebrae by the junction of notches on adjacent vertebrae.

The *cervical vertebrae* have well-developed articular processes to facilitate the large amount of movement normally found in the neck region. The other processes are less well developed in cervical vertebrae than in other regions. All domestic mammals have seven cervical vertebrae.

The *atlas* is the first cervical vertebra. The spinous process is absent, and the body is fused to the axis as the dens.

The *axis* is the second cervical vertebra. The spinous process is broad but not high.

The remaining cervical vertebrae are similar, with small spinous processes and small transverse processes but rather large articular processes. With the exception of the last cervical vertebra, each cervical transverse process contains a foramen known as the transverse foramen.

Thoracic vertebrae are marked by well-developed spinous processes. In the shoulder region these spinous processes form the basis for a dorsal prominence known as the *withers*.

Costal fovea (articular facets) on the bodies of adjacent thoracic vertebrae form cavities for articulation with the heads of the ribs. Each transverse process also has a transverse costal fovea (facet) for articulation with the tubercle of the rib of the same number as the vertebra.

Lumbar vertebrae have large, flat transverse processes that project laterally. They form the long arm of bone in a T-bone steak. The spinous processes are similar to those of the last few thoracic vertebrae. The articular processes are better developed than those of the thoracic vertebrae, but not as large as the articular processes in the cervical region. The body and caudal articular processes of the last lumbar vertebra articulate with the sacrum.

The *sacral vertebrae* are fused to form a single wedge-shaped bone known as the sacrum, which articulates with the lumbar vertebrae cranially, with the caudal (coccygeal) vertebrae caudally, and with the wings of the ilia craniolaterally. The intervertebral foramina are represented by a dorsal and ventral row of *sacral foramina* on each side of the sacrum. These foramina, as other intervertebral foramina, give passage to spinal nerves.

Caudal (coccygeal) vertebrae form the bony basis for the tail. Consequently the number varies considerably from species to species and even within the same species. Size of the vertebrae decreases rapidly in a caudal direction, until the last few caudal vertebrae are merely small rods of bone.

Sternum and Ribs

The *sternum* forms the floor of the bony thorax and gives attachment to the costal

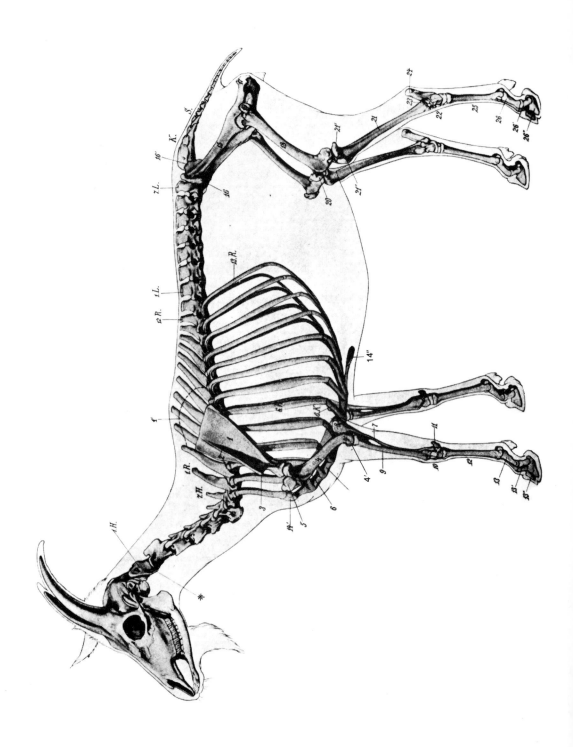

Fig. 8–6.   Goat. (Ellenberger, Baum and Dittrich, Atlas of Anatomy for Artists, Courtesy of Dover Publications, Inc.)

1H—1st cervical vertebra (Atlas)
7H—7th cervical vertebra
K—Sacrum
6K—Costal cartilage
1L—1st lumbar vertebra
7L—7th lumbar vertebra
1R—1st thoracic (dorsal) vertebra
6R—6th rib
12R—12th thoracic (dorsal) vertebra
13R—13th rib
S—Caudal vertebra
*—Ala of Atlas
1—Scapula
1'—Border of scapular cartilage
2—Spine of scapula
3—Acromion
4—Humerus

4'—Lateral epicondyle
5—Major (lateral) tuberosity
6—Deltoid tuberosity
7—Ulna
8—Olecranon
9—Radius
10—Carpus
11—Os pisiforme (accessory)
12—Metacarpus
13—Proximal phalanx
13'—Middle phalanx
13"—Distal phalanx
14—Sternum
14'—Manubrium
14"—Xiphoid cartilage
15—Ossa pelvis

16—Tuber coxae
16'—Tuber sacrale
17—Tuber ischiadicum
18—Femur
19—Trochanter major
20—Patella
21—Tibia
21'—Lateral condyle of tibia
21"—Tuberosity of tibia
22—Tarsus
23—Lateral malleolus tibia
24—Tuber calcanei
25—Metatarsus
26—Proximal phalanx
26'—Middle phalanx
26"—Distal phalanx

cartilages of the *sternal (true) ribs* as well as forming a place of origin for the pectoral muscles. The cranial extremity of the sternum is the *manubrium*; the middle portion is the *body*; and the caudal extremity is the *xiphoid process*. The sternum consists of segments called *sternebrae* which tend to fuse together as age advances. The number of sternebrae varies with species as follows: pig and sheep, 6 each; cow and goat, 7; and horse and dog, 8 each.

The *ribs* form the lateral walls of the *bony thorax*. Usually the number of pairs of ribs is the same as the number of thoracic vertebrae. Rarely an extra rib or pair of ribs may be located either cranial or caudal to the thoracic vertebrae. *Sternal (true)* ribs extend from their respective thoracic vertebra to the sternum, where they are connected directly by costal cartilages. The number of sternal ribs corresponds with the number of sternebrae in the animal. The ribs caudal to the sternal ribs are called *asternal (false) ribs* because they are not directly connected with the sternum. The *costal cartilages* at the ventral extremity of most of the asternal ribs overlap and thus indirectly connect the asternal and sternal ribs. Sometimes the last one or two pair of ribs have no connection with other ribs at the ventral end. Such ribs are called *floating ribs*. The spaces between adjacent ribs are called the *intercostal spaces*, and are numbered to correspond with the number of the rib in front of the space.

Table 8–2. Comparison of Pectoral and Pelvic Bones

Pectoral limb	Pelvic limb
Pectoral girdle (shoulder girdle)	Pelvic girdle (os coxae)—pelvis
Scapula	Ilium
Clavicle	Ischium
Coracoid	Pubis
Humerus—arm	Femur—thigh
	Patella
Radius—forearm	Tibia—leg
Ulna "	Fibula "
Carpus—knee	Tarsus—hock
Metacarpus—cannon	Metatarsus—cannon
Phalanges—digits	Phalanges—digits

A typical rib consists of a curved shaft, a sternal extremity ventrally, and a vertebral extremity dorsally. With the possible exception of floating ribs, the sternal extremity is extended by a costal cartilage. The vertebral extremity consists of a spherical head connected to the rib by a constricted neck, and a tubercle which bears a facet that articulates with the transverse process of a thoracic vertebra. The head articulates with the bodies of two adjacent vertebrae.

APPENDICULAR SKELETON

The appendicular skeleton is made up of the bones of the limbs (Fig. 8–7). The bones of the front (pectoral) limb are compared to those of the hind (pelvic) limb by region in Table 8–2.

Pectoral Limbs

The *scapula (shoulder blade)* in all animals is a rather flat, triangular bone. The distal portion, forming a joint with the *humerus (arm bone)*, is known as the *ventral (articular) angle*, and it forms the only true joint between the scapula and another bone in most domestic animals. Anthropoids, birds, and cats have a *clavicle (collar bone)*, which forms a joint with part of the scapula. In most quadrupeds, the clavicle is represented by the *clavicular tendon*, a connective tissue band within the brachiocephalicus muscle. Poultry also have a *coracoid* as a separate bone, in addition to the scapula and clavicle. The fused clavicles are called the *furcula* or *wishbone* in birds. The coracoid in man and our domestic mammals has been reduced to the coracoid process (a bony prominence) which protrudes medially from the scapula near the ventral angle.

The lateral face of the scapula has a ridge extending from the ventral angle to the dorsal border (vertebral border). This ridge is called the *spine*, and it divides the lateral side of the scapula into two depressions. One is the *supraspinous fossa*, which is cranial and above the spine, and the other is the

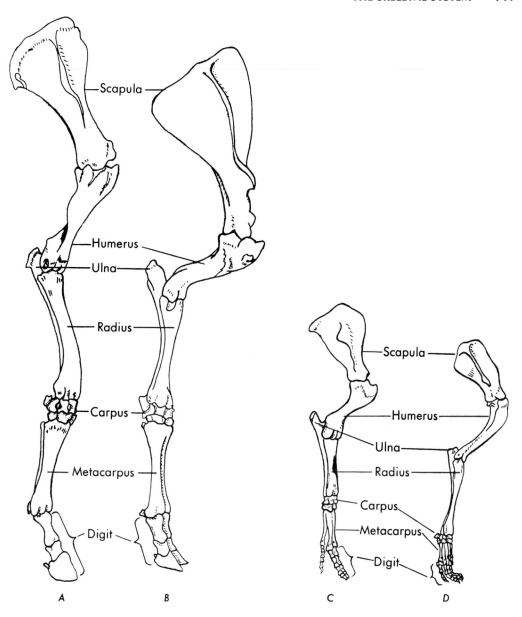

Fig. 8–7.   Forelimb skeletons of domestic animals. *A*, Horse; *B*, cow; *C*, pig; *D*, dog.

infraspinous fossa, which is caudal and below the spine.

The costal (medial or deep) face of the scapula gives attachment to many of the muscles that connect the limb to the body. It also has a depression known as the *subscapular fossa.*

The humerus (arm bone) is a typical long bone that varies only in minor details from one animal to another. It has a shaft and two extremities. The proximal (upper) end joins the ventral angle of the scapula to form the *shoulder joint.* The prominence produced by this end of the humerus is called the *point of the shoulder.* The upper end of the humerus has a number of irregular prominences (tuberosities) resulting from the pull of the strong muscles that attach here. The distal end of the humerus forms the elbow joint with the proximal ends of the radius and ulna.

The *radius* is the larger of the two forearm bones, and the *ulna* is the smaller in mammals but not in birds. The radius is well developed in all species. It enters into the elbow joint proximally and the carpus (knee joint) distally. The radius is a long bone located on the medial side of the forearm, where it can be felt immediately beneath the skin. "Radial" is a term frequently used as an adjective meaning medial in relation to the front limb. "Ulnar" may be used in place of lateral.

The *ulna* varies in its degree of development from species to species. The *olecranon process (point of the elbow)* is found in all animals, where it projects above and behind the elbow joint. This process forms a lever for attachment of the muscles that extend the elbow. In the horse the proximal portion of the shaft of the ulna is well developed but fused to the radius. The cow, sheep, goat, and pig each have a complete ulna, but with restricted or no movement between the ulna and radius. The cat and dog have considerably more movement between these bones, but not nearly as much as man.

The *carpus* in all animals is a complex region that includes two rows of small bones. Those in the proximal row are called (from medial to lateral) *radial, intermediate,* and *ulnar,* while those in the distal row are numbered 1, 2, 3, and 4. In addition, an accessory carpal bone projects backward from the lateral side of the carpus.

The *metacarpal* or *(cannon)* region is immediately distal to the carpus. In the horse it includes one *large metacarpal (cannon)* bone, representing the base for the third digit or middle finger, and two *small metacarpal (splint) bones.* The second metacarpal bone is on the medial side, and the fourth is on the lateral side. Fusion of these small bones to the cannon bone with excess bone formation results in a condition known as *splints,* which may cause lameness in the horse (Fig. 8–8).

The cannon bone of the cow and sheep results from a fusion of the third and fourth metacarpal bones. A vertical groove on the front of the cannon bone indicates the original line of fusion.

The pig has four metacarpal bones. The first is absent; the second and fifth are reduced; and the third and fourth bear most of the weight.

In the dog and cat, each of the five metacarpal bones is separate and distinct. Each forms the basis for a digit (toe). The first metacarpal bone is usually poorly developed, as is the dewclaw that is attached to it.

The *digits (toes* or *fingers)* vary from one to five in number. The horse, having only one digit, figuratively walks on the tip of his middle finger, or third digit. The digits, like

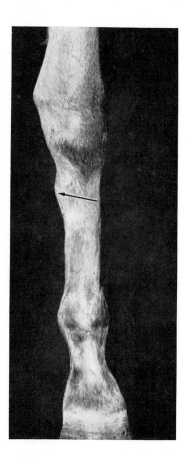

Fig. 8–8.   Medial splint. (From Adams, O. R.: Lameness in Horses. ed. 3. Philadelphia, Lea & Febiger, 1974.)

the metacarpal bones, are numbered from one to five from medial to lateral. Each complete digit is made up of three phalanges *(proximal phalanx, middle phalanx,* and *distal phalanx)*. These are numbered 1, 2, and 3 from proximal to distal and should not be confused with the first, second, and third digits. The proximal phalanx is also called the *long pastern bone;* the middle phalanx, the *short pastern bone;* and distal phalanx, the *coffin bone.* Each digit also includes two *proximal sesamoid bones* at the junction of the metacarpal and proximal phalanx and a *distal sesamoid bone* at the junction of the middle and distal phalanges.

The cow, sheep, and goat have two principal digits or toes, the third and fourth, while the second and fifth digits are represented only by the small dewclaws at the back of the pastern. In the pig the dewclaws are much better developed and in fact *are* the second and fifth digits. The dog and cat normally have five digits on each front limb.

The first digit again is only a dewclaw and corresponds in position to the human thumb.

Pelvic Limbs

The pelvic girdle consists of three bones on each side, which are fused to form two irregular bones, the *os coxae* (Fig. 8–9). Each os coxae, or *pelvic bone* of one side, is firmly attached to its fellow at the *symphysis* ventrally to form the *ossa coxarum (pelvis)* and is joined to the axial skeleton dorsally by a very strong joint on each side, the right and left *sacroiliac articulations.* The bones entering into the formation of the os coxae are the ilium, the ischium, and the pubis. These bones unite at the *acetabulum* (socket) of the hip joint.

The *ilium* is the largest and most dorsal of the bones. It is irregularly triangular in shape, with the apex at the acetabulum and the base projecting craniodorsally. The me-

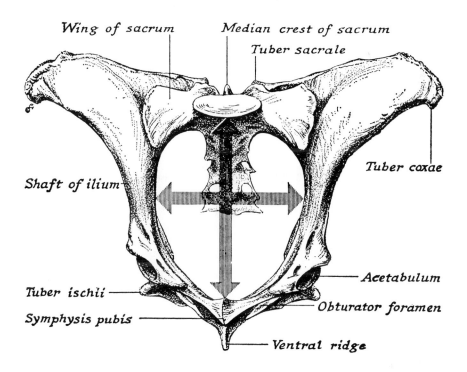

Wing of sacrum   Median crest of sacrum
Tuber sacrale
Tuber coxae
Shaft of ilium
Tuber ischii
Acetabulum
Symphysis pubis
Obturator foramen
Ventral ridge

Fig. 8–9.   The pelvic bones of the cow (viewed from in front and somewhat below), through which the calf must pass at birth. The arrows indicate the greatest transverse and dorso-ventral diameters of the pelvic girdle. *(In* Salisbury and VanDenmark, Physiology of Reproduction and Artificial Insemination of Cattle, courtesy of W. H. Freeman & Co., copyright 1961.)

dial angle is called the *tuber sacrale* and is close to the sacroiliac joint near the midline. The lateral angle is called the *tuber coxae* and is known as the *point of the hip*, or *hook bone*. The broad, flat portion between the *tuber coxae* and tuber sacrale is called the wing of the ilium, and the anterior dorsal margin is known as the *crest of the ilium*. The shaft of the ilium projects downward and backward between the wing and acetabulum and helps form the lateral wall of the pelvis.

The *ischium* projects backward and ventrally from the acetabulum, forming much of the floor of the pelvis. The ischium has a large roughened caudal prominence, the *tuber ischiadicum (tuber ischii)*, commonly called the *pin bone*.

The *pubis* is the smallest of the three bones and forms the cranial part of the floor of the pelvis. The pubis also enters into the formation of the acetabulum and meets the pubis of the opposite side at the symphysis. The pubis and ischium form the boundaries of the largest foramen in the body, the *obturator foramen*.

The *femur (thigh bone)* extends from the hip joint to the *stifle* (the joint corresponding to the human knee). When seen in cross section in round steaks, the femur is known as the *round bone*. The proximal end of the femur has a nearly spherical head that articulates with the acetabulum of the os coxae to form the hip joint. There are also several roughened prominences known as *trochanters* for the attachment of heavy thigh and hip muscles. The shaft of the femur is nearly circular on cross section and of considerable length. The distal end has two condyles for articulation with the tibia and a trochlea for articulation with the *patella*, which is the largest sesamoid bone in the body.

The *tibia* and *fibula* correspond to the radius and ulna in the forelimb, with the tibia being the larger and located medially. The fibula is much smaller and is located on the lateral side of the leg. The terms *tibial* and *fibular* are sometimes used as adjectives, meaning medial and lateral respectively.

The tibia has an expanded proximal end that enters into the stifle joint. The shaft is elongated but triangular in cross section. The distal end of the tibia has two sagittal concave depressions that form the hinge joint of the hock with the *tibial tarsal bone (talus)*.

In the dog, pig, and man, the fibula is a long, thin bone extending from the proximal end of the tibia to the lateral side of the tarsus (hock). Both the proximal end and shaft are present in the horse, but only a vestige of the proximal end of the fibula is present in the cow, sheep, and goat.

The *tarsus (hock)* is composed of small bones much like the carpus (knee) in the front limb. The proximal row of tarsal bones consists of two large bones. The *tibial tarsal bone (talus)* dorsally has two spool-like ridges for articulation with the tibia. The *fibular tarsal* bone *(calcaneus)* projects upward and backward to form the point of the hock. The calcaneus acts as a lever for the muscles extending the hock, and corresponds to the human heel.

In the horse, the central row of tarsal bones is represented by one bone, the *central tarsal*. The bones of the distal row are again numbered from medial to lateral, 1, 2, 3, and 4. These bones of the hock are bound tightly together by short strong ligaments. The fourth tarsal and central tarsal bones are fused in ruminants and swine.

The metatarsus and digits of the hindlimb are similar to the metacarpus and digits of the forelimb. The hindlimb of the dog may lack the first digit (dewclaw), or it may be present or even double but lack one or more phalanges.

Chapter 9

Microanatomy and Physiology of Bone

MICROANATOMY AND EMBRYOLOGY OF BONE

Mature bone consists of *osteocytes* (bone cells) surrounded by an intercellular matrix composed of calcified osteoid material. The osteocytes are located in small cavities in the bone called *lacunae* (meaning little lakes). A system of tiny canals called *canaliculi* connect the lacunae within the substance of the bone. Even though bone is highly vascular, with capillaries close together, the canaliculi transmit tissue fluid which is essential for maintaining the life of the osteocytes.

Both the lacunae and canaliculi are formed because the *osteoblasts* (bone-forming cells) are interconnected by cytoplasmic processes at the time the osteoid material is laid down. Thus the cells and their processes act as a mold until the osteoid tissue is set and probably mineralized. The cytoplasm is then partially withdrawn, leaving the cells, now known as osteocytes, in the lacunae, which are connected by canaliculi containing cytoplasmic extensions.

According to Ham, the osteoblasts are responsible for formation of osteoid tissue and almost immediately secrete the enzyme *phosphatase*, which is necessary for deposition of calcium salts in the osteoid tissue, thus forming true bone.

Osteoblasts usually come from *mesenchymal cells*, the parent cells of all connective tissues. The osteoblasts divide readily, but only a portion of the new cells actually secretes osteoid substance and forms bone; the rest is held in reserve as the *osteogenic layer* of the *periosteum* and of the *endosteum* within the marrow cavity and *Haversian canals*. These reserve cells function (divide and form more osteoblasts) whenever more bone is needed, as in repair of fractures, response to stress, or simply increase in bone size. Bone can be added only on the surface, because the intercellular matrix is unyielding, and the *osteocytes* (mature osteoblasts) probably have lost the ability to divide.

Resorption of bone occurs both under normal and abnormal conditions. Whenever bone is being resorbed, large multinucleated

145

cells called *osteoclasts* usually are found. These cells are assumed to take an active part in bone destruction. Ham suggests that erosion of bone may be the result of failure of the covering cells to protect the bone by active secretion of phosphatase. Any bone surface exposed to tissue fluid tends to erode if not covered by osteogenic cells.

Ossification

Regardless of the location, the sequence of actual bone formation consists of osteoblasts laying down osteoid tissue that is subsequently calcified under the influence of phosphatase. A localized area of bone formation is called a *center of ossification.* The environment in which bone forms determines whether the type of ossification will be called *heteroplastic ossification, intramembranous ossification,* or *endochondral ossification.*

Heteroplastic Ossification. Bone formed in tissue other than the skeleton is called *heteroplastic bone.* With the exception of the os penis of certain animals and the os cordis of the bovine heart, heteroplastic bone formation is usually pathologic.

Endochondral (Intracartilaginous) Ossification. The bone is preformed in cartilage in the fetus. Most long bones are developed by this method. The cartilage becomes mineralized and then is gradually replaced by bone tissue. A long bone can continue to grow in length as long as the cartilage between the epiphysis and diaphysis (epiphyseal cartilage) continues to grow. When all of this cartilage has changed to bone, increase in length is impossible. If this occurs too early in life, it results in an *achondroplastic dwarf* with a fairly normal body but short extremities. In man, this fusion of epiphysis normally occurs during the late teens or early twenties.

Long bones increase in diameter by producing new bone from the periosteum surrounding the cortex of the bone. As new bone is laid down, portions of the deeper bone are removed to increase the size of the marrow cavity (Fig. 9–1).

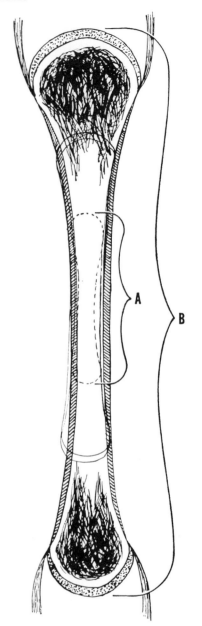

Fig. 9–1. Diagram to illustrate remodelling that occurs as a long bone increases in size. Both resorption and deposition of bone take place. *A,* Size of young bone. *B,* Size of mature bone. (After Grant, A method of Anatomy, Williams & Wilkins Co.)

During development of the fetus, the majority of the bones of the skeleton have a cartilage pattern formed, which is gradually replaced by bone. This process is called endochondral ossification. After several centers of ossification form in the cartilage model of a long bone, it continues to grow in length at the *epiphyseal plates*, the junctions of *diaphysis* and *epiphyses*. These junctions are known as *metaphyses*. Each epiphyseal plate, also called the *epiphyseal line,* may be divided into several zones, which are named according to the activity occurring in each (Fig. 9–2). Starting at the epiphyseal plate and ending at the metaphysis, the zones are:

1. zone of growth
2. zone of cartilage transformation
3. zone of ossification

It is fairly obvious that cartilage-cell multiplication in the zone of growth will force the epiphysis away from the diaphysis, thus lengthening the epiphyseal plate. Subsequent removal of cartilage and deposition of bone in the zone of ossification in turn will lengthen the diaphysis (shaft) of the bone. Increase in diameter of the bone results from activity of the osteogenic layer of the periosteum.

Intramembranous Ossification. Many of the flat bones are preformed in a fibrous membrane, or matrix, which is infiltrated with *osteoid tissue.* This bone-like osteoid tissue becomes calcified to form true bone. Additional bone then is formed by the layers of periosteum on either side of the bone.

COMPOSITION AND PHYSIOLOGY OF BONE

Bone consists of living cells and an intercellular matrix that is impregnated with mineral salts. Calcium phosphate makes up

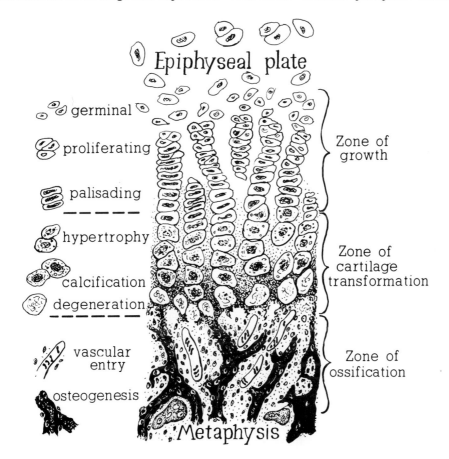

Fig. 9–2.   Diagrammatic representation of the mechanism of endochondral bone formation, providing longitudinal bone growth. (From Bojrab, M. J. (ed.): Pathophysiology in Surgery. Philadelphia, Lea & Febiger, in press.)

about 80% of the mineral matter, with the remainder composed largely of calcium carbonate and magnesium phosphate.

One hundred cubic centimeters of bone contain 10,000 mg of calcium, as compared with 6 mg per 100 cc for most tissues, and about 10 mg per 100 ml for blood. Thus, bone serves as a mineral reservoir that is constantly being either replenished or depleted. According to Boyd (1953), no tissue in the body is capable of as much overgrowth and as much absorption as is bone.

Adult bone cells are found in the lacunae within the matrix of the bone. Throughout life, osteoblasts (osteogenic cells) are found in the deep layer of periosteum surrounding the bone, and in the endosteum of the marrow cavity and Haversian canals. These cells function in bone growth and in fracture repair.

Ossification is the formation of true bone by the deposition of calcium salts in a matrix of osteoid tissue. Calcification refers to the deposition of calcium salts in any tissue.

The enzyme phosphatase hydrolyzes phosphoric esters into inorganic phosphates in young growing bones, but it is not present in cartilage until a center of ossification appears. Absorption of bone occurs normally whenever rearrangement of structure takes place, as in ordinary bone growth and fracture repair. Bone tissue may be absorbed because of hormonal imbalance *(hyperparathyroidism)*, inflammation, pressure, old age, and certain bone diseases.

Osteoclasts (bone-destroying cells) and osteocytes, in conjunction with an increased blood supply to the area, function in resorption of bone in both normal and pathologic conditions. The resorption and deposition of bone will be detailed in Chapter 32 under parathyroid function.

Bone, even in a fresh carcass, appears hard, dense, inelastic, and almost lifeless. Actually, bone as a tissue is highly responsive to environmental changes, such as changes in pressure, blood supply, and nutrition. Bone can decrease in size *(atrophy)*, increase in size *(hypertrophy)*, repair

breaks, and rearrange its internal structure to best resist stresses and strains. Under both normal and pathologic conditions, bone can reshape itself according to good engineering principles to sustain a maximum of stress with a minimum of bone tissue. Atrophy of bone occurs when pressure is constant and excessive, when periods of pressure exceed periods of release, and when there is little or no stress, as in weightlessness. Proliferation of bone, however, occurs in response to concussion or intermittent pressure. Thus, under pressure, either bone atrophy or bone proliferation occurs, depending on the degree and duration of stress as well as the maturity of the bone. Excessive pressure on growing bone will slow down or stop bone growth, while in mature bone it may stimulate a response of either excess growth or rearrangement of structure.

Elasticity is the characteristic of a substance that enables it to change form when subjected to stress but return to its original shape when the stress is removed. Bone is relatively inelastic. A rod of bone can be elongated only about 1/200 part of its length before breaking. However, even this much deformity is not perfectly elastic; the deformity is permanent and the bone will not return completely to its original length if stretched near its breaking point. This characteristic of deforming under stress without returning to the original shape is exaggerated in bone diseases such as *rickets*.

In addition to tension (stretching), bone is subjected to compression, shearing, and bending, and torsion (twisting) stresses. Steindler (1955) cites resistance of bone to tension as 10 kg/mm^2, and to compression as 16.86 kg/mm^2. Other types of stress are more difficult to measure. A bone will support considerably more weight in a static situation (supporting weight without moving) than under a dynamic load. A dynamic load results from impact of the bone against an object or an object against a bone. For example, the leg bones of a horse bear a static load when the horse is standing quietly, but bear a dynamic load when the horse is running, jumping, or kicking. Compression, bending, and shearing stresses of the leg bones are all involved in this type of activity. When a horse or other animal pivots with one or more feet bearing weight in contact with the ground, torsion or twisting is added to the other stresses. This is seen particularly well in the action of cutting horses.

Muscles and tendons that run parallel to a bone tend to act like guy wires and reduce stresses, particularly bending and shearing stresses.

FRACTURES AND FRACTURE HEALING

A fracture of bone is simply a break in the continuity of a bone.

Among the many types of fractures described are the following (see Fig. 9–3):

A *simple fracture* is one in which the skin over the fracture site is unbroken.

A *compound fracture* is one in which a wound from the exterior contacts the bone at the point of the fracture. This may be caused by a broken end of bone perforating the skin or by a penetrating object such as a bullet causing the fracture.

A *greenstick fracture* is one in which one side of the bone is broken or splintered and the other side only bent. This type of fracture usually is found only in young animals.

A *complete fracture* is one in which the bone is broken entirely across.

An *epiphyseal fracture* is one that occurs at the junction of an epiphysis and the diaphysis of a bone. This type of fracture also is limited to young animals.

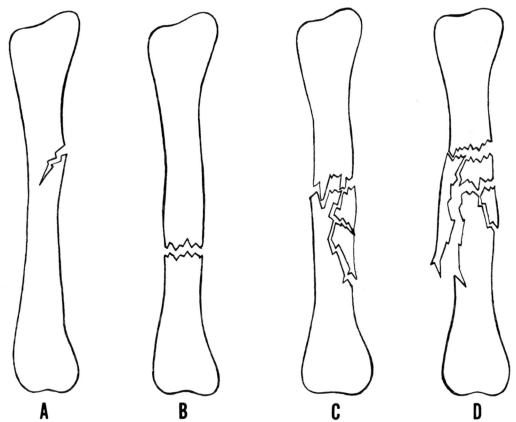

A   B   C   D

Fig. 9–3. Types of fractures shown diagrammatically. *A*, Greenstick; *B*, complete; *C*, comminuted, and *D*, compound (if fragment punctured skin). (After Kahn, Man in Structure and Function, courtesy of Alfred A. Knopf.)

A *comminuted fracture* is one in which a number of small fragments are formed due to the bone being splintered or crushed.

If the broken ends of a fractured bone are brought into apposition (touch) and are immobilized (prevented from moving), the normal process of healing will take place (Fig. 9–4). At the time the fracture occurs, some blood vessels are ruptured, releasing blood around the broken ends of the bone. This forms a clot that is invaded by connective tissue cells forming granulation tissue and new blood capillaries. The osteoblasts from the surface of the bone, from the periosteum, and from the endosteum lining the marrow cavities and Haversian canals divide rapidly and produce a massive amount of osteoid tissue called a *callus*. This osteoid tissue fills the gap between the broken ends of the bone, fills the marrow cavity for a distance, and completely encircles the broken ends of the bone, forming an effective splint which usually prevents movement between the segments. As soon as the callus becomes mineralized, it has changed into true bone. The healing process is then completed by reorganization of the callus to form a typical bone shaft with a marrow cavity. Misalignment of the fractured bone will be corrected to some extent by the action of osteocytes and osteoclasts, which also will remove excessive internal and external callus. As soon as the bone is put to use, functional orientation of the callus begins with a tendency to straighten imperfections in the alignment of the bone. The callus will increase in size on the concave side, where stress is greatest and tend to erode on the convex side, thus tending to correct any deformity.

The amount of spontaneous correction that is possible in fractures depends on a number of factors, including age of the animal, blood supply to the bone, degree of correction necessary, presence or absence of infection, and amount of damage to surrounding tissues.

Excessive separation of fragments, which may be caused by too much traction or incomplete immobilization of a fracture, may result in non-union, with fibrous tissue filling the gap between fragments.

Quickest fracture healing occurs in young animals, particularly if the fracture site has a good blood supply and is completely immobilized with the ends of the fragments in apposition. In man, a fracture may heal completely within one month in an infant, but a similar fracture in a person past middle age may require six months or longer to heal.

Occasionally bone is repaired by grafting another piece of bone into the area. If the bone is from the same species and particu-

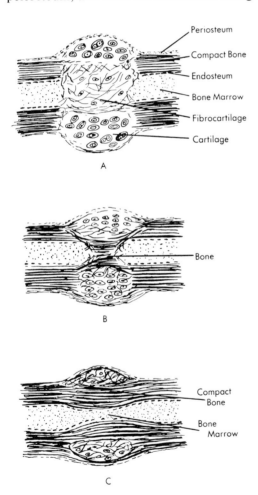

Fig. 9–4. Some stages in healing of a fracture of a long bone. *A*, Early soft callus replaces blood clot; *B*, intermediate callus; *C*, nearly healed hard callus.

larly from the same animal, the portion of the bone in contact with tissue fluid may survive and the osteoblasts become active. At the same time osteoclasts remove the dead portions of the graft, which are replaced by healthy bone if the graft is functional and subjected to the proper amount of stress. If the graft is taken from an animal of a different species, all osteoblasts in the graft will die because the animal body tends to reject any foreign protein.

OTHER PATHOLOGIC CONDITIONS

Other pathologic conditions of bones may be caused by infections, tumors, endocrine disturbances, or nutritional imbalances.

Tuberculosis of bone and *osteomyelitis*, which means inflammation of the bone and bone marrow, are two infections sometimes seen in bone. In man, osteomyelitis usually is caused by staphylococcus or streptococcus bacteria which may gain access to the bone by way of the blood stream, as a general infection, or by way of a wound, in which case the infection may remain localized.

Bone tumors are named according to the cells of the bone from which they originate. A tumor of bone tissue itself is called an *osteoma*, but most bony growths from the surface of a bone are called *exostoses* and are simply due to the response of the bone to irritation. A *fibroma* of bone grows from the outer layer of the periosteum.

A *chondroma* may develop from the epiphyseal cartilage or from unabsorbed islands of cartilage which preceded the development.

oping bone. Giant cell tumor is a tumor of the osteoclasts and is sometimes called an *osteoclastoma.*

The preceding tumors are considered benign; that is, they are slow growing and not likely to cause death. Malignant tumors grow rapidly and will kill the animal if not stopped. Malignant tumors include *osteogenic sarcoma* of the bone proper and *multiple myeloma* of the bone marrow.

Most endocrine disturbances that affect bone involve the parathyroid glands. *Osteitis fibrosis*, also called *von Recklinghausen's disease*, is believed to be caused by malfunction (excess secretion) of the parathyroid glands.

Rickets and *osteomalacia* usually are due to lack of vitamin D synthesis due to a deficiency of ultraviolet irradiation of the skin to change 7-dehydrocholesterol into vitamin D, with the resultant failure to lay down calcium in the bones. Although rickets usually is due to lack of vitamin D, it may be caused by an imbalance or lack of calcium and/or phosphorus in the ration. Rickets is essentially a disease of young bones that chiefly affects the growing areas. Osteomalacia, sometimes called adult rickets, affects the entire bone, since there are no rapidly growing areas in adult bone.

Achondroplasia is a hereditary condition in which the metaphyses fuse early in life but the bones continue to increase in diameter. An animal affected with the disease is called an *achondroplastic* dwarf. The dachshund is a breed of dogs selectively bred for this condition. Dwarfism in cattle closely resembles achondroplasia.

Chapter 10

Joints

Arthrology is the study of the articulations (unions) between bones, which are commonly called joints. These articulations may be immovable, slightly movable, or freely movable, and are known respectively as synarthroses (Fig. 10–1), amphiarthroses, and diarthroses (synovial joints).

CLASSIFICATION OF JOINTS

Based on their structure and the material that unites them, joints may be classified as fibrous joints, cartilaginous joints, and synovial joints. These classifications can be combined as follows:

Fibrous Joints

These contain no joint cavity. The bones are united by fibrous tissue.

Syndesmosis refers to joints with a fibrous-tissue uniting medium which permit slight movement. The normal union of the shafts of the *splint bones* and *cannon bone* of the horse is an example of syndesmosis.

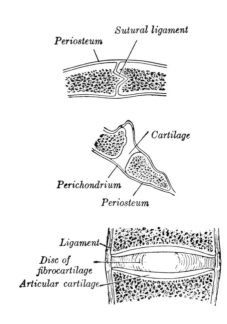

Fig. 10–1. Types of synarthrodial joints. (From Goss, C. M. (ed.): Anatomy of the Human Body. ed. 29. Philadelphia, Lea & Febiger, 1973.)

Suture refers to the junction between bones of the skull which are united by fibrous tissue early in life but may ossify after maturity.

Gomphosis refers to the articulation of teeth in their sockets in the mandible and *maxillae* (and premaxillae in nonruminants).

Cartilaginous Joints

These contain no joint cavity. The bones are united by cartilage.

Synchondrosis (hyaline cartilage joints) refers to an immovable joint in which the uniting medium is cartilage. The union of the *diaphysis* and *epiphysis* of an immature bone is an example of synchondrosis.

Symphyses (fibrocartilaginous joints) (certain median-line joints) are united by flattened discs of *fibrocartilage* as found between adjacent pelvic bones, and between the bodies of adjacent vertebrae.

Synostosis refers to a joint in which the uniting medium is bone. This type of joint may be a pathologic or normal development from other types of joints. The normal os-sification of the *epiphyseal cartilage* of a long bone produces a synostosis.

Synovial (Diarthrodial) Joints

The general structure of most synovial joints is similar and includes the following: articular surfaces, articular cartilages, articular cavity, joint capsule, and ligaments (Fig. 10–2).

The *articular surfaces* are specialized layers of compact bone on the surfaces that articulate with other bones.

The *articular cartilage* is a layer of *hyaline cartilage* covering the articular surface. *Periosteum* covers the remainder of the bone.

The articular cavity is a *potential space* between adjacent bones and is surrounded by the joint capsule.

The *joint capsule* consists of two layers. The deeper layer is the *synovial membrane,* which is a delicate sleeve-like layer of specialized connective tissue extending from the edges of the articular cartilages of the adjacent bones, but does not cover either articular cartilage. This membrane secretes

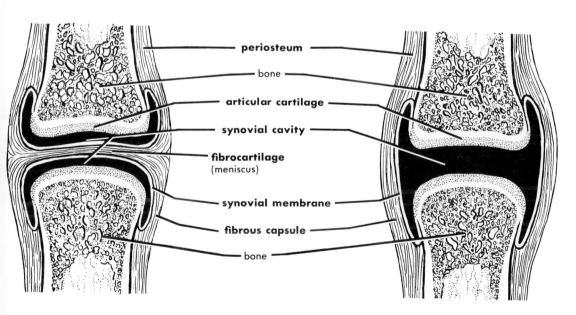

periosteum

bone

articular cartilage

synovial cavity

fibrocartilage
(meniscus)

synovial membrane

fibrous capsule

bone

Fig. 10–2.   Types of synovial articulations. (From Crouch, J. E.: Functional Human Anatomy. ed. 3. Philadelphia, Lea & Febiger, 1978.)

the *synovial fluid* (joint oil), which lubricates the normal joint. The inner surface of the synovial membrane may be increased by folds *(plicae synoviales)*, which may contain fat pads and project into the joint cavity. Villi *(villi synovales)*, finger-like projections, may also project into the joint cavity.

The superficial layer of the joint capsule is the *fibrous membrane (capsular ligament)*, which is a heavier fibrous sleeve covering the synovial membrane. This capsular ligament may be thickened in certain areas to form the extracapsular (or periarticular) ligaments, which connect adjacent bones and help stabilize the joint.

Ligaments are connective tissue bands that extend from bone to bone. They are named according to their location in relation to the joint capsule.

Intracapsular (intra-articular) ligaments are found within joints and are surrounded by the joint capsule. Examples include the *cruciate ligaments* of the stifle and the ligaments that hold adjacent carpal or tarsal bones together.

Extracapsular (periarticular) ligaments are outside the joint capsule and include collateral, dorsal, palmar, and annular ligaments. *Collateral ligaments* are located on the medial and lateral sides of a joint. *Dorsal* and *palmar* (or *plantar*) *ligaments* are located in front of and behind the joint. *Annual ligaments* surround the joint, and the fibers generally run in a circular fashion around the joint to strengthen and protect the joint capsule.

MOVEMENTS OF JOINTS

Synovial (true) joints may exhibit one or more of the following movements: gliding or sliding, flexion, extension, hyperextension, rotation, adduction, abduction, and circumduction (Fig. 10–3).

Flexion refers to movement in the sagittal plane that tends to decrease the angle between segments making up a joint. The carpus (knee) must be flexed when a horse's front foot is picked up for trimming.

Extension is the reverse of flexion and refers to movement in the sagittal plane that tends to increase the angle between segments forming the joint.

Hyperextension refers to movement in which the angle between segments is increased beyond 180° or a straight line. In some instances hyperextension is also called *dorsal flexion*. The fetlock joint of the horse is hyperextended in the normal standing position.

Rotation consists of a twisting movement of a segment around its own axis. Turning the head from side to side as in indicating "no" is perhaps the best example of rotation.

Adduction refers to movement of an extremity toward the median plane. *Abduction* refers to movement of an extremity away from the median plane.

Circumduction results from a combination of the preceding movements and may be defined as a movement in which an extremity describes a cone and the distal end of the extremity describes a circle. A horse that "paddles" exhibits circumduction.

Pronation is a movement that tends to rotate an extremity so that the dorsum is up. *Supination* is a movement that tends to rotate an extremity so that the palmar (volar) or plantar aspect of the limb is up. Pronation and supination are rarely seen to any extent in domestic animals.

Types of Synovial Joints

Synovial *(diarthrodial)* joints are classified according to the type of joint surface and movements possible. Simple joints involve only two articulating bones, while compound joints include more than two bones within the same joint capsule. The types of synovial joints commonly found in domestic animals include: ginglymus, arthrodial, trochoid, and spheroid (enarthrodial). Additional types of joints, described particularly in the dog, are condyloid, ellipsoid and saddle joints.

Ginglymus (hinge) joints move only in the

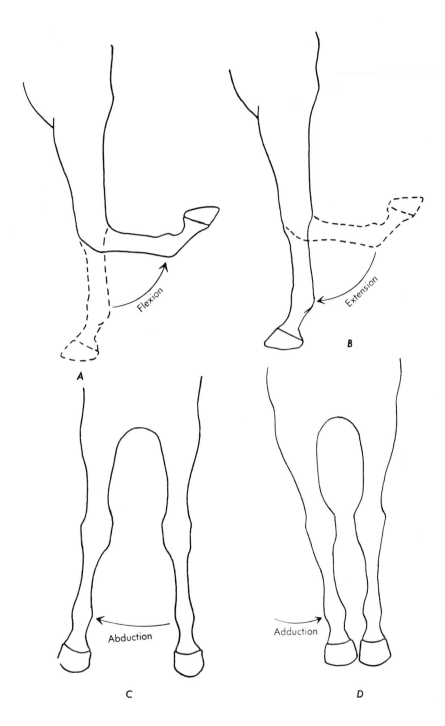

Fig. 10–3.   Movements of the front limb. *A*, Flexion; *B*, extension; *C*, abduction; and *D*, adduction.

sagittal plane. The movements possible in this type of joint are flexion, extension, and in some joints, hyperextension. The fetlock joint is a good example of a ginglymus joint.

Arthrodial (plane) joints have only a slight gliding movement between relatively flat opposed surfaces. These surfaces are called *facets*. The joints between adjacent carpal bones are examples of arthrodial joints.

A *trochoid (pivot) joint* is one in which rotary movement occurs around one axis. The *atlanto-axial joint* is the only good example of a trochoid joint in domestic animals.

Spheroid (enarthrodial or ball-and-socket) joints permit movement in nearly any direction. A spherical head on one bone fits into a cup-shaped depression in the other segment of the joint. Flexion, extension, adduction, abduction, rotation, and circumduction are all possible movements in enarthrodial joints. The *coxo-femoral (hip) joint* is the best example of an enarthrodial joint.

In the *condylar* (condyloid) *joint*, convex articular condyles articulate with somewhat concave articular surfaces. The temporomandibular joint and stifle are examples. They resemble ginglymus (hinge) joints, but permit more movement.

The *ellipsoid joint* has an articular surface that is expanded more in one direction than another, forming an ellipse. The joint between the distal end of the radius and proximal row of carpal bones is ellipsoid. In our domestic animals this joint has been called a ginglymus or hinge joint, and it is similar to a hinge joint.

The saddle joint has surfaces that resemble an English or flat saddle. It permits all types of movement except rotation. The carpo-metacarpal joint of the thumb of man is the best example, but the interphalangeal joints of the dog are sometimes classified as saddle joints.

JOINTS OF THE AXIAL SKELETON

The joints of the skull are chiefly of the *suture* type, with adjacent bones united by fibrous tissue. In old age these ossify, becoming solid bone. The *fontanel* (soft spot) in a baby's head is an example of the fibrous tissue connecting adjacent bones.

Exceptions to the suture type of joint in the skull are the *symphysis* of the *mandible* and the *synchondrosis* at the junction of the sphenoid bone and occipital bone at the base of the skull.

The first movable joint in the axial skeleton is the *temporomandibular joint* between the *mandible* (jaw bone) and the *temporal bone* of the skull. This joint consists of two articular surfaces, one on the skull and one on the mandible, with a plate of cartilage (*articular disk* or *meniscus*) between. The temporomandibular joint acts as a *ginglymus (hinge) joint* when the mouth is opened and closed and as an *arthrodial*, or sliding-gliding, *joint* when the jaw is moved from side to side and forward and back, as in grinding food. The temporomandibular joint may be classified as a condylar joint.

The *atlanto-occipital* joint between the skull and first cervical (neck) vertebra is strictly a *ginglymus (hinge)* joint. Two *condyles* (convex ridges) of bone on the skull fit into corresponding depressions in the *atlas* (first cervical vertebra). The only movements possible are flexion and extension in the sagittal plane as in nodding the head "yes."

Rotation of the head occurs almost entirely between the atlas and axis. The *dens*, a tooth-like projection from the cranial extremity of the *axis* (second cervical vertebra), projects into the *vertebral foramen* of the *atlas*, where it is held by a strong *annular ligament* that permits considerable rotary movement. The atlanto-axial joint is the best example of a pivot joint, in which one segment rotates around the long axis of another.

The *symphyseal (amphiarthrodial) joints* between adjacent vertebrae throughout the rest of the vertebral column exhibit relatively little motion. The bodies of adjacent vertebrae are united by a heavy disk of fibrocartilage that is flexible enough to permit some bending in any direction, or even twisting. This fibrocartilage has a soft center known as the *nucleus pulposus,* which may abnormally protrude through the surrounding *annulus fibrous* into the spinal canal and cause pressure on the spinal cord. The resulting condition is called a ruptured *intervertebral disk* and may cause paralysis of the body caudal to the involved disk. The articular processes of adjacent vertebrae have flat surfaces that are apposed to form an *arthrodial* (sliding) *joint*. These surfaces are larger; and the movements, more extensive toward the head, decrease in the thoracic region and are more extensive again in the lumbar region. The joints between sacral vertebrae fuse completely, and the *sacrum* becomes a single bone with the segments joined by *synostoses.*

The *ribs* are attached to the vertebral column by two separate joints: one joint is between the head of the rib and a depression located between the bodies of two adjacent thoracic vertebrae; and one joint is between an articular facet a short distance from the head of the rib and a facet on the transverse process of the vertebra of the same number as the rib. The first joint is of the pivot type, and the second is of the arthrodial type.

The ventral ends of the first few ribs are directly attached to the sternum by bars of cartilage known as *costal cartilages.* These are the *sternal* or *true ribs (costae verae).* The cartilages of the ribs behind these are attached to the costal cartilages of the true (sternal) ribs and are called *asternal* or *false ribs (costae spuriae). Floating ribs* have no sternal attachment either directly or indirectly. Whenever an animal has an extra pair of ribs, the last pair is likely to be floating.

JOINTS OF THE APPENDICULAR SKELETON

Joints of the Front Limb

The *scapula* (or shoulder blade) has no true bony connection with the *bony thorax.* It is held in place by a number of muscles and ligaments. This type of joint is called a *synsarcosis.*

The *shoulder joint* proper *(scapulohumeral joint)* is a *spheroid (enarthrodial* or *ball-and-socket)* joint. Movements in all directions including rotation are possible. However, in our domestic animals, the arrangement of shoulder muscles practically limits movement to a hinge type of action in the sagittal plane. Thus, extension and flexion are the chief movements. The head of the *humerus* is a segment of a large sphere much more extensive than the comparable cavity of the scapula. The joint capsule is extensive, with poorly developed ligaments. The muscles surrounding the shoulder joint on all sides act rather effectively as ligaments, with the added advantage of being able to contract or relax, thus giving greater movement to the joint.

The *elbow joint* is a true *ginglymus* (hinge) *joint* formed by the *condyles* (spool-like distal end of the humerus) meeting the proximal ends of the *radius* and *ulna.* The proximal end of the radius is slightly concave and expanded to give an extensive surface for support. Combined with the *semilunar notch* of the ulna, the radius forms a half circle embracing the humeral condyles. Movement in the elbow is limited to flexion and extension in the horse. In man and to a lesser degree in the dog, the joint between the radius and ulna permits rotation, specifically supination and pronation.

The *carpus* (knee) is a complex joint which not only permits flexion and extension between the radius and proximal row of carpal bones, but also between the proximal and distal rows of carpal bones (Fig. 10–4). The entire joint absorbs considerable shock because of the many small *arthrodial joints* formed by adjacent carpal bones connected by short ligaments. The joint between the distal row of carpal bones and the *metacarpus (cannon bones)* is almost entirely arthrodial, with little movement except sliding and gliding.

The fibrous layer of the *joint capsule* of the carpus is extensive, being a long sleeve extending from the radius to the metacarpus and enclosing the carpal bones. The *synovial*

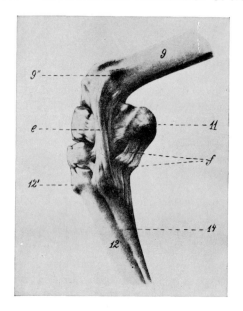

Fig. 10–4. Lateral view of the carpus of the horse.
9.   Distal end of radius
9″. Lateral tuberosity of radius
11. Accessory carpal
12. Third (large) metacarpal
12′. Tuberosity of third metacarpal
14. Fourth (small) metacarpal
e.   Lateral ligament of carpus
f.   Ligaments of accessory carpal.
(Ellenberger, An Atlas of Animal Anatomy for Artists, courtesy of Dover Publications, Inc.)

are present between adjacent metacarpals as well as between the metacarpals and carpus.

The *fetlock (metacarpo-phalangeal) joint* is formed by the distal end of the *metacarpus*, the proximal end of the *first phalanx*, or *long pastern bone*, and the two *proximal sesamoid bones*. It is a ginglymus joint that in the standing position is hyperextended or in dorsal flexion.

The *pastern joint (proximal interphalangeal joint)* is a ginglymus joint between the first and second phalanges (the long and the short pastern bones). Although it is a ginglymus joint, it is rather limited in motion.

The *coffin joint (distal interphalangeal joint)* is formed by the second and third phalanges and the *distal sesamoid (navicular) bone*. The coffin joint is largely encased within the hoof and is essentially a ginglymus joint.

The foregoing descriptions of the fetlock, pastern, and coffin joints apply to the digit of the horse. A somewhat similar pattern is followed for each digit in animals that have more than one digit per foot, as in ruminants and pigs.

membrane, however, forms three separate sacs: a *radiocarpal sac,* an *intercarpal sac,* and a *carpometacarpal sac.*

In the horse there is normally little movement between the large metacarpal (cannon) bone and the small metacarpal (splint) bones. If much movement occurs, inflammation will follow, resulting in a "splint," which is a painful swelling where the shafts of the large and small metacarpal bones meet. Later this swelling may ossify and form a bony prominence which may not cause any lameness at all. (See Fig. 8–8.)

In the cow and sheep, the third and fourth metacarpal bones are fused to form the single cannon bone, so the only true joint present in this area is an arthrodial joint between the carpus and metacarpus. In the dog and pig, the sizes of the metacarpal bones are more nearly equal, so arthrodial joints

Joints of the Hindlimb

The *sacroiliac* joint is the only bony connection between the axial and appendicular skeletons. The sacroiliac is a true joint in which the *articular surface* of the sacrum is held tightly in apposition with the wing of the ilium by a number of short, strong ligaments. Movement in this joint is normally limited, but may become more extensive just preceding parturition, when the ligaments stretch under the influence of the hormone *relaxin.*

Excessive movement of the sacroiliac joint can be painful if some of the nerves in the area are injured by pressure. Ligaments in this area include dorsal and ventral *sacroiliac* and *sacrotuberous (sacrosciatic) ligaments.* The latter is a strong, wide band in the cow, sheep, and horse that helps form the lateral wall of the pelvis.

The *hip joint (coxofemoral joint)* is the

best example of a *spheroid (enarthrodial or ball-and-socket) joint*. The head of the *femur* is about two-thirds of a sphere that fits into the less extensive *cotyloid cavity (acetabulum)* of the *os coxae*. The margin of the acetabulum is reinforced and deepened by a marginal cartilage, which increases the depth of the cavity.

The *joint capsule* of the hip joint is extensive, but not so extensive as that of the shoulder. The *ligament of the femoral head (round ligament)* of the femur connects the head of the femur with a nonarticular area in the acetabulum. Movements in all directions are possible in the hip joint, but, as in the shoulder joint, extension and flexion are the movements chiefly employed. Dislocation of the hip of the dog is fairly common, particularly when the dog has been struck by a car.

The *stifle joint* corresponds to the human knee (Fig. 10–5). The stifle joint is made up of the *condyles* of the distal end of the femur, separated from the proximal end of the *tibia* by two *semilunar cartilages (menisci)*. Each meniscus is a half-moon-shaped disk that is flattened on the lower side to conform to the surface of the tibia, and concave on the upper surface to fit the respective condyle of the femur. These menisci help keep the joint congruent and also absorb shock. The stifle joint is held in apposition by a *medial* and a *lateral collateral ligament* on either side and by two *intra-articular cruciate* (X-shaped) *ligaments* that extend from the tibia to the femur in the middle of the joint. Also associated with the stifle joint is the *patella (knee cap)*, the largest *sesamoid* bone in the body. The patella rides on the *trochlea* of the femur, helps reduce friction, and changes the direction of pull of the *quadriceps femoris* muscle, which is the large *extensor muscle* of the stifle, located on the front of the *thigh*.

The *tarsus (hock joint)*, like the carpus, is a complex joint (Fig. 10–6). The *ginglymus* portion is formed between the distal end of the tibia and the *tibial tarsal bone (talus)*. This portion of the joint is held together by

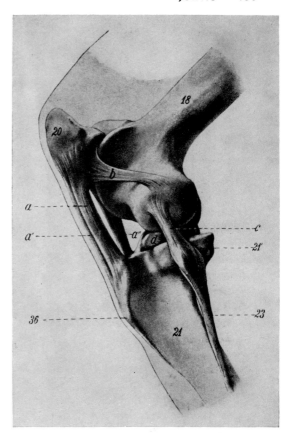

Fig. 10–5.   Lateral view of stifle of horse. *18*, Distal end of femur; *20*, patella; *21*, tibia; *21'*, lateral condyle of tibia; *23*, fibula; *a*, lateral patellar ligament; *a'*, middle patellar ligament; *a"*, medial patellar ligament; *b*, lateral femoro-patellar ligament; *c*, lateral femoro-tibial ligament; *d*, lateral meniscus. (Ellenberger, An Atlas of Animal Anatomy for Artists, courtesy of Dover Publications, Inc.)

the strong medial and lateral collateral ligaments of the hock.

The *fibular tarsal bone (calcaneus)* projects upward and backward to form a lever for attachment of the *tendon of Achilles* and hence the extensor muscles of the *hock*. The calcaneus is firmly attached to the remaining tarsal bones by many short, strong ligaments. The ligaments are less extensive over the craniomedial aspect of the hock, where, in the horse, the joint capsule may bulge, producing a condition known as *bog spavin*. In the horse and dog, movement between adjacent tarsal bones is limited and then is

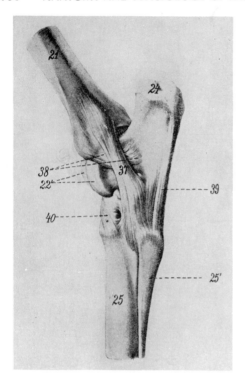

Fig. 10–6.   Lateral view of hock of horse.
21. Tibia
22. Tibial tarsal
24. Tuber calcis (point of hock)
25. Third (large) metatarsal
25'. Fourth (small) metatarsal
37. Lateral long ligament of hock
38. Lateral short ligament of hock
39. Plantar ligament of hock
40. Dorsal ligament of hock
   (Ellenberger, An Atlas of Animal Anatomy for Artists, courtesy of Dover Publications, Inc.)

only of the *arthrodial* type. However, in the cow, sheep, and pig, the *proximal intertarsal joint* has some hinge movement.

Below the hock the joints are similar to those of the forelimb.

PATHOLOGY OF JOINTS
AND RELATED STRUCTURES

Since diarthrodial joints depend on free movement for effective functioning, anything that interferes with their mobility can be serious. Conditions affecting joints may be due to injuries, infections, or inflammations.

Injuries to joints include dislocations, fractures, sprains, cuts, and puncture wounds. A *dislocation*, also known as a *luxation*, of a joint refers to a condition in which one or more segments of the joint are out of place. Dislocation of a joint nearly always involves stretching or tearing of *ligaments* and if the dislocation is severe enough, the *joint capsule* also may be torn. The usual treatment for dislocation consists of replacing the joint into its normal position, frequently followed by the application of a splint or cast. Replacement may be difficult unless the animal is put completely to sleep so that all muscles will be relaxed. Early treatment is important to prevent the joint cavity from filling with connective tissue. Because of the excessive stretching or tearing of ligaments, recovery from a dislocation may be less satisfactory and take longer than recovery from a properly treated fracture.

Occasionally a fairly functional joint, called a *false joint*, may develop, even though the dislocated joint has never been replaced. In a false joint the fibrous connective tissue that grows around the end of the bone permits considerable movement even though no joint capsule or cartilage develops as in true joints. False joints may also form at a fracture site if the ends of the bone are not immobilized.

Fractures, or breaks of bones, may involve one or more of the segments making up a joint. In young animals the fracture may be simply a separation of the *epiphysis* of the bone from the *diaphysis* close to or within the joint. Bone fractures within or close to a joint are difficult to *reduce* (bring segments into proper alignment) and to immobilize after reduction because of the short length of at least one of the segments.

A *sprain* of a joint is a condition in which the ligaments are stretched but the joint does not remain dislocated. The term "*strain*" is sometimes used in place of "sprain." "Strain" is used more frequently to denote excessive stretching of a muscle or tendon. Although a considerable amount of swelling may follow a sprain, the affected joint usu-

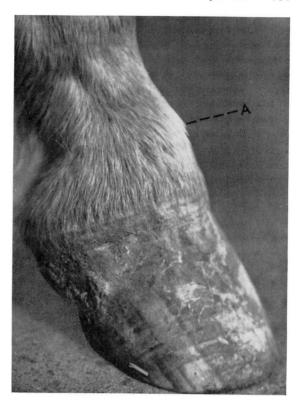

Fig. 10–7. Clinical appearance of high ring bone on the distal end of the first phalanx and proximal end of the second phalanx. Notice the bulging effect approximately 1 inch above the coronary band (A). (From Adams, O.R.: Lameness in Horses. ed. 3. Philadelphia, Lea & Febiger, 1974.)

ally will recover spontaneously if rested adequately.

Cuts such as those from barbed wire may extend into a joint cavity, with subsequent loss of *synovial fluid.* A condition of this nature, called an open joint, may be serious and difficult to treat successfully. The danger is not from the loss of synovial fluid, but from infection of the joint cavity. Synovial fluid is a good medium for bacterial growth, and the many recesses of most joint capsules make drainage and treatment of an infected joint difficult. There is always danger of permanent damage to the articular cartilage from infection.

Puncture wounds involving joints may result from penetration by sharp objects such as nails, wire, or thorns. Since the object causing the puncture rarely is sterile, a puncture wound of a joint resembles an infected cut. However, the puncture wound is more insidious because it may not be discovered for several days and there usually is little chance for drainage. Cuts and puncture

wounds may involve *bursae* and *synovial sheaths* of tendons, with results similar to those involving joints.

Infections of joints may result from cuts or punctures as mentioned above, or the infection may reach the joint by way of blood or lymph stream. *Erysispelas* of swine and *joint ill* of foals are two diseases that frequently result in joint infections. In conditions of this nature, the disease must be treated systemically rather than treating only the affected joint.

Arthritis is inflammation of a joint, involving swelling and pain; it usually accompanies each of the conditions previously mentioned. In addition, injury from kicks, blows, and falls may result in inflammation of a joint without any infection being present. If no complications develop, the animal should recover readily.

Some specific conditions (usually in horses) involving joints or related structures are listed in Table 10–1.

Table 10–1.   Pathologic Disorders of Joints and Related Structures

Name of Condition	Involvement
Arthritis	Inflammation of any joint from any cause
Bicipital bursitis	Inflammation of the bursa between the biceps brachii tendon and the humerus near the point of the shoulder
Bog spavin	Distension of the joint capsule of the hock—swelling on the cranio-medial side of the hock
Bone spavin (jack)	Exostosis (extra bone formation) of tarsal bones and/or metatarsal bones near the hock
Bowed tendon (tendosynovitis) (Fig. 11–9)	Stretching (possibly with tearing) and inflammation of the superficial and deep digital flexor tendons and their synovial sheaths in the area of the cannon—usually front leg
Bursitis	Inflammation of any bursa from any cause
Capped elbow	Inflammation of the superficial or deep bursa over the olecranon process of the ulna (the point of the elbow)
Capped hock	Inflammation of the bursa over the tuber calcis (point of the hock)
Carpitis (popped knee)	Inflammation of the carpal joint capsule and/or carpal bones and ligaments
Curb (curby hocks)	Thickening of the plantar ligament of the hock at the caudal surface of the hock
Dislocation (luxation)	Out of joint—one or more segments of a joint out of proper position
Fistulous withers	Inflammation and infection of the supraspinous bursa between the ligamentum nuchae and thoracic vertebrae
Herniated intervertebral disk	Prolapse of the nucleus pulposus of an intervertebral fibrocartilage into the vertebral canal—may cause pressure on the spinal cord resulting in pain and/or paralysis
Laminitis (Fig. 13–9)	Inflammation of the sensitive laminae located between the distal phalanx and the hoof wall
Navicular disease	Inflammation of navicular bursa, deep digital flexor tendon, and/or navicular bone (distal sesamoid bone) in the region of the coffin joint.
Osselets	Inflammation of proximal end of proximal phalanx and/or distal end of third metacarpal
Poll evil	Inflammation (usually with infection) of the atlantal bursa between the ligamentum nuchae and atlas
Popped ankle (wind gall)	Inflammation of fetlock joint capsule or other synovial structure in the area
Quittor (Fig. 14–4)	Infection of the collateral cartilages of the distal phalanx
Ring bone (Fig. 10–7)	Exostosis of the phalanges (usually the proximal and middle phalanges)
Side bone (Fig. 14–3)	Ossification of the collateral cartilages of the distal phalanx
Splints (Fig. 8–8)	Ossification and exostosis of the joint between the shaft of a splint bone and the cannon bone (usually the second and third metacarpal bones are involved)
Sprain	Stretching of the ligaments of any joint
Stifling (upward fixation of the patella)	Locking of the patella over the medial ridge of the trochlea of the femur—keeps the stifle extended and indirectly extends the hock
Subluxation	Partial dislocation of any joint
Synovitis	Inflammation of any tendon synovial sheath
Thoroughpin	Swelling of the synovial sheath of the deep digital flexor tendon above the hock
Trochanteric bursitis	Inflammation of the bursa between the tendon of the middle gluteal muscle and the greater trochanter of the femur

Chapter *11*

Anatomy of the Muscular System

Figures 11–1 to 11–4 show major muscles of the horse, cow, and goat.

The three types of muscle tissue found in the body are smooth muscle, involuntary striated muscle, and voluntary striated muscle.

Smooth (involuntary, visceral, unstriated) muscle has no visible striations, and is found in the systems that are chiefly automatic in their functioning. Smooth muscle is found in the wall of the digestive tract, where it moves and mixes food from the stomach into the intestines and through the intestines without any conscious control. The walls of the urogenital system contain a considerable amount of smooth muscle. The diameter of blood vessels and consequently the quantity of blood flowing to a given area is controlled rather extensively by the smooth muscle within the vessel walls. Contraction of smooth muscles is inherent (requires no nerve stimulus); however, its contraction is regulated by the *autonomic ner-* *vous system* and is affected by certain drugs. The individual muscle cells are spindle-shaped, with a centrally located nucleus. The cells are usually arranged in sheets, bundles, or a network, although occasionally individual smooth muscle cells are scattered through a tissue, as the smooth muscle fibers within the skin (arrectores pilorum) that raise the hair.

Involuntary striated muscle is also known as *cardiac muscle,* since it is found only within the heart. These cardiac muscle cells are arranged in the form of a network. Contraction of cardiac muscle is inherent and rhythmic, requiring no nerve stimulus. However, its rate is regulated by the autonomic nervous system. Usually there is no conscious control of the heart muscle. The cells are striated, and the nuclei are centrally located.

We are familiar with *voluntary striated (skeletal)* muscle as the flesh (meat) of our domestic animals. The individual cells, as the name implies, appear striated (striped)

163

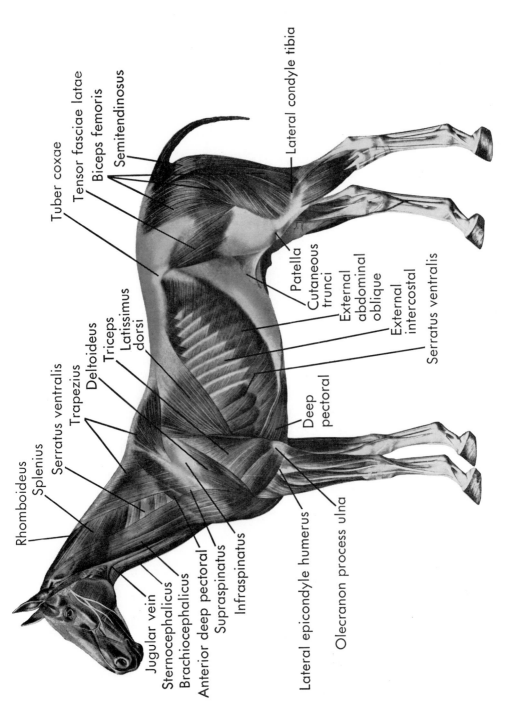

Fig. 11–1. Superficial muscles of the horse. (Ellenberger, Baum, and Dittrich, Atlas of Animal Anatomy for Artists, reprinted with permission of Dover Publications, Inc.)

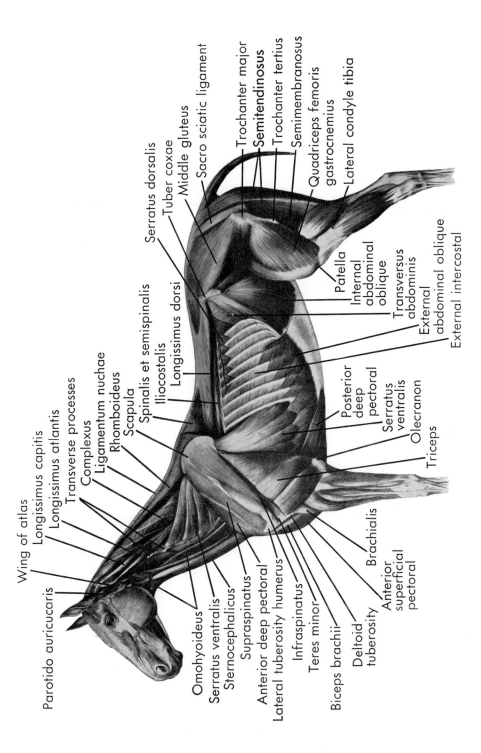

Wing of atlas
Parotido auricucaris
Longissimus capitis
Longissimus atlantis
Transverse processes
Complexus
Ligamentum nuchae
Rhomboideus
Scapula
Spinalis et semispinalis
Iliocostalis
Longissimus dorsi

Serratus dorsalis
Tuber coxae
Middle gluteus
Sacro sciatic ligament
Trochanter major
Semitendinosus
Trochanter tertius
Semimembranosus
Quadriceps femoris
gastrocnemius
Lateral condyle tibia

Patella
Internal
abdominal
oblique
Transversus
abdominis
External
abdominal oblique
External intercostal

Posterior
deep
pectoral
Serratus
ventralis
Olecranon
Triceps

Brachialis
Anterior
superficial
pectoral
Deltoid
tuberosity
Biceps brachii
Teres minor
Infraspinatus
Lateral tuberosity humerus
Anterior deep pectoral
Supraspinatus
Sternocephalicus
Serratus ventralis
Omohyoideus

Fig. 11–2.   Deeper muscles of the horse. (Ellenberger, Baum, and Dittrich, Atlas of Animal Anatomy for Artists, reprinted with permission of Dover Publications, Inc.)

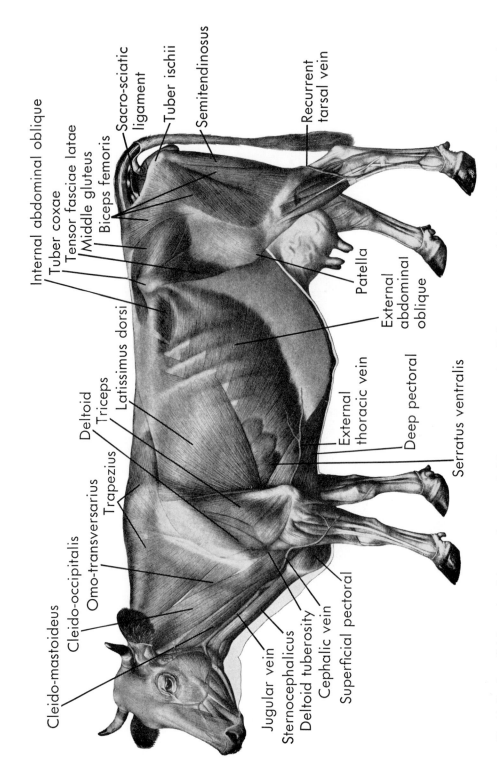

Fig. 11–3. Superficial muscles of the cow after removal of the cutaneous muscle. (Ellenberger, Baum, and Dittrich, Atlas of Animal Anatomy for Artists, reprinted with permission of Dover Publications, Inc.)

when viewed under a microscope. Each cell contains several nuclei (multinuclear) which are located near the cell surface. Each muscle cell (fiber) is covered by a cell membrane (sheath) known as the *sarcolemma*. This covering acts as a connecting link between muscle fibers and tendons and gives elasticity to the muscle fiber. It is composed of the plasma membrane and the basement membrane.

Each skeletal muscle fiber is insulated from all other muscle fibers and is controlled directly by a branch from a *voluntary nerve (motor neuron),* and usually is under conscious control. The functional unit of voluntary striated muscle, called a *motor unit*, consists of a motor neuron and all the muscle fibers it innervates (Fig. 11–5).

STRIATED MUSCLES

Muscle fibers are arranged in bundles surrounded by fibrous connective tissue. The connective tissue between individual muscle fibers is called *endomysium*. The sheath surrounding bundles of muscle fibers is called *perimysium*, and the connective tissue around an entire muscle is known as *epimysium*.

The proportion of connective tissue to muscle tissue and the amount of *marbling* (fat interspersed between muscle bundles) largely account for the relative toughness or tenderness of a cut of meat. Thus a cut from the rump or loin of an animal will be more tender than a shank end, where much of the connective tissue is concentrated to form the tendon of Achilles.

Muscle fibers may be arranged in a parallel manner: in sheets, as in the abdominal muscles, or bands, as in the *sartorius muscle* located on the medial side of the thigh. Other arrangements of muscle fibers include spindle-shaped muscles and various penniform (feather-like) arrangements (Fig. 11–6). In the penniform arrangements, a tendon represents the quill, and the muscle fibers attaching to the tendon at an angle

represent the vane of the feather. If the fibers come from only one side, the arrangement is called *unipennate*; from two sides, *bipennate;* and from three or more sides, *multipennate*.

A parallel arrangement of muscle fibers gives the greatest distance of shortening but is a relatively weak arrangement, while the pennate arrangement increases the power of a muscle but at the expense of distance of contraction.

Muscle Attachments

If a muscle appears to come directly from the bone, it is said to have a *fleshy attachment*. The muscles attaching to the *scapula* (blade bone) have fleshy attachments. If these muscles are peeled from the bone, as in boning beef, the *periosteum* is stripped from the bone and stays with the muscle. In reality, the muscle fibers attach to very short tendons, which in turn attach to the periosteum of the bone or may even penetrate the surface of the bone for a short distance.

Tendons proper are composed of dense, regular connective tissue. The fibers are arranged in parallel bundles. Most tendons are cords or bands and attach spindle-shaped or pennate muscles to bones. Other tendons, however, are flat sheets known as *aponeuroses* and usually are associated with flat muscles. The heavy fibrous sheets found covering the muscles of the loin are good examples of aponeuroses.

Most muscles have attachments to two different bones. The least movable attachment is called the *origin* and the more movable attachment is called the *insertion*. As an example, the *biceps brachii* muscle extends from the scapula to the *radius*. The scapula usually moves less than the radius, so the origin of the biceps is its attachment to the scapula, and the insertion is its attachment to the radius. In the extremities the origin usually is proximal and the insertion distal. Since the only thing a muscle can actively do (when stimulated) is to contract, it will

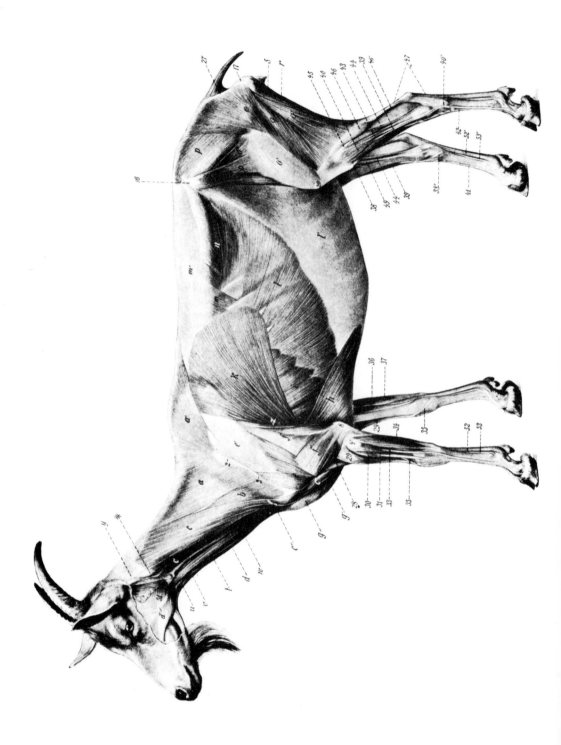

Fig. 11–4.   Goat. (From Ellenberger, Baum, and Dittrich, Atlas of Animal Anatomy for Artists, reprinted with permission of Dover Publications, Inc.)

a,a′–trapezius
b–omotransversarius
c–brachiocephalicus (cleido-occipitalis)
c′–brachiocephalicus (cleidomastoideus)
c″–brachiocephalicus (cleidobrachialis)
c‴–clavicular tendon
d–sternomandibularis
e–deltoideus
e′–aponeurosis of deltoideus
f,f′–triceps brachii
g,g′–superficial pectoral
h–deep pectoral
i–serratus ventralis thoracis
k–latissimus dorsi
l–external abdominal oblique
l′–aponeurosis of l
m–serratus dorsalis caudalis
m′–thoracolumbar fascia
n–internal abdominal oblique
o,o′–tensor fasciae latae
o′–fascia lata
p–middle gluteus
q,q′–biceps femoris

r–semitendinosus
s–edge of semimembranosus
t–sternothyroideus
u–omohyoideus
v–sternohyoideus
w–scalenus
y–aponeurosis of brachiocephalicus
z–tensor fasciae antebrachii
*–wing of atlas
2–spine of scapula
3–acromion
4′–lateral epicondyle of humerus
8–olecranon process of ulna
16–tuber coxae
17–tuber ischiadicum
19–trochanter major of femur
20–patella
27–sacrospinotuberal ligament
     (sacrosciatic ligament)
28–brachialis
29–extensor carpi radialis
30–medial digital extensor
31–common digital extensor

33–lateral digital extensor
34–extensor carpi ulnaris
35–abductor pollicis longus
36–flexor carpi radialis
37–flexor carpi ulnaris
38–tibialis cranialis
38′–tendon of tibialis cranialis
39–long digital extensor
40,40′–peroneus longus
41,42–tendon long digital extensor
43–lateral digital extensor
44–deep digital flexor
45–soleus
46–gastrocnemius
46′–tendon of Achilles
47–tendon of superficial digital flexor
49–long digital flexor
52–superficial and deep digital flexor
     tendons front limb
52′–superficial and deep digital flexor
     tendons hind limb
53–interosseous front limb
53′–interosseous hind limb

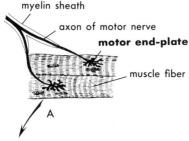

myelin sheath

axon of motor nerve

motor end-plate

muscle fiber

A

Fig. 11–5. Myoneural junction or motor end-plate. (From Crouch, J. E.: Functional Human Anatomy. ed. 3. Philadelphia, Lea & Febiger, 1978.)

nearly always tend to bring its origin and insertion closer together, thereby causing one or both of the bones to move.

Functional Grouping of Muscles

If a muscle is located on the side of the limb toward which the joint bends in decreasing the angle between the segments, it will be a *flexor* of that joint. If the muscle is located on the opposite side it will be an *extensor*. The biceps brachii, being on the front of the limb, flexes the elbow toward the front. The *triceps brachii* (usually called simply ''triceps''), located at the back of the elbow, takes origin from the scapula and humerus and inserts on the ulna. Thus the triceps is an extensor of the elbow.

Muscles that tend to pull a limb toward the median plane are classed as *adductors*, while those that tend to move the limb away from the median plane are *abductors*. Muscles that pass over more than one joint often have different classifications depending on the joint on which they are acting. The *gastrocnemius* (the large muscle in the gaskin or calf of the leg) is a flexor of the stifle and an extensor of the hock.

Muscles that surround an opening, whether they are striated or smooth, are called *sphincters*. The smooth muscle surrounding the opening from the stomach to the intestine forms the *pyloric sphincter*, which controls passage of food from the stomach. The *orbicularis oculi* muscle is composed of striated muscle fibers in the eyelids, which closes the eyelids. This is an example of a striated sphincter.

Cutaneous muscles are developed in the superficial fascia between the skin and the deep fascia covering the chief skeletal muscles. These cutaneous muscles attach to the

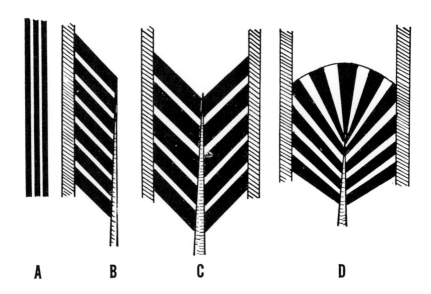

A   B   C   D

Fig. 11–6. Arrangements of muscle fibers. *A*, Parallel; *B*, unipennate; *C*, bipennate; and *D*, multipennate. (After Grant, A Method of Anatomy, 4th ed., Williams & Wilkins Co.)

skin and are responsible for movement of the skin. When a fly rests on a horse, the *cutaneous trunci muscle* enables the horse to shake the skin in order to dislodge the fly.

The muscles involved in a specific action, such as extension of the elbow, may be classified according to the part each plays in the action. The *agonists* (prime movers) are the muscles directly responsible for producing the desired action. The *antagonists* are muscles that may oppose the desired action; they have an action directly opposite that of the agonists. *Synergists* are muscles that oppose any undesired action of the agonists. For example, in extension of the elbow, the triceps brachii and *anconeus* are the agonists because they extend the elbow. The biceps brachii and *brachialis* are antagonists because they produce the opposite action, flexion of the elbow. Since the long head of the triceps can flex the shoulder joint as well as extend the elbow, any muscle that opposes flexion of the shoulder joint is a synergist. The *supraspinatus* and *brachiocephalicus* muscles are synergists for this particular action. The term "*fixators*" is sometimes used in place of synergists since these muscles usually stabilize one or more bones.

Whether a given muscle will be classified as an agonist, an antagonist, or a synergist depends entirely on the specific action being considered. It is obvious that if flexion of the elbow is the desired action (instead of extension), the biceps brachii and brachialis muscles become agonists, while the triceps brachii and anconeus muscles become antagonists.

Synovial Structures

Synovial structures of the body include *joint capsules, bursae,* and *synovial sheaths.* The inner layer of each consists of a connective tissue membrane that produces synovial fluid for the purpose of reducing friction.

As described in Chapter 10, the inner (synovial) layer of the joint capsule normally produces just enough *synovial fluid* to keep the apposed joint surfaces well lubricated. Inflammation of the joint *(arthritis)* may result in the production of excess synovial fluid, with resultant swelling and pain in the affected joint.

A *bursa* is simply a synovial sac located between two structures that tend to rub against each other. Examples of bursae are *superficial bursae* between the skin and *olecranon process* of the ulna at the point of the elbow, and between the skin and *superficial digital flexor* tendon at the point of the hock; the *bicipital bursa* between the biceps brachii tendon and the proximal end of the humerus; the *atlantal bursa* between the *ligamentum nuchae* and *atlas*; and the *supraspinous bursa* between the ligamentum nuchae and the spinous process of the second thoracic vertebra. Normally a bursa contains only enough fluid to reduce friction between adjacent parts. Excess fluid produced by the lining of a bursa, causing swelling in cases of inflammation of the bursa, is called *bursitis.*

A bursa gives adequate protection to structures that move only a short distance in relation to each other. However, tendons that must travel a long distance (sometimes as much as several inches) over a bone or other structure require protection for the entire length of the tendon that moves. This protection is afforded by a synovial sheath.

A *synovial sheath* resembles an elongated bursa placed between the tendon and underlying tissue, with the edges of the bursa (sheath) reflected around the tendon until they meet (Fig. 11–7). This results in an

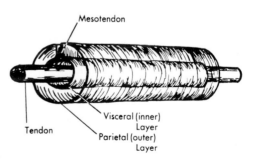

Fig. 11–7. **Diagram of a synovial sheath.**

inner layer of synovial membrane surrounding the tendon and a superficial layer of the synovial membrane outside the tendon, forming a closed sac which contains enough synovial fluid to reduce friction between the tendon and adjacent structures. The double fold of membrane formed where the edges of the synovial sheath meet is called the *mesotendon*. Synovial sheaths are also called *vaginal sheaths,* so inflammation of a synovial sheath is called *synovitis* or *vaginitis* (not to be confused with inflammation of the genital tract). If the tendon is involved as well as the synovial membrane, the condition is called *tendosynovitis* or *tendovaginitis*.

MUSCLES OF THE FRONT LIMB

Muscles Acting on the Shoulder Girdle

The *scapula* is subject to a number of complex movements in man, but in the domestic animals the chief movement is a pendulum-like swing forward and backward of the articular (ventral) angle. The pivot point is about the middle of the junction of the dorsal one-fourth and the ventral three-fourths of the scapula. The muscles that hold the scapula in place contribute to this swinging movement. From superficial to deep, these muscles include the trapezius, the omotransversarius, the rhomboideus, and the serratus ventralis (Fig. 11–8).

The *trapezius* is a triangular flat muscle that takes origin along the dorsal midline from the head as far back as the lumbar vertebrae. The trapezius inserts chiefly on the spine of the scapula. That portion taking origin cranial to the scapula will help swing the scapula forward, that attaching behind will swing it back. The entire trapezius also aids in holding the scapula against the body.

The *rhomboideus* is a heavier muscle just deep to the trapezius. The rhomboideus also takes origin from the dorsal midline both cranial and caudal to the scapula. The rhomboideus inserts on the deep (medial) face of the dorsal end of the scapula.

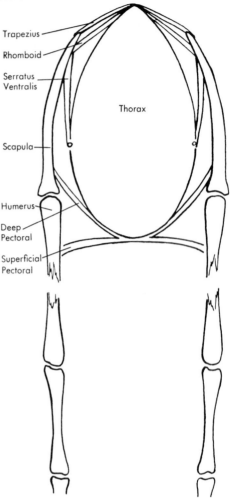

Fig. 11–8.   Diagram of a cross section through the thorax and forelegs showing muscles that attach the forelegs to the trunk.

The *serratus ventralis* is the largest and most important muscle attaching the front limb to the trunk. It is a large, fan-shaped muscle. The origin of the serratus ventralis is the widest part and extends from the transverse processes of the cervical vertebrae and ribs along a curved line just above the *sternum* as far back as the tenth costal cartilage. The insertion is on the medial side of the dorsal portion of the scapula. The serratus ventralis muscles from each side form a sling that supports the trunk between the front legs. Each muscle also acts to swing the scapula; and the cranial (cervical) portion, on contraction, tends to swing the lower part of the scapula backward, while the caudal (thoracic) portion swings it forward.

The *omotransversarius* muscle is found in most domestic species except the horse. It takes origin from the transverse processes of the cervical vertebrae and inserts on the lower part of the spine of the scapula. With these attachments, the omotransversarius usually pulls the lower part of the scapula forward, although with the animal in the standing position, it would assist lateral flexion of the neck.

Muscles Acting on the Shoulder Joint

The shoulder joint is a ball-and-socket joint and can undergo all types of movement. In the quadruped, however, its chief actions are extension and flexion.

Extensors of the Shoulder. The *brachiocephalicus*, as the name implies, extends from the arm to the head. The origin is from the *occipital bone* of the skull and transverse processes of the cervical vertebrae. It inserts on the lateral side of the proximal part of the *humerus* above the *deltoid tuberosity*. The brachiocephalicus is the heavy muscle covering the cranial aspect of the point of the shoulder. It is effective in raising the shoulder and pulling it forward. The brachiocephalicus is the principal extensor of the shoulder and also acts as a lateral flexor of the neck. In the horse the brachiocephalicus is a single muscle, while in the dog, cow, and sheep it can be divided into three parts, which all meet at the *clavicular tendon* (area representing the *clavicle*). The parts extending up the neck from the clavicular area are the *cleidomastoideus*, which originates from the *mastoid process* of the *temporal bone*, and the *cleido-occipitalis*, which originates from the cranial part of the dorsal midline of the neck and occipital bone. The *cleidobrachialis* is the remaining portion, which extends from the clavicular tendon to the humerus and is comparable to the *anterior deltoid* of man.

The *supraspinatus muscle* originates from the *supraspinous fossa* of the *scapula* in front of the spine on the lateral side. It inserts on the *major (lateral) tuberosity* (both major and minor in the horse) of the humerus. The supraspinatus may assist in extending the shoulder but acts chiefly as a ligament of the shoulder joint. This is one of the muscles that atrophies or shrinks in the condition known as *sweeny* in horses, in which the *suprascapular nerve* is paralyzed.

Flexors of the Shoulder. The *teres major* originates from the upper part of the axillary border of the scapula and inserts on the *teres major tuberosity* on the medial side of the shaft of the humerus. It is a strong flexor of the shoulder joint.

The *latissimus dorsi* is a wide triangular muscle that originates from the spinous processes of the thoracic and lumbar vertebrae by means of a wide aponeurosis, the *lumbodorsal fascia*. It inserts with the teres major on the medial side of the humerus and is a strong flexor of the shoulder. Also, it pulls the front limb backward, or, if the limb is fixed, advances the trunk.

The *infraspinatus muscle* originates from the *infraspinous fossa* just behind and below the spine of the scapula. It inserts into the caudal part of the lateral (greater) tuberosity of the humerus. The infraspinatus also acts as a strong ligament of the shoulder joint and may serve to abduct, flex, and outwardly rotate the shoulder. This muscle also atrophies in cases of sweeny.

The *teres minor* muscle lies below and adjacent to the infraspinatus muscle and has the same actions as the infraspinatus muscle. The teres minor originates from the axillary border of the scapula and inserts on the *teres minor tuberosity* of the humerus located just distal to lesser tuberosity of the humerus.

Adductors of the Shoulder. The *pectoral muscles* form the substance of the brisket. They originate from the *sternum* and insert mainly on the proximal part of the humerus. Commonly they are divided into the superficial pectoral muscle and the deep pectoral muscle. These pectoral muscles are effective adductors of the forelimb and the deep pectoral also serves to advance the trunk when the limb is fixed.

The *coracobrachialis* is a small muscle extending from the *coracoid process* on the medial side of the scapula to the medial side of the shaft of the humerus. It has little function except to hold the joint in apposition.

The *subscapularis* is another muscle holding the shoulder joint in close apposition. It originates from the *subscapular fossa* on the medial side of the scapula below the attachments of the *rhomboideus* and *serratus ventralis muscles*. It inserts on the *medial (minor) tuberosity* of the humerus and may serve as an adductor of the shoulder joint.

Abductors of the Shoulder. The *deltoideus* extends from the spine of the scapula to the deltoid tuberosity of the humerus. It is an abductor and flexor of the shoulder joint. In man, the deltoid is one of the most important muscles of the arm, being the only one that can effectively abduct the arm.

Muscles Acting on the Elbow

Since the elbow is a hinge joint, the muscles acting on it are either flexors or extensors. Those in front of the elbow are flexors and those behind are extensors. In quadrupeds, the extensors are stronger than the flexors because they support the weight of the body by maintaining the limbs in an extended position.

Extensors of the Elbow. The *triceps* has three heads. The long head originates from the caudal (axillary) border of the scapula, while the medial and lateral heads originate from the respective sides of the *humerus*. In the dog there is an accessory head that also originates from the humerus between the medial and lateral heads. All heads insert on the *olecranon process* of the *ulna* (point of the elbow). The triceps is the strongest extensor of the elbow. The long head may also act to flex the shoulder.

The *anconeus*, located deep to the triceps, is a rather small muscle that covers the back of the joint capsule of the elbow. It also originates on the humerus, inserts on the ulna, and extends the elbow.

Flexors of the Elbow. The *biceps brachii* originates on the *supraglenoid tuberosity* just above and in front of the articular surface of the scapula. It inserts on the *radial tuberosity* of the *radius* at the front of the proximal end of the radius. The biceps assists in holding the shoulder joint in apposition and may extend it to some extent. However, the chief action of the biceps is flexion of the elbow. In addition, in animals with a separate radius and ulna, it tends to supinate the forearm (rotate it outward).

The *brachialis* is strictly a flexor of the elbow, since it originates on the humerus and inserts on the front of the radius or ulna.

The *pronator teres*, found in the dog and ruminant but not in the horse, is primarily a flexor of the elbow, although it may tend to pronate the forearm in the dog. It originates on the medial epicondyle of the humerus and inserts on the medial side of the radius.

Extensor muscles of the carpus and digit, which originate on the *lateral epicondyle* of the humerus, may assist in flexion of the elbow as a secondary function.

Muscles Acting on the Carpus

The *carpus*, like the elbow, acts essentially as a hinge joint. However, the muscles acting on it are extensors in front and flexors behind.

Extensors of the Carpus. The *extensor carpi radialis* is the largest extensor of the carpus. It extends from the *lateral epicondyle* of the *humerus* to the proximal end of the *metacarpal region*. The exact insertion varies with the species. In the dog it inserts on the dorsal (cranial) surface of the proximal ends of the second and third *metacarpal bones*. (Remember the term dorsal here refers to the front of the forelimb.) In the horse it attaches only to the dorsal surface of the proximal end of the third metacarpal *(cannon)* bone. This is the most prominent muscle on the front of the forearm. It is the most medial muscle of the group. As the name implies the extensor carpi radialis acts primarily as an extensor of the carpus.

The *extensor carpi ulnaris (ulnaris lateralis)* is the most lateral of the extensor group of muscles. It also takes origin from the lateral epicondyle of the humerus but passes downward over the lateral side of the carpus to insert on the most lateral metacarpal bone. In most domestic animals this muscle flexes the carpus, although by origin and nerve supply it belongs with the extensor group.

In addition, the extensor muscles of the digits whose tendons pass over the dorsal surface of the carpus may act secondarily as extensors of the carpus.

Flexors of the Carpus. Starting from the medial side of the volar surface of the forearm, the *flexor carpi radialis* is the first muscle encountered in the horse. It takes origin from the *medial (flexor) epicondyle* of the humerus and inserts on the volar aspect of the proximal end of the metacarpus (medial side).

On the lateral side the flexor carpi ulnaris gains considerable leverage as a flexor of the carpus by inserting on the *accessory carpal bone* which projects in a palmar (volar) direction from the lateral side of the carpus.

These muscles are, of course, primarily flexors of the carpus, but they may act slightly in extending the elbow.

Muscles Acting on the Digit

Extensors of the Digit. The *common digital extensor* is the longest extensor muscle in the forelimb. It originates from the lateral epicondyle of the humerus close to the *extensor carpi radialis*. The insertion is on the extensor process of the third phalanx. The tendon is single in the horse, double in the cow, sheep, and goat, and split into four separate tendons in the pig, dog, and cat, where it inserts on the second through the

fifth digits. This muscle is an extensor of all joints of the digit including the *fetlock joint*. It may also assist in extending the *carpus*, and even in flexing the *elbow*.

The *lateral digital extensor* is found in all species. Its origin is just lateral to the common digital extensor, and the insertion varies according to the number of digits present. In the dog and cat, it inserts on the fifth digit; in two-toed animals, on the fourth digit; and in the horse, on the first phalanx of the third (and only) digit.

The *medial digital extensor* goes to the third digit of two-toed animals, and may be considered part of the common digital extensor. It is absent in the horse.

The extensor and abductor of the thumb or first digit is known as the *abductor digiti I (policis) longus* in the dog. It originates from the distal portion of the dorsal surface of the *radius,* and its tendon crosses obliquely over the tendon of the extensor carpi radialis. In the dog, it inserts on the first metacarpal bone. In animals without a first metacarpal bone, this muscle inserts on the most medial metacarpal bone, which is the second in the horse and the third in the cow and sheep. In these animals it is known as the *extensor carpi obliquus.*

Flexors of the Digit. In all animals the principal digital flexors are the superficial and the deep digital flexors.

The *deep digital flexor (flexor digitorum profundus)* lies the closest to the metacarpal bones. It originates from the humerus, *radius,* and *ulna.* The long tendon extends distally through the *carpal canal,* then along the palmar side of the metacarpus to insert on the palmar surface of the third phalanx. As with the common digital extensor tendon, the number of tendons and insertions depends on the number of digits. If the tendon is cut, the respective toe cannot be held against the ground, but will point up whenever weight is placed on the foot. The deep digital flexor is the only muscle that flexes the *distal interphalangeal joint.* Secondarily, it will also flex the more proximal joints of the digit and the carpus. The deep digital flexor also is important in supporting the *fetlock*.

The *superficial digital flexor* is similar to the deep digital flexor, but it inserts on the base of the second phalanx of each digit except the first. In the horse the superficial digital flexor tendon inserts on the volar aspect of the proximal end of the second phalanx and the volar aspect of the distal end of the first phalanx. Tendons of both the superficial digital flexor and deep digital flexor can be palpated (felt) at the back of the cannon region. *Bowed tendons* of horses involve one or both of these tendons in the cannon region (Fig. 11–9).

Interosseous muscles are present as muscles between the *metacarpal* bones of the dog. In the larger animals most of the muscle tissue has disappeared, and these structures are known as the *suspensory ligaments*.

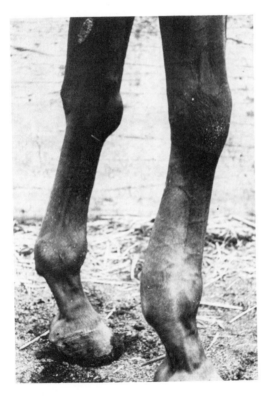

Fig. 11–9. Tendosynovitis (bowed tendon). Note swelling on the volar aspect above the fetlock in the area of the flexors.

They support the *proximal sesamoids* and hence the fetlock, and a band extends dorsally on each side of the digit to attach to the common digital extensor tendon.

MUSCLES OF THE HINDLIMB

The *hip joint* is a ball-and-socket joint, and as such can move in nearly any direction. However, the chief movements are extension, or backward movement, of the femur, and flexion, or forward movement, of the femur. Adduction and abduction are also fairly common movements and rotation is possible.

Muscles Acting on the Hip Joint

Extensors of the Hip. The chief extensor muscles of the hip are the so-called *hamstring muscles*, which pass behind the hip joint from the *tuber ischiadicum* (*tuber ischii* or *pin bones*) to the proximal end of the *tibia* or *fibula*. They include the *biceps femoris* (the most lateral of the posterior muscles of the thigh), the *semitendinosus* (the middle muscle of the posterior group), and the *semimembranosus* (the medial muscle of this group). The divisions between these muscles can be seen as vertical grooves in animals that are not too fat. In the horse, the biceps femoris and semitendinosus extend dorsad over the rump to attach to the *sacral* and *coccygeal vertebral spines*. In many other animals the hamstring muscles originate only from the tuber ischiadicum.

The *middle gluteus (gluteus medius) muscle* is another strong extensor of the hip. It originates from the wing of the *ilium* and inserts on the *trochanter major* of the femur, which is a lever projecting above the hip joint.

Flexors of the Hip. Flexors of the hip are located cranial to the femur. The most important are the *iliacus* and *psoas major*, which insert on the *trochanter minor* on the medial side of the femur. Together they are called the *iliopsoas muscle*. The iliacus originates from the ventral surface of the wing of the ilium. The psoas major originates from the ventral surfaces of the lumbar transverse processes. The psoas major and minor make up the *tenderloin*. The *sartorius* is a thin, straplike muscle that extends from the *tuber coxae* to the tibia, diagonally crossing the medial surface of the *thigh*.

Abductors of the Hip. Abductors of the hip extend laterally over the hip joint so that either a lever or pulley-type action moves the leg away from the median plane. The *deep gluteus (gluteus profundus)* extends from the spine of the ischium laterad over the proximal part of the *hip joint* to insert on the trochanter major. The top of the femur, when pulled mediad, moves the rest of the limb laterad.

The *superficial gluteus* extends from the sacral vertebral spines to the *trochanter tertius* just below the trochanter major. The *tensor fasciae latae* extends from the tuber coxae to the *lateral femoral fascia*, which attaches to the patella. In addition to abducting the hip joint, this latter muscle also flexes the hip joint and extends the *stifle*.

Adductors of the Hip. Adductors of the hip joint pull the limb toward the median plane. They are all located on the medial side of the thigh and extend from the *os coxae* to either the femur or the tibia. The *gracilis* is the most medial muscle extending from the *symphysis of the pelvis* to the tibia.

The *pectineus*, a small spindle-shaped muscle under cover of (lateral to) the gracilis, is both an adductor and flexor of the hip.

The *adductor muscle* is the largest muscle on the medial side of the thigh. It extends from the ventral aspect of the *pelvis* to the medial side of the femur and tibia. It is a strong adductor but may also help to extend the hip.

The *quadratus femoris* is an adductor and outward rotator of the thigh. Several other small muscles extending from the area of the *obturator foramen* are outward rotators of the thigh. They include the *obturator externus*, the *obturator internus*, and the *cranial* and *caudal gemelli*.

Muscles Acting on the Stifle

The stifle is essentially a hinge joint, so the muscles acting on it are either extensors or flexors.

Extensors of the Stifle. One large muscle, the *quadriceps femoris*, does most of the extending of the stifle. This muscle has four heads. The longest head, the *rectus femoris*, originates from the *ilium* just above the *acetabulum*. The other three heads, *vastus medialis*, *vastus intermedius*, and *vastus lateralis*, originate from the respective areas of the shaft of the *femur*. All four heads insert on the patella (knee cap). The patella, being fastened to the front of the *tibia* by the patellar ligaments, extends the stifle when it is pulled proximad by the quadriceps femoris. The *tensor fasciae latae* may also pull on the patella, thus helping extend the stifle.

Flexors of the Stifle. The chief flexors of the stifle are the *hamstring muscles*, which also extend the hip. In addition, those extensor muscles of the *hock* that originate on the caudal surface of the distal end of the femur may also flex the stifle. These muscles include the *gastrocnemius* and the *superficial digital flexor*. The *popliteus* is a relatively small muscle located behind the stifle. Its chief action is flexion of the stifle, although it may slightly rotate the leg (tibia and *fibula*) inward.

Muscles Acting on the Hock

The principal actions in the *hock* are extension and flexion.

Extensors of the Hock. Extensors of the hock primarily attach to the *tuber calcis (point of the hock)* by way of the *tendon of Achilles*. The *gastrocnemius* and *superficial digital flexor* originate from the distal end of the posterior surface of the femur and make up the bulk of the tendon of Achilles. They are joined in part by a portion of the *biceps femoris* and *semitendinosus*, which also enter into the tendon of Achilles and assist in extending the hock, as well as extending the hip and flexing the *stifle*. The *deep digital flexor* also extends the hock.

Flexors of the Hock. Flexors of the hock include the *tibialis cranialis (anterior)* and the *peroneus muscles*, whose tendons pass over the anterior surface of the hock to insert on the *tarsus* and *metatarsus*. The *peroneus tertius* is the only peroneal muscle named in the horse. The *peroneus longus* is found on the cow, sheep, goat, pig, and dog. The digital extensors also flex the hock.

Muscles Acting on the Digit

Digital extensors of the forelimbs tend to *extend the carpus*, while *digital extensors* of the hindlimb tend to *flex the hock*. Of course *digital flexors* of the forelimb tend to *flex the carpus*, while *digital flexors* of the hindlimb tend to *extend* the *hock*.

Muscles acting on the hind digits are similar to those of the digits of the front limb.

Extensors of the Digit. The *long digital extensor* originates from the distal end of the *femur* and passes down the limb to insert on the extensor process of the third phalanx. As with the common extensor in the forelimb, the tendon has one part in the horse, two parts in the cow, goat, and sheep, and four parts in the pig, dog, and cat.

The *lateral digital extensor* tendon of the horse joins the long digital extensor about the middle of the *cannon (metatarsus)*.

Flexors of the Digit. The superficial and deep digital flexors are arranged in the hindlimb as they are in the front. However, the tendon of the *superficial digital flexor* also attaches to the *tuber calcis* in the hindlimb.

MUSCLES OF THE TRUNK, NECK, AND HEAD

Extensor Muscles of the Trunk, Neck, and Head

The group of muscles located dorsal to the transverse processes of the vertebrae on either side of the spinous processes *(epaxial muscles)* make up the loin muscles and continue forward to the head. They are called the *erector spinae (sacrospinalis)* muscles. In our domestic animals, the largest of these loin muscles is known as the *longissimus* muscle. It is composed of innumerable small bundles of muscle fibers that extend from vertebral transverse processes to spinous processes, from transverse processes to transverse processes, or from spinous processes to spinous processes. As these attachments may extend from one vertebra to the next or overlap one or more vertebrae, there are many possibilities for naming individual muscles and many chances for individual muscle actions. However, in our domestic animals, these muscles are responsible for extension and lateral flexion of the *spinal column*. They may also cause slight rotation (twisting) of the spinal column, as seen when a bucking horse throws his front feet to one side and his hind feet to the opposite side.

The longissimus can be subdivided into segments named according to location: in the lumbar region, the *longissimus lumborum*; in the thoracic region, the *longissimus thoracis*; and in the cervical region, the *longissimus cervicis*, *longissimus capitis*, and *longissimus atlantis*.

Other muscles closely related to the longissimus may also be subdivided according to location. These include the *musculi iliocostalis, spinalis, semispinalis, multifidi, rotatores, interspinales,* and *intertransversarii.*

The same general arrangement of muscles is continued into the neck and head, where much greater flexibility is evidenced. The dorsal neck muscles, which extend (raise) the head and neck, are well developed because of the added load due to the mechanical disadvantage resulting from the head's being located at the end of the neck, which acts as a long lever. The large extensor muscles of the head originate from the vertebrae in the region of the *withers* and insert on the *occipital bone* of the skull. The most superficial of these muscles (other than the trapezius, which does not originate from the vertebrae) is the *splenius* and deep to it is the *complexus*. Other muscles that actively extend the head and neck include the *rhomboideus*, the *longissimus capitis et atlantis*, and the *dorsal oblique* and *dorsal straight muscles* of the head. Deeper muscles of the neck that extend from one vertebra to the next also aid in movements of the neck. In addition to these muscles, a heavy elastic band, the *ligamentum nuchae*, reaches from the withers to the *skull*. This ligamentum nuchae gives considerable aid to the muscles that extend (raise) the head and neck.

Flexor Muscles of the Head and Neck

Gravity is the most powerful force involved in flexing or lowering the neck and head of domestic animals. The ventral muscles of the neck which aid in flexing the head and neck include the *sternocephalicus*, which extends from the *sternum* to the *mandible* in the horse and to the mandible and *mastoid process* of the skull in the ruminant and dog. In addition, the *sterno-thyro-hyoideus*, *longus colli*, and *longus capitis* are flexors. Muscles ventral to the transverse processes of the vertebrae are called *hypaxial muscles*.

Abdominal Muscles

The muscles that form the bulk of the abdominal wall have a number of functions. They support the organs of digestion and many of the reproductive organs, particularly in the female during gestation. The abdominal muscles may act to flex the *vertebral column* (arch the back). If contracting on one side only, they flex it laterally, or even twist the vertebral column. These muscles are important in emptying the contents of the digestive tract *(defecation)*, urinary tract *(micturition* or *urination)*, and female reproductive tract at the time of giving birth to the young *(parturition)*. The abdominal muscles are used in *regurgitation*

and *vomiting* and serve as strong muscles for active expiration of air from the lungs, as seen during coughing or sneezing. (The horse rarely if ever vomits.)

The abdominal muscles are arranged in layers much like plywood, with the muscle fibers running in different directions. Most of these muscles have broad aponeurotic insertions that meet at the midventral line at an area known as the *linea alba* (white line).

The *external abdominal oblique* muscle is the most superficial. The fibers of this muscle are directed obliquely downward and backward. Its origin is from the last few *ribs* and *thoracolumbar (lumbo-dorsal) fascia* over the back and loins. The insertion is by means of a broad flat tendon (aponeurosis) that meets the insertion of the muscle from the opposite side at the linea alba. Caudally, the muscle is continued by an aponeurosis (fascia), sometimes called the *inguinal ligament*. This aponeurotic ligament forms the superficial wall of the *inguinal canal* for the passage of the *spermatic cord* of the male. It contains a slit, the *external inguinal ring*, through which the spermatic cord passes from the inguinal canal into the scrotum.

The *internal abdominal oblique muscle* is immediately deep to the external abdominal oblique muscle. It originates from a deeper layer of the thoracolumbar fascia and the inguinal ligament. The fibers pass obliquely downward and forward, and the muscle also inserts on the linea alba by means of an aponeurosis. In some animals this muscle forms the deep wall of the inguinal canal and also of the *internal inguinal ring*. The most caudal group of fibers from the internal abdominal oblique muscle passes through the inguinal canal with the spermatic cord and attaches to the outer covering of the *testicle (tunica vaginalis communis)*. This muscle is the *external cremaster muscle*, which functions in pulling the testicle toward the inguinal canal. In some animals, such as rodents and elephants, the testicle is retracted into the abdominal cavity except during breeding seasons.

The *transversus abdominis muscle* is the

deepest of the abdominal muscles. It originates from the deepest layer of thoracolumbar fascia, and the fibers are directed straight downward to insert on the linea alba.

The *rectus abdominis muscle* forms the muscular floor of the abdomen. It originates from the cartilages of the ribs and the *sternum*. The fibers run directly caudad in a frontal plane (horizontally) to attach to the pubis by means of a strong tendon, the *prepubic tendon*.

Muscles of Respiration

The muscles of respiration are either expiratory, forcing air out of the lungs by decreasing the size of the *thorax (chest)*, or they are inspiratory, causing air to enter the lungs by increasing the size of the thorax.

Inspiratory Muscles. The *diaphragm* is the chief muscle of inspiration. It is a dome-shaped sheet of muscle separating the thoracic and abdominal cavities. It projects into the thorax. Contraction of the fibers of the diaphragm tends to straighten the curvature of the diaphragm and force the abdominal viscera out of the thorax and into the abdomen. This in effect increases the size of the thorax and creates a partial vacuum in the thorax, causing air to enter the *lungs*.

The *external intercostal muscles* extend from each rib to the next rib behind. The fibers are directed downward and backward in a direction similar to that of the external abdominal oblique muscle. When these muscles contract, they tend to rotate the ribs upward and forward, thereby increasing the size of the thorax.

The *levatores costarum* and *rectus thoracis* muscles may also aid in inspiration.

Muscles of Expiration. As mentioned previously, the abdominal muscles may act as muscles of expiration by forcing the abdominal viscera against the diaphragm, thus decreasing the size of the thorax. In addition to these muscles, the *internal intercostals*, which lie deep to the external intercostals, are said to rotate the ribs backward, thus decreasing the size of the thorax. They run from each rib to the next one in front, and the fibers are directed downward and forward.

Some authorities believe that both the external intercostal muscles and the internal intercostal muscles may function in both inspiration and expiration.

The *retractor costae* and *transversus thoracis* muscles may also aid in expiration.

Chapter *12*

Microanatomy and Physiology of Muscle

Smooth Muscle
  Structure
  Plasticity
  Excitation, Contraction, and Relaxation
Cardiac Muscle
  Excitation and Contraction

Voluntary Striated Muscle
  Structure
  Excitation, Contraction, and Relaxation
  Heat Production by Muscle
  Stimulus for Muscle Contraction
  Factors Influencing Contraction
  Measurement of Contraction

The basis for movement in living cells involves *contractile proteins*, which can convert chemical energy into the mechanical energy of tension and motion. Proteins that have such contractile properties have been extracted from many cells other than just muscle cells. For example, such proteins are responsible for the migration of some white blood cells, for the movements of mitochondria, and the movement of the cilia on some epithelial cells.

Muscle cells are highly specialized for the function of contraction. Many responses of vertebrate organisms to environmental change depend on muscle contraction. These responses include such diverse activities as walking, breathing, the ingestion, transport, and elimination of food, blood circulation, and most activities associated with reproduction.

Connective tissue is closely associated with all muscle cells or fibers to form a slightly elastic harness, so that the pull exerted by muscle contraction can be usefully applied. The connective tissue between muscle cells also serves as a path for the vessels and nerves of the muscle.

Muscle fibers appear either striated or smooth (nonstriated) and are voluntary or involuntary, depending on the type of nerve supply. Involuntary muscle receives autonomic nerves and is not under conscious control. The nerves are not required for contraction, since contraction is an inherent property of smooth and cardiac muscle; the function of the nerve is to regulate the contraction. Voluntary muscle is supplied chiefly by somatic nerves and can be consciously controlled. Each voluntary muscle fiber must receive a nerve impulse in order to contract.

The three types of muscle usually de-

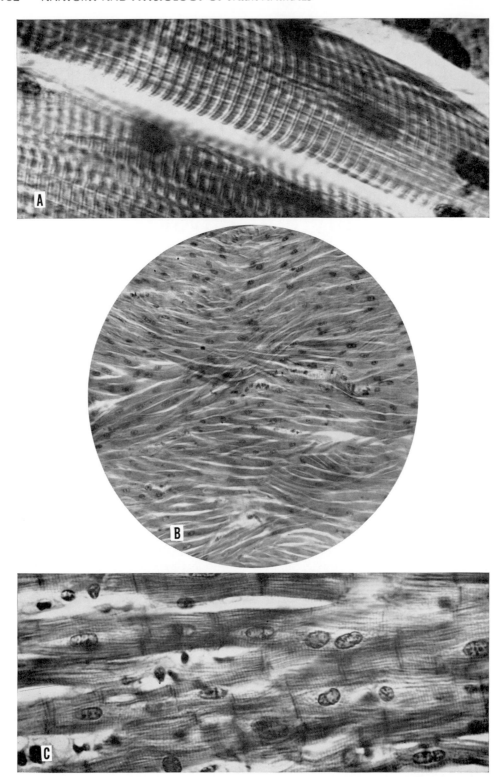

Fig. 12–1. *A*, Striated voluntary muscle; *B*, smooth (involuntary) muscle; and *C*, cardiac (involuntary striated) muscle. (Turtox Biological Supplies, 65 Catalogue, courtesy of General Biological Supply House, Inc.)

scribed are involuntary smooth muscle, involuntary striated muscle, and voluntary striated muscle (Fig. 12–1).

SMOOTH MUSCLE

Smooth muscle is also called *involuntary, unstriped, visceral,* or *plain muscle.* The terms are synonymous.

As the term "visceral" implies, smooth muscle is largely found in visceral structures associated with the digestive system, urogenital system, respiratory system, and vascular system.

About 99% of the smooth muscle of the animal body is of the visceral type, which is also called single-unit or unitary smooth muscle because the cells are closely packed together and form a network that may be called a syncytium. About 1% of the smooth muscle of the animal body is arranged as multiunit smooth muscle, which occurs in the iris and ciliary body of the eye and in the pilomotor fibers that erect the hair in the skin. These discrete groups of smooth muscle fibers have a more specific autonomic nerve supply and perform more specific functions than the single-unit visceral smooth muscle, which usually has a generalized action on an entire organ such as the stomach or intestine.

Structure

The smooth muscle cell appears to be simply a fusiform (spindle-shaped) contractile unit with a centrally located nucleus. Size of smooth muscle fibers varies considerably. Most cells range between 50 and 250μ in length and from 5 to 10μ in greatest diameter. The major portion of the cell consists of *sarcoplasm*. No cross striations, myofibrils, or sarcolemma are easily visible with the light microscope. Filaments are present as actin and myosin molecules, but there are no orderly arrangements to form striations. However, there are myosin molecule cross-bridges, and the actin filaments enter dense bodies analogous to Z-lines. Even small amounts of troponin and

tropomyosin have been found. A sarcoplasmic reticulum, which accumulates calcium, is simply referred to as smooth endoplasmic reticulum. There are no transverse tubules or triads.

Plasticity

Smooth muscle exhibits a special property called *plasticity*, which is also referred to as *stress-relaxation*. This is the ability to adjust to being stretched without increasing the final tension or the pressure exerted on the contents within a hollow viscus surrounded by smooth muscle. As it is stretched, the tension increases at first, but then in a few seconds or a few minutes the smooth muscle relaxes again to its original tension, even though it is still elongated.

This plasticity occurs in the stomach when it is being filled with food, in the intestines as the processed food moves along, in the blood vessels when the blood volume increases, in the urinary bladder as it increases its volume of urine, and in the uterus as pregnancy develops.

Plasticity allows expansion or stretch within physiologic limits without an increase in pressure and without pain; the smooth muscle does not lose its contractile ability. The reverse occurs upon emptying a visceral organ when the stretched muscle shortens back to its original length; i.e., all tension is lost at first, but returns again shortly. Plasticity is believed to be due to changes in the arrangement of the myosin and actin molecules upon stretch or shortening.

The increase in size of the uterine wall during pregnancy to several times its nonpregnant volume is due in a considerable measure to an increase in the amount of smooth muscle in the wall. There are three ways in which this increase may occur. Individual muscle fibers may increase in size, as is seen in voluntary striated muscle. Smooth muscle cells may divide mitotically to increase the number of cells. Finally, smooth muscle cells may form from undifferentiated mesenchymal cells.

Smooth muscle cells are believed to be

surrounded always by connective tissue, even though it may be only a small amount of reticular tissue. These reticular fibers join the larger *collagenous* and elastic fibers that make up the major part of the connective tissue associated with smooth muscle.

Excitation, Contraction, and Relaxation

Smooth muscle cells in the walls of the hollow organs are arranged so that only a fraction of the cells is supplied by autonomic nerves. These can bring about contraction, but nerve stimulation is not required for normal smooth muscle contraction, since it has various pacemaker-cell points for its own depolarization and contraction resulting from stimuli such as distention, chemical or hormonal influences, or myogenic self-excitation without any extrinsic stimulus. The innervation of such muscle is mostly regulatory.

The contraction impulse (action potential) spreads across the tissue because of syncytial connections between the fibers (where the plasma membranes of adjacent cells touch). Thus, smooth muscle cells can be linked electrically while remaining independent chemically (no secretion of transmitter substance required). This direct transmission is called *ephaptic conduction*. Current flows across readily, and the membrane resistance is low. The threshold for producing an action potential is about -35 mv, while the resting potential is only -55 to -50 mv (inside negativity). Even rapidly stretching the muscle will depolarize it and cause contraction. Smooth muscle is sensitive to stimuli all over, not just at specific neural plates as is the case with skeletal neuromuscular junctions. Hence, smooth muscle contraction can be initiated by stretch, neural stimuli, hormones, chemical stimuli, and mechanical stimuli.

Smooth muscle cells respond to norepinephrine released by sympathetic nerves, and to acetylcholine released by parasympathetic nerves, the one being antagonistic to the other. Some smooth muscle consists of distinctly separated fibers that require nerve stimulation to contract. This is called multiunit smooth muscle and includes the *pilomotor* smooth muscle cells in the skin and the smooth muscle cells in the iris and ciliary body of the eye.

The characteristic slow sustained contractions of smooth muscle are undoubtedly associated with the large amount of sarcoplasm and the apparent absence of myofibrils, striations, and Z lines in smooth muscle cells. Contractions of smooth muscle are often rhythmic in nature, as seen in peristalsis in the intestine. Gradual stretching of smooth muscle is possible without much change in tension, as occurs when the bladder fills with urine. Sudden stretching, however, increases the tension considerably and usually stimulates contraction of smooth muscle. Myogenic or self-excitation is apparently the result of sodium and calcium both leaking into the fiber, which causes the resting potential to decay down toward threshold as a prepotential. However, the sodium and calcium are pumped back out before threshold is reached, so the membrane resting potential is restored. This cycle is repeated continuously in a sinusoidal pattern. The resting potential is not stable but is constantly oscillating, forming pacemaker waves that are subthreshold in magnitude.

The pacemaker cells that produce pacemaker waves are located throughout visceral smooth muscle. In the presence of an adequate stimulus (usually chemical or from distention of the viscera), action potentials become superimposed on the crests of the pacemaker waves. These action potentials produce *peristalsis* (contraction waves) along the hollow viscera of the gastrointestinal tract, the bile ducts, the ureters, and the uterus during parturition.

Ca^{++} diffuses through the cytoplasm in 200 to 300 msecs. This is a *latent period* between the initial excitation and the beginning of contraction and accounts for the much slower response time of smooth muscle (20 to 30 times slower) compared to skeletal muscle. It also accounts partly for the much longer duration of the contraction itself. Even the calcium pump operates slowly in bringing about relaxation by pumping Ca^{++} back to the endoplasmic reticulum, to the mitochondria, and to the extracellular fluid.

Calcium is responsible, as it is in skeletal muscles, for producing smooth muscle tension, contraction, and relaxation. However, it is much more difficult to fatigue and to tetanize smooth muscle because the slow process consumes only 25% as much oxygen as skeletal muscle and the filaments tend to stick together, delaying the sequence.

The fibers of the autonomic nervous system (ANS) travel between the smooth muscle cells in a branching network of terminal fibrils. These fibrils have *varicosities* (bead-like enlargements) at intervals along their axons. When action potentials depolarize them, the transmitter substance is released and diffuses to the smooth muscle cell membranes, where stimulation occurs. The innervation is usually dual, i.e., both divisions of the ANS innervate smooth muscle except in the skin, where the pilomotor fibers, sweat glands, and cutaneous vessels receive only sympathetic innervation. Acetylcholine (ACh) is released from the parasympathetic (cholinergic) nerve fibers, and norepinephrine (NE) from the sympathetic (adrenergic) fibers. For example, ACh enhances intestinal peristalsis, whereas NE inhibits peristalsis.

CARDIAC MUSCLE

Cardiac muscle (involuntary striated muscle) has many characteristics that are similar to voluntary striated muscle fibers, although the striations are fainter than in skeletal muscle. Both types of muscle consist largely of sarcoplasm, myofibrils, a sarcoplasmic reticulum, transverse tubules, nuclei, and a sarcolemma. The most striking difference is the tendency for cardiac muscle fibers to join, forming a network. The heart is made up of cells that are separate entities; however, unique structures found in cardiac muscle are the *intercalated disks*. These disks are interposed between segments of muscle 50 to 120μ in length. They may cross the fiber in an irregular manner. Usually, each segment contains only one nucleus. These disks represent apposed cell membranes where gap junctions occur. Action potentials can readily spread from cell to cell through the intercalated disks, causing the atria and the ventricles to *each* act electrically and mechanically like a *functional syncytium,* as if it were a single cell mass.

Blood vessels and lymphatic vessels are both plentiful in cardiac muscle. A generous blood supply is essential, because cardiac muscle undergoes rhythmic contraction from early fetal life continuously until death of the animal.

Excitation and Contraction

Cardiac muscle does not require nerve stimulation. It has its own intrinsic or inherent ability to generate action potentials rhythmically. This is done by the normal pacemaker, the *S–A node*, which depolarizes faster than any other part of the heart muscle. Although cardiac muscle is innervated by the sympathetic and parasympathetic nervous systems, the function of these systems is limited to altering or regulating the heart rate, which the pacemaker normally sets.

The cardiac action potential is much slower than that of skeletal muscle. It lasts for 0.15 sec in the atria and 0.3 sec in the ventricles, as opposed to 0.005 to 0.01 sec in skeletal muscle. Also, the contraction time in cardiac muscle lasts as long as the action potential does. Instead of a sharp spike-potential, the cardiac action potential has a long *plateau*, which extends the time of both the action potential and the muscle contraction. This extended period provides time for pumping the blood out of the ventricles and filling them again before the next beat. It also explains why it is rare to get summation effects or tetany in heart muscle—the time-delay allows repolarization and relaxation.

Hypertrophy (increase in cell size) occurs in cardiac muscle when the heart has excessive work to do. In man this condition is sometimes called athlete's heart. Living in high altitudes may also cause hypertrophy of the heart. *Brisket disease (high-mountain disease)* of cattle involves enlargement of the heart as well as edema of the brisket and involvement of the lungs.

VOLUNTARY STRIATED MUSCLE

Voluntary striated muscle is also called *somatic* or *skeletal muscle.*

Structure

The *voluntary muscle fiber* is actually a multinucleated cell with cross striations. It consists of the sarcolemma (a thin, translucent envelope consisting of the plasmalemma or cell membrane and an external basal lamina and reticular fibers), numerous nuclei immediately deep to the sarcolemma, a large number of myofibrils (tiny fibers arranged parallel to the long axis of the muscle fiber), the sarcoplasmic reticulum, the transverse tubules of the sarcotubular system, and the sarcoplasm (intervening cytoplasm).

The sarcolemma is a thin membrane closely related to the *endomysium*, the

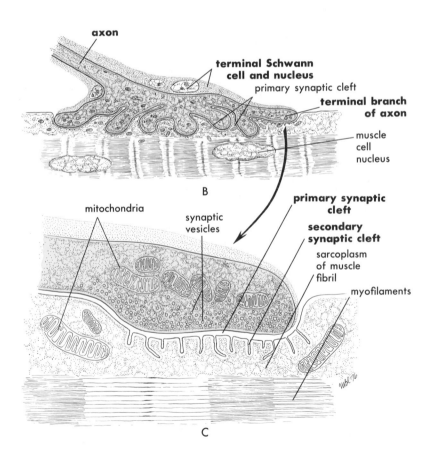

Fig. 12–2.   *A*, One motor end-plate, greatly enlarged. *B*, One terminal branch of an axon greatly enlarged to show in detail the structures involved in activating a muscle. (From Crouch, J. E.: Functional Human Anatomy, ed. 3. Philadelphia, Lea & Febiger, 1978.)

deepest connective tissue that surrounds individual muscle fibers. The sarcolemma and endomysium contribute to the elasticity of muscle, and connect the muscle fiber to the tendinous part of the muscle or tendon.

Each muscle fiber has a thickened part of its membrane surface called the *motor end-plate*. This surface has an irregular contour, like wrinkles, which interdigitates with the contour of the sole feet of the highly branched naked terminal ends of the appropriate branch of the motor neuron axon. There is no protoplasmic continuity between the nerve terminal ends and the motor end-plate, since there is a *synaptic cleft* between the two, and transmission of the nerve impulse is by means of the chemical transmitter substance, acetylcholine. This synaptic junction involving nerve ending and thickened muscle membrane is called the *neuromuscular junction* (or *myoneural junction*). (See Fig. 12–2.)

Long muscle fibers may contain several hundred nuclei. In the adult they are ovoid, dark-staining structures located just deep to the sarcolemma. In the fetus, however, nuclei of voluntary muscle fibers may be located near the center of the fiber.

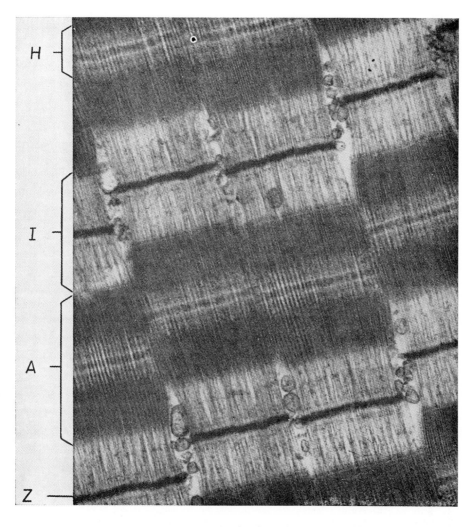

Fig. 12–3. Electron micrograph showing H, I, and A bands, and Z discs of rabbit striated voluntary muscle (Copenhaver, Bailey's Textbook of Histology, 15th ed., courtesy of Williams & Wilkins Co.)

Each striated muscle fiber may contain from several hundred to several thousand *myofibrils*, and each myofibril contains about 1500 myosin and 3000 actin filaments.

Each myosin filament is made up of hundreds of myosin molecules with a molecular weight of 332,000 each. (As a comparison, hydrogen [H_2] has a molecular weight of 2.)

An actin filament is composed of 600 molecules of actin with a molecular weight of 70,000 each.

On casual examination with a light microscope, the cross striations of voluntary muscle appear to be disks throughout the entire fiber. However, with the electron microscope the striations appear only in the

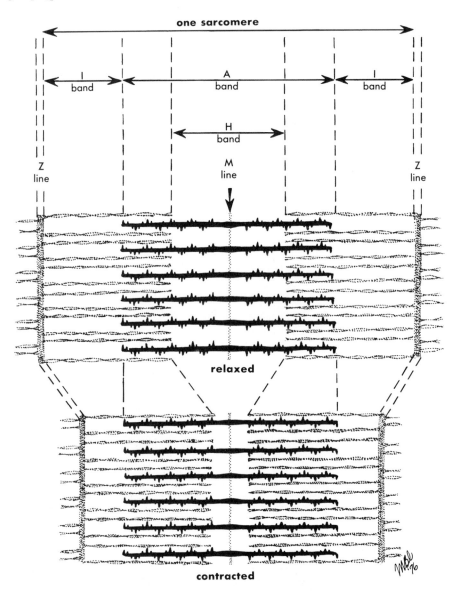

Fig. 12–4.   Schematic diagram of a single sarcomere to show the changing relationships of the I, A, and H bands as contraction takes place. Note that the thin actin filaments slide between the dark myosin filaments and the I and H bands partially disappear. The A band remains constant in length. (From Crouch, J. E.: Functional Human Anatomy. ed. 3. Philadelphia, Lea & Febiger, 1978.)

myofibrils and not in the sarcoplasm. The alternate light and dark bands of all fibrils appear at the corresponding places in the fiber (Fig. 12–3). The fact that corresponding bands of adjacent myofibrils are in register makes these bands seem to extend completely across the whole fiber. The apparent bands of myofibrils are due to relative density and partial overlapping of myosin and actin filaments (Figs. 12–4, 12–5). Usually letters are used to designate the different bands.

The light I-bands contain only *actin* filaments. They are called *I-bands* because they are *isotropic* to polarized light, meaning that a light beam passing across the I-band is scattered equally in all directions because the actin filaments are all the same density. The dark A-bands are located where actin and myosin filaments overlap. They are called *A-bands* because they are *anisotropic* to polarized light, meaning that they scatter the light unequally because the filaments have different densities and are therefore *birefringent.*

The sarcomere is bounded at each end by a *Z-line*, which is composed of noncontractile protein. The actin filaments are attached to the Z-lines at each end of the sarcomere. Notice from the illustrations that the Z-lines bisect the I-bands; therefore, an A-band and two halves of two I-bands make up a sarcomere. The Z-lines are in register from one myofibril to the next, so the dark and light bands are also in register, giving a striated appearance to the whole fiber.

At the normal resting length, the actin filaments nearly meet in the middle of the sarcomere. At this length the sarcomere can generate its greatest force of contraction. However, when the muscle is slightly stretched from its resting length, the actin filaments are then separated, leaving an *H-zone* in the middle of the A-band. Only myosin exists in the H-zone, which is where there are no actin filaments. An *M-line* sometimes seen in the center of the H-zone may be caused by transversely oriented slender filaments that possibly function to hold the heavy myosin filaments in register.

Sarcoplasm is the cytoplasm of the muscle cell. Delicate tubules within the sarcoplasm are called the *sarcoplasmic reticulum,* which is agranular (contains no ribosomes) and functions as part of the excitation-contraction coupling process.

The sarcoplasmic reticulum is similar to, but not identical to, the endoplasmic reticulum of other cells. It consists of a network of agranular tubules scattered among the myofibrils and oriented parallel to them.

Another network of tubules, the transverse tubules (or T system) is continuous with the plasma membrane and extends into

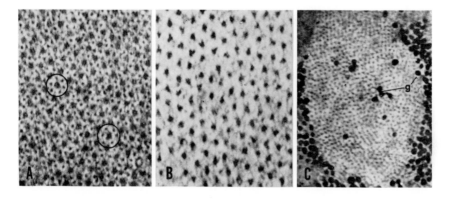

Fig. 12–5. **Human quadriceps femoris tissue under high magnification. A,** Cross section through an A band, showing both thick and thin myofilaments. Six thin filaments appear to surround each thick filament. (× 130,000.) **B,** Cross section of an H zone. Only thick filaments are present. (× 130,000.) **C,** Cross section of an I band. Only thin filaments are present. (× 80,500.) *g,* Glycogen granules (Prince, courtesy Amer. J. Med.)

the interior of the muscle fiber at right angles to the myofibrils and sarcoplasmic reticulum. The T system transmits the action potential from the sarcolemma into the interior of the muscle fiber to initiate contraction of the entire fiber. Together, the transverse tubules and the sacroplasmic reticulum *(longitudinal tubules)* form the *sarcotubular system*.

The transverse tubules pass through the myofibrils at the junction of the A- and I-bands, or in some animal species, at the Z-lines. Therefore, two sets of T-tubules may pass through each sarcomere. At the points where the T-tubules pass through the sarcomere, the longitudinal tubules butt up against the T-tubules from both sides and bulge to form two lateral sacs or cisterns, one on either side of the T-tubule. This places the two longitudinal tubules in juxtaposition with a T-tubule, forming a *triad* wherever the three components meet. This

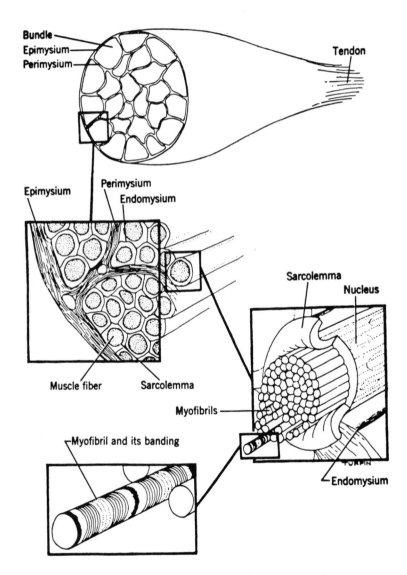

Fig. 12–6.   Architecture of a skeletal muscle and its fibers. (Reproduced by permission from Torrey, Morphogenesis of the Vertebrates, courtesy of John Wiley & Sons.)

arrangement is important in the excitation-contraction coupling process. A *Golgi apparatus* and large numbers of *mitochondria* as well as glycogen and fat inclusions also are found in muscle fibers.

Figure 12–6 shows the architecture of a skeletal muscle and its fibers. Voluntary muscle fibers range in diameter from 10 to 100μ. In general, the large fibers appear to be longer and tend to be found in large rather than small muscles. Animals on full feed are reported to have larger fibers than animals on restricted feed. It is generally accepted that males have larger muscle fibers than females. Length of voluntary muscle fibers is highly variable, depending on the length of the muscle and arrangement of muscle fibers (parallel or pennate). Probably some fibers in parallel muscles extend the entire length of the muscle.

It is generally believed that voluntary muscle fibers are such specialized cells that little if any multiplication of fibers or formation of new fibers occurs after birth except following injury to the muscle fiber. All increase in size of muscles at any stage in life following birth is due to hypertrophy (increase in size) of individual muscle fibers, with the synthesis of more myofibrils and an increased vascular supply. It is well known that exercise can cause increased muscular development, such as that seen in weight-lifters. This, of course, is accomplished by increase in size of existing individual muscle fibers. If the nerve supply to a muscle is destroyed, the muscle fibers decrease to practically nothing, a condition called *denervation atrophy*. This is seen in "sweeny" of draft horses, when the suprascapular nerve is crushed by a collar, resulting in shrinking of the supraspinatus and infraspinatus muscles of the shoulder.

Excitation, Contraction, and Relaxation

Neuromuscular Junction. Voluntary-striated muscle contraction is triggered by the generation of an action potential on the sarcolemma (muscle fiber membrane). This action potential is initiated by the firing of a motor neuron whose axon branch terminates at the neuromuscular junction or myoneural junction near the midpoint of the muscle fiber. However, the action potential of the nerve does not travel beyond the terminal ending. Instead, depolarization of the motor nerve ending releases a chemical transmitter substance, acetylcholine, which diffuses across the space between the nerve ending and the muscle fiber membrane. The space, the *synaptic cleft*, averages 300 Å (300 nm) across.

Acetycholine (ACh) is synthesized in the cytoplasm of the nerve ending by the enzyme *choline acetyltransferase* (also called *acetylase*), which combines acetyl-CoA with choline. The ACh is stored in vesicles in the *end-feet* or *sole feet* at the end of the nerve fiber.

When ACh diffuses across the cleft of the myoneural junction, it acts on that specialized part of the sarcolemma of the muscle fiber located directly under the end-feet. This greatly thickened and specialized sarcolemma is referred to as the *postjunctional membrane* (PJM) or *subneural apparatus*. This specialized part of the sarcolemma has an irregular contour, like wrinkles or folds, which interdigitate with but do not touch the end-feet of the nerve terminal branch because the synaptic cleft is between them.

End-Plate and Action Potentials. The ACh released from the end-feet depolarizes the postjunctional (PJM) membrane from the resting potential of about −85mv down to about −10mv. This local depolarization of the PJM produces a localized flow of current, which *then* depolarizes the adjacent sarcolemma to its threshold potential, and an action potential results. The action potential is then propagated all over the sarcolemma of the muscle fiber.

Since the T-tubules (transverse) are inward continuations of the sarcolemma, the action potential (or impulse) travels along these tubules throughout the muscle fiber. Where the transverse tubules pass by the longitudinal tubules (the sarcoplasmic reticulum), there is an electrotonic spread of current at these triads into the longitudinal tubules. This ionic current flow causes the release of calcium ions from the longitudinal tubules, where the calcium is stored, particularly in the lateral cisternae at the triad level. Calcium is released into the surrounding sarcoplasm of the muscle fiber and diffuses into the myofibrils. Here it initiates the linking together of the actin and myosin filaments, which results in the actin filaments sliding toward the center of each sarcomere. This sliding action shortens the sarcomeres, which shortens the myofibrils, which shortens the muscle fibers, and so the muscle contracts.

Myosin and Actin Filaments. Each myosin filament in a sarcomere is a protein made up of about 200 myosin molecules. Each molecule has two parts: (1) a *light meromyosin* (LMM) part, which lies parallel to other light meromyosin molecules, making up the *length* of the myosin filament; and (2) a *heavy meromyosin* (HMM) part, which projects outward like an arm from the end of the LMM filament. The HMM also has two parts: the arm projecting and a head attached at the free end of the arm. The arm is flexible, like a hinge, where it joins the light meromyosin and also where it joins the head. These hinged heavy meromyosin arms, called *cross-bridges*, protrude from all around the myosin filament. They extend away from the center in both directions, so there are no cross-bridges in the center of the myosin filament. The cross-bridges extend toward the surrounding actin filaments.

Each *actin* filament is made up of three components: actin, tropomyosin, and troponin. The base unit is the *F-actin molecule,* which consists of two long strands wound around each other in a spiral. Each strand is made up of *G-actin molecules,* and each of these has an adenosine diphosphate (ADP) attached. The ADP sites are believed to exist where the heads of the HMM of the cross-bridges attach to the actin to cause actual contraction.

Lying in the grooves of the two F-actin spiral strands are polypeptide strands of *tropomyosin* molecules attached together to also form long strands. The third protein, *troponin*, is attached to each tropomyosin molecule. Together they are called the *troponin-tropomyosin complex.*

Contraction Mechanism. The best current explanation indicates that the calcium ions released from the sarcoplasmic reticulum (longitudinal tubules) combine with the troponin to produce a molecular change in the tropomyosin molecules, which uncovers, or releases from inhibition, the active ADP sites on the G-actin molecules. This allows the HMM-heads to attach to the actin active sites; when they do, the bonding forces change at the hinge between the HMM head and arm. That causes the head to tilt inward toward the center of the sarcomere, dragging the actin filament with it.

The tilting of the head apparently exposes an ATP on the head, and an ATPase enzyme dephosphorylates the ATP to ADP, releasing energy. The energy causes detachment of the head and tilts the head back upright again. The head then attaches to the next available ADP on a G-actin molecule on the actin filament. The process is thereby repeated, pulling the actin filament another step toward the center. This is repeated with machine-gun rapidity, making and breaking like a ratchet, and so it is referred to as the *ratchet theory.* Table 12–1 is a summary of these events. (See Fig. 12–7.)

The resultant contraction shortens the sarcomere and shortens the I-bands. The A-band always remains the same length. During shortening, the actin filaments slide over the myosin filaments as they are drawn from both ends, pulling the Z-lines closer together. (See Fig. 12–3.) The filaments themselves, actin and myosin, do not shorten.

Relaxation. Muscle contraction will continue as long as there is an excess of Ca^{++} ions present in the sarcoplasm, but when the effect of the current-spread at the triads ends, the Ca^{++} is then sequestered back into the longitudinal tubules (Fig. 12–8). This is

Table 12–1. Summary of Excitation and Contraction

Excitation: action potential propagated along sarcolemma

↓

Depolarization of T-tubules (electrotonic spread of current)

↓

Local current flow to terminal cisternae of sarcoplasmic reticulum

↓

Ca^{++} released into sarcoplasm

↓

Ca^{++} bound by troponin

↓

Configurational change in tropomyosin, exposing ADP active sites on G-actin

↓

Release of inhibition of actomyosin with link between actin and HMM-S$_1$

↓

change in bonding forces;

↓

HMM head tilts inward, pulling actin

↓

ATPase dephosphorylates exposed ATP Energy detaches HMM head

↓

HMM head tilts back and attaches to another ADP site of G-actin

(Ratchet mechanism continues in presence of Ca^{++} and active sites)

accomplished by an active Ca^{++}-pump that uses the energy of ATP to pump the Ca^{++} from the sarcoplasmic fluid back into the tubules, ready for the next depolarization. (Without ATP the muscle cannot relax.)

Only a small amount of Ca^{++} is left out in the sarcoplasm of the relaxed resting muscle; not enough to act on the troponin-tropomyosin complex. Therefore, during relaxation the actin and myosin filaments are dissociated, allowing the elasticity of the muscle to return it to its resting length, which pulls the Z-lines and actin filaments back to their original positions.

Replenishment of ATP. A great amount of ATP is needed because the energy for contraction is derived from hydrolyzed (dephosphorylated) ATP. Also, ATP is used by the muscle fiber to sequester Ca^{++} back into the sarcoplasmic reticulum. It is also needed during recovery of the membrane after depolarization—the Na-K-ATPase system.

The concentration of ATP in skeletal muscle is relatively small, supplying only enough energy to maintain contraction for a brief period. Since muscles continue to contract after the initial supply of ATP has been used up, the resulting ADP is phosphorylated again from another source, *creatine phosphate* (CP).

There is normally about five times as much CP stored in the sarcoplasm of skeletal muscle as there is ATP. When the ATP is used for contraction and relaxation, transphosphorylation occurs from creatine phosphate to the resulting ADP, forming ATP again, as follows: CP + ADP $\xrightarrow{\text{kinase}}$ C + ATP. This replenishment reaction occurs

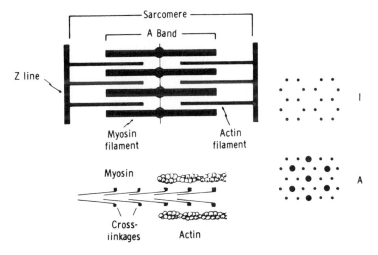

Fig. 12–7. *Top left:* Arrangement of actin and myosin filaments in skeletal muscles. *Right:* Cross sections through I band and through A band lateral to H band. *Bottom left:* Probable fine structure of actin and myosin, showing cross-linkages. Myosin appears to be made up of units arranged on either side of the sarcomere in such a way that their heads form the cross-linkages. Actin appears to be made up of two helical chains of globular units. (Ganong, Review of Medical Physiology, courtesy of Lange Medical Publications.)

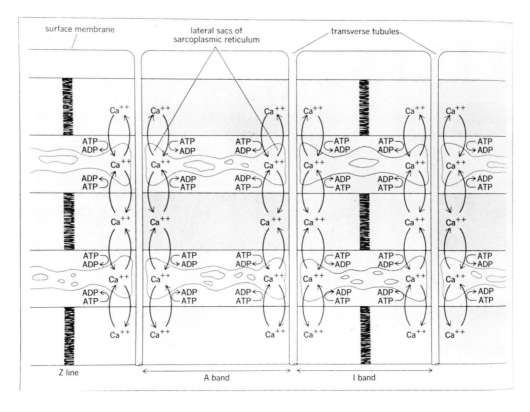

Fig. 12–8. Release and active uptake of calcium ions by lateral sacs of sarcoplasmic reticulum in mammalian skeletal muscle. Transverse tubule located at the A-I junction. (From Vander, A. J., et al.: Human Physiology. ed, 2. New York, McGraw-Hill, 1975.)

almost as fast as ATP is being used. Therefore, the ATP level changes little until the concentration of CP gets low. CP acts as the immediate energy source for the resynthesis of ATP as the initial supply of ATP is used. This is a convenient means of transferring energy needed for muscle contraction.

The concentration of creatine phosphate is also limited. Thus, if muscle contraction continues for any length of time, the CP and new ATP eventually have to be replaced by the citric acid cycle (Kreb's cycle) in the mitochondria of the muscle fibers during relaxation. Meanwhile, as long as the muscle continues to be used, *lactic acid* will build up in the active muscle, because glycolysis, the degradation of glucose to lactic acid, is mostly taking place in the cells, instead of the citric acid cycle. The glucose is obtained from the blood supply to the muscle, and from the glycogen stored *in* the muscle

fibers, which is then broken down to glucose by the process called *glycogenolysis.* Glycogenolysis and glycolysis are complex processes involving a number of reactions, enzymes, and intermediate compounds.

Once the muscle relaxes, some of the accumulated lactic acid is converted to pyruvate, which then goes through the citric acid cycle in the muscle's mitochondria, from which ATP and CP are reformed in the muscle, or it is converted to glucose and glycogen in the muscle. The rest of the lactic acid enters the capillaries in the muscle and is carried, in the blood, to the liver, where it is converted back to glucose or glycogen to replenish these supplies in the animal.

Oxygen from the blood must also be supplied to the mitochondria in muscles in order for the citric acid cycle to operate and result in oxidative phosphorylation of ADP to ATP. While lactic acid was mostly being produced anaerobically during muscle contraction, an *oxygen debt* was building up. This oxygen debt must be repaid during relaxation before optimal muscle activity can resume.

The chain of reactions involved in supplying energy for muscle contraction and recovery may be summarized as follows:

The maximum amount to which a muscle fiber can contract is about one-half its resting length (Fig. 12–9). In man, the *strength of muscle contraction* is believed to be somewhere between 35 and 150 pounds per square inch of cross sectional area. Whenever a muscle fiber receives a sufficiently strong nervous impulse to create an action

Adenosine triphosphate (ATP) $\rightarrow$ Adenosine diphosphate (ADP) + Phosphoric acid (H_3PO_4) + Energy (for immediate use in contraction)

Creatine phosphate (CP) $\rightarrow$ Creatine + Phosphoric acid (H_3PO_4) + Energy (for resynthesis of ATP from ADP)

Glycogen $\rightarrow$ Lactic acid + Energy (for resynthesis of Creatine phosphate from Creatine and Phosphoric acid)

$1/5$ of Lactic acid (formed above) + Oxygen (O_2) $\rightarrow$ Water (H_2O) + Carbon dioxide (CO_2) + Energy (for resynthesis of remaining $4/5$ of lactic acid back to glycogen)

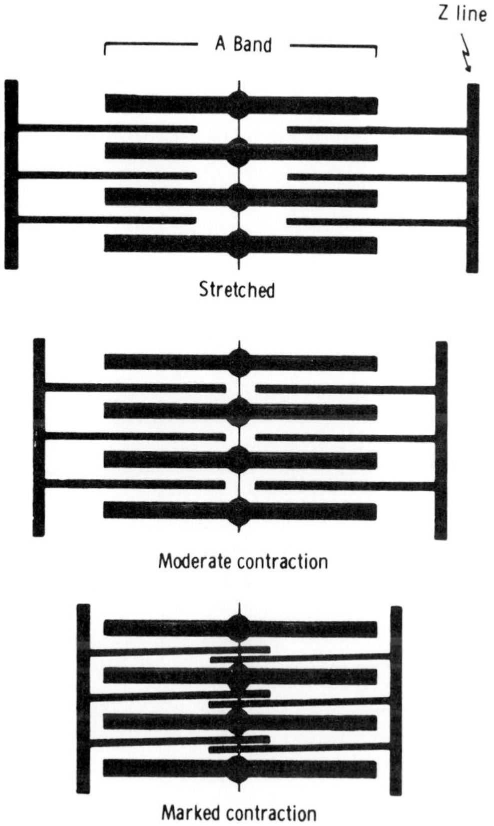

Fig. 12–9. Diagrammatic representation of muscle filaments in various states. Note that with strong contraction, the actin filaments probably slide over each other. (Ganong, Review of Medical Physiology, courtesy of Lange Medical Publications.)

potential on it, the potential will be propagated over the entire fiber and cause the whole fiber to contract. This is the "*all-or-none law*" of muscle contraction. However, the *force* of contraction depends on the state of the fiber at the time, *i.e.,* is it warmed up, is it fatigued, is it stretched, is the calcium supply low, etc. Under optimum conditions, any increase in strength of contraction of a whole muscle is due to a greater number of fibers contracting, since each fiber contracts to its maximum ability.

Heat Production by Muscle

Contraction is the primary function of muscle fibers, but only about one-fourth of the energy used is available for actual work in the physical sense of weight times distance, usually measured in foot-pounds. The rest of the energy is dissipated as heat. Although the mechanical efficiency of muscle is not high, it compares favorably with some types of engines.

Whenever environmental temperature is much below the normal body temperature, heat production by muscles is a definite advantage. In fact, when air temperature is extremely low, muscles may undergo spasmodic contractions called *shivering* to produce enough heat to maintain normal body temperature.

Heat production occurs in two distinct phases, the *initial heat* (heat of actual contraction), and the *heat of recovery*. The initial heat includes *heat of activation and maintenance, heat of shortening,* and *heat of relaxation*. The initial heat of contraction is the same whether the muscle contracts in oxygen or in nitrogen, because oxygen consumption does not occur until contraction and relaxation are over.

About nine-tenths of the heat of recovery is derived from oxidation of food and one-tenth from anaerobic (without oxygen) metabolic processes. In the presence of oxygen, recovery is rapid, with heat production almost equal to initial heat. However, under anaerobic conditions, recovery extends over a period of 20 minutes, and the heat produced is equivalent to only about one-fifth of the initial heat.

Stimulus for Muscle Contraction

The description of the nerve impulse (Chapter 6) indicates that it is basically a membrane phenomenon in which an electrical action potential is produced by a change in the balance of ions on the inside and outside of the nerve fiber due to an increased permeability of the membrane. However, the action potential, which is simply electrical activity of the nerve, does not travel beyond the nerve ending. Instead, depolarization of the nerve ending releases a chemical transmitter substance, acetylcholine, from synaptic vesicles in the end-bulb or terminal of the nerve fiber at the neuromuscular junction. The released acetylcholine crosses the cleft between the nerve ending and the muscle fiber membrane (motor end-plate) to initiate a depolarization wave that travels along the fiber membrane in all directions at approximately 5 m/sec. This excitation wave reaches the myofibrils by way of the sarcotubular system, and initiates the contraction by subsequent release of Ca^{++}.

The presence of a chemical mediator of nerve impulses was first suspected when the similarity of action of *epinephrine (Adrenaline)* and stimulation of the sympathetic nervous system was observed. Later *acetylcholine* was found to stimulate organs supplied by parasympathetic nerves and was also found in fluid surrounding the motor end-plates of striated muscle fibers following stimulation of their motor nerves.

Acetylcholine is released only at a nerve ending. The depolarization wave initiated by acetylcholine is due to increased permeability of the muscle fiber membrane to Na^+, and the wave reaches the individual myofibrils by way of the *triads*, which are where the longitudinal sarcoplasmic reticulum lies in juxtaposition with the transverse tubules that pass all the way through a muscle fiber at the junction of the A and I bands. The transverse tubules may pass through at the Z line in some species.

The sarcoplasmic reticulum is the longitudinal tubular network within the fiber. It contains the Ca^{++} stores that are released when the membrane depolarization is spread throughout the fiber preceding contraction of the whole fiber.

From the time the impulse reaches the muscle fiber until contraction occurs, there is a latent period of about 0.002 sec.

Almost as soon as acetylcholine initiates the impulse for muscle contraction, the acetylcholine is inactivated by an enzyme called *acetylcholinesterase*. This enzyme, which splits acetylcholine, is found in conductive tissue synapses, including the neuromuscular junction.

Acetylcholinesterase in turn is irreversibly inhibited by certain alkylphosphates, which is the basis of some effective insecticides and the so-called nerve gases that have been studied extensively by the armed forces since World War II.

These insecticides, known both as *organic phosphates* and *phospate esters,* include such products as Malathion, Parathion, Diazinon, Thimet, and Cygon. Products for both external application and oral administration are included in the organic phosphate insecticides. If improperly used, any of the organic phosphates is extremely dangerous, not only to domestic animals, but also to the person using it. Therefore, it is imperative that this class of insecticides be used under proper supervision, and that instructions for use be followed exactly. Poisoning will give a picture of parasympathetic stimulation as described in Chapter 6. Some of the symptoms include constriction of the pupil of the eye, cramps, vomiting, diarrhea, and weakness. The organophosphates are anticholinesterases; therefore they inhibit the action of acetylcholinesterase, and acetylcholine builds up, causing muscular spasm and asphyxiation. Neostigmine and physostigmine are commonly used anticholinesterase drugs.

Another group of drugs that affects the neuromuscular junction are the *curariform drugs*. These drugs act like *curare*, which is the deadly poison that South American Indians use on their arrowheads. It binds to the postjunctional membrane so that ACh cannot act on it to produce an EPP. Also, curare is not destroyed by acetylcholinesterase (AChE); therefore, a muscle contraction cannot be produced because an action potential is not elicited. Death can result from asphyxiation because the muscles needed for breathing are unable to contract. Any curariform drug, such as gallamine, will do this in varying degrees depending on the drug concentration. These drugs produce varying amounts of paralysis, as when used to relax muscles during certain types of surgery.

Another group of drugs blocks the release of acetylcholine from the nerve terminal end-feet. One of the most dramatic in this group is the *botulinus toxin*, which is produced by the bacterium *Clostridium botulinum*. It causes a type of food poisoning and is deadly. Flaccid paralysis results because ACh is blocked and no action potentials can be produced for muscle contraction. This condition gives rise to the term "limber neck" for poisoning with botulinus toxin.

The *"all or none" law* states that when a muscle fiber is stimulated to contract, the whole fiber contracts and it will contract to the maximum of its ability under the particular conditions, or it will not contract at all. Another way of stating this law is that a stimulus to a muscle fiber either causes an action potential to travel over the entire fiber, causing contraction, or it fails to stimulate the muscle fiber at all.

The "all or none" law applies to a single muscle fiber or a single motor unit (a motor nerve and all the muscle fibers it supplies); it does not apply to an entire muscle. The "all or none" law also does not state that a muscle fiber will always contract with the same speed or the same force but only that for the conditions at the time of stimulation the muscle fiber will contract to its maximum. The size of the stimulus as long as it is above the threshold has no relationship to the speed or strength of contraction of a muscle fiber. The size of stimulus to an entire muscle, however, has a direct relationship to the strength of contraction, because the larger the stimulus the more motor units are caused to contract; hence the greater strength of contraction of the muscle.

A *muscle twitch* is a single brief response of a single motor unit, and so a twitch is the smallest quantum of contraction possible. The action potential essentially is over before the contraction begins. Frog gastrocnemius muscle at 21°C. shows a muscle twitch which lasts about 0.1 second. Three phases of the twitch are described: (1) a *latent period* between the application of the stimulus and the beginning of the response (about 0.01 sec); (2) a *period of contraction*, during which the muscle shortens (about 0.04 sec); and (3) a *period of relaxation* (about 0.05 sec) (Fig. 12–10).

Much of the physiologic information about voluntary muscle activity has been obtained from experiments using a *muscle-nerve preparation* connected to a recording instrument and a source of electrical stimulation. A muscle-nerve preparation consists of an isolated muscle, often the gastrocnemius muscle of the frog, with one end attached to a clamp and the other end at-

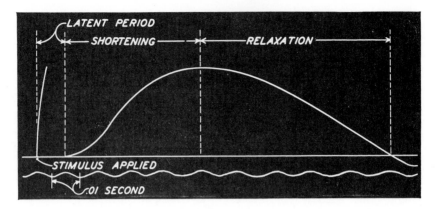

Fig. 12–10. A single twitch of a frog muscle recorded on a rapidly moving smoked plate employing a lever. (Carlson, Johnson and Cavert, The Machinery of the Body, courtesy of the University of Chicago Press.)

tached to a lever from which a record is made on paper as the lever moves. The nerve supplying the muscle (tibial branch of the sciatic nerve for the gastrocnemius muscle) is exposed and electrically stimulated. The response of the muscle to stimulation under various conditions, such as changes in load, changes in frequency of stimulation, and changes in strength of stimulation, can be analyzed by study of the record traced on the paper drum by the lever.

Electronic amplifiers and recorders are more advanced devices that have replaced the kymograph, and are used almost exclusively today for such measurements. The electronic devices also permit controlled electrical stimulation in such experiments on muscle physiology, with provisions for varying the voltage and frequency. Such electrical stimulation is more accurately controlled than other types of stimuli. Nevertheless, striated muscle can also be caused to contract by mechanical stimuli such as tapping, stretching, or pinching, by chemical stimuli such as acids or salts, and by the application of heat.

The primary function of muscle is to contract, that is, develop tension and shorten. However, contraction is often described as four types: concentric (shortening), eccentric (lengthening), isometric (same length but increased tension), and isotonic (same tension but length changes).

Concentric contraction is the usual form of contraction, in which the muscle moves a bone or segment by shortening. An example would be flexion of the elbow by contraction of the biceps brachii.

Isometric contraction occurs naturally whenever a limb or portion of the body is held stationary against equal resistance such as gravity. In order to hold the head up in a fixed position, the dorsal neck muscles must contract isometrically.

Eccentric contraction occurs in the extensor muscles of the neck when an animal lowers its head gradually. Antagonistic muscles may also undergo eccentric contraction when unsuccessfully opposing the actions of a prime mover.

Isotonic contraction refers to a contraction in which the length of the muscle changes but the tension remains the same. This occurs primarily when a muscle lifts a given weight. The weight is constant; therefore the tension does not change.

Factors Influencing Contraction

Treppe. Treppe *(staircase effect)* is the repeated increase in strength of contraction of a muscle fiber due to successive stimulations a few seconds apart (Fig. 12–11). The strength of contraction continues to increase for about 30 contractions. This effect may be due to an increasing concentration of Ca^{++}

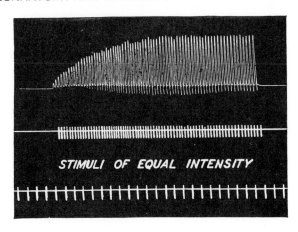

Fig. 12–11. The staircase phenomenon. Application of electrical stimuli in rapid succession to a frog heart whose spontaneous beat is arrested induces contractions of gradually increasing strength. Changes occur in the heart muscle as a result of one stimulus, making it more contractile when stimulated a second time, unless too long an interval elapses between stimuli. Skeletal muscle also displays this phenomenon. Time is shown in 5-second intervals. (Carlson, Johnson and Cavert, The Machinery of the Body, courtesy of the University of Chicago Press.)

ions within the muscle fiber, which increases activation of the myofibrils.

Although this phenomenon may appear to violate the "all or none" law, remember that each contraction is a separate entity, and for the given conditions each contraction will be maximal or will not occur. Thus, the conditions change for each contraction, but the law still holds. Treppe is generally regarded as a "warm-up" phenomenon wherein a rested muscle builds up greater contraction strength to its maximum ability by repeated stimulation at optimal frequency. The frequency, however, must not exceed that which allows for a complete return of the recorded spike to its recovery baseline, as seen in Figure 12–11.

Summation. Apart from Treppe, each *gross* muscle is capable of contracting with varying degrees of strength. This is the re-sult of summing the contractions in two ways.

Multiple motor unit summation occurs when more motor units are stimulated to contract simultaneously in the gross muscle. Therefore, more muscle fibers and bundles are contracting and producing greater strength in the whole muscle.

Wave summation occurs when the frequency of stimulation is increased to a motor unit or units. That is, the frequency of stimulation is such that the first contraction is not over by the time the second contraction begins. The two become additive, which increases the contraction strength. Ordinarily, in normal muscle function, both types of summation occur at the same time.

Tetany (Tetanus). When the frequency of stimulation (wave summation) becomes so rapid that no further increase in frequency

Fig. 12–12. Tetanus in skeletal muscle. When stimuli are applied to a muscle at a gradually increasing rate of frequency (indicated by signal), the individual muscle twitches blend together, so that when the stimuli are applied in rapid succession, a smooth, sustained contraction results. Note that the height of contraction is greater in tetanus than in a single twitch. Time is shown (bottom line) in 5-second intervals. (Carlson, Johnson and Cavert, The Machinery of the Body, courtesy of the University of Chicago Press.)

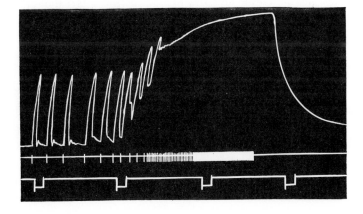

will increase the tension of contraction, then the greatest force that the muscle can develop will have been reached. This is called *tetany, tetanus,* or the *state of tetanization.* All these terms are defined as a continuous tonic spasm of muscle or a steady state of contraction (Fig. 12–12). However, the disease caused by the toxin from *Clostridium tetani,* which produces spasm of the masseter muscles (lockjaw) followed by a spasm of other muscles, is specifically referred to as tetanus. In this case, the only difference is the chemical cause, not the manifestation of spasm. Tetany (tetanus) is also caused by such conditions as hypoparathyroidism, vitamin D deficiency, hypophosphatemia, and hypocalcemia (low levels of calcium).

Fatigue. Fatigue is a decrease in work capacity caused by work itself. More specifically, the length of time that muscle tension or contraction can be maintained depends on the ability to supply calcium and energy, in the form of ATP, to the contractile protein filaments. As the total available ATP supply is decreased, the force of contraction decreases and the muscle gets progressively weaker and weaker. This drop in contraction force following prolonged stimulation is called *muscle fatigue* (Fig. 12–13). The time of its onset varies considerably with the type of fiber and muscle involved.

Fatigue can occur at *any* state of contraction or frequency of stimulation that is reasonably prolonged, including tetany. The nerve impulses to the muscle, the neuromuscular junction, and the muscle action potentials continue without fatiguing, so that it is only the energy supplied by ATP and CP in the myofibrils that becomes exhausted. This, of course, also depends on the blood supply to the muscle for adequately bringing in the nutrients and oxygen, and taking away the metabolic wastes. Muscle contraction compresses the blood vessels in the muscles and thereby decreases blood flow during prolonged contraction. This produces *ischemia* (lack of blood) which, along with fatigue, and the buildup of lactic acid, causes *muscle cramps.*

Rigor and Rigor Mortis. If most of the ATP becomes depleted in a muscle, the calcium can no longer be sequestered back into the sarcoplasmic reticulum by the calcium pump. Therefore, relaxation cannot occur, because the actin and myosin filaments become bound in a continuous contracted state. This is the state of extreme fatigue that is called *rigor* or *physiologic contracture;* it is sustained until more ATP is made available to sequester the calcium back into the longitudinal tubules. Relaxation of muscle requires a high concentration of ATP, whereas contraction persists at low concentrations of ATP.

Rigor mortis is essentially the same as rigor, except that it occurs a few hours after death. ATP is no longer available, the muscle loses its tone, and calcium is gradually released from the sarcoplasmic reticulum. The muscles of the whole animal progressively become stiff and rigid because the filaments lock together or seize in the presence of the calcium, without ATP to sequester the calcium and separate the cross-bridges. The rigidity continues until cell au-

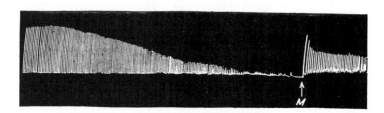

Fig. 12–13.   Fatigue. Contractions of a muscle (recorded by means of a muscle lever) induced by rapidly repeated stimuli to the nerve of the muscle. (Carlson, Johnson and Cavert, The Machinery of the Body, courtesy of the University of Chicago Press.)

tolysis and protein degradation breaks down the muscle to the relaxed state.

Tone. The term "muscle tone" refers to the slight tension exhibited by all muscles at rest. It is due to the continuous transmission of impulses at very low frequency from the spinal cord to the muscles. Tone keeps muscles in a state that is receptive to contraction-strength stimuli and prevents them from hanging flaccid (flabby-like), as occurs in paralysis.

When an animal becomes anxious, fearful, or excited, the muscle tone becomes intensified. Therefore the muscles become more taut (tension increases), and the animal will then respond faster to any stimulus. This is often seen in the "skittish," "nervous," or "jumpy" animal. During sleep, on the other hand, muscle tone is low to allow for optimal relaxation.

Measurement of Contraction

Abnormalities of contracture, as well as normal function, can be tested by a procedure called *electromyography*. This involves placing electrodes on the skin over a muscle, or inserting pin-electrodes through the skin into the muscle, and then recording the potentials produced as changes occur in the polarity of the muscle membrane. The recording obtained is called an *electromyogram* (EMG). The measurable changes are in principle like those of an electrocardiogram of the heart (ECG).

Elasticity of a muscle fiber is due largely to the sarcolemma and connective tissue surrounding the fiber. If the tendons are cut, a muscle will shorten about 20% of its normal resting length, due to elasticity. This new length with zero tension is called the *resting length*. The fiber can be stretched about one and one-half times the resting length without permanent damage. When stretched excessively, rupture of a muscle fiber usually occurs at less than three times resting length.

The rate of contraction and amount of shortening of a muscle depend on the load it must lift. With no load at all, the speed of contraction and amount of shortening are greatest. As the load increases, both speed and amount of shortening decrease. With a load too heavy to lift, the speed becomes zero but the tension is maximum, producing an isometric contraction.

The maximum amount a muscle fiber can contract is to about one-half of its resting length. This would also be true of a complete muscle only if the fibers are equal and parallel, as in the abdominal muscles.

Reciprocal innervation of muscles is an arrangement whereby the antagonists relax when the agonists are stimulated to contract in a given muscular action. This arrangement produces efficient use of muscles by ensuring that the muscles producing a specific action (the agonists) do not have to overcome resistance from muscles with opposite actions (the antagonists).

If the muscle fibers are arranged in a pennate manner, distance of contraction will be about one-half the length of the individual fibers. This distance, which may be called the *physiologic length* of the muscle, is the distance from the origin of the muscle fiber to the place on the tendon of insertion where the particular fiber attaches.

Likewise, measurement of the strength of contraction of a muscle must be based on the *physiologic cross-sectional area* of the muscle and not simply by cutting across the muscle at right angles to the tendon (unless the muscle fibers are parallel). The physiologic cross-sectional area is difficult to measure or calculate for pennate muscles, as all muscle fibers must be cut at right angles. Estimates of strength of contraction of human muscle fibers range from 35 to 150 lbs/inch^2.

The physiologic cross-sectional area of parallel muscles is small compared with the physiologic cross-sectional areas of pennate muscles. The physiologic length of parallel muscles is relatively greater than the physiologic length of pennate muscles. For the same volume of muscle fibers, long parallel muscles have a greater distance of contraction but are relatively weak, while pennate muscles have a shorter distance of contraction but are much stronger.

Since almost all bones act as levers and most joints act as fulcrums, the law of levers can be used to determine the mechanical advantage or disadvantage of a particular muscle. The *law of levers,* which applies equally well to all three classes of levers (Fig. 12–14), states that resistance times the resistance arm equal force times the force arm (R × RA = F × FA). The pivot point, called the *fulcrum,* is the point on the lever about which the lever rotates. The fulcrum may be located at either end of the lever or any place between the ends. The *force arm* is measured from the fulcrum to the point of application of the force. In the body the force is usually applied where the tendon of insertion of a muscle attaches to the bone. The *resistance arm* is measured from the fulcrum to the point on the lever where the resistance is applied. In some cases in the animal body resistance may be represented simply by the weight of a limb, or a segment of a limb. In extreme cases the weight of the entire animal may represent the resistance.

Most of the levers used in everyday life exhibit a mechanical advantage because the force arm is longer than the resistance arm. For example, a relatively small person can lift one wheel of a heavy car off the ground by placing a pole over a block located near the axle of the car. The segment of the pole from the fulcrum (block) to the resistance (axle) is the resistance arm. The long segment from the fulcrum to the point where the force is applied is the force arm. If the force arm is 10 feet long and the resistance arm is 1 foot long, every pound of force applied to the force arm will lift 10 pounds on the resistance arm. However, for every foot the resistance arm is raised, the force arm must be depressed 10 feet, so the gain in force is offset by the greater distance the force arm must move.

In most instances in the animal body the muscles are working at a mechanical disadvantage. The force arm is shorter than the resistance arm, so the muscles must exert a much greater force than the resistance they overcome. Thus we see the desirability of having pennate muscles attached to the short arm of a bony lever. The pennate arrangement gives increased strength at the expense of distance, while the lever with a mechanical disadvantage requires greater force but gives increased distance of move-

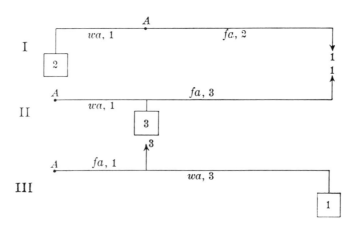

Fig. 12– 14.   The three classes of levers. The long straight lines are the levers; *A,* is the axis; the squares represent the weight or resistance and the arrows the force or pull of muscle; *fa,* force-arm; *ra,* resistance weight-arm. Numerals in the squares and beside the arrows are the magnitudes of the weights (or resistances) and of the effort forces respectively. The other numerals indicate the length of the lever arm. (From Rasch, P. J., and Burke, R. K.: Kinesiology and Applied Anatomy, ed. 6. Philadelphia, Lea & Febiger, 1978.)

ment. Examples of this combination of pennate muscles attaching to the short arm of a lever include the *triceps brachii*, which attaches to the olecranon process of the ulna; the *middle gluteus*, which attaches to the greater trochanter of the femur; and the gastrocnemius, which attaches to the *tuber calcis* of the hock. In each of these examples the limb distal to the joint where the muscle attaches is the resistance arm.

Angle of pull, the angle at which a tendon meets the segment (bone) to which it attaches, is also an important factor in the efficiency of muscle action. The force exerted by a muscle usually results in two components. The *rotary component* is that portion of the total force which tends to cause movement (rotation) in the joint. The other component, the *stabilizing component*, is that portion of the total force that tends to hold in apposition the segments making up the joint. If the muscle pulls at right angles (exactly 90°) to the segment to which it attaches, the entire force acts as a rotary component. However, if the pull is parallel to the segments (0°), the entire force acts as a stabilizing component. The larger the angle of pull up to 90°, the larger is the rotary component, and the smaller is the stabilizing component. The smaller the angle of pull, the greater is the stabilizing component, and the smaller is the rotary component.

If the angle of pull and the total force are known, both the rotary component and the stabilizing component can be calculated by trigonometry or by a scale drawing of a parallelogram of forces.

The graphic determination of rotary and stabilizing components is illustrated in Figure 12–15, using 30° as an example of a specific angle of pull. A right triangle is constructed on a scale diagram. The base of the triangle extends along the segment to which

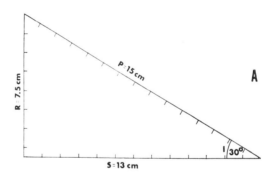

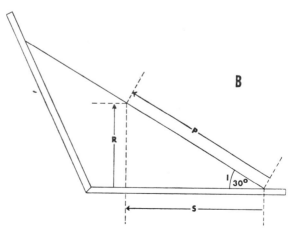

Fig. 12–15. Construction of a right triangle for determining components of muscular force.

the tendon of insertion attaches (usually the distal segment). The hypotenuse extends along the line of pull of the muscle meeting the segment at the predetermined angle (30° in this example). The pull of the muscle in pounds, converted to convenient units of linear distance, is then measured along the hypotenuse from the angle. If the total force (pull) of the muscle is assumed to be 150 lbs, 15 cm ($\frac{150}{10}$) is measured along the line of pull from its intersection with the distal segment. The altitude of the right triangle is constructed at right angles to the base so that it (the altitude) intersects the line of pull exactly 15 centimeters from the apex of the original angle. The altitude of this triangle represents the rotary component, which can now be determined by measuring the line in centimeters and multiplying by 10 to convert the linear measure to pounds. Likewise, the base of the triangle represents the stabilizing component, which can also be converted to pounds by multiplying by 10, since 1 cm represents 10 lbs. In this example the following may be found:

ric means. Since the sine of an angle in a right triangle is the ratio of the side opposite (rotary component) to the hypotenuse (side opposite divided by the hypotenuse), the value of the hypotenuse multiplied by the sine of the angle gives the value of the side opposite (rotary component). In our example, the hypotenuse (total force of 150 lbs) multiplied by the sine of 30° (the angle of pull), which is 0.5, equals 75 lbs, the rotary component.

The cosine of an angle is the ratio of the side adjacent to the angle (stabilizing component) divided by the hypotenuse. The cosine of 30° is 0.866. To find the stabilizing component in our example, the hypotenuse (total force of 150 lbs) is multiplied by 0.866 (cosine of 30°), which equals 129.9 or approximately 130 lbs.

Either the graphic method or the trigonometric method can be used for any angle of pull and any force to calculate the rotary component and the stabilizing component. However, as the muscle moves the distal segment by contracting, the angle of pull

hypotenuse	= line of pull	= 15.0 cm = 15.0 × 10 = 150 lbs
altitude	= rotary component	= 7.5 cm = 7.5 × 10 = 75 lbs
base	= stabilizing component	= 13.0 cm = 13.0 × 10 = 130 lbs

Anyone familiar with plane geometry will recognize this method as an application of the *Pythagorean theorem*, which states the relationship of the sides of any right angle: "the square of the hypotenuse is equal to the sum of the squares of the other two sides."

By using a table of sines and cosines, the value of the total force, and the angle of pull, the rotary component and the stabilizing component can be calculated by trigonomet-

constantly changes, so that the relationship of stabilizing component to rotary component changes at the same time.

Thus we see that the final effect of contraction of a single muscle is influenced by a number of factors, which include the physiologic cross section of the muscle, the mechanical advantage or disadvantage of the muscle (law of levers), and the angle of pull of the muscle.

Chapter *13*

The Skin and Associated Structures

The skin consists of two layers: a superficial covering of stratified squamous epithelium, the *epidermis,* and a deeper layer of dense irregular connective tissue, the *dermis* (also known as the *corium*). This general arrangement of two layers of the skin is found throughout the body, including areas of modified epidermal structures such as hair, horns, hooves, chestnuts, and ergots.

EPIDERMIS

The epidermis is stratified squamous epithelium that in most areas can be divided into a deep growing layer, the *stratum basale (germinativum),* and a superficial hornlike layer, the *stratum corneum* (Fig. 13–1). The stratum basale follows the contour of the underlying papillary layer of the dermis, to which it is closely applied. Epidermal cells range in shape from cuboidal or columnar cells, which are undergoing mitosis in the deepest layers of epidermis, to spindle-shaped cells of the *stratum granulosum* and flattened cells of the stratum corneum.

Cells in the deepest layers of the stratum germinativum undergo active mitotic division, which pushes the more superficial layers still farther from the blood vessels in the corium. As distance from nutrients increases, the cells flatten and die. The drying and hardening of the superficial cells, a process called both *keratinization* and *cornification*, probably are related to the decreased nutrition of these cells.

The stratum corneum actually appears as stratified squamous epithelium, since the cells are flat and plate-like. These keratinized cells with degenerate nuclei are constantly in the process of flaking off the

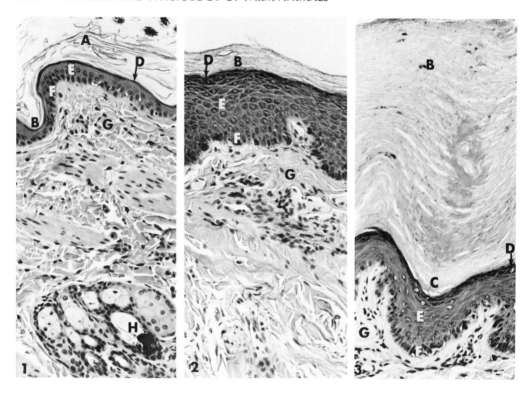

Fig. 13–1. Epidermis, cat. *1*, Hairy skin with thin epidermis, lumbar region. *2*, Nonhairy skin with thicker epidermis, nose. *3*, Footpad with thick stratum corneum. Stratum disjunction *(A)*; stratum corneum *(B)*; stratum lucidum *(C)*; stratum granulosum *(D)*; stratum spinosum *(E)*; stratum basale *(F)*; superficial layer of the dermis *(G)*; hair follicle *(H)*. H & E × 200. (From Dellmann, H–D., and Brown, E. M.: Textbook of Veterinary Histology. Philadelphia, Lea & Febiger, 1976.)

surface of the skin in the form of *dandruff*. The thickness of the stratum corneum is greatest in areas subjected to considerable wear, such as ordinary calluses and the foot pads of dogs.

The rate of cell division in the deeper layers of the epidermis increases under the influence of a number of different factors. Increased blood supply to the dermis from any cause will stimulate production of epidermal cells. Irritation or pressure will also stimulate increased cellular production, as seen in *callus* formation.

Modified epidermal structures produced by specialized areas of the stratum germinativum, including hair, hooves, and horns, are described later in this chapter.

DERMIS

The dermis, also known as the corium, can be subdivided into a papillary layer immediately deep to the epidermis and consisting of ridges and nipple-like projections, and a deeper reticular layer that makes up the major part of the dermis.

Arteries, veins, capillaries, and lymphatics of the skin are concentrated in the dermis. Sensory nerve fibers, in addition to supplying the dermis, also extend a short distance into the epidermis. Hair follicles, especially those of tactile hairs, are well supplied with sensory nerves. Sympathetic nerves from the gray rami communicans of the spinal nerves supply sweat glands, sebaceous glands, and arrector pili muscles in the dermis.

COLOR OF SKIN

Color of skin is due to the presence of pigment granules, *melanosomes,* within the cytoplasm of the pigment cells *(melano-cytes)*. The pigment is melanin; the dark colors result from the dispersion of melanin granules into the cell cytoplasmic processes or surrounding tissues, whereas light colors are a result of concentration of granules near the nucleus. Dispersion of pigment is under the influence of *melanocyte-stimulating hormone* (MSH, intermedin), which is released from the intermediate lobe of the pituitary gland. In lower forms of life, this hormone permits rapid changing of skin color, but higher vertebrates do not have this ability. Absence of pigment in the skin (albinism), which may be partial or total, can be dangerous because it makes the animal more susceptible to the effects of sunlight, particularly after ingestion of certain feeds, including *buckwheat* and *alsike clover*. This condition, in which the unpigmented areas of the skin become edematous (filled with fluid) and may even slough off, is called *photosensitization*. Lack of pigment in the iris as well as lack of pigment in the skin surrounding the eye may cause extreme sensitivity to light; this condition appears in *albinos*. Cattle with white skin surrounding the eyes are much more susceptible to cancer of the eye than cattle with dark skin surrounding the eyes.

HYPODERMIS

In nearly all areas of the body, the dermis is separated from underlying structures such as bone and deep fascia by a layer of loose (areolar) connective tissue. This areolar connective tissue, known as the *superficial fascia, subcutis,* or *hypodermis,* is important because it permits movement of the skin without tearing. It is also important because it permits a layer of fat (panniculus adiposus) to be interposed between the skin and deeper structures. This is not possible if the skin is adherent to these structures, as in the case of a *tie*, where the dermis is attached to one or more vertebral spinous processes.

HAIR

Hair covers almost the entire body of most domestic animals, but many variations in hair structure exist between species and in different areas of an individual animal. A *hair follicle* develops first as a thickening and then as an ingrowth of epidermis into the corium of the skin (Fig. 13–2). This forms a column of epithelial cells with a bulbous enlargement on the deep end, into which a connective tissue papilla is invaginated. The hair follicle consists of a connective tissue sheath surrounding a double-layered epithelial sheath. The internal epithelial root sheath intimately covers the root of the hair and is continuous with the epithelial cells covering the papilla. The external epithelial root sheath surrounds the internal root sheath, is continuous with the epidermis, and gives rise to the sebaceous glands that are associated with hair follicles. The epithelial cells covering the papilla actually form the hair itself. Growth and multiplication of these cells extrude the hair from the follicle, causing it to grow.

When a hair is ready to shed, the epithelial cells over the papilla stop multiplying and become cornified. The papilla atrophies and the hair may fall out, be pulled out, or be pushed out by a new hair that develops from epithelial sheath cells in a manner similar to the hair formation just described.

A typical hair consists of an inner *medulla,* an outer *cortex,* and a thin covering, the *cuticle* (Fig. 13–3). The medulla may contain pigment, which has little effect on hair color, but air between medullary cells is believed to give a white or silver color to the

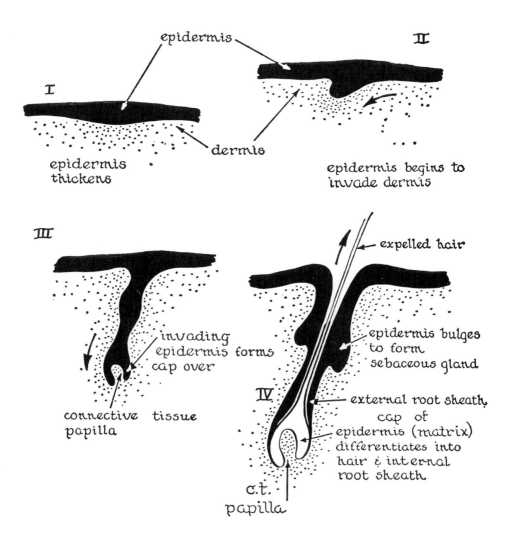

Fig. 13–2.   Sketches illustrating the embryologic development of a hair follicle and a sebaceous gland. (Redrawn and slightly modified from Addison: Piersol's Normal Histology, J. B. Lippincott Co.)

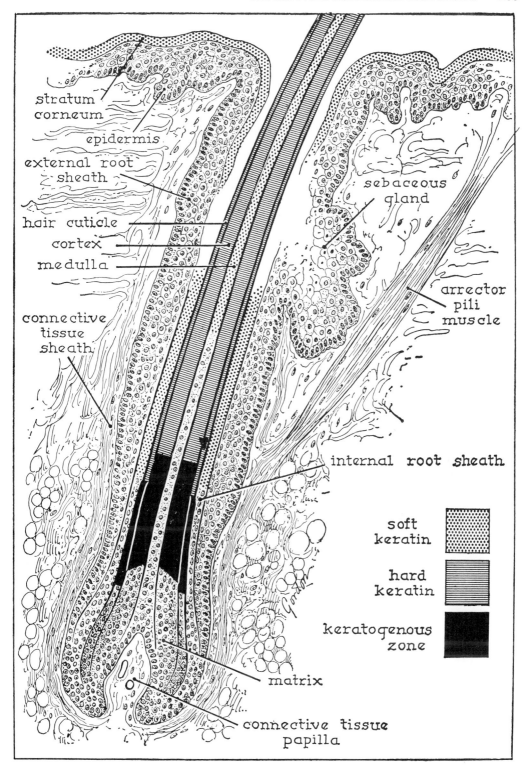

stratum corneum

epidermis

external root sheath

hair cuticle

cortex

medulla

connective tissue sheath

sebaceous gland

arrector pili muscle

internal **root sheath**

soft keratin

hard keratin

keratogenous zone

matrix

connective tissue papilla

Fig. 13–3.   Diagram of a hair follicle, showing the distribution of soft and hard keratin and the keratogenous zone in which hard keratin is produced. (Based on C. P. Leblond: Ann. New York Acad. Sc., *53*, 464.)

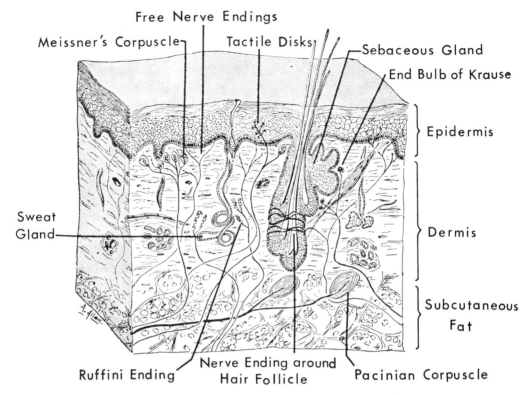

Fig. 13–4. Schematic representation of the nerve supply to the skin. (Modified after Woolard et al. 1940 and Gardner, 1963. In Miller, Christensen, and Evans, Anatomy of the Dog, courtesy of W. B. Saunders Co.)

hair if the cortex lacks pigment. The major part of the hair is the cortex, which consists of several layers of cornified cells. The amount and type of *melanin* in cortical cells determine whether the hair will be black, brown, or red. The cuticle is a single layer of thin, clear cells covering the surface of the cortex.

In addition to regular cover hair, domestic animals have wool hairs and tactile hairs. *Wool* forms the fleece of sheep. It is crimped (wavy) and lacks a medulla, and the connective-tissue portion of the follicle is sparse. *Tactile hairs (pili tactiles)*, used as probes or feelers, are also called *sinus hairs* because a large blood sinus is located in the connective-tissue portion of the follicle. Sinus hairs are particularly well supplied with sensory nerve endings that are sensi-

tive to the slightest movement of the hairs (Fig. 13–4).

Coat Color in Horses

A study by Gremmel (1939) gave most of the following information about *coat color* in horses. Hair color is due to only one pigment, and differences in color are caused by variations in the amount and location of the pigment. The pigment was never found scattered diffusely throughout the hair but always as clusters of granules. Scattered small smooth clusters of granules permit light to pass through the hair and produce a light color coat such as light chestnut. Densely packed, large, irregular clusters of pigment permit no light transmission, giving a black color to the hair. Variations in pigment clusters between these extremes were found in intermediate coats, including liver chestnuts and mahogany bays. The diluted appearance of dun horses was believed to be caused by a greater concentration of pigment on one side of the hair shaft than on the other. A lack of pigment clusters in the superficial part of the cortex was seen in hairs from brown or white muzzles of dark horses.

Standard colors of horses include black, brown, bay, chestnut, ysabella, dun, gray, roan, pinto, and possibly albino.

Black consists of uniformly black hairs, including the mane and tail. *Brown* is a modification of black, with reddish hair on the muzzle, on the flanks, and under the eyes.

Bay is a reddish coat with black mane and tail.

Chestnut varies from somewhat golden to red, with mane and tail of about the same color, but never black.

Ysabella, which includes *palomino*, varies from a golden to red coat, but the mane and tail are flaxen or silver.

Dun resembles a diluted bay or chestnut with black mane and tail and a dark stripe on the dorsal mid-line.

Gray consists of an approximately equal mixture of white and black hairs. Gray horses are usually born black or some other dark color, and the proportion of white hairs to dark hairs increases with age.

Roan is a mixture of white hairs with some other color. Blue roan consists mostly of white and black hairs with possibly a small amount of some other color. Strawberry roan consists of a mixture of white hairs and chestnut hairs. Other colors may be mixed with white to give the respective roan color.

Pinto (paint) has irregular white areas alternated with colored areas. If the colored areas are black, the coat is called *piebald,* but if they are any color except black, the coat is called *skewbald.*

In all colors except *albino*, the skin is pigmented, but the true albino lacks pigment both in the skin and in the hair. The white hair of the pinto, roan, and gray indicates a partial albino.

ARRECTORES PILORUM MUSCLES

Arrectores pilorum muscles are bundles of smooth muscle fibers that extend from the deeper portion of the hair follicle at an angle toward the epidermis. Hair follicles usually are at an angle to the surface of the skin other than 90°, and the arrectores pilorum muscles are attached to the side of the follicle, forming an obtuse angle with the surface of the skin, so that contraction of the muscle will straighten the hair. This action has the obvious advantage of increasing the insulating value of the coat during cold weather and may also be used by some animals immediately preceding and during battles, presumably as a means of bluffing the opponent by increasing the apparent size of the animal. These arrectores pilorum muscles are supplied by sympathetic nerves.

SEBACEOUS GLANDS AND SUDORIFEROUS GLANDS

Sebaceous glands are classified as holocrine glands because the secretory products are produced by disintegration of epithelial cells within the glands. The glands derived from hair follicles are located in the triangle between the hair follicle, the surface of the skin, and the arrector pili muscle; they empty into the hair follicle. Contraction of the arrector pili muscle compresses the glands and aids in emptying them. Sebaceous glands that open directly onto the skin surface include sebaceous glands in the ear canal, tarsal sebaceous glands of the eyelid, sebaceous glands around the anus, sebaceous glands on the penis, prepuce, and labia vulvae, and in the sheep, sebaceous glands in the infraorbital pouches, interdigital pouches, and inguinal pouches. Sebaceous glands of sheep produce the product called *lanolin.*

With a few exceptions, *sudoriferous glands* or *sweat glands* (tubular skin glands) can be found over the entire bodies of farm animals, including the horse, cow, sheep, pig, and dog. However, the horse is the only farm animal that sweats readily. The nose of the dog lacks sweat glands, but the *planum nasolabiale* of the cow, *planum nasale* of the sheep, and *planum nasale* of the pig (all areas of the muzzle) have tubular glands that are not generally classed as sweat glands. Many modified epithelial structures, including hooves and horns, lack sweat glands.

MODIFIED EPIDERMIS

Much of the modified epithelium is based on a connective-tissue corium (dermis) that is in the form of papillae or in the form of laminae (sheets). In some places this corium is directly continuous with the underlying *periosteum*. Although the corium is often called the sensitive portion of the foot or horn, implying that it produces the corresponding insensitive structures, the insensitive portion actually represents the stratum corneum and is produced by the deepest layer of the epidermis, the stratum basale (germinativum).

FOOT OF THE HORSE

The foot of the horse has a bony base that consists of the distal one-half of the second phalanx, the entire third phalanx and the distal sesamoid (navicular) bone. Covering the bone and some adjacent structures is a highly vascular modified dermis called the *corium of the foot*. The corium is regionally named according to the insensitive structures it underlies and includes the *perioplic corium, coronary corium, laminar corium, corium of the sole*, and *corium of the frog*. Figure 13–5 shows the blood and nerve supply of the foot, and Figure 13–6 shows the horny structures and parts of the hoof.

The *hoof* is the insensitive cornified layer of epidermis covering the distal end of the digit. Corresponding sensitive structures underlie all insensitive structures, and pigmentation of the germinating (sensitive) layer determines the color of the hoof

proper. *White hooves* are found where the hair at the upper margin of the hoof is also white, and *dark hooves* are associated with dark hair in this area. Black hooves are much tougher and stronger than *nonpigmented* (white) *hooves*, which tend to be somewhat brittle and chalky.

The insensitive structures of the hoof include the periople, wall, bars, laminae, sole, and frog. Each is produced by a corresponding sensitive structure consisting of the germinating layer of epidermis closely applied to the underlying corium of the same name, which is well supplied with vessels and nerves. With the exception of the ribbon-like laminae, all sensitive structures present papillae that produce some type of insensitive horn tubules.

Hoof Wall

The hoof wall is the portion of the foot that is visible when the horse is in a standing position. It is divided into a toe region in front, medial and lateral quarters on the sides, and medial and lateral heels behind that turn sharply forward at the angles to be continued by the bars. The wall consists of three layers: the periople and tectorial layer superficially, the tubular layer making up the bulk of the wall, and the laminar layer that connects the hoof wall with the third phalanx (see Figs. 13–7 to 13–10).

The major portion of the wall consists of parallel horn tubules cemented together by intertubular horn (cornified material between tubules). The tubules are produced by thousands of papillae on the convex surface of the *coronary band (coronet)*, a crown-shaped cushion that fits into the coronary groove in the top of the hoof wall and marks the junction of the skin and hoof. The tubules extend distally from the coronary band to the ground surface of the hoof. The *tectorial layer* of the hoof wall is the dense cornified surface of the hoof. The proximal part of the tectorial layer is covered by periople.

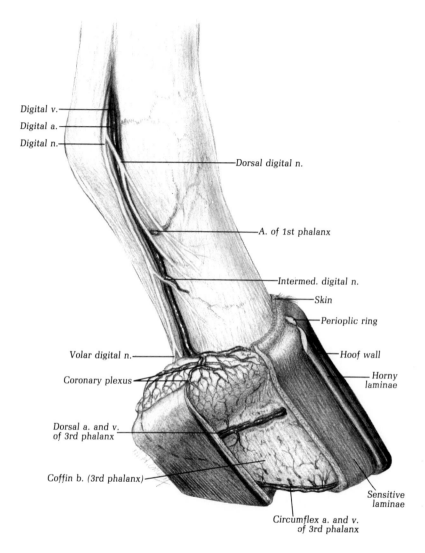

Digital v.

Digital a.

Digital n.

Dorsal digital n.

A. of 1st phalanx

Intermed. digital n.

Skin

Perioplic ring

Volar digital n.

Hoof wall

Coronary plexus

Horny laminae

Dorsal a. and v. of 3rd phalanx

Coffin b. (3rd phalanx)

Sensitive laminae

Circumflex a. and v. of 3rd phalanx

Fig. 13–5.   Lateral view of blood and nerve supply of digit. (From Emery, L., Miller, J., and Van Hoosen, N.: Horseshoeing Theory and Hoof Care. Philadelphia, Lea & Febiger, 1977.)

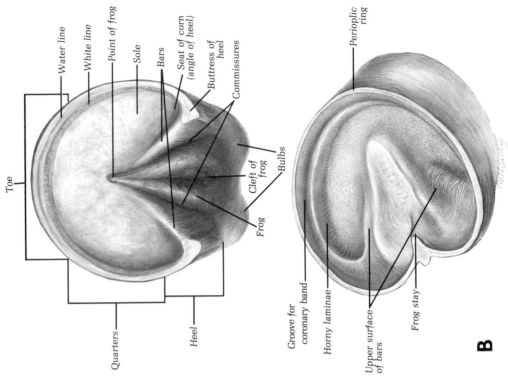

Fig. 13–6. (A) Horny structures of hoof. (B) Parts of the hoof. (From Emery, L., Miller, J., and Van Hoosen, N.: Horseshoeing Theory and Hoof Care. Philadelphia, Lea & Febiger, 1977.)

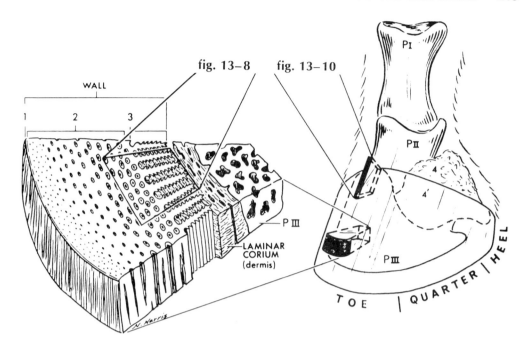

Fig. 13–7.   Frontolateral view, equine foot. The wall of the hoof is composed of three layers; (1), stratum externum, stratum medium (2), stratum internum (laminar layer) (3); proximal *(PI)*, middle *(PII)*, distal *(PIII)* phalanges; lateral cartilages of the hoof (4) and (4'). (From Stump, J. E.: Anatomy of the normal equine foot, including microscopic features of the laminar region. J. Am. Vet. Med. Assoc., *151*:1588, 1967.)

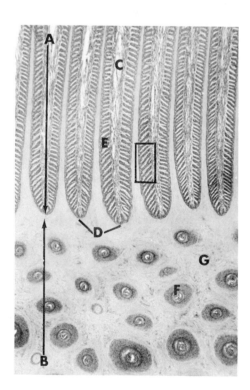

Fig. 13–8.   Wall of hoof, horse, from area marked in Figure 13–7. Stratum internum*(A)*; stratum medium*(B)*; laminar corium *(C)*; primary lamina *(D)*; secondary laminae*(E)*; tubular horn*(F)*; intertubular horn*(G)*. H & E × 38. (From Dellmann, H. -D.: Veterinary Histology: An Outline Text-Atlas. Philadelphia, Lea & Febiger, 1971.)

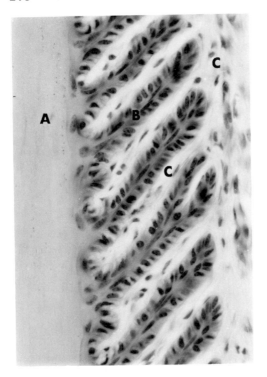

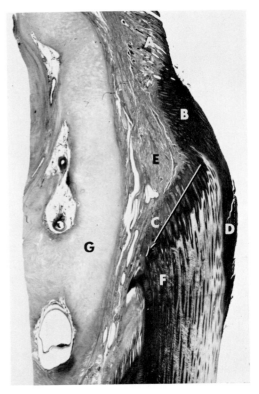

Fig. 13–9.   Secondary laminae, hoof, horse. See area marked in Figure 13–8. Primary lamina of the wall (A); secondary lamina (B); laminar corium (C). H & E, × 435. (From Dellmann, H.-D.: Veterinary Histology: An Outline Text-Atlas. Philadelphia, Lea & Febiger, 1971.)

Fig. 13–10.   Vertical section of hoof, horse. See area marked in Figure 13–7. Skin (A); periople (B); epidermis lining the coronary groove (C); stratum externum (D); coronary corium (E); stratum medium (F); hyaline cartilage (G). Trichrome. × 3. (From Dellmann, H.-D., and Brown, E. M.: Textbook of Veterinary Histology. Philadelphia, Lea & Febiger, 1976.)

Periople

The periople is a thin layer of tubular horn that covers the wall for a variable distance distally from the coronet, usually about an inch. It turns a milky white when the hoof is soaked in water. The periople is produced by the narrow *perioplic band* just above and concentric with the coronary band.

Laminar Corium

The laminar corium is adherent to the periosteum over the convex surface of the third phalanx. The primary sensitive laminae radiate from the laminar corium like vertical ribbons with one edge attached to the corium and the other touching the tubular part of the hoof wall. Each primary lamina has up to 100 secondary laminae that are also parallel to the wall tubules but are at right angles to the primary laminae. Alternating with the sensitive laminae and related to them are an equal number of insensitive laminae attached to the tubular wall. Weight or force applied to the third phalanx is transmitted by this system of interlocking leaves to the wall of the hoof, so that in a sense the weight of the horse is suspended from the hoof wall by the combination of sensitive and insensitive laminae. This arrangement also permits the hoof wall to slide (grow) distally in relation to the third phalanx without disrupting the attachment, because the insensitive laminae move with the wall and the sensitive laminae remain attached to the periosteum of the third phalanx.

Sole

The sole of the foot is a concave plate that attaches to much of the volar surface of the third phalanx. It includes all of the ground surface of the foot not occupied by the wall or the frog. The angles of the sole project caudally between the bars and heels of the wall. Normally, the concavity of the sole allows the wall and frog to bear most of the weight and wear. (See Fig. 13–11.)

Most of the *corium of the sole* is attached to the periosteum on the volar side of the third phalanx. It is covered by papillae that produce short horn tubules to make up the insensitive sole. The sole covers all of the volar side of the foot between the wall (and bars) and the frog.

Where the outer margin of the sole meets the inner margin of the wall, a narrow white mark appears that is known as the *white line*. It is useful as a landmark for driving nails in

shoeing. A properly directed nail started at or outside the white line will not touch any sensitive structures of the foot.

Frog

The *sensitive frog* is separated from the third phalanx, the navicular bone, and the insertion of the deep digital flexor tendon by the *digital cushion*, a thick wedge of fibro-fatty subcutaneous tissue. Papillae of the sensitive frog form the insensitive frog, a thick triangular structure with the apex pointing craniad and the base located between the heels. Each side of the frog is flanked by a deep groove called the *collateral sulcus* that separates each side of the frog from the respective bar. The *central sulcus of the frog* is a sagittal groove in the middle of the volar side of the base of the frog. The *frog stay* is a sagittal ridge on the dorsal surface of the insensitive frog above

Fig. 13–11.   Typical attitude of a horse with laminitis. The rear feet are carried up further forward to help take more weight off the forefeet, which are extended anteriorly. This horse had laminitis following a respiratory infection. He was beginning to lose the hoof walls as evidenced by cracking at the coronary band. Hoof wall changes were minimal but the sole had dropped and the third phalanges were protruding through the soles of the forefeet. (From Adams, O. R.: Lameness in Horses. ed. 3, Philadelphia, Lea & Febiger, 1974.)

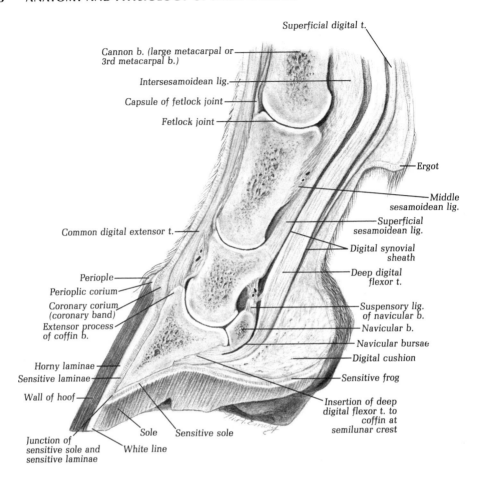

Superficial digital t.

Cannon b. (large metacarpal or 3rd metacarpal b.)

Intersesamoidean lig.

Capsule of fetlock joint

Fetlock joint

Ergot

Middle sesamoidean lig.

Superficial sesamoidean lig.

Common digital extensor t.

Digital synovial sheath

Deep digital flexor t.

Periople

Perioplic corium

Coronary corium (coronary band)

Extensor process of coffin b.

Suspensory lig. of navicular b.

Navicular b.

Navicular bursae

Digital cushion

Horny laminae

Sensitive laminae

Sensitive frog

Wall of hoof

Insertion of deep digital flexor t. to coffin at semilunar crest

Sole   Sensitive sole

Junction of sensitive sole and sensitive laminae

White line

Fig. 13–12.   Sagittal section of digit. (From Emery, L., Miller, J., and VanHoosen, N.: Horseshoeing Theory and Hoof Care. Philadelphia, Lea & Febiger, 1977.)

the central sulcus. It cannot be seen unless the entire frog is removed from the foot.

Figure 13–12 shows a sagittal section of the foot of the horse.

FEET OF OTHER ANIMALS

The individual digit (claw) of the cow, goat, sheep, and pig in a general way resembles the digit of the horse, except for the presence of bars and frog in the horse and their absence in the other animals.

A convenient terminology for the digits of *artiodactyla* (even-toed animals) is to refer to the digits by number (III and IV in cow and sheep), and then relate each digit to the midline of the respective foot. The *axial* side of the digit is the side closest to the midline of the foot and the *abaxial* side is the side farthest from the midline of the foot.

The *hoof wall* consists of a nearly vertical axial portion that reflects sharply caudad at the toe line to be continuous with the abaxial portion of the wall. The toe is the area of junction of axial and abaxial portions of the wall at the ground surface. The *toe line* is the sharp ridge on the cranial side of the digit that extends from the toe in a proximal direction as far as the *perioplic band*.

Both the axial and abaxial surfaces of the hoof wall are continuous caudally with the bulb of the heel. The *bulb* forms the major part of the ground surface of the digit because the true sole is restricted to a small zone at the toe and a narrow strip adjacent to the wall.

Each insensitive structure (wall, periople, bulb, and sole) is related to a corresponding sensitive structure. The *perioplic corium* is a narrow band with long papillae at the junction of skin and coronary corium.

The *coronary corium* is a much wider band than in the horse and extends as much as one-third of the distance from the perioplic band to the ground. The width of the coronary band is maintained as it passes caudad to blend with the *bulbar corium*. This occurs about three-quarters of the distance back on the abaxial side and about half the way back on the axial side. Papillae of the bulbar corium are longer than those of the coronary corium.

The *laminar corium* is much less extensive than in the horse. It is restricted to the area on both axial and abaxial surfaces, that is, cranial to the bulbar corium and distal to the coronary corium. The corium of the sole, although less extensive, resembles that of a horse.

HORNS

Horns of cattle and sheep are formed over the *horn process*, a bony core that projects from the frontal bone of the skull (Fig. 13–13). The corium of the horn completely envelops the horn core and fuses with its periosteum. The corium at the base of the horn is thick where it joins the skin proper and has many long slender papillae. The papillae become shorter and more sparse toward the apex of the horn, and some laminae are found parallel to the long axis of the horn. The horn itself consists largely of horn tubules that extend from the base of the horn toward the apex of the horn, with only a few laminae inside the horn associated with the laminae of the corium. A soft type of horn called the *epikaras* covers the surface of the horn at the base and extends a variable distance toward the apex of the horn. The epikaras resembles periople of the hoof.

Seasonal variations in level of nutrition of the animal are reflected in variations in growth of horn, resulting in a series of rings on the horn. The age of the animal may be estimated by counting the rings on the horn.

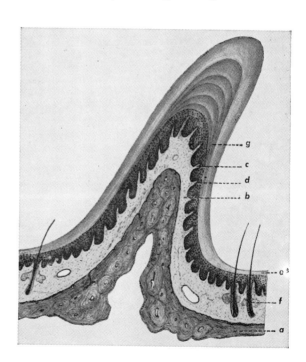

Fig. 13–13. Longitudinal section through the horn and cornual process of the calf. *a*, Horn process of the frontal bone; *b*, corium covering *a*; *c*, papillae; *d*, stratum germinativum; *e*, stratum corneum of the skin; *f*, hairs with sebaceous glands; *g*, stratum corneum of the cornual epidermis. (Trautman and Fiebiger, Fundamentals of the Histology of Domestic Animals, courtesy of Comstock Publishing Associates.)

Dehorning can be accomplished by destroying the corium when only *"buttons"* are present, either by surgical removal of the button, or by its destruction with a hot iron or with caustic material. After the horn has started to develop, the entire corium must be removed along with the horn and horn core to ensure complete dehorning. If ¼ inch of skin at the base of the horn is removed with the horn, there will be no chance for regrowth of horn. If any corium is left, a crooked horn stub may develop.

DEWCLAWS

Other areas of modified epidermis are the coverings of the dewclaws of the cow, the pig, and the sheep, and the chestnuts and ergots of horses. A *dewclaw* is essentially a miniature digit, and its covering resembles a hoof of the same animal. The medial dewclaw represents digit number II and the lateral dewclaw represents digit number V, except in the dog, in which the dewclaw is digit number I. Dewclaws of the pig have a bony basis similar to other digits; those of cattle and sheep have neither metacarpal bones nor phalanges. Front dewclaws of dogs usually have phalanges; hind dewclaws usually do not.

CHESTNUTS

Chestnuts are horn-like growths on the medial sides of horses' legs. The front chestnuts *(torus carpalis)* are located above the carpus on the medial sides of the forearms, and the hind chestnuts *(torus tarsalis)* are located on the medial sides of the hocks. Chestnuts are larger and heavier in work horses than in riding horses, and may even be absent in some light breeds.

ERGOTS

Ergots *(torus metacarpalis* and *metatarsalis)* are small projections of cornified epithelium in the center of the caudal part of the fetlock. The tuft of hair at the fetlock hides the ergot in most instances.

Some authorities consider the chestnut to be a vestige of the first digit and the ergot to be a vestige of the second and fifth digits of extinct forms of the horse.

Chapter 14

Anatomy and Physiology of the Foot of the Horse

Structure
  Tendons
  Ligaments
  Synovial Structures
  Cartilages

Function
  Stay Apparatus
  Concussion-Absorbing Mechanisms
  Considerations in Shoeing

The anatomy of the hoof was described in the preceding chapter. Insensitive structures discussed included the periople, the wall, the laminae, the sole, and the frog. The corium of each respective part was also discussed.

A common definition of the *foot* of the horse is "the hoof and all of the structures contained within it." However, if the feet of the horse are considered equivalent to the hands and feet of man, the front foot *(manus)* will include all structures from the carpus (knee) distally and the hind foot *(pes)* will include all structures from the tarsus (hock) distally. This concept is desirable for a relatively complete discussion of the function of the foot, since it involves much more than just the hoof and its contents.

STRUCTURE OF THE FOOT

Other structures relating to the foot include the three *phalanges*: proximal (first),

middle (second), and distal (third); the *metacarpus* (cannon), the two *proximal sesamoid bones* at the back of the fetlock, and the *distal sesamoid (navicular) bone* located at the volar side of the *coffin joint*. There are also a number of ligaments, tendons, and synovial structures that are important in this area.

Tendons

No muscle bellies extend below the carpus or tarsus in the mature horse. The tendons of several muscles in the forelimb and several muscles in the hindlimb continue into the foot, where each tendon inserts on one or more phalanges, as described in "Muscles Acting on the Digit," p. 175.

The tendon of the *deep digital flexor muscle* passes down the volar side of the metacarpus, across the fetlock, and over the proximal and distal sesamoids; it inserts on the volar portion of the distal phalanx, which is the most distal extent of any tendon.

221

The *superficial digital flexor tendon* passes distally on the metacarpal region just superficial to the deep digital flexor tendon. Below the fetlock the superficial digital flexor tendon divides into two branches, which pass on each side of the *deep digital flexor tendon* and insert at the proximal end of the middle phalanx and the distal end of the proximal phalanx. These two muscles, as their names imply, are flexors of the digit. Their tendons are involved in *bowed tendon*, a disorder seen commonly in race horses and occasionally in other riding horses.

The *common digital extensor tendon* passes down the dorsal aspect of the metacarpus, over the fetlock, and inserts on the extensor process of the distal phalanx.

In the forelimb, the *lateral digital extensor* tendon inserts on the proximal end of the proximal phalanx after pursuing a course lateral to the common digital extensor tendon. In the hindlimb, the lateral digital extensor tendon joins the tendon of the *long digital extensor muscle*, which is similar to the common digital extensor tendon of the forelimb.

Ligaments

The ligaments of the foot include the medial and lateral collateral ligaments of each joint: the fetlock joint, the pastern joint, and the coffin joint (Fig. 14–1). These are the typical ligaments found in any *ginglymus joint*. In addition, there is a special ligament known as the *suspensory ligament*. In animals with more than one digit, a considerable amount of muscle tissue is usually present in this structure; in such animals, it is called the *interosseous muscle*.

The suspensory ligament or interosseous muscle is found between the metacarpal bones and the deep digital flexor tendon. It attaches proximally to the proximal end of the metacarpal bones (metatarsal in the hindleg) and to the distal row of carpal (or tarsal) bones. It passes down between the small metacarpal bones on the volar surface of the large metacarpal bone in the horse.

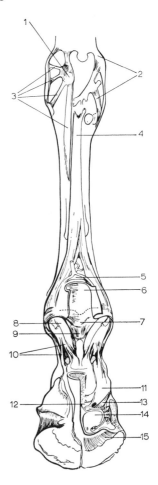

Fig. 14–1. Diagrammatic illustration of some structures in the stay apparatus. Some accessory structures are also shown. *1*, Accessory carpal bone; *2*, medial collateral ligaments of the carpus; *3*, ligaments of the accessory carpal bone; *4*, suspensory ligament; *5*, diverticulum of metacarpophalangeal (fetlock) joint; *6*, volar annular ligament of the fetlock (cut and reflected); *7*, intersesamoidean ligament; *8*, middle or oblique distal sesamoidean ligament; *9*, superficial or straight sesamoidean ligament; *10*, volar ligaments of proximal interphalangeal (pastern) joint; *11*, medial collateral ligament of the pastern joint; *12*, diverticulum of the distal interphalangeal (coffin) joint; *13*, suspensory ligament of the navicular bone; *14*, flexor surface of navicular bone; *15*, insertion of deep digital flexor tendon. (From Adams, O. R.: Lameness in Horses. ed. 3. Philadelphia, Lea & Febiger, 1974.)

Upon reaching the fetlock, the suspensory ligament divides into several branches. The main continuation of the suspensory ligament attaches to the proximal sesamoid bones and the *intersesamoidean ligament*, which binds these two bones together. In addition, there is a band extending across the fetlock on each side—a medial band and a lateral band, each of which passes across the fetlock to attach to the tendon of the common digital extensor muscle. This attachment is in the area of the proximal phalanx. The suspensory ligament acts as a strong supporting mechanism for the fetlock joint in addition to the deep digital flexor tendon and the superficial digital flexor tendon.

The *distal sesamoidean ligaments* of the proximal sesamoid bones bind these sesamoid bones primarily to the proximal phalanx, but also have some attachment to the middle phalanx. The distal sesamoidean ligaments include a superficial ligament, a middle ligament and two deep ligaments. The *deep sesamoidean ligaments*, also known as the *cruciate ligaments*, pass from a proximal sesamoid bone diagonally to the opposite side of the proximal end of the first phalanx, about the same level as the short ligaments.

The *middle sesamoidean ligament* extends from the distal end of the proximal sesamoid bones to attach to the volar aspect of the first phalanx.

The *superficial sesamoidean ligament* extends from the volar end of the proximal sesamoid bones distally to the proximal end of the middle phalanx.

The *short sesamoidean ligaments* pass from each sesamoid to the respective side of the proximal phalanx. These can be seen only by opening the joint capsule and looking downward.

The *distal sesamoid bone* has a number of ligaments associated with it. It has the *collateral sesamoidean ligaments (suspensory ligament of the distal sesamoid)* attached to each end of the distal sesamoid bone, and an additional ligament extends from the proximal side of the distal sesamoid to the T ligament that passes from the middle of the middle phalanx across to the deep digital flexor tendon.

The *proximal digital annular ligament* is a thickening of the deep fascia in the area of the fetlock. The fibers tend to run transversely, and this ligament binds the tendons of the superficial and deep flexor muscles into the groove on the volar side of the proximal sesamoid bones.

The *distal digital annular ligament* is located more distally and binds the deep digital flexor tendon at the very termination of the superficial digital flexor tendon, holding it close to the pastern.

Synovial Structures

Synovial structures related to the foot include the synovial sheath surrounding the superficial and deep digital flexor tendons in the area of the metacarpus. This synovial sheath occasionally is involved, as well as the tendons, in bowed tendon. The digital synovial sheath in the area of the fetlock extends as far distad as the T ligament going from the middle of the second phalanx to the deep digital flexor tendon. Just distal to this is the joint capsule of the coffin joint and also the *navicular bursa (bursa podotrochlearis)*, which is related to the distal sesamoid and the deep digital flexor tendon.

There is, of course, a joint capsule associated with each of the joints—the fetlock joint, the pastern joint, and the coffin joint. There are also several bursae relating to the tendons of the common digital extensor and the lateral digital extensor as they pass over the fetlock joint on the way to the extensor process of the distal phalanx and first phalanx.

Cartilages

The *collateral cartilages* are two rhomboid-shaped cartilages attached to the angles of the distal phalanx (Fig. 14–2). These cartilages extend caudad and proximad into the area of the heel proximal to the coronary border of the hoof. The cartilages can be felt above the heel and should be flexible. Their elasticity aids in the proper

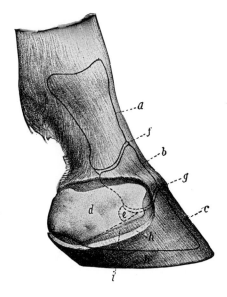

Fig. 14–2. Digit of horse showing surface relations of bones and joints. The collateral cartilage is largely exposed. *a*, First phalanx; *b*, second phalanx; *c*, third phalanx; *d*, collateral cartilage; *e*, distal sesamoid or navicular bone; *f*, pastern joint; *g*, coffin joint; *h'*, cut edge of wall of hoof *(h)*; *i*, laminar corium. (Adams, Lameness in Horses, ed. 3. Lea & Febiger, 1974.)

functioning of the foot in pumping blood away from the foot.

Ossification of the cartilages is a condition called *sidebones* (Fig. 14–3). Infection involving the collateral cartilages produces a condition called *quittor* (Fig. 14–4).

FUNCTION

The primary function of the foot can be summed up in the word "locomotion." A secondary function is that of standing support. As an aid to efficient locomotion, the foot absorbs concussion and provides leverage for muscles that insert on bones of the foot and produce the drive.

Support in standing is provided by both the stay apparatus of the foreleg and the stay apparatus and the reciprocal apparatus of the hind leg.

The Stay Apparatus

The stay apparatus may be defined in both the forelimb and hindlimb as those structures that permit the horse to stand with relatively little muscular activity in the limbs.

The stay apparatus forms a flexible and somewhat elastic support of the fetlock and is essentially the same in both the front leg and in the hindleg. Structures making up the stay apparatus include the suspensory ligament, the intersesamoidean ligament between the two proximal sesamoids, the distal sesamoidean ligaments of the proximal sesamoids, and the short sesamoidean ligaments. These ligaments, together with the proximal sesamoid bones, form a sort of sling across the caudal surface of the fetlock that helps prevent excessive hyperextension (settling) of the fetlock. The collateral ligaments of the fetlock and the collateral sesamoidean ligaments are sometimes included as part of the stay apparatus because they help to hold the fetlock and sesamoid bones in position and prevent lateral or medial deviation of the segments.

Forelimb. In the forelimb, with the exception of the long head of the *triceps muscle,* all structures of the stay apparatus are either completely tendinous or are tendinous portions of certain foreleg muscles (Fig. 14–5). Tendinous parts of the *serratus ventralis muscle* form a sling to support the trunk between the two scapulae, even with the muscular portion relaxed. The *biceps brachii* muscle has a tendon running throughout its length from the scapula to the front of the radius. When the elbow is extended by the triceps, the tension on the distal end of the biceps will tend to keep the shoulder joint extended also. A part of the biceps brachii tendon also connects to the fascia covering the *extensor carpi radialis* muscle and in this way indirectly maintains extension of the carpus. The common digital extensor tendon has no action as long as the horse remains standing without moving the foot.

The *superior check ligament* or *accessory ligament* (also called the radial head of the superficial digital flexor) is a heavy ligamentous structure that attaches to the

Fig. 14-3. Ossification of collateral cartilages of the third phalanx (sidebones). (From Adams, O. R.: Lameness in Horses. ed. 3. Philadelphia, Lea & Febiger, 1974.)

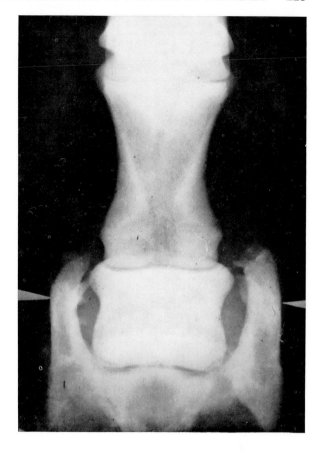

Fig. 14-4. Clinical appearance of typical quittor. Arrows point to two draining tracts. This horse was cured by making an elliptical incision above the coronary band. The anterior tract led posteriorly, and only the posterior tract had to be followed to necrotic cartilage. (From Adams, O. R.: Lameness in Horses. ed. 3. Philadelphia, Lea & Febiger, 1974.)

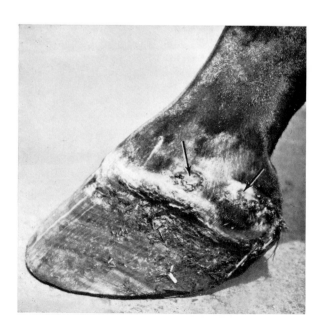

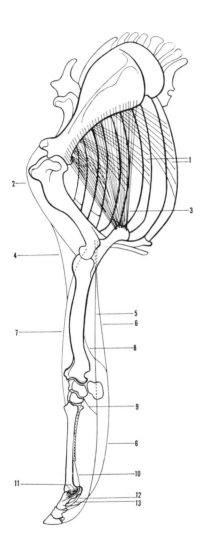

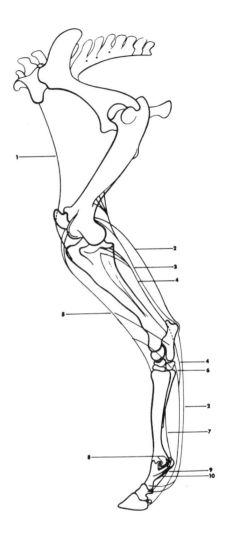

Fig. 14–5. Stay apparatus of forelimb (not all structures are shown). *1*, Fibrous sheet of serratus ventralis; *2*, tendon of biceps brachii; *3*, long head of triceps; *4*, lacertus fibrosus; *5*, deep digital flexor; *6*, superficial digital flexor; *7*, extensor carpi radialis; *8*, proximal (superior) check ligament; *9*, distal (carpal) check ligament; *10*, suspensory ligament; *11*, combined collateral sesamoidean ligament and collateral ligament of fetlock joint; *12*, superficial (straight) distal sesamoidean ligament; *13*, middle (oblique) distal sesamoidean ligament. (From Adams, O. R.: Lameness in Horses. ed. 3. Philadelphia, Lea & Febiger, 1974.)

Fig. 14–6. Stay apparatus of hindlimb (not all structures are shown). *1*, Tensor fascia lata; *2*, superficial digital flexor; *3*, gastrocnemius; *4*, deep digital flexor; *5*, peroneus tertius; *6*, tarsal (inferior) check ligament; *7*, suspensory ligament; *8*, combined collateral sesamoidean ligament and collateral ligament of fetlock joint; *9*, superficial (straight) distal sesamoidean ligament; *10*, middle (oblique) distal sesamoidean ligament. (From Adams, O. R.: Lameness in Horses. ed. 3. Philadelphia, Lea & Febiger, 1974.)

caudal side of the distal end of the radius and to the tendon of the superficial digital flexor. The *inferior check ligament* has a proximal attachment to the distal row of carpal bones and to the proximal end of the large metacarpal (cannon) bone. Distally it joins the tendon of the deep digital flexor. Both the superior and inferior check ligaments assist the suspensory ligament in supporting the fetlock even if the muscular portions of the digital flexors are relaxed.

Hindlimb. In addition to structures supporting the fetlock described previously, the stay apparatus of the hindlimb includes the tensor fasciae latae, peroneus tertius muscle, superficial digital flexor muscle, deep digital flexor muscle and its tarsal check ligament, and possibly the gastrocnemius muscle.

RECIPROCAL APPARATUS OF THE HIND LEG. The hind leg has a reciprocal apparatus not found in the foreleg. The reciprocal apparatus consists of the *peroneus tertius muscle* on the front of the leg, extending from the femur to the tarsus, and the *superficial digital flexor muscle* on the back of the leg, extending from the femur to the tuberosity of the calcaneus (point of the hock). Both of these muscles are almost entirely tendinous and contain little if any actual muscle tissue in the horse.

These two muscles, in combination with the distal end of the femur and the tarsus, form a parallelogram, with the *stifle joint* and *hock joint* acting as pivots. This arrangement forces the hock joint and the stifle joint to move in unison; when the stifle extends, the hock extends, and when the stifle flexes, the hock also flexes. In other words, both joints must extend and flex at the same time. Thus, if the stifle is maintained in extension, the leg distal to the stifle will bear the weight of the horse with little additional muscular effort. The part of the superficial digital flexor that passes from the point of the hock to the digit has no effect on the stifle and therefore does not function as a part of the reciprocal apparatus. Although the gastrocnemius muscle is not entirely tendinous, sometimes it is included in the reciprocal apparatus.

Concussion-Absorbing Mechanisms

A large part of the *mechanism* for *absorbing concussion* depends on angulation of the joints of the limbs at the time of impact and immediately following contact of the foot with the ground. The muscles, tendons, and ligaments act as springs that absorb the shock of impact by permitting some flexion of all the limb joints except the fetlock joint, the pastern joint, and the coffin joint, which hyperextend on bearing weight. The elasticity of the ligaments and tendons of the digits also aids propulsion by helping to straighten the digit before it leaves the ground, thus adding impetus to the drive.

The hoof and its contents absorb concussion because of the elasticity of the hoof wall, the collateral cartilages, the digital cushion, and the frog. As the frog strikes the ground, both the digital cushion and the frog are compressed between the phalanges and the ground. This causes them to become wider and thinner. Pressure on the bars, the collateral cartilages, and the wall spreads the heels and also forces blood out of the vascular bed of the foot. The direct cushioning effect of the frog and digital cushion is enhanced by the resiliency of the wall and the hydraulic shock-absorbing effect of the blood confined within the hoof wall. At the same time the hoof is expanded by frog pressure, blood is forced out of the vascular sensitive structures of the foot against some resistance, which not only absorbs concussion but also pumps blood out of the foot and into the veins of the leg against gravity. This pumping action of the foot is an important means of returning venous blood from the foot to the general circulation.

Elasticity of the Hoof. Elasticity of the hoof is associated with moisture content of the horn material. Smith (1912) gives moisture content of the wall as 24.735%; of the sole, 37.065%; and the frog 42.54%. The frog is more elastic than the sole or wall. There is an increasing elasticity of the wall from the toe to the heel that is correlated with the decreasing thickness of the wall in this direction, and with the decreasing age of the hoof from the toe to the heel. The young, thin wall of the heel is more elastic than the older, thick wall at the toe. To take full advantage of this elasticity, the shoe should be nailed only as far back as the quarters.

Considerations in Shoeing

So-called *physiologic horseshoeing* maintains normal function of the foot by interfering as little as possible with most structures of the foot. The ground surface of the hoof wall is leveled in a manner to maintain the normal axis of the foot without lowering either the heels or toes excessively. To preserve moisture in the hoof, the outside of the hoof wall should be rasped only below the nails to form a groove for the clinches, and the surface of the sole should be left intact to prevent loss of moisture. To maintain frog pressure, the frog should never be lowered; only loose strands of tissue should be removed.

After the hoof wall is leveled, the shoe should be fitted to the foot rather than fitting the foot to the shoe. The heel of the shoe should be about ¼ of an inch longer than the heel of the foot, and should be about ⅛ of an inch wider at the heel ($^1/_{16}$ of an inch on each side) than the foot to permit weight bearing during expansion of the heels when the foot bears weight.

The nails should be started at the white line with the bevel toward the inside of the shoe, so the nail will bend away from the sensitive structures of the foot. It is desirable to have the nails emerge in an even line about ¾ of an inch above the junction of the hoof and shoe.

Contraction of the heels, because of lack of frog pressure, is a common result of shoeing that does not follow physiologic principles.

Chapter *15*

Blood and Other Body Fluids

Single-celled organisms that live in sea water have an external environment that provides all the needs of the organisms, such as food, disposal of excreted wastes, and relatively constant conditions for maintenance of life. As the complexity of organisms has increased, the problem of supplying each cell with a proper environment has become more acute. Higher forms of animals have developed circulating blood and the fluids derived from it as a means of maintaining a relatively constant environment for all cells.

Blood consists of cells bathed with a fluid called plasma. Most blood cells remain within blood vessels but the leukocytes may migrate through vessel walls to combat infections.

Most of the functions of blood are included in the following list:

1. Blood carries nutrients made available by the digestive tract to body tissues.

2. It carries oxygen from the lungs to the tissues.

3. It carries carbon dioxide from tissues to the lungs.

4. Waste products from various tissues are carried to the kidneys for excretion.

5. Hormones are carried from endocrine glands to other organs of the body.

6. Blood plays an important part in temperature control by transporting heat from deeper structures to the surface of the body.

7. Water balance is maintained partly by the blood.

8. Buffers such as bicarbonate in the blood help maintain a constant pH of tissues and body fluids.

9. The clotting ability of blood prevents excess loss of blood from injuries.

10. Blood contains important factors for defense of the body against disease.

229

FORMED ELEMENTS OF BLOOD

The formed elements of the blood include red blood cells, white blood cells, and blood platelets. Because the red blood cells and the platelets both lack nuclei, they are not typical cells (see Fig. 1–9).

Erythrocytes

Red blood cells or *erythrocytes* (Gr. erythro—red, cyte—cell) are cells averaging 7.5μ in diameter which specialize in the transportation of oxygen. They are biconcave disks, having a thick, 1.5-μ circular margin, and a thin center (Figs. 15–1, 15–2). The biconcave disk has a relatively large surface area for oxygen exchange across the cell membrane.

The presence of *hemoglobin* within the erythrocyte is responsible for its ability to transport oxygen and for the red color of the erythrocytes. Chemically, hemoglobin is a complex organic compound composed of four red porphyrin pigments (hemes), each of which contains an atom of iron, plus globin, which is a globular protein consisting of four amino acid chains (Fig. 15–3). Hemoglobin combines with oxygen from the air of the lungs to form *oxyhemoglobin*, which in turn readily gives up its oxygen to tissue cells within the body. Because of the presence of hemoglobin, blood can carry about 60 times as much oxygen as a similar quantity of water under the same conditions.

Oxygen from the lungs forms a loose combination with each iron of hemoglobin (Hb), and the product is oxyhemoglobin (HbO$_2$). This process is *oxygenation* and not a true oxidation. It requires the presence of ferrous iron in the hemoglobin molecule. The combined oxygen is proportional to the amount of iron present, with two atoms of oxygen combined with each atom of iron. Each gram of hemoglobin will transport about 1.34 ml of oxygen. When the blood reaches tissues deficient in oxygen, the loosely held oxygen of the oxyhemoglobin is given up readily.

The iron is absorbed from the diet by epithelial cells of the duodenal mucosa after the food leaves the stomach (Fig. 15–4). From there the iron enters the blood capillaries in the mucosa, where the β-globulin *transferrin* combines with and carries the iron. Most of the iron goes to the bone mar-

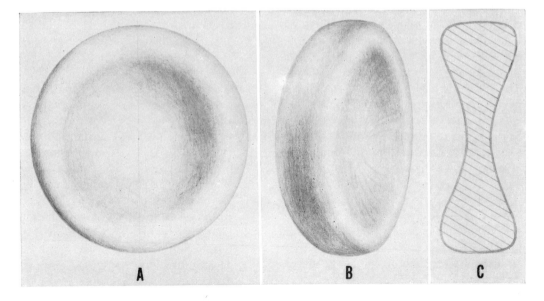

Fig. 15–1.   Red blood cell (erythrocyte). *A*, Viewed from above; *B*, viewed from an angle; and *C*, cross section.

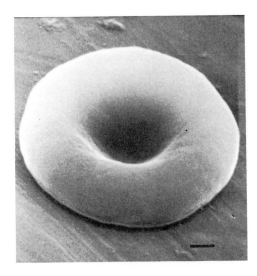

Fig. 15-2. The normal mature erythrocyte as visualized by the scanning electron microscope (× 9800). (Courtesy of Dr. Wallace N. Jensen. From Wintrobe, M. M.: Clinical Hematology, 7th ed. Philadelphia, Lea & Febiger, 1974.)

Succinyl coenzyme A + glycine
↓
δ-aminolevulinic acid
↓
porphobilinogen
↓
uroporphyrinogen III
↓
coproporphyrinogen III
↓
protoporphyrin IX + iron
↓
Heme
↓
4 heme + globin ——→ hemoglobin

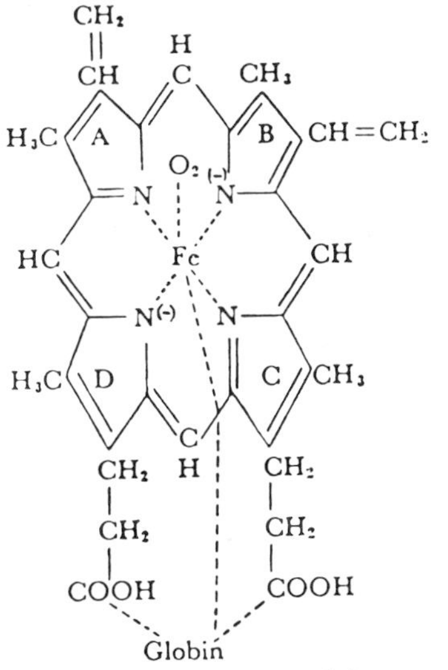

Fig. 15-3. Structure of hemoglobin.

row to become part of the heme molecules for developing erythrocytes. A small amount is used in forming myoglobin in the muscles. About 25% combines with *apoferritin* in tissue cells to form *ferritin*, which is a temporary storage form for the iron especially in the liver and spleen. Iron is lost from the animal body in the feces, urine, and sweat. The female gives up iron to the developing fetus during pregnancy and during nursing of the newborn.

Methemoglobin is a true oxidation product of hemoglobin that is unable to transport oxygen because the iron is in the ferric (Fe^{+++}) rather than the ferrous (Fe^{++}) state. Certain chemicals, such as nitrite and chlorates, produce methemoglobinemia (presence of methemoglobin in the blood). Nitrate poisoning has been reported in cattle grazing on highly fertilized rank plant growth. In these cases, nitrates in the plants are converted to nitrites in the rumen and cause the formation of methemoglobin when absorbed into the blood. Chlorates are sometimes used as weed killers and might be eaten by livestock.

Carboxyhemoglobin is a more stable compound formed when carbon monoxide (present in exhaust fumes) combines with hemoglobin. CO + Hb ——→ COHb. The affinity of Hb for CO is 210 times greater than its affinity for O_2. The carboxyhemoglobin is unable to carry oxygen, and the animal essentially dies of suffocation, although the blood is typically cherry red in color.

Cyanide poisoning, also called *prussic acid poisoning,* produces asphyxia (suffocation) by interference with internal respiration, the utilization of oxygen by tissues. It has no effect on the oxygen-carrying ability

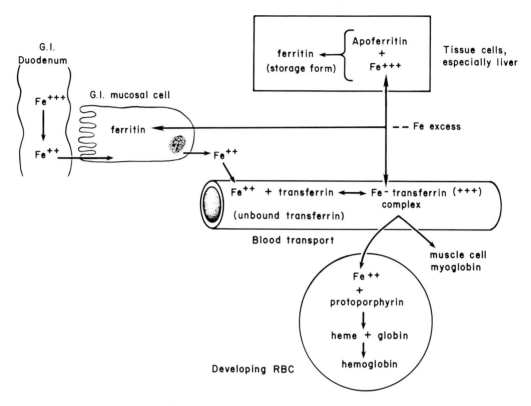

Fig. 15–4.   Iron absorption and distribution.

of the blood. Cyanide poisoning may occur when cattle eat stunted or frosted grain sorghums. *Methylene blue* is used in the treatment of cyanide poisoning because it forms methemoglobin in the blood, which reacts with the cyanide to form *cyanmethemoglobin*, a relatively inactive compound that is slowly degraded and detoxified by the body.

Formation of red cells in the adult occurs normally in the red bone marrow, which also produces granular leukocytes. However, in the fetus, red cells are also produced by the liver, the spleen, and the lymph nodes. Although mature red corpuscles of mammals have no nuclei, the immature cells, erythroblasts, from which they are derived, are nucleated. In birds, nuclei persist in the red cells throughout the life of the cells.

Destruction of red cells occurs after three to four months in the circulation. The red cells disintegrate, releasing Hb into the blood, and the broken cell debris is removed from the circulation by the *reticuloendothelial system*, which consists of special cells in the liver, spleen, bone marrow, and lymph nodes. These reticuloendothelial cells phagocytize (engulf) the debris. The fragments are digested and released into the blood. The globin protein fraction of the hemoglobin is degraded to amino acids. The iron is picked up by the globulin *transferrin* and is then either deposited in bone marrow for use again, combined and stored in the liver as *ferritin* for future use, contributed to form myoglobin in muscle, or stored in tissue cells as *hemosiderin*.

After the protein and iron are broken away from the Hb, a green pigment, *biliver-*

din, remains. This becomes reduced to *bilirubin*, which is transported to the liver by blood albumin. Here it is conjugated and passes to the gallbladder in the bile and finally into the intestine, where most of it is reduced to *bilinogens*. These are either excreted in the feces (giving the brown color to feces), or are excreted in the urine as *urobilinogen*. (See Fig. 15–5.) The reduction is accomplished by microorganisms in the intestine.

If an excess of bilirubin accumulates in the vascular system as a result of pathologic conditions in the liver-to-intestine phases, the visible mucous membranes, such as the mouth and eye, become yellow, a condition called *jaundice* or *icterus*.

Icterus may be caused by liver damage, by occlusion of the bile ducts, or by destructive blood diseases. In case of either liver damage or blockage of the bile ducts, the bile pigments are not secreted into the intestine but are resorbed into the circulatory system, causing icterus. When blood damage is excessive, as in some parasitic blood diseases such as *anaplasmosis*, the bile pigments are liberated into the blood faster than the liver can conjugate and secrete them, and icterus results.

Hemolysis is a breakdown of red cells so that the hemoglobin escapes into the plasma. It may be caused by bacterial toxins, snake venoms, blood parasites, hypotonic solutions, and many chemical substances. The resulting hemoglobin in the plasma gives it a reddish color, and the condition is called *hemoglobinemia*. If hemoglobin is excreted in the urine, the condition is called *hemoglobinuria (red water)*.

Hemagglutination is a clumping of red cells of blood. Usually cells from one species will agglutinate when injected into the blood of an animal of another species. Clumping may occur within the same

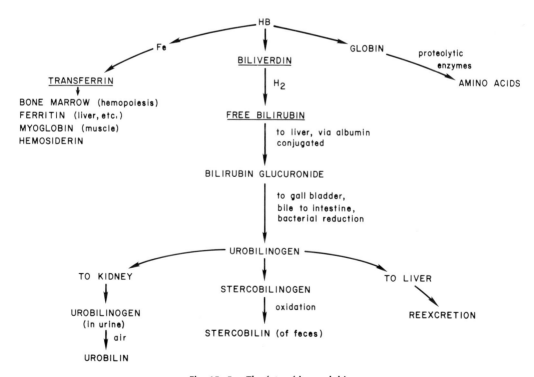

Fig. 15–5.   The fate of hemoglobin.

species, such as man, if blood of the wrong *type* is used. There appear to be a number of blood types in horses, so matching of the blood is desirable before attempting transfusion. Usually, little trouble is encountered in transfusing cattle or dogs with blood from another animal of the same species.

Sedimentation rate is a measure of the distance the red cells settle in citrated blood in a given period, usually thirty minutes or one hour. Standard *hematocrit tubes* are filled with blood and placed in an absolutely vertical position. The amount of settling is measured in millimeters at specified intervals. Sedimentation rates are increased in cases of acute general infections, malignant tumors, and pregnancy. Normal sedimentation rates and other blood values are shown in Table 15–1.

Blood counting provides a useful laboratory procedure for estimating the numbers and types of cells in the circulating blood of a given animal at a given time. Total cell counts are expressed as number of cells per cubic millimeter of whole blood. This is true of both red-cell counts and white-cell counts, although the equipment and technique are slightly different for each (Fig. 15–6).

Total red-cell count is determined by diluting a definite small amount of whole blood with a specific amount of diluting fluid in a red-cell pipette to produce a dilution of one part of blood to 200 parts of diluting fluid. The blood and fluid are thoroughly mixed in the special pipette and the counting chamber of a special slide is then filled with the mixture to a depth of 0.1 mm. One square millimeter of the counting chamber is ruled into 400 smaller squares. The red cells are counted in the 400 squares or a specified fraction of them. The number of red cells thus counted is multiplied by the proper number to give the total number of red cells

Table 15–1. Normal Values in Circulatory System

	Horse	Cow	Sheep	Pig	Dog
Sedimentation rate (mm/min)	2 to 12/10 15 to 30/20	0/30 0/60	0/30 0/60	0 to 6/30 1 to 14/60	1 to 6/30 5 to 25/60
Red blood cell count (million/cu mm)	7	7	11	7	7
Diameter of red cells (μ)	5.6	5.6	5.0	6.2	7.3
Hemoglobin (gm/100 ml)	12.5	12	11	12	13.5
Hematocrit (volume % of red cells)	42	40	32	42	45
White blood cells (thousands/cu mm)	9	9	8	15	12
Differential white count (%)					
Neutrophils	55	30	40	40	60
Eosinophils	4	5	4	2	5
Basophils	1	1	1	1	1
Monocytes	10	5	6	8	8
Lymphocytes	30	60	50	50	25
Blood pH (average and range)	7.4 (7.35 to 7.43)	7.3 (7.20 to 7.55)		7.4	7.5 (7.32 to 7.68)
Coagulation time (minutes)	11.5	6.5	2.5	3.5	2.5
Specific gravity	1.060	1.043	1.042	1.060	1.059
Heart rate/min (average and range)	32 to 44	60 to 70	70 to 80	60 to 80	70 to 120
Blood pressure (mm Hg, syst/diast)	80/50	134/88	114/68	169/108	148/100
Carotid pressure (mm Hg, average and range)	169 (159 to 194)	125 to 166	114 (90 to 140)	169 (144 to 185)	155 (120 to 176)
Blood volume (% of body weight)	9.7	7.7	8.0		7.2

*Data compiled from standard references, including Benjamin, Dukes, Payne, and Spector.

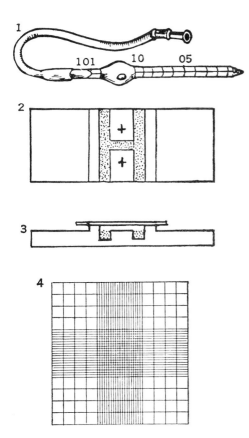

Fig. 15–6. Equipment for blood counting. Hemocytometer for counting the red blood cells. *1*, Pipette for diluting blood sample; *2*, glass slide, provided with two platforms on each of which ruled squares marked by +, and shown highly magnified in *4*, are engraved. Each square has an area of 1/400 sq mm; *3*, slide in cross-section with cover glass in position. (Best and Taylor, The Living Body, courtesy of Henry Holt and Co.)

blood due to hemorrhage from wounds or because of parasites such as stomach worms or lice. It is also caused by deficient secretion of *intrinsic factor* from the stomach; this factor makes vitamin B_{12} absorption possible. Anemia also occurs when blood cells are being hemolyzed faster than new ones can replace them, or if the red blood cells fail to mature normally.

The anemias have a considerable effect on the cardiovascular system. Obviously, the oxygen-carrying capacity of the blood is decreased. Also, a reduced concentration of RBCs means that the viscosity of the blood is reduced, and therefore it flows faster. Hypoxia occurs at the tissue level, which stimulates the heart to pump faster to try to deliver more oxygen. The heart is stressed to work harder. When the animal then works or is exercised hard, the heart cannot supply enough oxygen to the tissues and the efficiency of the heart decreases, which can produce acute heart failure.

Hemoglobin concentration is measured in grams per 100 ml of blood. Normal hemoglobin concentration ranges are 11 in sheep, 13.5 in dogs, 12 in cows and pigs, and 12.5 in the horse.

Hematocrit value, or packed cell volume, is a term that means the percentage (by volume) of whole blood that is constituted by red blood cells. It is determined by filling a hematocrit tube with blood treated so that it will not clot and then centrifuging the tube until the cells are packed in the lower end. The hematocrit value then is read directly or indirectly from the tube (Fig. 15–7). Normal hematocrit values are 32 in the sheep, 45 in the dog, 40 in the cow, and 42 in the horse and pig. The hematocrit is generally considered to be as useful as total red cell count, and is much easier to perform.

Hemoconcentration is the opposite of anemia, which means that the ratio of red cells to fluid is above normal. This is indicated by an excessively high red cell count or high hematocrit value. The total number of red cells in the body may be increased (a condition called polycythemia), or there

in 1 cu mm of diluted blood, and this number in turn is multiplied by the dilution to give the number of red cells in 1 cu mm of whole blood. Most domestic animals have a red-blood-cell count of about 7 million/cu mm.

Anemia (Gr. *an*—without; *emia*—blood) results if either the number of functional red cells or the quantity of hemoglobin is decreased much below normal. Anemia may be due to deficient blood formation because of poor nutrition, including dietary deficiency of iron, copper, vitamins, or amino acids. Anemia may also be caused by loss of

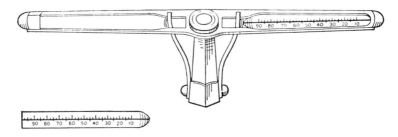

Fig. 15–7. Hematocrit. Blood to which sodium oxalate or other anticoagulant agent has been added is drawn into the graduated tubes which are then placed in the holder and rotated in a centrifuge at a rate of 3000 revolutions per minute. The blood is thus separated into a red (cells) and a straw-colored portion (plasma), the proportions of each being easily determined by means of the graduations on the tubes. (Best and Taylor, The Living Body, courtesy of Henry Holt and Co.)

may be a decrease of fluid. Either a lowered intake of water or excess loss of water can cause hemoconcentration, which then is a result of dehydration. Vomiting and diarrhea as well as diseases causing high temperatures, if continued over a long period, result in dehydration.

To correct *dehydration* it may be necessary to supply water to the animal in the form of physiologic saline or glucose solution *parenterally*. This means that it is given by some route other than by mouth, since an animal that is vomiting may be stimulated to vomit even more upon drinking water. Fluid may be injected *hypodermically* (under the skin), *intravenously* (into a vein), or *intraperitoneally* (into the peritoneal cavity in the abdomen).

Platelets

Blood platelets, also called *thrombocytes*, are fragments of *megakaryocytes*, large cells formed in bone marrow. Thrombocytes measure 2 to 4μ in size. They are surrounded by a plasma membrane and contain microtubules, lysosomes, mitochondria, and Golgi vesicles, but not nuclei. Thrombocytes range from 350,000 to 500,000/cu mm of blood. They are important in the clotting of blood.

The appearance of platelets in a stained smear may be considerably different from their actual appearance in circulating blood, where they are oval disks. In smears they may appear as circular disks, star-shaped fragments, or clumps of irregular shape. Electron microscope studies have shown that platelets contain mitochondria, vesicles, and granules, but relatively little *RNA* (ribonucleic acid).

Platelets function chiefly to reduce loss of blood from injured vessels. By adhering to vessel walls and to each other in the area of the injury, platelets may form a hemostatic plug upon which a white thrombus (clot) forms that can occlude the vessel and prevent further loss of blood. Materials released by platelets stimulate formation of an ordinary clot (as described later in this chapter), assist the retraction of a clot making it more solid, and help cause local constriction of the injured blood vessel. This last action is due to a substance called *serotonin* that is carried by the platelets.

Leukocytes

White blood cells, or leukocytes (Gr. *leuco*—white), differ considerably from erythrocytes in that they are nucleated and are capable of independent movement. Leukocytes are classified as follows:

Granulocytes
　Neutrophils
　Eosinophils
　Basophils

Agranulocytes
　Monocytes
　Lymphocytes

The life span of the white blood cells (WBCs) varies considerably—from only a few hours for granulocytes, to potentially months for monocytes, and years for lymphocytes. In the bloodstream itself, most of the white blood cells are nonfunctional and are only being transported to tissues when and where they are needed.

Granulocytes, as the name implies, contain granules within the cytoplasm that stain with common blood stains, such as Wright's stain. These stains contain an acid dye, eosin, which is red, and a basic dye, methylene blue, which is bluish. Granulocytes are named according to the color of the stained granules. The nuclei of granulocytes appear in many shapes and forms, leading to the name polymorphonuclear leukocytes (Gr. *poly*—many; *morpho*—form). Common usage restricts the term polymorphonuclear leukocyte to neutrophils. In the normal adult the granulocytes are formed in the red bone marrow.

Neutrophils contain granules that stain indifferently and are not notably red or blue. They constitute the first line of defense against infection by migrating to any area invaded by bacteria, passing through the vessel walls, and engulfing the bacteria to destroy them. In the process, many of the neutrophils also degrade dead (necrotic) tissue in the area, and the resulting semiliquid material is known as *pus.* A localized accumulation of pus is called an *abscess.* Actinomycosis (lump jaw) in cattle and distemper in horses frequently result in abscess formation in the mandibular lymph nodes.

The number of neutrophils in the blood increases rapidly whenever acute infection is present. A blood count showing this increase is useful in diagnosis of infections.

The neutrophils constitute the greatest number of all the WBCs. They reside to a great extent along the inner margins of the capillaries and small vessels—a phenomenon called *margination.* When tissue injury occurs, the neutrophils are mobilized from their marginal sites to the injury area, and they squeeze through the capillary walls between the cells *(diapedesis),* whereupon they migrate by ameboid movement into the tissues to phagocytize the foreign particles. The neutrophils are attracted to these sites because, when a tissue is injured, invaded, or otherwise insulted, *chemotoxic substances* are released from damaged cells or as toxins from bacteria. Not only do these result in inflammation, but they attract the neutrophils (and monocytes).

Upon phagocytizing (engulfing) the offending material, the lysosomal enzymes of the neutrophils "digest" the material. When its phagocytic capacity is reached, the neutrophil self-destructs (autolysis) and releases the degraded materials into the tissue fluids, where they can be carried away by the lymph. Also, the autolyzed neutrophil releases its lysosomal enzymes, which act on the surrounding tissue to release more chemotoxic substances, which attract more neutrophils into the area, until no more autolysis occurs.

The injured and damaged cells also release histamine, which helps to initiate the process of *inflammation.* Histamine dilates the capillaries, venules, and arterioles. This causes *hyperemia,* an increased localized blood flow, which accounts for the redness of the inflamed site. Dilation of the capillaries increases their permeability, which allows more fluid and protein to leak out and thereby creates a "brawny edema." In addition, fibrinogen leaks out of the vessels and causes coagulation in the tissues, which helps to produce a barrier against spreading of an infective agent, "walling off" the area of damage.

The inflamed tissue also apparently releases a globulin into the blood called *leukopoietic factor* or *colony-stimulating factor,* which acts on the bone marrow to (1) release some of its large reserve store of neutrophils into the blood, and (2) increase the rate of granulocyte formation. The resultant increase in the number of circulating neutrophils is called *neutrophilia.* Neutrophilia occurs whenever tissue damage is extensive. It also occurs during disseminated bacterial infection, cancer, metabolic poisoning, hemorrhage, and physiologically during exercise because the increased rate of blood flow decreases margination of the neutrophils along the inside of the blood vessels.

Eosinophils, also known as *acidophils*, show red-staining granules in the cytoplasm. These cells, which normally are scarce, increase in numbers in certain chronic diseases, such as infection with parasites.

Eosinophils are also ameboid and somewhat phagocytic. Their primary function seems to be the detoxification of either foreign proteins introduced into the body via the lungs or gastrointestinal tract, or toxins produced by bacteria and parasites. Their number also increases in allergic reactions.

Basophils, which contain blue-staining granules, are also rare in normal blood. Since they contain heparin (an anticoagulant), it is postulated that they release this in areas of inflammation to prevent clotting and stasis of blood and lymph. Being involved with inflammation, there is apparently a delicate balance between basophils and eosinophils in the initiation and control of inflammation. Basophils also contain some histamine. They may also possibly be the precursors of *mast cells*.

Agranulocytes (Gr. a—without) usually show few granules in the rather sparse cytoplasm. These cells include monocytes and lymphocytes.

Monocytes, the largest white blood cells, like neutrophils, are phagocytic; that is, they have the ability to engulf foreign matter such as bacteria. However, while the neutrophils act mainly in overcoming acute infections, the monocytes are called into action by less acute infections such as *tuberculosis*. When monocytes from the blood enter tissues, they develop into larger phagocytes called *macrophages*.

Lymphocytes are variable in size and appearance, and have a relatively large nucleus surrounded by a small amount of cytoplasm. One of the major functions of lymphocytes is their response to antigens (foreign substances) by forming antibodies that circulate in the blood or in the development of cellular immunity which will be discussed later in this chapter.

Total white cell counts are made in a manner similar to red cell counts. However, since white cells are much less numerous than red cells, the blood is not diluted as much, and the counting squares on the slide are larger. White cell counts are given in thousands per cubic millimeter of whole blood. The normal white cell count per cubic millimeter is 8 thousand in the sheep, 15 thousand in the pig, 9 thousand for the horse and cow, and 12 thousand for the dog.

Differential counts indicate the percentage of each type of white cell in the blood sample. If the total leukocyte count is much above normal for the particular species, this is important to know.

A differential count is made by spreading a drop of whole blood thinly on a glass slide to form a blood smear. The smear is dried and stained with a blood stain such as Wright's stain. After staining is complete, the slide is examined with a microscope and the number of white cells of each kind is tabulated, until a predetermined total number of white cells has been counted. The number counted is usually a multiple of 100 and the percentage of each leukocyte type observed in a given sample of blood is called the differential leukocyte count or differential white cell count. The normal percentage of each type of leukocyte for each species is shown in Table 15-1. At present, both red and white cell counts are semiautomatically determined by more sophisticated laboratory equipment, which eliminates the need for laborious counting by viewing the slide squares through a microscope.

An increase in the number of leukocytes usually indicates that infection is present. However, a cancer of the leukocyte-producing tissues also results in an abnormally high white cell count; this type of cancer is called *leukemia*.

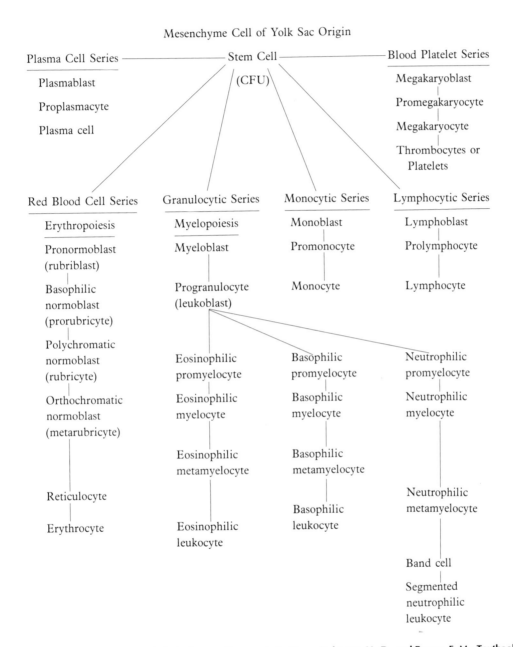

Fig. 15–8. Unitarian or monophyletic theory of hemopoiesis. (From Delmann, H.-D., and Brown, E. M.: Textbook of Veterinary Histology. Philadelphia, Lea & Febiger, 1976.)

HEMOPOIESIS

Hemopoiesis is the formation of erythrocytes, leukocytes, and platelets. As shown in Figure 15–8, all blood cells in the adult animal have a common origin—the primordial *stem cells* in the bone marrow. The process of erythrocyte formation is called *erythropoiesis*. The process of leukocyte formation is called *leukopoiesis*.

Regulation of Erythropoiesis

The erythropoietic activity of the bone marrow is governed by the level of oxygen in the tissues. When oxygen availability is reduced for any reason below the needs of the tissues and cells (hypoxia), the glycoprotein hormone *erythropoietin* (also called *hemopoietin* or *erythropoietic stimulating factor*) appears in the plasma. The enzyme that acts on the plasma precursor globulin of this hormone is called *renal erythropoietic factor*.

Erythropoietin appears in the plasma within one hour after the onset of hypoxia; it is formed due to low oxygen content of the arterial blood or a reduced oxygen affinity of hemoglobin. There is no *direct* response of the bone marrow to hypoxia. (See Fig. 15–9.) It usually takes three days from the onset of hypoxia for the body to begin to produce and empty increased amounts of RBCs into the blood from the marrow. The mechanism of erythropoiesis continues as long as needed, and is turned off again when the hypoxic state of the cells is eliminated. So, the concentration of RBCs is controlled by negative feedback. If the hypoxic cause is eliminated, the excess RBCs will be decreased by normal attrition and degeneration after about 120 days without replacement.

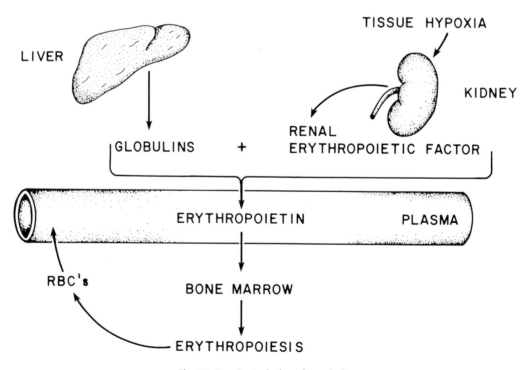

Fig. 15–9. Control of erythropoiesis.

PLASMA

When a sample of blood is treated to prevent clotting and permitted to stand undisturbed, the cells gradually settle to the bottom of the container, leaving a straw-colored fluid above (Fig. 15–10). This fluid portion of the blood, called *plasma*, was referred to by Claude Bernard as the "internal environment" which directly or indirectly bathes all cells of the body and protects them from external influences. Thus the plasma of the blood of higher vertebrates replaces the sea water in which primitive life probably developed.

Plasma is made up of about 92% water and 8% other substances. The kidneys are responsible for maintaining constant proportions of water and other constituents of the plasma by selective filtration and resorption of water and other substances from the blood plasma. These substances include about 90% proteins and 0.9% inorganic matter; the remainder is nonprotein organic matter.

The substances other than water that comprise 8% of the plasma can be subdivided on the basis of their molecular weights (MW). Those having a MW greater than 50,000 gm/mole are the *proteins*, which comprise 7⁄8 of this plasma fraction (7 gm/100 ml). Those having a MW less than 50,000 gm/mole include glucose, lipids, amino acids, hormones, NaCl and other electrolytes, inorganic mineral salts, and metabolic waste products, such as urea, uric acid, and creatinine. These make up the other 1⁄8 fraction of the plasma.

Protein Constituents

The plasma proteins consist of two major types: *albumin* and *globulins*. The primary globulins are classed in types based on their migration or separation by electrophoresis. The types are alpha-1, alpha-2, beta-1, beta-2, and gamma (α_1, α_2, β_1, β_2, γ). The alpha- and beta-globulins are synthesized in the liver. The gamma-globulins are synthesized in the reticuloendothelial tissue by plasma cells and lymphocytes when these cells are stimulated by antigens. Most of the known antibodies are included in the gamma-globulin fraction. *Fibrinogen* is a β_1-globulin that is synthesized in the liver. It is an essential part of the blood clotting mechanism described later in this chapter.

Albumin, the most abundant protein in the plasma, is the major protein produced by the liver. Albumin is important in binding and

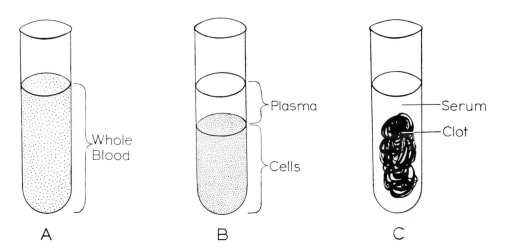

Fig. 15–10.   Blood. Diagram illustrating different physical states of blood. *A*, Unclotted blood, cells dispersed uniformly throughout; *B*, blood treated with anticoagulant. Cells permitted to settle, leaving clear plasma. *C*, Clotted blood. Serum separated from clot.

transporting many substances in the blood, and it is responsible for about 80% of the total *potential osmotic pressure* (oncotic pressure) of the plasma. This is because albumin and the other large MW proteins do not pass readily through the vessel or capillary walls, and so they aid in keeping fluid in the vascular system.

Functions of the Plasma Proteins. CARRIER FUNCTION. Many plasma substances are insoluble in water, but in association with plasma proteins, they are solubilized and thereby easily carried in the plasma. Examples are iron, thyroxine, and cortisol. This carrier function also provides a temporary storage "pool" of some substances in the plasma, which can then replace the free form of the substance in the plasma when the concentration of the free form gets low. For example, thyroxine is carried as an inactive hormone when complexed in equilibrium with plasma protein. When it is needed at the tissue level, it leaves the carrier protein, becomes active, and induces a cellular response.

IMMUNITY FUNCTION. The gamma-globulin fraction of the plasma proteins is associated with immunity and resistance to disease. It provides the immune response, i.e., antibodies to react with antigens, such as bacteria or foreign proteins, to either neutralize the antigen or to help to break it down. The gamma-globulin content of the blood therefore increases following vaccination and during recovery from disease.

BUFFERING FUNCTION. The plasma proteins help to prevent great changes in the pH (degree of acidity or alkalinity) of the blood. This buffering can occur because proteins have ionized carboxyl and amide groups, which can either accept excess hydrogen ions in the plasma or donate hydrogen ions to the plasma. However, other more important blood buffers are bicarbonate, sulfates, phosphates, and hemoglobin.

MAINTENANCE OF OSMOTIC PRESSURE. The total osmotic pressure of plasma at normal body temperature is about 290 mOsm/L. The large molecular-weight proteins (colloids) contribute only 1 or 2 mOsm/L; all the rest is produced by the small-molecular-weight proteins, even though their concentration or mass is small. This occurs because osmotic pressure depends on the *number* of osmotically active particles in solution, not the mass of the particles, and the number of small-molecular-weight proteins is tremendous compared to the number of proteins with large molecular weight.

Other Constituents

The other organic compounds in plasma include lipids, cholesterol, hormones, enzymes, and nonprotein nitrogenous material.

The *nonprotein nitrogen* fraction contains both amino acids, which are used by body cells to build protein, and waste products of metabolism, such as urea, uric acid, creatine, creatinine, and ammonium salts.

Glucose and lipids, as well as the amino acids, are nutritive substances absorbed into the blood following digestion.

The inorganic chemicals consist chiefly of chlorides, carbonates, sulfates and phosphates of sodium, potassium, calcium, and magnesium. Some of these compounds are essential for cell metabolism, and some function as buffers to maintain the pH of the blood within a normal range. Most of the carbon dioxide from cell metabolism is given back as waste to the blood. The greater part of it enters the erythrocytes to form carbonic acid, which then dissociates to the bicarbonate ion (HCO_3^-) and the hydrogen ion (H^+) to be carried ultimately back to the lungs, where it is dissociated to CO_2 and water. The oxygen carried to the cells from the lungs is almost entirely combined with the hemoglobin of the red cells.

SERUM

When blood clots in a test tube, a solid red mass is formed. However, on standing longer, the clot will contract, expressing out a supernatant yellow fluid which is called *serum*. Essentially, serum is plasma minus fibrinogen and most clotting factors. The fact that serum contains antibodies that the animal may have formed makes it useful in prevention and treatment of disease.

Immune serum or *hyperimmune serum* is produced by inoculating an animal with disease-producing agents such as bacteria or viruses (usually killed organisms). When the animal is repeatedly injected with a specific antigen (disease agent), it produces a large excess of antibodies against that particular antigen. Serum from that animal can then be injected into an animal susceptible to the same disease to provide passive protection for as long as the antibodies remain in the susceptible animal. This provides merely a temporary immunity, which leaves the animal as susceptible to the disease after the serum wears off as before it was administered. For example, hogs injected only with hog-cholera serum will be protected from hog cholera for a period of one or two weeks, and then will be as susceptible as before. However, if some live or modified hog-cholera virus is given at the same time the immune serum is given, the hogs not only will receive passive protection from the serum, but also will develop active immunity by producing their own antibodies in response to the injected virus.

BLOOD pH

The pH of the blood refers to the hydrogen-ion concentration, which determines the relative acidity or alkalinity of the solution. In distilled water, the hydrogen ions (H^+) (which are acid) equal the hydroxyl ions (OH^-) (which are basic or alkaline); the pH is 7, indicating it is neutral, neither acid nor alkali. Solutions with pH between 1 and 7 are acid; the smaller the number, the more acid the solution. The pH of alkaline solutions ranges from 7 to 14; the larger the number, the more alkaline the solution.

Normally the pH of blood lies between 7.35 and 7.45, just slightly on the alkaline side of neutral.

The pH of blood is kept within rather narrow limits by the presence of chemical buffers, chiefly sodium bicarbonate. Buffers react with strong acids or strong alkalies to produce a neutral salt and a weak acid or weak base. An example is the sodium-bicarbonate, carbonic-acid system:

$$HCl + NaHCO_3 \rightarrow NaCl + H_2CO_3$$
$$NaOH + H_2CO_3 \rightarrow NaHCO_3 + H_2O$$

This ability to neutralize acids resulting from metabolism leads to the term *alkali reserve* as a synonym for available bicarbonate in the blood. The resulting carbon dioxide is removed from the blood when it passes through the lungs. Thus hyperventilation, by removing too much carbon dioxide, can result in a temporary *alkalosis* of the blood.

In some diseases and conditions the alkali reserve is decreased enough to cause an acid condition of the blood *(acidosis)*, created by the presence of too much CO_2.

BLOOD CLOTTING

Blood clotting, or *coagulation*, occurs in blood that is drawn into a container and allowed to stand. A jelly-like mass results which then shrinks to produce a firm clot and some clear fluid, the blood serum. The actual clot consists of filaments of fibrin that enmesh red blood cells, white blood cells, and platelets.

When a blood vessel in an animal is cut or ruptured, the first thing that happens is a sudden pinching together of the walls of the vessel. This is caused by: (1) myogenic contraction of the smooth muscle, as a local spasm, and (2) a sympathetic nerve reflex stimulating the adrenergic fibers that innervate the smooth muscle of the vessel wall locally. This constriction narrows the vessel opening to reduce the flow of escaping blood. The spasm lasts about 20 minutes, which allows time for a *platelet plug* to form and for coagulation to occur.

The second event in *intravascular hemostasis* (clotting *within* a blood vessel) is formation of the platelet plug. As the platelets in the blood come in contact with the exposed subendothelium or basement membrane of a damaged or cut vessel, they adhere to the collagen and elastin fibers of the exposed lining. This causes the blood platelets to swell and undergo a process called *viscous metamorphosis* (transformation), whereby they become sticky by an alteration of their membrane surface. They also secrete ADP, which helps to trigger the metamorphosis in other platelets in the area, causing them to stick together as well. This build-up of platelets sticking together is called *platelet aggregation*. Platelet metamorphosis and aggregation, then, is the reaction that forms a platelet plug of the hole or cut in the vessel; if the plug covers damage to a vessel wall, it thereby provides a site for the formation of a thrombus.

Platelets contain epinephrine, norepinephrine, and serotonin (5-hydroxytryptamine), all of which can be used to induce platelet aggregation. These are selectively secreted by the platelets. Nearly all the serotonin in blood exists in the platelets, and since serotonin causes local vasoconstriction, it enhances spasm of the vessel. Platelets also release a substance called *platelet factor 3* (PF–3). This is a phospholipid which then assists in forming *prothrombin activator* (also called *plasma thromboplastin)*, which is part of the coagulation process within blood vessels, as will be explained and illustrated.

When some of the platelet membranes break down in the process, ATP and a contractile protein called *thrombosthenin* are released. These also enhance the vascular spasm. Also, they stimulate retraction of the clot to about 40% of its initial size within 24 hours after coagulation occurs. The retraction forces serum out of the clot, a process called *syneresis*. The clot retraction pulls the opening of the ruptured or cut vessel further together. If the vessel hole or cut is small,

the platelet plug can, by itself, stop further blood loss. Larger holes must depend on coagulation to stop the bleeding.

Clotting, or coagulation, begins anywhere from 15 seconds to 2 minutes after injury, and is generally complete in about 5 minutes. This is followed by a gradual *organization* of the clot, wherein fibroblasts move into the clot and form fibrous tissue over the course of 7 to 10 days; sutures are left in wounds that long to hold an incision together until the fibrous tissue forms. However, when blood is disseminated locally into tissues, as in the case of a hematoma, the clots will be gradually dissoluted (broken down in solution) instead of becoming fibrous, and be resorbed by the lymphatic system.

The steps in the process of coagulation are illustrated schematically in Figure 15–11; it involves the actions and interactions of various substances known as *factors*. The factors and their synonyms are listed in Table 15–2. Formation of the clot itself will be explained first, then the pathways by which it occurs (1) outside the blood vessels in the tissues, and (2) inside the blood vessels.

Fibrin is a substance that forms a loose clot; naturally, fibrin cannot be present in its active form in the circulating blood. However, its precursor, *fibrinogen* (factor I) is present in plasma as a soluble protein, which is synthesized in the liver. Fibrinogen consists of three polypeptide chains. *Thrombin*, which is a proteolytic enzyme, acts on the fibrinogen to hydrolyze it into fibrin monomers. These monomers then polymerize (join) together, end-to-end, to form long fibrin threads. This forms the clot *reticulum* (web or network), producing a loose clot. Then factor XIII (fibrin stabilizing factor) acts as an enzyme to bond together these loose threads by forming cross-links between the threads, and a firm clot results.

Naturally, thrombin also cannot be present in the blood in its active form or coagulation would occur in normal circulation; it, too, has a precursor in the blood called *prothrombin* (factor II). This factor is an α_2-

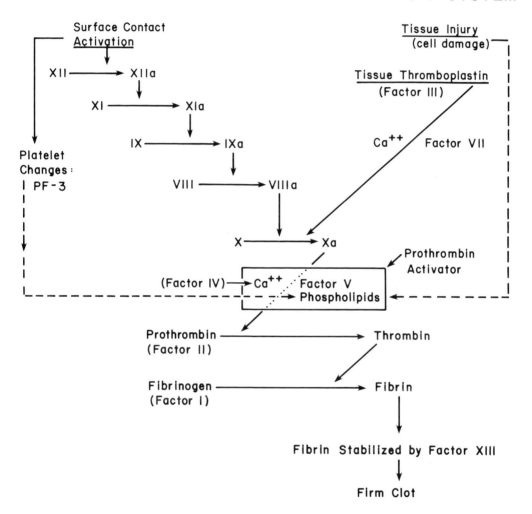

Fig. 15–11.   Mechanisms involved in causing blood to clot.

Table 15–2. International Nomenclature of Blood Coagulation Factors with Synonyms

Factor	Synonyms
I	Fibrinogen
II*	Prothrombin
III	Thromboplastin
IV	Calcium
V	Labile factor, proaccelerin, Ac-globulin
VII*	Stable factor, proconvertin, serum prothrombin conversion accelerator (SPCA)
VIII	Antihemophilic globulin (AHG), antihemophilic factor A
IX*	Christmas factor, plasma thromboplastin component (PTC), antihemophilic factor B
X*	Stuart-Prower factor
XI	Plasma thromboplastin antecedent (PTA), antihemophilic factor C
XII	Hageman factor
XIII	Fibrin stabilizing factor

The first four factors are well known by their names which are likely to remain in use, but the international nomenclature (Roman figures) for the other factors is now becoming general.

* These factors are affected by the anticoagulant drugs (coumarins and indanediones) much used in the treatment of thrombotic diseases.

(Bell, Davidson and Scarborough, Textbook of Physiology and Biochemistry, 27th ed, Churchill Livingstone, Edinburgh.)

globulin formed by the liver in the presence of vitamin K. During coagulation, the prothrombin is acted on by a complex called *prothrombin activator*, which splits off the enzyme thrombin from prothrombin.

The formation of the complex called prothrombin activator occurs by one of two different pathways, depending on the origin of the damage that leads to clotting. The pathways are: (1) the *extrinsic system*, which begins by cell damage in the tissues outside the blood vessels, and (2) the *intrinsic system*, which begins inside the vascular system (see Fig. 15–11). These systems usually operate together by virtue of the extent of damage from injuries, but they can also operate independently.

In the extrinsic pathway of coagulation, blood gets into the tissues because of capillary or vessel damage or inflammation. Also, the tissue cells that are damaged release tissue thromboplastin (factor III) and phospholipids. Factor III then, along with factor IV (calcium) and factor VII, reacts to activate factor X (Stuart-Prower factor). Activated factor X (Xa) then complexes with Ca and factor V and the phospholipids to form prothrombin activator, which splits off thrombin from prothrombin. Then the clotting proceeds as already described.

The process in the intrinsic system of coagulation, as shown on the left half of Figure 15–11, begins with trauma or injury to the inside of blood vessels. This results in an abnormal roughened inner surface along the vessel wall which is usually smooth. For example, such roughening occurs with bruises, atherosclerotic plaques, and calcium plaques. This change in the surface activates factor XII and the platelets as they come in contact with the abnormal surface. Factor XII is the Hageman Factor, and it activates factor XI, which is plasma thromboplastin antecedent (PTA). The PTA activates factor IX, which is plasma thromboplastin component (PTC), also called the Christmas factor (named after the discoverer). Factor IX then activates factor VIII, which is the antihemophilic factor (AHF). Factor VIII then activates factor X, which then complexes with calcium and factor V and the platelet phospholipid factor (PF–3) to form prothrombin activator. The subsequent clotting steps are the same as explained previously.

Factor V, also known as proaccelerin, and factor VII, also known as proconvertin, together are called "accelerators of prothrombin conversion," because in their absence the conversion to thrombin occurs slowly. A deficiency of either factor, therefore, lengthens the clotting time. (Note that no factor VI has been found or assigned.)

In summary, then, fibrinogen, calcium, and prothrombin circulate normally in the blood until damage occurs to cause the release or activation of the factors that will lead to splitting thrombin free from prothrombin. The thrombin enzyme then acts on fibrinogen to produce the fibrin monomers and the clot reticulum, which is then made firm by factor XIII. (Note that other names have been given for the factors and other diagrams of the events, depending on various authorities and researchers.)

Blood clots often break up and disappear in the body, a process called *fibrinolysis*. This is brought about by the action of a normal blood constituent called *plasminogen*, which is the precursor of a proteolytic enzyme, *plasmin*, which breaks down the fibrin clot into soluble products. Its action is

prevented in the normal blood state by the presence in blood of an antiproteolytic enzyme, *antiplasmin*. Plasminogen is activated only in the interstices of a clot.

Prevention of Coagulation. There are various means of preventing the clotting of blood drawn from an animal. (See Fig. 15–12.) Whipping fresh blood with a glass rod defibrinates the blood by causing the fibrin to adhere to the glass rod; this allows the blood to remain fluid indefinitely. Rapid chilling of blood to about 0°C retards coagulation by interfering with thromboplastin formation, and inhibiting the activity of enzymes. Using agents that provide a "nonwettable surface," such as silicone, to coat the inside of test tubes or syringes, or using Silastic plastic vessels, will slow down the activation of factor XII and therefore retard the coagulation time of blood samples.

Another method is to add sodium oxalate or ammonium oxalate to blood removed

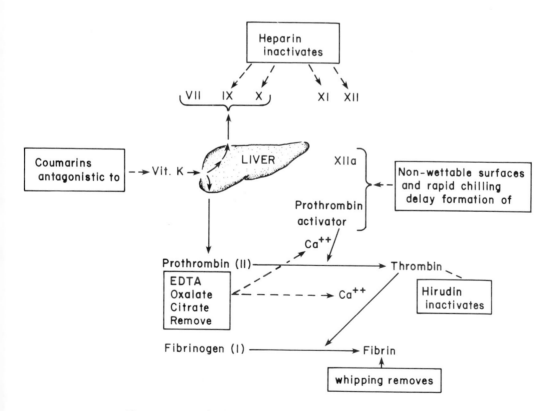

Fig. 15–12. Mechanisms that inhibit or prevent clotting of blood.

from the animal. This will delay coagulation indefinitely by precipitating calcium, thereby preventing its action. However, sodium citrate, potassium citrate, or ammonium citrate are preferred because they are essentially nontoxic. They all remove calcium ions from the blood solution either by precipitation or by deionizing it. EDTA (sodium-ethylenediaminetetra-acetic acid) is a useful anticoagulant also because it is a chelating agent that takes up calcium ions. Any of these means can be used to prevent or slow down clotting in blood that has been withdrawn from the animal for use in laboratory tests.

Other means are used to delay or prevent intravascular coagulation of the blood. The *coumarins*, such as dicumarol (bishydroxycoumadin) and sodium warfarin, are used clinically. They act in the liver where they interfere with the synthesis of factors II, VII, IX, and X. Medically, they lessen the danger of intravascular coagulation because they are antagonistic to *vitamin K*, which is essential to synthesis of the four factors.

Dicoumarin, found in sweet clover, inhibits the clotting of blood because it is antagonistic to vitamin K, thus reducing the amount of prothrombin in the blood. *Sweet clover disease* is the hemorrhagic condition resulting from excess dicoumarin. In this condition, small cuts or bruises result in bleeding that is difficult to stop. Therefore routine surgery, such as dehorning or castration, should be avoided while animals are being fed sweet clover hay or are grazing on sweet clover pasture. Dicoumarin is used commercially in rodent poisons, and rats and mice that eat these poisons usually die from internal bleeding following bruising.

In the absence of vitamin K in the diet, poultry and mammals can develop fatal hemorrhages. Vitamin K is obtained mostly from the diet. Although it is normally synthesized by bacteria in the mammalian intestine, very little from this source becomes absorbed. Vitamin K is essential. A low plasma concentration of the four vitamin K-dependent clotting factors is referred to as *hypoprothrombinemia*.

Vitamin K deficiency most often results from poor absorption of fats from the gut, since dietary vitamin K is taken up across the intestinal mucosa by first becoming adsorbed to triglycerides. If liver disease or an obstruction of the bile duct is present, the resultant lack of bile in the gut reduces the absorption of lipids and vitamin K. For example, this occurs in hepatitis and cirrhosis.

Heparin is a mucopolysaccharide—a polymer of glucuronic acid and glucosamine. It was named heparin because it was first isolated from the liver (hepatic tissue). It is synthesized and stored in the metachromatic granules of mast cells. Mast cells are located in the connective tissue surrounding capillaries and in the walls of blood vessels. They are especially abundant around the liver and lung capillaries. Various forms of shock caused by a decrease in the effective blood volume cause the mast cells to release a lot of heparin to prevent coagulation of blood during the crisis. Heparin is the most powerful anticoagulant known, and it is extracted from animal tissues for clinical use. Clinically it is injected, acts rapidly, and lasts three to four hours. It acts by inactivating blood factors IX, X, XI, and XII, thereby inhibiting the formation of the prothrombin activator complex.

Dicoumarol is also used clinically to prevent clotting. The buccal glands of the leech contain the anticoagulant *hirudin*, an antithrombin. The venoms of certain snakes contain anticoagulants that act by interfering with the action of thromboplastin or by destroying blood fibrinogen.

The normal blood clot contracts to about 40% of its initial volume within 24 hours. This requires *thrombosthenin* from blood platelets.

Coagulation Time. Coagulation time is the length of time from drawing a fresh blood sample until coagulation occurs. It may simply be determined by placing 1 ml of blood in each of three test tubes. One tube is tilted at thirty-second intervals to test for coagulation. As soon as coagulation in the first tube occurs, the second tube is tilted, and then the third. *Coagulation time* is measured from the time blood enters the syringe till the blood in the third tube coagulates. Coagulation time for the dog and sheep is 2½ min; pig, 3½ min; man, 5 min; cow, 6½ min; and horse, 11½ min. Variations in technique may cause appreciable differences in coagulation time.

SPECIFIC GRAVITY OF BLOOD

Specific gravity is an index, or ratio, of the weight of a substance compared to the weight of an equal volume of water. A substance that weighs less than an equal volume of water will have a specific gravity of less than 1.000; if it weighs more than the same volume of water, its specific gravity will be more than 1.000. Specific gravity is commonly measured with an instrument called a *hydrometer*. The amount of antifreeze in a radiator and the charge of a storage battery are both determined by the use of a hydrometer to measure specific gravity of the fluid involved.

Whole blood has a slightly higher specific gravity than water primarily because of the blood cells: the red cells are heavier than the white cells, and both of them are heavier than the plasma. Specific gravity of blood varies slightly between species, with that of the sheep being 1.042; cow, 1.043; dog and man, 1.059; and horse and pig, 1.060.

BLOOD VOLUME

Blood volume refers to the total amount of blood in an animal's body. It could be determined directly by bleeding an animal as completely as possible and then washing out the remaining blood that cannot be removed by ordinary bleeding. However, a known volume of dye can also be injected into the blood and the volume calculated from the dilution of the dye after it is thoroughly mixed with the blood. This is an indirect method that does not interfere with the life of the animal.

Blood volume can be readily calculated if the percentage of body weight normally comprised of blood is known. Average figures, in percentage of body weight due to blood, are: dog 7.2, cow 7.7, sheep 8.0, and horse 9.7.

LYMPH

Much of the fluid that passes through the capillary walls into the tissue spaces is reabsorbed into the venous capillaries. The remainder is tissue fluid in the tissue spaces. Excess tissue fluid that is not absorbed by the blood capillaries is picked up by a system of capillaries called lymphatics. As soon as the tissue fluid enters the lymph capillaries it is called *lymph*. (The lymphatic system is described in Chapter 16.)

Lymph is a clear, colorless liquid somewhat similar to blood plasma from which it is derived. There may be a few red cells and numerous *lymphocytes* as well as inorganic salts, glucose, nonprotein nitrogenous substances, and some proteins. Neutrophilic leukocytes normally are not present in great numbers except during acute infections.

The quantity of protein in lymph is considerably less than in plasma, but the content of simple chemical substances, crystalloids, is about the same.

Lymph derived from the intestine during digestion may contain large quantities of lipids, giving it a milky appearance. This milky lymph, called *chyle*, results from the absorption of lipids into the *lacteals*, the small lymphatics of the intestine. Eventually all lymph is returned to the circulation by way of large veins cranial to the heart.

CEREBROSPINAL FLUID

Cerebrospinal fluid is formed by *choroid plexuses* (tufts of capillaries) in the ventricles of the brain. It circulates throughout the subarachnoid space, between the *pia mater* and *arachnoid membrane*, over the entire surface of the brain and spinal cord. (See Chapter 5 for a description of the ventricles and meninges.)

Cerebrospinal fluid also resembles blood plasma from which it is derived, but has less protein, glucose, and K⁺, and few if any cells except some lymphocytes. It probably serves partly as a nutritive medium for the brain and spinal cord as well as cushioning these structures against shock.

SYNOVIAL FLUID

Synovial fluid is a thick, tenacious liquid found in joint cavities, tendon sheaths, and bursae. It owes its physical properties and lubricating ability to the presence of mucopolysaccharides and possibly hyaluronic acid. Besides reducing friction in joints, synovial fluid probably helps to nourish the articular cartilages.

SEROUS FLUIDS

Serous fluids found in the respective body cavities include peritoneal fluid, pleural fluid, and pericardial fluid. Normally these fluids are present as a thin film that reduces friction between apposed surfaces. Inflammation or infection of the serous membranes causes increased production of serous fluids. Examples are *traumatic pericarditis* (hardware disease) of cattle, *pleuritis* (pleurisy), and *peritonitis*.

OTHER BODY FLUIDS

Other body fluids include the *aqueous humor* of the eye and the *perilymph* and *endolymph* of the inner ear. They are discussed in Chapter 7.

MACROPHAGE SYSTEM (RETICULOENDOTHELIAL SYSTEM) AND IMMUNITY

The reticuloendothelial system (RES) refers to the network of macrophage (large eater) cells throughout the body. The reticuloendothelial system is responsible for destruction of red blood cells and necrotic tissue from the animal and destruction of foreign organisms such as bacteria and some parasites.

The name reticuloendothelial system came from an early belief that the reticular cells in lymph nodes and so-called endothelial cells lining the sinusoids of the liver and lymphatic organs were the cells that actually engulfed these undesirable substances in the animal. Recent evidence indicates that the functional cells in the reticuloendothelial system are actually macrophages originally derived from stem cells in the bone marrow, probably related to the monocytes. The term macrophage system may be more appropriate than reticuloendothelial system.

Immunity

In addition to the macrophage system (reticuloendothelial system) for protection of the animal body against foreign materials and organisms, a mechanism of *acquired immunity* protects against antigens (toxins and organisms) that have been previously introduced into the body.

The two types of acquired immunity—cellular (lymphocytic) and humoral (relating to antibodies in the blood)—are dependent on specially processed lymphocytes for the development of immunity. Lymphocytes can form hundreds of different types of sensitized lymphocytes and antibodies, each type being specific for a specific antigen, and each type being capable of multiplying into a large number (called a *clone*) when excited by a sufficient number of the specific antigens.

Cellular (lymphocytic) immunity results when an antigen contacts and sensitizes the so-called *T lymphocytes* (thymus lymphocytes). The T lymphocytes are derived from lymphocytes that originate from bone marrow stem cells and are processed in the thymus before they migrate to the lymphoid tissue of the animal. The "processing" in the thymus begins shortly before birth and continues for a few months after birth.

When T lymphocytes are exposed to proper antigens, they are stimulated to multiply rapidly and produce many more T lymphocytes, which are also capable of acting directly against the specific antigen. Antigens that produce chronic diseases tend to stimulate cellular immunity by way of T lymphocytes. These antigens include such agents as fungi, tubercle bacilli, Brucella organisms, cancer cells, and transplanted organs.

In addition to attaching directly to the invading agents and destroying them, the T lymphocytes also produce a *transfer factor* that sensitizes other small lymphocytes to attack the agent in the same manner. A macrophage chemotaxic factor is also released that may attract as many as 1,000 macrophages into the vicinity of each sensitized lymphocyte.

Humoral immunity results from antibodies that are produced in response to a specific antigen interaction with preprocessed lymphocytes called *B lymphocytes*. In birds these lymphocytes are processed in the bursa of Fabricius, a lymphoid organ located near the cloaca (termination of the intestine) of young birds, hence the term B lymphocyte. In mammals, the B lymphocytes are processed in tissue called the bursa equivalent, probably in the liver or spleen.

In humoral immunity, a B lymphocyte, which is specific for a foreign antigen, enlarges to form a *lymphoblast*. Some of these then form *plasmoblasts*, which then divide to form many *plasma cells*. It is the plasma cells that synthesize the antibodies. These antibodies are then secreted into the lymph, and from there they enter the circulation.

The antibodies circulate as free gammaglobulin proteins in the plasma. Also, new B lymphocytes are formed from the lymphoblasts, so that greater amounts of antibodies can be produced if the animal is exposed later to the same antigen. This gives the animal a greater immunity upon second exposure.

Each antibody is specific in acting against one specific antigen. However, for convenience, the antibodies are grouped into five classes: IgA, IgD, IgE, IgG, and IgM (Ig stands for immunoglobulin). Nearly three-fourths of the antibodies are in class IgG.

Antibodies accomplish their job of preventing the antigen from "gaining a foothold" in the body in one of three primary ways: (1) by acting directly on the antigen, causing them to either agglutinate or precipitate, or by neutralizing or lysing them; (2) by activating the *complement system,* which consists of inactive enzymes in the plasma that become active when an antibody binds with an antigen—this activation can cause agglutination, neutralization, lysis, or inflammation to wall-off the antigen, or opsonization (altering the antigen surface so it can be phagocytized); (3) by activating the *anaphylactic system*—IgE antibodies attach to cell membranes, especially mast cells and basophils, and when these complexes react with the antigen, the cells swell up, rupture, and release histamine, lysosomal enzymes, a chemotoxic factor, and a "slow-reacting anaphylactic substance." This last substance causes prolonged smooth muscle contraction, which affects the ability to breathe. The anaphylactic response can be dangerous to life while attempting to confine or immobilize the antigen.

Chapter 16

The Circulatory System

The circulatory system consists of a four-chambered pump, the heart, and a system of vessels for circulating the blood.

Vessels that carry blood away from the heart are called *arteries*. Vessels that carry blood toward the heart are called *veins*. In addition, a system of vessels that carry tissue fluid or lymph to large veins are called *lymph vessels,* or *lymphatics*.

HEART

The heart is a cone-shaped, hollow, muscular structure. The base is directed dorsally or craniodorsally and is attached to other thoracic structures by large arteries, veins, and the pericardial sac. The apex of the heart is directed ventrally and is entirely free within the pericardium. (In this book illustrations show the right side of the heart on the right side of the diagram and the left side of the heart on the left side of the diagram,

which conforms closely to the orientation of the heart in the living animal.)

Pericardium

The heart is partially surrounded by a serous sac called the *pericardium*, or pericardial sac. The pericardium, like other serous sacs (the pleura and peritoneum), is a completely closed sac that contains only a small amount of fluid for lubrication. The heart is invaginated into the pericardium much as would occur if one thrust a fist into the side of an inflated balloon. This arrangement results in two distinct layers of pericardium. The inner layer, which is intimately adherent to the outer surface of the heart, is called *visceral pericardium*, or *epicardium*. The outer layer, called *parietal pericardium*, is continuous with the visceral layer at the base of the heart and is reinforced by a superficial fibrous layer, which in turn is

252

covered by a layer of mediastinal pleura (also called pericardial pleura). (See Figs. 16–1, 18–6.)

Structure

The heart wall consists of three layers: an outer serous covering called *epicardium*, an inner endothelial lining called *endocardium*, and a thick muscular layer called *myocardium* (Fig. 16–1).

The epicardium is actually the visceral layer of pericardium. The endocardium is a layer of simple squamous endothelial cells that lines the chambers of the heart, covers the heart valves, and is continuous with the lining of the blood vessels.

The myocardium consists of cardiac muscle, which is also called involuntary striated muscle. Cardiac muscle has been described in Chapter 12, where muscle was considered as a tissue. Cardiac muscle cells do have cross-striations, but the nuclei are more centrally located than in voluntary striated

muscle cells. The muscle fibers making up the heart are arranged in whorls or spirals because the heart develops from a single tube which becomes divided and twists upon itself. Details of this developmental process may be found in standard embryology texts.

The heart is divided into a right and a left side (Fig. 16–2). Each side consists of an *atrium*, which receives blood by way of large veins, and a *ventricle*, which pumps blood from the heart by way of a large artery. Between the atrium and the ventricle of each side is a large valve called the *atrioventricular valve*, or A–V valve. The left A–V valve is also called the *bicuspid valve*, because in man it has two distinct flaps or cusps. Another synonym is *mitral* valve, because of the imagined resemblance of the left A–V valve to a bishop's miter, or two-sided hat. The right A–V valve is also called the *tricuspid valve* because it has three flaps or cusps; each cusp is somewhat triangular. The upper border is attached to the inner wall of the ventricle at the junction of atrium

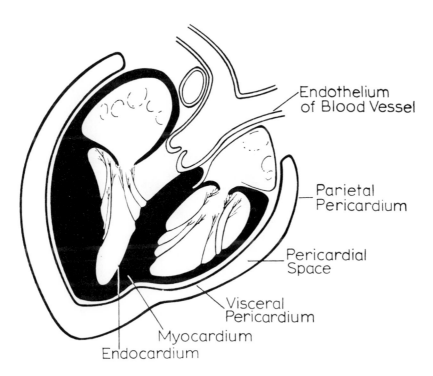

Endothelium of Blood Vessel

Parietal Pericardium

Pericardial Space

Visceral Pericardium

Myocardium

Endocardium

Fig. 16–1. The heart and its coverings.

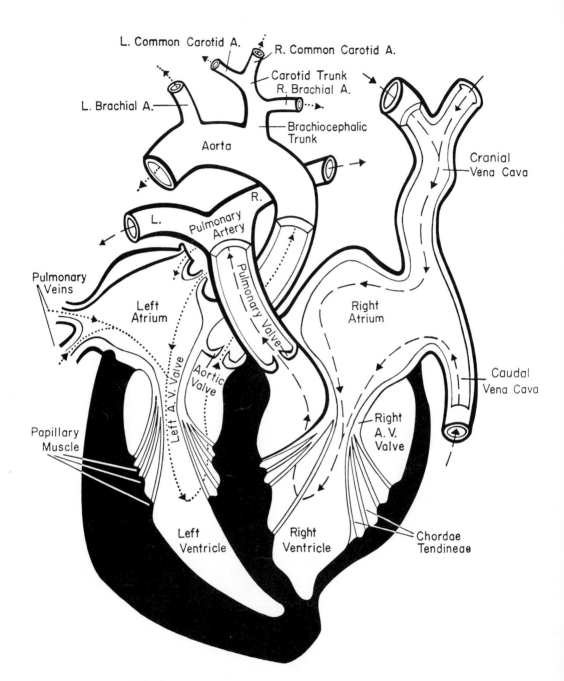

Fig. 16–2.   Structure of the heart. Arrows indicate direction of blood flow. Dotted lines represent oxygenated (arterial) blood. Broken lines represent unoxygenated (venous) blood.

and ventricle. The free margin or margins of the cusp are indirectly attached to the ventricular wall by means of fibrous cords called *chordae tendineae*. These chordae tendineae, which resemble strings on a parachute, prevent the valve from everting into the atrium when the ventricle contracts and closes the A–V valve by forcing blood against the ventral side of the valve.

The *aortic semilunar valve* is a three-cusped valve located at the junction of the left ventricle and aorta. The *pulmonary semilunar valve* is a similar valve located at the junction of the pulmonary artery and right ventricle. Each semilunar valve prevents blood from returning into the respective ventricle when the ventricles relax.

The simplest way to get an idea of the internal arrangement of the heart is to follow the course of the blood through the heart and lungs. Blood returning to the heart from the systemic circulation, commonly called venous blood, is relatively low in oxygen content. Since this same blood is also carried to the lungs by the pulmonary artery, the term venous seems somewhat inappropriate, so in this text it will be called unoxygenated blood rather than venous blood. The blood returned to the heart by pulmonary veins and subsequently distributed to the body by way of systemic arteries, commonly called arterial blood, is relatively high in oxygen content. In this text it will be called oxygenated blood rather than arterial blood.

Unoxygenated blood returns to the heart by the *cranial* and *caudal venae cavae*. These large veins enter the right atrium of the heart, which is a thin-walled area for collection of returning blood.

Next, the blood passes through the right A–V valve into the right ventricle. The right ventricle does not quite reach the apex of the heart, as the apex is formed entirely by the more muscular left ventricle. From the right side, the right ventricle spirals around the cranial side of the heart and terminates as the *conus arteriosus* at the left side of the base. The conus arteriosus is the *funnel-shaped* origin of the pulmonary artery.

Just beyond the pulmonary semilunar valve, the *pulmonary artery* divides, each branch carrying unoxygenated blood to the capillaries of the respective lung where CO_2 in the blood is exchanged for O_2 from the alveolar air.

The *pulmonary veins* return oxygenated blood from the lungs to the left atrium, another large thin-walled chamber of the heart. From the left atrium, blood passes through the left A–V valve into the thick-walled left ventricle.

The left ventricle then pumps the oxygenated blood past the aortic semilunar valve into the *aorta*. The aorta and its subdivisions carry oxygenated blood to all parts of the body, including the heart and lungs themselves.

VESSELS

Blood vessels resemble the branching of a tree, in that the arteries start as large vessels and divide into smaller and smaller branches. The smallest arteries are called arterioles. The *arterioles* in turn are continuous with the smallest blood vessels, capillaries. *Capillaries* again unite to form *venules*, which in turn unite to form larger and larger veins. The largest veins finally empty into the atria of the heart.

Arteries

Arteries are tubular structures that carry blood away from the heart. The largest arteries are known as elastic arteries because a large portion of the arterial wall consists of elastic tissue. This elasticity is important in maintaining blood pressure during diastole, the period during which the ventricles are relaxed.

Smaller arteries contain a large amount of smooth muscle in the arterial wall in place of the elastic tissue. This smooth muscle controls the size of the vessel and consequently the amount of blood that can flow through it during a given period of time.

Arterioles, the smallest arteries, are muscular immediately before giving rise to capillaries. The heavy, circular, smooth muscle surrounding the terminations of the arterioles is important because it controls the amount of blood each capillary receives. Tension of the muscle around the arterioles also aids in maintaining blood pressure throughout the arterial system. In case of shock, the arterioles dilate or relax, and a large part of the blood volume is lost within the capillary beds, particularly those of the viscera.

Capillaries

Capillaries are tiny tubes almost entirely composed of endothelium, a continuation of the simple squamous epithelium that lines the heart and blood vessels (Fig. 16–3). These thin-walled vessels are only large

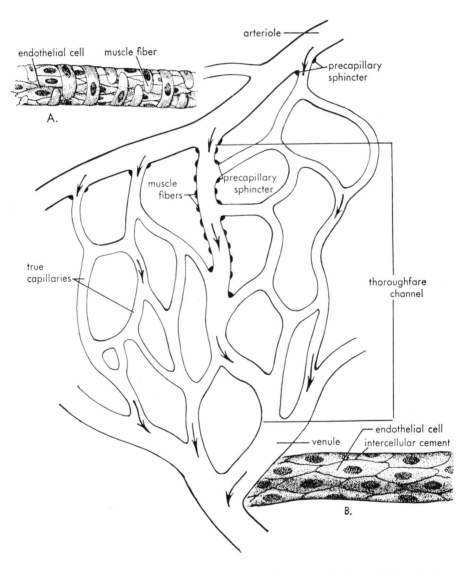

Fig. 16–3.   Schematic representation of a capillary bed. Insert *A* shows some of the muscle fibers of the proximal part of a thoroughfare channel. Insert *B* shows a part of a true capillary. (From Crouch, J. E.: Functional Human Anatomy. ed. 3. Philadelphia, Lea & Febiger, 1978.)

enough in diameter to accommodate a single file of erythrocytes. The wall acts as a selectively permeable membrane that permits water, oxygen, and nutrients to leave the blood for tissue cells and permits waste products from tissue cells to enter the blood. Much of the fluid that passes out of the capillaries into tissue spaces again returns to the blood by passing back through the capillary walls. Some fluid remains in the tissues as tissue fluid, and the excess fluid normally is removed by lymph vessels. In addition to the capillary networks or capillary beds, which are interposed between arterioles and venules, there are larger connections called *arteriovenous anastomoses* or *shunts*. These direct anastomoses permit more blood to flow through a given part than could get through the capillaries alone. This increased blood flow aids in sudden necessary shifts in blood volume, as in heat elimination from the skin and in increasing oxygen loading at the lungs.

Veins

As previously mentioned, capillaries unite to form venules, which in turn form larger and larger veins. Veins are larger than the arteries they accompany and have much thinner walls, with only a slight amount of muscle tissue present. Valves, usually consisting of two cusps each, are scattered at irregular intervals throughout the venous and lymphatic systems. A valve frequently is present where two or more veins unite to form a larger vein. The valves are always directed so blood will flow only toward the heart. These valves prevent blood from being forced back into capillary beds and also permit muscle contractions and movement of body parts to aid the flow of blood toward the heart. Blood pressure in veins is low, since little arterial pressure is transmitted through the capillaries to the veins. This situation may be compared to water from a river entering a lake with considerable force, while the water leaving the other side of the lake has little of the force found at the inlet.

All veins are tributaries to larger veins which eventually enter the right or left atrium of the heart.

Lymphatics

The walls of capillaries are thin enough to permit fluid as well as nutrients and gases to escape into spaces between tissue cells. Much of this intercellular fluid (tissue fluid) does not re-enter capillaries or veins directly, but is picked up by thin-walled lymph vessels, which resemble veins in that they contain numerous valves permitting the contents to flow only toward the heart. The smallest lymph vessels are capillary-sized structures that begin blindly in intercellular spaces, where they accumulate tissue fluid, which is then transported to larger and larger lymph vessels and finally emptied into the cranial vena cava or one of its tributaries.

This movement of *lymph*, as tissue fluid within lymph vessels is called, is produced largely by gravity or changing pressures of adjacent structures. For example, contraction of a muscle applies pressure to the adjacent lymphatic vessels and forces the lymph further toward the heart, since the valves effectively prevent backflow. The lymph is filtered by nodular structures called *lymph nodes* (or lymph glands) scattered along the course of most lymph vessels.

CIRCULATORY SYSTEMS

Pulmonary Circulation

The pulmonary circulation is that part of the vascular system that circulates all the blood through the lungs. The right atrium receives unoxygenated blood from the caudal and cranial venae cavae. The blood then passes through the right A–V valve into the right ventricle, and then into the pulmonary artery. The pulmonary semilunar valve prevents backflow of blood from the pulmonary artery into the right ventricle, and elasticity of the artery ensures a continuous flow

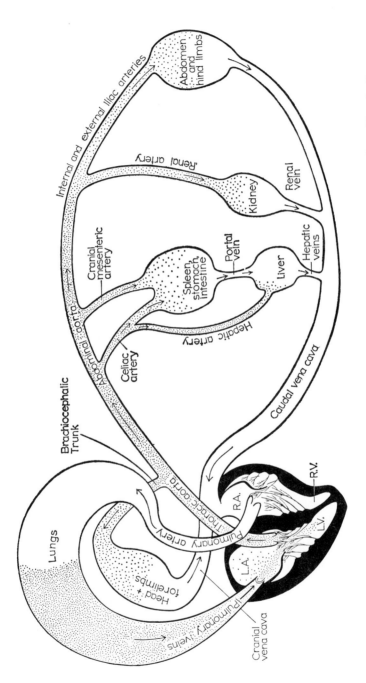

Fig. 16–4. General scheme of the adult circulation. Relatively higher oxygen content of blood is indicated by stippling.

of blood through the capillary bed of the lungs.

After a short distance the pulmonary artery divides into a right branch going to the right lung and a left branch going to the left lung. Each branch again subdivides into lobar arteries going to each of the lobes of the lungs. The lobar arteries again subdivide many times, finally forming arterioles that supply the extensive capillary beds of the lungs.

Lung capillaries are intimately associated with alveoli (the smallest terminations of air passages) of the lungs. Here a minimal amount of tissue separates the blood of the pulmonary circulation from air within the alveoli, thus affording an opportunity for oxygen of the air to be exchanged for carbon dioxide in the blood. As this gaseous exchange occurs, the color of the blood changes from the bluish color of unoxygenated blood, called venous blood, to the bright red of oxygenated blood, called arterial blood. It is worth noting that in the adult the pulmonary circulation is the only place where unoxygenated blood is found in arteries and oxygenated blood is found in veins.

After the blood is forced through the capillary bed of the lungs, it enters the venules, which combine to form pulmonary veins. These pulmonary veins, after leaving the lungs, immediately empty oxygenated blood into the left atrium, thus completing the pulmonary circulation.

Systemic Circulation

Systemic circulation, also called *somatic circulation*, refers to the movement of oxygenated blood to all areas of the body and the subsequent return of unoxygenated blood to the heart (Fig. 16–4). The systemic circulation can be divided into a number of circulations, each of which supplies a specific region or part of the body. These circulations include such subdivisions as circulation of the head, circulation of the front limb, circulation of the hind limb, etc.

Each regional circulation in turn can be broken down still further to the circulation of any given part of the region. For example, we can study the circulation of the biceps brachii muscle, or the circulation of the eye. No matter how small or how large a segment of systemic circulation we consider, the basic pattern is the same with the exception of circulation of the kidneys and portal circulations. Arteries divide into arterioles, which supply blood to capillaries; then the capillaries in turn recombine to form venules, which again form veins that drain blood from the area.

The systemic circulation will be discussed in the following order:

The aorta, origin and course
The thoracic aorta and its branches
The abdominal aorta and its branches
The cranial (anterior) vena cava and its tributaries
The caudal (posterior) vena cava and its tributaries
The hepatic portal system

The following descriptions of blood vessels are based mainly on the horse (see Figs. 16–5, 16–6). Animals having different digestive systems, such as ruminants, and those having more than one digit per limb will, of course, have a somewhat different arrangement of arteries and veins.

AORTA

The left ventricle receives oxygenated blood from the left atrium and then pumps the blood throughout the systemic circulation by way of the largest artery in the body, the *aorta*. The aortic valve, located at the junction of the left ventricle and aorta, prevents backflow of blood from the aorta into the left ventricle when the ventricle relaxes.

After leaving the heart, the aorta first passes dorsad and then caudad just ventral to the bodies of the thoracic vertebrae. The thoracic aorta continues caudad through the aortic hiatus between the two roots of the diaphragm to become the abdominal aorta. Ventral to the last few lumbar vertebrae, the aorta terminates by dividing into two *external iliac arteries* and two *internal iliac ar-*

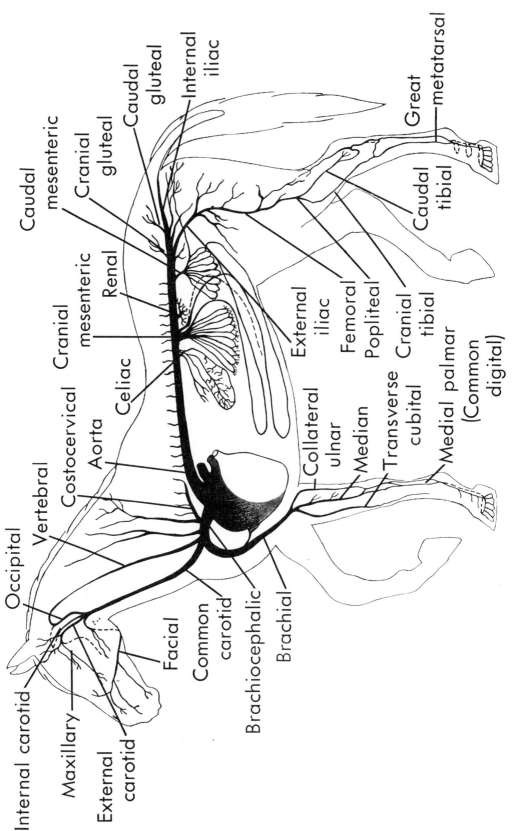

Fig. 16–5. Arteries of the horse.

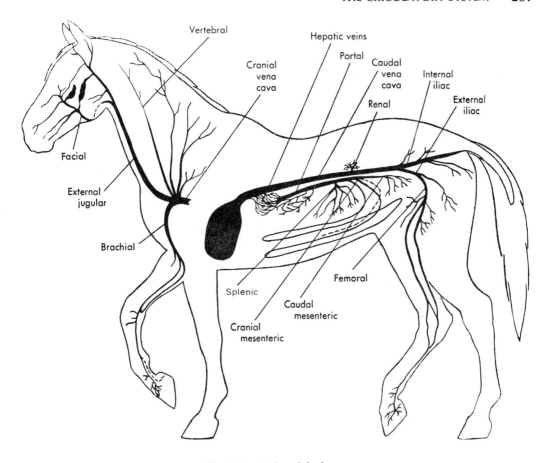

Fig. 16-6.   Veins of the horse.

teries. This division can be compared to the four fingers of your hand, with the index finger and little finger representing the right and left external iliac arteries and the middle and ring fingers representing the internal iliac arteries. In some species a *middle sacral artery* emerges between the two internal iliac arteries.

Thoracic Aorta and Its Branches. The first branches of the aorta are given off before the aorta leaves the heart. These are the *right* and *left coronary arteries*, which form a crown-shaped ring around the base of the heart and supply the heart muscle itself (myocardium) with blood. The term *coronary thrombosis*, or *heart attack*, refers to a clot in a coronary artery or one of its branches and may cause severe damage to the heart from lack of oxygen and nutrients.

Most of the blood from the capillary bed of the heart is returned to the right atrium by way of the *coronary veins*, which empty into the *coronary sinus* of the right atrium. However, some of the venous blood from the coronary circulation passes directly through the heart wall into the chambers of the heart.

BRACHIOCEPHALIC TRUNK. The first branch of the aorta after the coronary arteries are given off is the *brachiocephalic trunk* which, in the horse, gives rise to the left *subclavian (brachial)* artery and then divides into the right subclavian (brachial) artery and *bicarotid trunk*. The bicarotid trunk in turn divides into *right* and *left common carotid arteries*, which pass up the respective sides of the neck to supply a great part of the blood to the head and face region. Much of this blood is then returned to the cranial vena cava by way of the jugular veins. The *external jugular veins* are present in all animals as the superficial veins along the neck. In cattle and dogs an additional vein, the *internal* jugular, passes caudad with each common carotid artery.

The *right* and *left subclavian arteries* follow essentially the same course on each side of the body, and each gives off similar branches. Each subclavian artery passes in front of the first rib on the respective side and supplies the shoulder, neck, and front limb of that side. Within the thorax the subclavian artery gives off a number of branches, including *vertebral, costocervical, deep cervical, superficial cervical,* and the *internal thoracic arteries*. These branches of the subclavian artery supply blood to the caudal part of the neck, the first few ribs, and the dorsal part of the shoulder. After the subclavian artery passes around the first rib, it continues through the axilla (arm pit) as the *axillary artery* as far as the insertion of the teres major muscle. From the tendon of the teres major to the elbow the main artery of the forelimb is called *brachial* and is continued beyond the elbow as the *median artery*. The largest terminal branch of the median artery is the *medial palmar (common digital) artery,* which passes distally in the metacarpus to the fetlock where it divides into *medial digital* and *lateral digital arteries*.

As the aorta passes backward in the thorax ventral to the bodies of the vertebrae, it gives off a number of small branches to thoracic structures. Branches are given to the esophagus, the diaphragm, and the lungs. The *bronchial arteries* pass along the bronchi and supply oxygenated blood to the lung tissues. This is in addition to unoxygenated blood carried to the lungs by the pulmonary artery. *Intercostal arteries* (most arising from the aorta) pass laterad and then ventrad immediately behind each pair of ribs. In other words, there is a pair of intercostal arteries for each pair of ribs. The muscular portion of the diaphragm is supplied with blood by the *phrenic* branches of the *thoracic aorta*.

Abdominal Aorta and Its Branches. Shortly after the aorta passes through the diaphragm, the *celiac artery* is given off. This is a large unpaired artery, which supplies, in general, the stomach, the spleen, and the liver by *gastric, splenic,* and *hepatic* arteries respectively. Of course, the exact branching of this artery depends to a great extent upon the type of stomach. The ruminant has a much more complex subdivision of the celiac artery than does the nonruminant or animals with a simple stomach.

Immediately caudal to the celiac artery is the *cranial mesenteric artery*. This is a large unpaired artery which soon divides into a number of smaller arteries that supply blood to most of the small intestine and much of the large intestine. The number and distribution of the branches of the cranial mesenteric artery vary among different species, with the horse having the most complex arrangement. The caudal part of the large intestine receives blood from a relatively small, unpaired artery called the *caudal mesenteric artery*.

The *renal arteries* supply blood to the kidneys. They are paired arteries that arise immediately behind the cranial mesenteric artery. Each renal artery appears large in relation to the size of the kidney. The function of the renal artery is not merely to supply arterial blood to the kidney, but to carry a large amount of the total blood to the kidney for filtration and purification. The *adrenal arteries* originate directly from the aorta, from the renal arteries, or from intercostal or lumbar arteries.

In the male, the testicles originate just behind the kidneys, so the blood supply for the testicles, the *testicular (internal spermatic) arteries,* likewise arise behind the respective renal arteries. The testicular arteries are paired arteries, each supplying the respective testicle. In the female, the comparable arteries are the *ovarian (utero-*

ovarian) arteries. These paired arteries supply blood to the cranial part of the uterine horns as well as to the ovaries.

The *abdominal aorta* gives rise to a number of paired lumbar arteries that arise behind the diaphragm. One pair of lumbar arteries passes laterad and ventrad behind each respective lumbar vertebra to supply the body wall in that area.

The *internal iliac arteries* are the most medial terminations of the aorta; they are paired right and left arteries. Each internal iliac artery and its many branches supply the region of the pelvis, the hip, and much of both the male and female genitalia. Branches include the *cranial gluteal*, the *obturator*, the *caudal gluteal*, and the *internal pudendal arteries*.

The *external iliac arteries* give some blood to the abdominal wall, scrotum or mammary gland, and continue into the hind legs as the *femoral arteries*. The femoral artery descends on the medial side of the thigh, giving branches to the large muscles surrounding the *femur*. The femoral artery is continued in the region of the caudal part of the stifle joint as the *popliteal artery*. After a very short course, the popliteal artery divides into a *cranial tibial artery* and *caudal tibial artery*. The caudal tibial artery supplies the muscles of the gaskin, or true leg. The cranial tibial artery is larger and passes forward between the *tibia* and *fibula* and descends on the front of the leg to the hock. The cranial tibial artery supplies branches to the hock joint and descends in the metatarsal region as the *dorsal (great) metatarsal artery*. At the fetlock the great metatarsal artery divides into *medial digital* and *lateral digital* arteries.

VEINS

With some notable exceptions, the veins may be said to accompany arteries of the same name. The veins are always larger than their respective arteries and frequently more numerous. For example, the brachial artery carrying blood to the forearm and digit may be accompanied by two or more brachial veins returning the same blood to the heart. Often veins are more superficial (closer to the skin) than their respective arteries. As indicated earlier, nearly all veins eventually drain into either the caudal vena cava or cranial vena cava, and thus unoxygenated blood returns to the right atrium of the heart.

Cranial Vena Cava and Its Tributaries. The cranial vena cava drains the head, neck, front limbs, and part of the thorax. Tributaries to the cranial vena cava include the *jugular veins* (internal and external), *subclavian veins, costocervical veins, internal thoracic veins, vertebral veins*, and the unpaired *azygos vein*. The external jugular veins drain much of the head region while the *internal jugular veins*, if present, along with the *vertebral veins* drain most of the blood from the brain. Each *subclavian* vein drains the same area that is supplied with blood by the subclavian artery and its branches which go to the shoulder, neck, and forelimbs.

Caudal Vena Cava and Its Tributaries. The caudal vena cava is formed by the junction of the paired *internal iliac veins* and *external iliac veins*. It receives in addition *lumbar veins, testicular* or *ovarian veins, renal veins, adrenal veins* and *intercostal veins*; also as the caudal vena cava passes by the liver, a number of short *hepatic veins* enter the caudal vena cava directly from the liver.

HEPATIC PORTAL SYSTEM

The hepatic portal circulation is an important exception to the usual arrangement of the systemic circulation, in which an artery breaks up into capillary beds which recombine to form veins that are direct tributaries to the cranial or caudal vena cava. In the hepatic portal circulation, most of the branches of the celiac artery and the cranial and caudal mesenteric arteries supply capil-

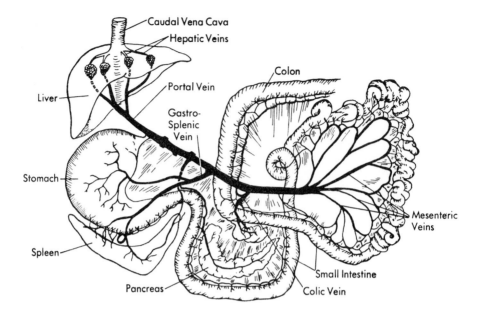

Fig. 16–7. Diagram of the hepatic portal circulation in the dog. See text for description.

lary beds of the *spleen* and digestive tract. (See Figs. 16–4, 16–7.)

Blood drained from the stomach, spleen, intestines, and pancreas is filtered through the liver by the hepatic portal circulation before it enters the general circulation. Blood from these areas drains into the *portal vein* which is the beginning of the hepatic portal system. Tributaries to the portal vein include the *gastric vein* from the stomach, the *splenic vein* from the spleen, the *mesenteric veins* from the intestines, and the *pancreatic veins* from the pancreas. The portal vein enters the liver and immediately breaks up into smaller and smaller branches in the liver, finally ending in the *sinusoids* (capillary network) of the liver. Here the blood comes into direct contact with cells of the liver cords. After being acted upon by the liver cells, the blood passes from the sinusoids of the liver into the *central vein* of each liver lobule. These central veins then combine and eventually form *hepatic veins* which empty their blood directly into the caudal vena cava.

It is desirable that blood drained from the digestive tract be exposed to the liver cells before entering the general circulation. This contact permits nutrients to be modified and/or stored in the liver for future use and gives the liver a chance to detoxify any harmful substances that may have been absorbed from the digestive tract.

The hepatic artery, a branch of the celiac artery, carries oxygenated blood to the liver. It enters at about the same place the portal vein enters the liver and the bile duct leaves the liver. Blood from the hepatic artery supplies oxygen and nutrients to the stroma of the liver and leaves by way of the liver sinusoids, central veins, and then hepatic veins.

OTHER PORTAL SYSTEMS

The arrangement in which a vein breaks up into capillaries and then recombines again to form another vein is spoken of as a portal system or portal circulation. A portal circulation is described in relation to the pituitary gland, the *hypophyseal portal circulation*. In birds, some reptiles, and amphibians, part of the blood returning from the hind limbs enters the kidneys to form the *renal portal circulation*.

Fetal Circulation

Throughout the entire gestation period, the fetus depends on the dam for nutrients, water, and oxygen needed for growth and for elimination of carbon dioxide and other waste products of fetal metabolism. This ex-

change for the most part occurs between fetal blood in the fetal placenta and maternal blood in the uterus of the dam without any actual interchange of blood from one to the other. The amount and types of material that can cross the placental barrier depend on the type of placenta and vary in different species (see Chap. 27). In effect, the fetal circulation performs functions that are carried on in the adult, by the lungs, the digestive system and the urinary system.

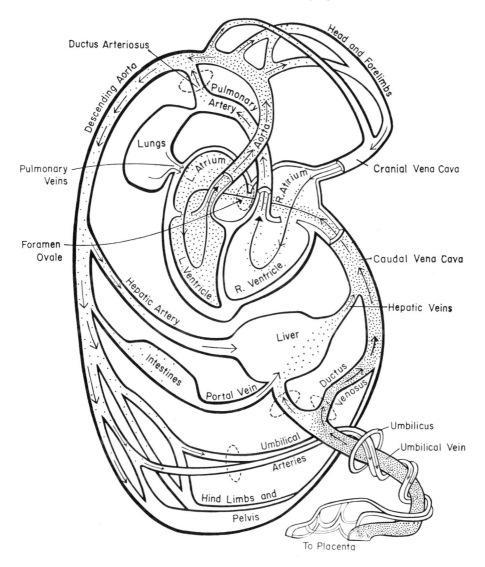

Fig. 16–8. Fetal circulation. Structures circled with dotted lines become nonfunctional at birth or shortly after and remain nonfunctional throughout the rest of the animal's life. These structures include the ductus arteriosus, the foramen ovale, the ductus venosus, the umbilical vein, and the umbilical arteries.

The fetal circulation differs from the adult circulation in several respects. (See Fig. 16–8.) Much of the blood from the caudal end of the aorta (internal or external iliac arteries) is transported to the placenta by means of two *umbilical arteries*. After passing through the placental capillaries, the blood is returned to the fetal heart by the *umbilical vein*.

In the adult, the same amount of blood passes through the pulmonary circulation as passes through the systemic circulation in a given period of time. However, since the lungs are nonfunctional in the fetus, a relatively small amount of the total blood volume is found in the pulmonary circulation at any specific time. There are two bypasses or shortcuts from the right side of the heart (and pulmonary artery) to the left side of the heart (and aorta). These bypasses are the *foramen ovale*, which connects the right and left atria and the *ductus arteriosus*, which connects the pulmonary artery and aorta.

The fetal blood that passes through the placental capillaries comes into relatively close contact with maternal blood circulating through the uterus of the dam. The amount of tissue between fetal blood and maternal blood varies with the species, but normally there is no direct exchange of fetal and maternal blood in mammals. Circulation of fetal blood through the placenta exchanges carbon dioxide and waste products in the fetal blood for oxygen and nutrients from the blood of the dam.

Since the fetal lungs are collapsed or, more properly, do not expand until the newborn animal takes its first breath, there is greater resistance to pulmonary blood flow than to systemic blood flow. The bypasses permit more blood flow through the systemic circulation than through the pulmonary circulation.

The course of blood through the fetal heart and related vessels has been studied extensively in the living lamb fetus by means of cineradiography (x-ray movies). Barcroft and Barclay, Franklin, and Pritchard have reported their work in considerable detail, in which radiopaque material was injected into various fetal vessels and its course followed with x-ray movies. These records, coupled with careful dissections and other experimental techniques, produced an accurate picture of the anatomy and physiology of fetal circulation in the lamb that presumably is similar to, if not identical to, the fetal circulation of other mammals.

The umbilical vein passes forward from the *umbilicus* in a peritoneal fold, the *falciform ligament*, and enters the liver close to the ventral border. Blood returning to the fetal heart from the placenta by way of the umbilical vein has the highest oxygen content of any fetal blood.

Several branches of the umbilical vein enter the substance of the liver before it communicates with the portal vein at the portal sinus. From the portal sinus, the *ductus venosus* forms a direct channel to the caudal vena cava. The ductus venosus appears to remain throughout fetal life in the ruminants and carnivora, but is present for only a short time if at all in the fetal pig and fetal horse. Blood enters the fetal liver by way of the *portal vein* and the *hepatic artery* and leaves the liver by the ductus venosus and *hepatic veins* that go directly from the liver to the caudal vena cava.

The caudal vena cava also drains the abdominal wall, kidneys, pelvis, and hind legs, as it does in the adult.

The caudal vena cava enters the right atrium, where a large part of its blood (still relatively high in oxygen content) is directed by a ridge, the *tuberculum intervenosum (crista intervenosa)* through the foramen ovale into the left atrium. Here this blood is joined by the small quantity of blood from the lungs, which enters the left atrium by way of the pulmonary veins.

From the left atrium, the blood from the caudal vena cava that passed through the foramen ovale and the blood from the pulmonary veins both pass through the left A–V valve into the left ventricle, and then are forced through the aortic semilunar valve to the aortic arch. This blood still has the highest oxygen content of any blood leaving the heart, even though it is a composite of blood from the umbilical vein, portal vein, hepatic artery, caudal vena cava, and pulmonary veins. The heart itself, the head, the neck, and the forelimbs all receive this relatively rich blood before it is mixed with blood from the cranial vena cava.

Blood returning to the heart from the cranial part of the fetus enters the right atrium by way of the cranial vena cava. This blood, together with the undiverted portion of blood from the caudal vena cava, passes through the right A–V valve into the right ventricle. From the right ventricle, it is forced through the pulmonary semilunar valve into the pulmonary artery.

A large part of the blood in the pulmonary artery is shunted directly into the aorta by way of the ductus arteriosus, which enters the aorta caudal to the branching of the brachiocephalic and/or subclavian arteries from the first part of the aorta. The smaller part of the blood in the pulmonary artery enters the lungs and is returned to the left atrium by the pulmonary veins, as already mentioned.

Beyond the entrance of the ductus arteriosus, the aorta contains a mixture of all the blood that enters and leaves the heart. The aorta of the fetus has the same branches as the aorta of the adult and, in addition, gives off directly or indirectly from the external iliac arteries or internal iliac arteries two large umbilical arteries that carry blood to the placenta, where it circulates through placental capillaries close enough to the maternal blood for exchange of fetal waste products for nutrients and oxygen from the dam's blood.

In summary, the umbilical vein contains the purest blood with the highest oxygen content, most nutrients, and fewest waste products of any blood vessel in the fetus. As the blood is carried toward the heart, it is diluted with less pure blood from the liver (the portal vein, hepatic artery, and hepatic veins) and from the caudal vena cava. This mixed blood enters the right atrium, and

most of it passes through the foramen ovale to the left atrium, where it is further diluted by blood returning to the heart by way of the pulmonary veins. This blood then supplies the heart, head, and forelimbs before further dilution occurs in the aorta with blood from the right ventricle that passes through the pulmonary artery and ductus arteriosus.

Barcroft describes closure of the foramen ovale followed by closure of the ductus arteriosus within a few minutes after ligation of the umbilical cord. Ultimate closure of the ductus arteriosus appears to be caused by smooth muscle within the wall, which is stimulated to contract by an increase in oxygen content of the blood reaching the ductus arteriosus. Attempts to correlate nervous stimuli with closure of the ductus arteriosus have been largely unsuccessful.

Respiratory movements in the fetus appear to be inhibited by a center located in the brain. This inhibition may be overcome and respiratory movements initiated by any one or combination of external stimuli, such as ligation or severing of the umbilical cord, handling the fetus, or simply exposing the fetus to a draft of air. The dam licking a newborn animal and the owner rubbing it with a rough cloth both may serve as a means of artificial respiration or stimulation.

LYMPHATIC SYSTEM

The lymphatic system includes both the lymphoid tissue of the body and the lymph vessels associated with the lymphoid tissue. It serves as a system for draining tissue fluid that parallels and augments the venous circulation and therefore assists in the control of interstitial fluid pressures (Fig. 16–9). It also forms antibodies and acts as a defense mechanism against noxious materials by filtering them out of tissue fluid and phagocytizing them, thereby assisting in the control of infection.

Lymphoid tissue consists of accumulations of *lymphocytes* trapped in the spaces between fibers of reticular connective tissue. The lymphoid tissue may be scattered

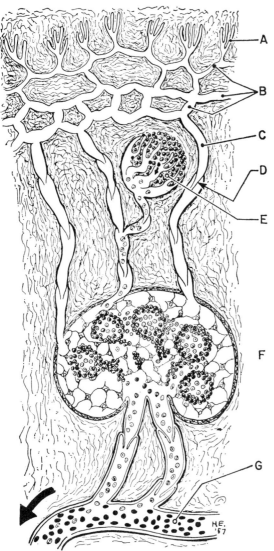

Fig. 16–9. A generalized diagram of lymphatic drainage. Lymph is, in essence, tissue fluid taken up by lymph capillaries (A). It streams slowly through vessels of increasing caliber (B, C), many of which are provided with valves (D). Lymphocytes, many produced in solitary lymph nodules (E), are added. Lymph is filtered through lymph nodes (F). There more lymphocytes and antibodies are added. Finally, it joins the venous circulation (G). (Elias and Pauly, Human Microanatomy, courtesy of Da Vinci Publishing Co.)

Lymph Vessels

The lymphatic vessels constitute a one-way channel that parallels the venous system and eventually empties into the cranial vena cava or some of its tributaries. The smallest lymphatics begin blindly between tissue cells as lymph capillaries, which collect the tissue fluid that is not absorbed by the venous system (Fig. 16–10). When the tissue fluid enters the lymphatic vessels, it is known as lymph, which consists of fluid originally derived from the blood and is on its way back to the blood.

The lymph capillaries form more or less complex networks throughout most tissues. These networks finally combine to form lymph vessels, which in turn unite to form larger and larger lymphatic vessels. All of the lymph collected from the body eventually returns to the venous system by way of the *thoracic duct, right lymphatic duct* (if present), and *tracheal ducts*. These ducts enter the cranial vena cava or the jugular veins as they unite to form the cranial vena cava.

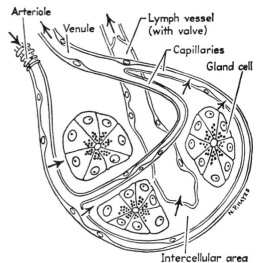

Fig. 16–10. Diagram illustrating the relations of the body cell to blood circulation and lymph drainage. (Leach, Functional Anatomy: Mammalian and Comparative, courtesy of McGraw-Hill Book Co.)

diffusely in some organs, as in the intestinal submucosa, or aggregations of lymphoid tissue may be encapsulated to form specific organs, including lymph nodes, the tonsils, the thymus, and the spleen.

In many ways lymph vessels resemble veins. The lymph vessels have numerous valves scattered throughout their course. Their walls are much thinner than those of arteries and usually thinner than veins. The valves, of course, permit the flow of lymph only in the direction toward the heart or great veins just cranial to the heart.

Lacteals (L. lact—milk) are a special group of the lymph vessels that drain the intestinal wall. These vessels absorb lipids from the small intestine, which then appear as a milky fluid called *chyle*.

Lymph Nodes

Lymph nodes, also called *lymph glands*, are discrete nodular structures scattered along the course of lymphatic vessels (Fig. 16–11). These lymph nodes serve as filters for the lymph and act as one of the first body defenses against infection by harboring lymphocytes and plasma cells, which produce antibodies.

Each lymph node is surrounded by a connective-tissue capsule that blends with the surrounding connective tissue and acts

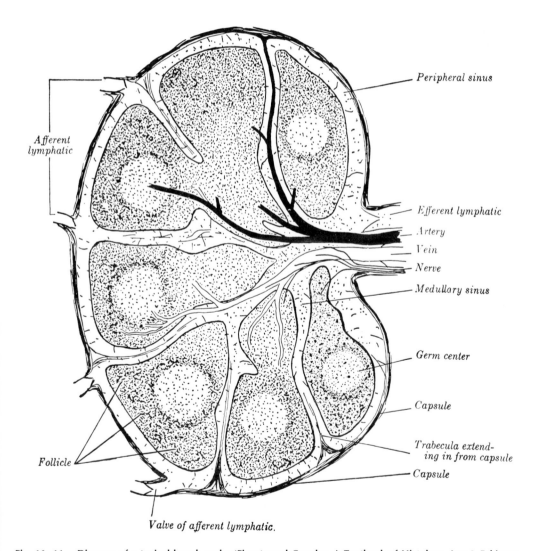

Fig. 16–11. Diagram of a typical lymph node. (Finerty and Cowdry, A Textbook of Histology, Lea & Febiger.)

as a means of holding it in place. The capsule also sends numerous connective-tissue *septa* (or *trabeculae*) into the substance of the node. The node is divided into a *cortex* and a *medulla*, which contain large numbers of lymphocytes. Those in the cortex are arranged in dark-staining groups known as *primary nodules*. Within the primary nodules are light-staining areas called *secondary nodules*. Secondary nodules are areas of rapid cell multiplication and, for this reason, are also called *germinal centers*. *Lymphocytes* in the medullary portion of the lymph node are arranged in cords rather than nodules.

In addition to the lymphocytes, lymph nodes also contain *plasma cells*, which are sometimes classified with the connective tissue cells. Plasma cells are an important source of antibodies produced by the animal body. They are somewhat larger than lymphocytes, with dark-staining granules in the nucleus that often are arranged in the form of a cart wheel or the dial of a watch. The cytoplasm is rich in RNA (ribonucleic acid) granules, suggesting extensive protein synthesis.

Immediately deep to the capsule of the node is a space—the lymph sinus of the cortex—that communicates with other lymph sinuses located in the cortex and in the medulla.

The lymph enters the sinus of the cortex and slowly percolates through the cortex and medulla, where it is filtered, to emerge finally at the hilus of the node, where the blood vessels and nerves enter and the efferent lymph vessels emerge.

The lymph vessels that carry lymph toward the lymph node enter through the cap-

Table 16–1.   Lymph Nodes of Cattle

Name of Node	Location of Node
Mandibular	In mandibular space, about 2 inches cranial to angle of mandible
Parotid	1 inch in front of and just below external meatus of ear
Suprapharyngeal	Dorsal to pharynx, close to midline
Atlantal	Ventral to wing of atlas
Cranial cervical	Cranial third of neck on common carotid artery
Middle cervical	Middle third of neck on course of common carotid artery
Prescapular (Postsuperficial cervical)	Above shoulder joint covered by brachiocephalicus muscle
Axillary	On medial side of shoulder near brachial plexus
Prepectoral (postcervical)	At entrance to thorax on each side of trachea
Popliteal	Behind stifle on gastrocnemius between semitendinosus and biceps femoris
Ischiatic	At lesser sciatic notch of pelvis
Prefemoral	In front of thigh just above stifle
Superficial inguinal (Supramammary)	Bulls—in front of external inguinal ring (Cows—above posterior part of udder)
Deep inguinal	Where circumflex iliac artery leaves external iliac artery
Sacral	Ventral surface of sacrum
External iliac	At bifurcation of circumflex iliac artery
Internal iliac	At junction of external iliac artery and aorta
Anal	Floor of pelvis lateral to anus
Lumbar	Sublumbar region along abdominal aorta
Renal	At hilus of kidney on renal artery
Gastric	On course of gastric blood vessels and between folds of stomach
Mesenteric	Along attached border of intestine between layers of mesentery
Splenic	At hilus of spleen
Hepatic or portal	At hilus of liver near vessels
Intercostal	Between ribs near thoracic vertebrae
Sternal	Dorsal surface of sternum on course of internal thoracic artery
Bronchial	On trachea near branching of main bronchi
Anterior mediastinal	Along trachea and esophagus caudal to thoracic inlet
Posterior mediastinal	Between esophagus and aorta cranial to diaphragm

sule and are known as *afferent vessels*. Lymph vessels that carry the filtered lymph away from the lymph node are known as *efferent vessels*. The terms efferent and afferent must be used in relation to a specific node, since the efferent vessels from one node frequently are the afferent vessels for the next node in the channel draining a given area.

In addition to the lymph vessels, each lymph node has its own blood supply and venous drainage. The lymph nodes are scattered throughout the body and, in general, the condition of each node reflects the health or disease of the area from which the afferent lymph vessels are derived. If an infection is present in a specific area, the lymph nodes in that area tend to increase in size to fight the infection. For example, a horse with distemper or strangles, which is an infection of the nasal cavity and pharynx, will frequently show great enlargement of the *mandibular lymph nodes*. Mandibular lymph nodes receive their afferent vessels from the nasal cavity, mouth, and pharynx.

If the first lymph node is unable to stop the infection, the bacteria or other infective agent will then pass on by way of the efferent vessels to the next lymph node on the lymphatic channel. This lymph node in turn responds to the infection by increasing in size.

Cancer cells as well as infections may spread throughout the body by way of the lymphatic channels. When a tumor (cancer) is removed surgically, it may be necessary to also remove the lymph nodes draining the cancerous area, if they are affected, to prevent further spread of the condition. The meat inspector studies the lymphatic system in order to determine whether a given part of a carcass should be condemned. For example, if a cow with a cancerous eye shows involvement of the lymph nodes of the head, neck, and thorax, the entire carcass probably will be condemned. However, if it appears that the cancerous condition has been stopped by the nodes immediately draining

the eye, perhaps only the head will be condemned, and the rest of the carcass may be passed for food.

The lymph nodes of cattle, described in USDA Circular 866, are listed in Table 16–1.

Hemal Lymph Nodes. These are small dark red or black structures found in cattle and sheep. They resemble lymph nodes but are interposed on the course of small vessels.

Spleen

The *spleen* is a lymphoid organ associated with the circulatory system. It is attached to the stomach either directly by connective tissue, as in the ruminants, where it is closely adherent to the rumen, or by the *gastrosplenic omentum*. The shape of the spleen varies considerably from one species to another. In the chicken, the spleen is nearly spherical in shape, while in other animals it is more or less elongated. The spleen has a thick capsule from which septa penetrate into the interior of the gland, forming a definite stroma.

Blood vessels enter and leave the spleen at the hilus of the organ. The splenic vein drains blood from the spleen and is a tributary to the portal vein. The spleen functions as a storage area for blood, so the size of the spleen varies from time to time even within a given individual, as well as from species to species, depending on the amount of blood present in the spleen at a given time.

The spleen is also a part of the reticuloendothelial system in that it phagocytizes fragile, worn-out red blood cells that break up in passing through the splenic pulp. The fate of the digested products was described in Chapter 13. Although the spleen is a very useful organ, it is not absolutely essential in the adult, because apparently all of its functions can be carried on by other organs. The spleen can be removed without apparent damage to a mature animal.

Chapter 17

Physiology of Circulation

Physiology of circulation is a complex subject. It involves details of all events in the cardiac cycle as well as dynamics of circulating fluid, pressure relationships, bioelectrical and nervous activity, and chemical and physical principles.

One somewhat useful analogy is a comparison of the circulatory system with a piston-pump water system for a residence. Although the water system is simple when compared with the circulatory system, some of the same problems have to be solved in each.

The heart is, in reality, two pumps, which receive blood into the atrial chambers (atria) and then pump this same blood from the ventricles to the tissues and back again. The heart valves open and close in proper sequence to ensure movement of the blood in one direction. The force exerted to propel the blood comes from the muscular action of the heart itself.

CARDIAC CYCLE

The *cardiac cycle* refers to the sequence of events that occurs during one complete heart beat. The events of the cardiac cycle, or the heart beat, occur in a specific sequence (Fig. 17–1). These are arbitrary divisions assigned by man as phases or periods conventionally used to describe the events, which are actually continuous.

Diastole (dilate, from Gr. *dia*—apart; *stello*—place or put) refers to the relaxation of a chamber of the heart just prior to and during the filling of that chamber. It may be right or left atrial diastole or right or left ventricular diastole.

Systole (contraction, from Gr. *syn*— together; *stello*—place) refers to the contraction of a chamber of the heart in the process of partially emptying that chamber. It also may be right or left atrial systole or right or left ventricular systole.

272

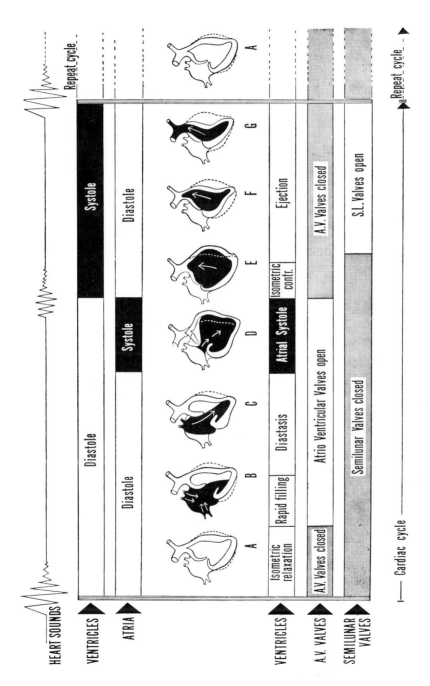

Fig. 17–1.   Events of the cardiac cycle.

When blood enters the right atrium from the systemic circulation of the body and the left atrium from the lungs, the volume and pressure rise in the atria. This occurs during diastole. When the atrial pressure exceeds ventricular pressure, the A–V valves open, allowing the blood to flow into the relaxed ventricles. This accounts for the major part of the filling of the ventricles (about 70%) and occurs before atrial contraction. The atria then depolarize and contract (atrial systole), forcing the rest of the atrial blood into the ventricles. This increases ventricular volume and pressure (Fig. 17–2).

As the atria relax (atrial diastole) the ventricles first depolarize and then they contract (ventricular systole). The now greater ventricular pressure forces the A–V valves closed (the first heart sound), and for a moment all heart valves are closed. This is the phase of isometric contraction (or isovolumetric), that is, when pressure and muscle tension are building up, but there is little change in the length of the muscle fibers.

Next, the ventricular buildup of pressure exceeds the arterial pressures, causing the aortic and pulmonary semilunar valves to open. The blood is ejected from the left ventricle into the aorta and from the right ventricle into the pulmonary artery.

This initial *rapid ejection phase* of systole is followed by a *reduced ejection phase*, during which ventricular pressure falls and repolarization occurs. Then comes the phase of *protodiastole*, when ventricular pressure is decreasing and arterial pressure starts to exceed ventricular pressure. The arterial pressure causes the blood to flow back, as a result of the elasticity of the arterial walls, which snaps shut the aortic and pulmonary semilunar valves (producing the second heart sound) (Fig. 17–3).

At this moment the A–V valves are still closed also, from the pressure of the blood forced against them at ventricular systole; and so we have an *isovolumic* (or isovolumetric) *relaxation* phase during which the heart muscle fibers are relaxed

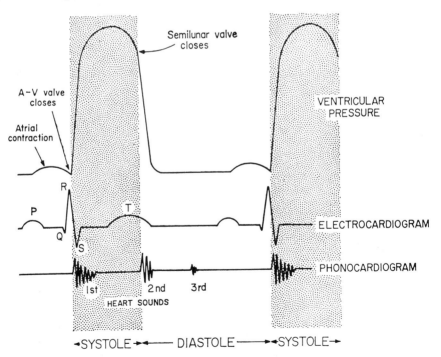

Fig. 17–2.   Relationship of ventricular pressure to the electrocardiogram and phonocardiogram during the cardiac cycle. (Guyton, Functions of the Human Body, courtesy of W. B. Saunders Co.)

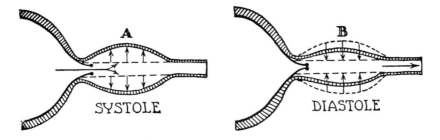

Fig. 17–3. Diagram to illustrate role of elastic walls of aorta in maintenance of circulation. *A*, Walls are distended as ventricular contents enter aorta. *B*, Following closure of aortic valves, elastic recoil of walls drives blood peripherally. Elastic walls serve to store energy during systole and release it during diastole. (After Rein *in* Ruch and Fulton, Medical Physiology and Biophysics, courtesy of W. B. Saunders Co.)

and there is no increase in muscle fiber length, since blood is not entering the ventricles to stretch the fibers (only blood from the direct coronary venous return is seeping into the ventricles). This phase has started diastole. The atria are again filling, and when their pressure exceeds ventricular pressure, the cycle will repeat.

Heart Sounds

If we place our ear or the receiver of a stethoscope on the wall of the thorax over the heart, two distinct sounds can be heard which are repeated indefinitely. The first sound is "lub" and the second sound is "dup." These sounds are separated by a short interval and followed by a longer pause. The slower the heart rate, the longer the pause.

The first sound, "lub," is produced by closure of the A–V valves at the time of contraction of muscle fibers of the ventricles. It is louder, lower pitched, and of longer duration than the second heart sound.

The second heart sound, "dup," is caused by vibrations of the vessel walls, blood columns, and closed semilunar valves.

Valve Disorders

A valve that fails to close completely permits blood to flow through in the wrong direction at the wrong time. This condition, called *valvular insufficiency* or *incompe-*

tence, results in an abnormal heart sound, or *murmur*.

On the other hand, a valve may fail to open completely because of thickening or presence of scar tissue, a condition called *stenosis*. The abnormal heart sound associated with stenosis is caused by the blood being forced through an opening that is too small.

Both insufficiency and stenosis increase the work load of the heart—insufficiency, because some of the blood is pumped twice for each beat; and stenosis, because of the greater resistance of the small opening.

Endocarditis, inflammation of the lining of the heart, is a common cause of pathologic changes in heart valves. *Erysipelas* infection in hogs frequently results in endocarditis, as does *rheumatic fever* in man.

CONDUCTION SYSTEM OF THE HEART

The heart beat originates in the *sino-atrial node (S–A node),* called the *pacemaker* of the heart. This is a collection of specialized cardiac muscle cells located at the junction of the cranial vena cava and the right atrium. The impulse from the S–A node spreads throughout the atria, causing them to contract in atrial systole. No special fibers have been demonstrated connecting the S–A node with the A–V node; only normal atrial muscle fibers have been described. However, physiologically it is apparent that a conduction system does exist, since the transmission speed is greater than could occur without one. There are also preferred pathways or routes of impulse conduction between the S–A and the A–V nodes.

The *atrioventricular node (A–V node)*, located in the septum between the atria, picks up the impulse from the depolarization of the atrial muscle membranes and conducts the impulse to the ventricular muscle by way of the *A–V bundle (bundle of His)* and the *Purkinje network* causing ventricular depolarization and systole. This pathway (A–V node, A–V bundle, and Purkinje network), composed of modified muscle fibers, constitutes the normal communication for impulse transmission from the atria to the ventricles.

Heart block refers to any interruption of this impulse pathway. The most common block occurs in the A–V bundle, which breaks the connection between atria and ventricles. Then the atria continue to beat at the normal rate, but the ventricular beat is much slower and completely dissociated from the atrial beat.

Control of Heart Rate

The intrinsic regulation of the heart beat by the S–A node, through the A–V node, A–V bundle, and Purkinje network, is adequate to keep a heart beating regularly without any outside nervous control (Fig.

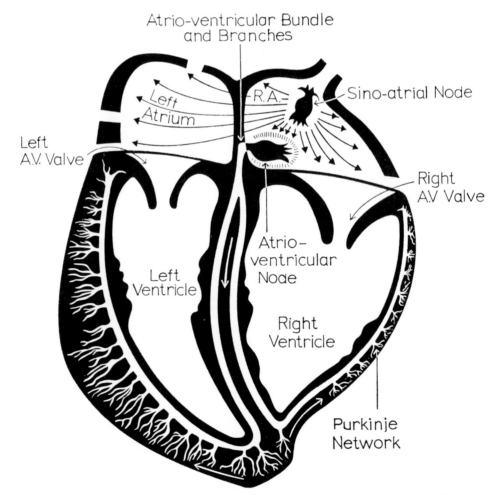

Fig. 17–4. Conduction system of the heart. (After Carlson and Johnson, The Machinery of the Body, courtesy of University of Chicago Press.)

17–4). However, rate of heart beat and strength of contraction are regulated by impulses from the autonomic nervous system. Parasympathetic fibers reach the heart from the two *vagus nerves,* and sympathetic fibers to the heart come from the area of the two *stellate ganglia* of the sympathetic nervous system.

Stimulation of the vagus nerves tends to inhibit action of the heart by decreasing the force of contraction of the heart muscle, rate of contraction, and rate of conduction of impulses within the heart. Secondary to these changes, the flow of blood through the coronary arteries is reduced. Sympathetic stimulation increases the activity of the heart by increasing force of contraction, rate of contraction, rate of impulse conduction, and coronary blood flow.

Thus, parasympathetic stimulation permits the heart to rest more when the remainder of the body is relatively inactive, but sympathetic stimulation increases heart activity to supply more blood to striated muscles, the liver, and brain for increased physical activity or during conditions of stress.

In general, the normal heart rate tends to be faster in small animals and slower as the size of the animal increases. For example, heart rate of the mouse ranges from 325 to 850 beats/min, while the heart of the elephant beats only about 20 times per minute. Ranges of normal heart rates of domestic animals is given by Dukes as: horse, 23 to 70; cow, 60 to 70; pig, 55 to 86; sheep, 60 to 120; goat, 70 to 135; dog, 100 to 130; and cat, 110 to 140.

Apex Beat

The heart shortens and rotates clockwise when viewed from above (dorsally) during ventricular systole, suddenly pressing against the thoracic wall. This *apex beat* is the pulsation that can be felt on the superficial surface of the thorax over the area of the heart, particularly near the apex of the heart.

BLOOD VOLUME AND PRESSURE

The quantity of blood in the body is at least 7% of the total body weight. For a 1000-pound horse, this would amount to about 70 pints, and for a 20-pound dog, 1 to 2 pints. For any size animal this represents a sizable mass of fluid which is constantly being moved through the body. The force necessary to propel this fluid mass is supplied primarily by the heart. Thus, blood under pressure is propelled from the ventricular chambers into the vessels leading from the heart.

In order that the heart may have a constant supply of blood with which to work, there must also be adequate return of blood to the heart at all times. The heart and the blood vessels constitute a closed system of circulation wherein blood is constantly moved from the heart to the periphery and back again. To maintain this constant movement, there must be a difference in pressure—a progressive decline, with the highest pressure at the ventricles and the lowest in the great veins as they empty into the atrial chambers of the heart.

Pressure Relationships in the Heart

Normally, in the adult, the pressures in the *left heart* (left atrium and left ventricle) are considerably higher than those in the *right heart* (right atrium and right ventricle). Although the same volume of blood is pumped by each side of the heart, the resistance of the systemic circulation is much greater than the resistance of the pulmonary circulation. Consequently, the pressure produced by the left heart must be much higher than that of the right heart.

Most of the reflexes affecting contraction of the heart are described in their relation to systemic circulation. Less is known about the mechanisms controlling pulmonary circulation; however, its correlations with systemic circulatory changes are well known today. If increased resistance to pulmonary circulation continues for a period of several days or weeks, the right side of the heart hypertrophies (increases in size of muscle cells) sufficiently to increase the pressure in the right ventricle to overcome the added resistance to pulmonary blood flow. Experimental obstruction of the pulmonary artery may result in pressures in the right ventricle that are as high as those in the left ventricle.

Relative pressures within the chambers and vessels of the heart determine when each of the valves closes and opens. In other words, whenever the pressure is higher in the atrium than in the respective ventricle, the A–V valve opens. A corresponding situation occurs with the semilunar valves. When ventricular pressure is higher than arterial pressure, aortic and pulmonary semilunar valves open, but when ventricular pressure falls below arterial pressure, the semilunar valves close.

Blood Pressure in Vessels

Blood pressure may be defined as the pressure blood exerts against the vessel walls. The initial pressure is produced by contraction of the ventricles of the heart and is the systolic pressure. Blood is forced into the large elastic arteries, stretching their walls and causing them to dilate.

When the ventricles relax, closure of the semilunar valves prevents the return of blood from the arteries to the heart, and the small arterioles impede the flow of the blood to the capillaries. Pressure exerted by the elastic walls of the arteries maintains pressure (diastolic pressure) within the arteries and keeps blood flowing smoothly into the capillaries while the ventricles are relaxed. This mechanism might be compared to a thin-walled garden hose with a small nozzle. Water will continue to flow through the nozzle for a time after the faucet is closed because of the elasticity of the wall of the hose.

The analogy to a water system may be carried even further, as shown in Figure 17–5. One side of the heart is represented by a one-cylinder piston pump; the A–V

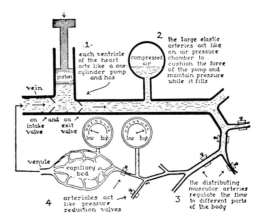

Fig. 17–5.   Diagram illustrating the mechanical functions that must be performed by the different parts of the circulatory system. (Ham and Leeson, Histology, courtesy of J. B. Lippincott Co.)

valves, by the intake valve; the semilunar valves, by the exit valve; and the elasticity of the large arteries, by the air-pressure chamber. In addition, control of distribution to various areas and maintenance of pressure are obtained by the muscular walls of arterioles, representing pressure-reducing control valves.

Distribution of Blood

Control of distribution of the amount of blood to different areas is obviously necessary because the needs of a given area differ greatly from one time to another. The leg muscles of a cow need more blood than any other area when she is running; the abdominal viscera need more blood while digestion is occurring; and the udder takes more blood during milk production. (This is a reason for not running dairy cattle, particularly before milking.)

Distribution of blood is controlled partially by arteries of moderate size, called distributing arteries. These arteries contain smooth muscle in the wall, which controls the size of the lumen (inside diameter) and consequently the amount of blood flowing through the arteries. An additional control is provided by the arterioles, the smallest of the arteries. They also maintain arterial diastolic pressure, as mentioned before, and reduce the pressure of blood entering the capillaries. This last function can be compared to the use of a fine-spray nozzle on a high-pressure hose to avoid washing out a newly planted lawn.

The drastic drop in pressure effected by the arterioles as blood enters the capillaries is essential, because the thin walls of the capillaries could not stand the high pressure found on the arterial side of the arterioles. The drop in pressure is enhanced by the fact that the many channels of the capillary bed constitute an increase in area in which the entering blood can spread out, thus reducing pressure by distributing the volume, which facilitates exchange through the capillary wall. Figure 17–6 shows a continued drop in pressure as the blood passes from arteries to capillaries, to venules, to veins, and finally

to the vena cava. In fact, a negative pressure (less than zero—a vacuum) may occur in the vena cava during the inspiratory phase of respiration.

Contraction of the diaphragm aids return of venous blood to the heart in two ways. The negative pressure in the thorax draws blood into the cranial and caudal venae cavae, where it is trapped by the large valves near the entrances of the veins into the thorax. In addition, the increased pressure on abdominal viscera caused by contraction of the diaphragm tends to force blood from abdominal veins into the thorax by way of the caudal vena cava.

Measurement of Blood Flow

Pressure alone does not produce blood flow, but difference in pressure from one end of a vessel to the other causes blood to

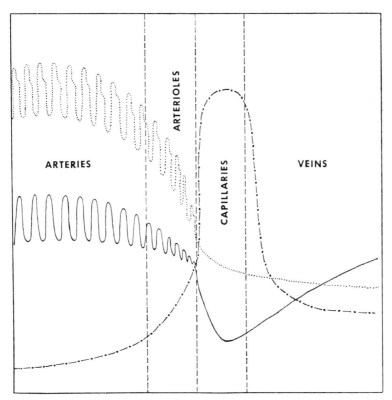

Fig. 17–6. Diagram showing relationship of pressure (. . . . . .) and velocity (————) to cross sectional area of vessels of the body (—•—•—•). Note the absence of rhythmic variations in pressure and velocity in the capillaries and veins. (After Best and Taylor, The Living Body, courtesy of Henry Holt and Co.)

move. For example, a steam boiler might have several hundred pounds pressure per square inch, but there will be little movement of water or steam until a valve is opened, giving an area of reduced pressure.

Flow is measured in units of volume per measurement of time, such as "gallons per minute" or "milliliters per second." It is related to both pressure and resistance. Amount of flow is directly proportional to pressure and inversely proportional to resistance.

Resistance to flow is due mainly to friction of the fluid on the vessel wall and friction between concentric layers of the fluid (being least in the very center and increasing outwardly). It is increased by greater vessel length and greater viscosity (thickness) of the fluid. However, friction and resistance decrease with greater vessel diameter. To summarize, resistance is directly proportional to vessel length and viscosity of the fluid, but resistance is inversely proportional to the fourth power of the vessel radius.

These relationships may be expressed by the following formulas, which are different ways of saying the same thing.

$$\text{Blood flow} = \frac{\text{Pressure}}{\text{Resistance}}$$

$$\text{Pressure} = \text{Blood flow} \times \text{Resistance}$$

$$\text{Resistance} = \frac{\text{Pressure}}{\text{Blood flow}}$$

A formula called *Poiseuille's law* gives blood flow when all factors, including pressure, vessel length, vessel diameter, and viscosity, are known. It states:

$$\text{Rate of flow} = \frac{P_1 - P_2}{8l} \times \frac{\pi r^4}{\eta}$$

P_1 and P_2 are the pressures at the ends of the vessel of length l and radius r, while η is the viscosity. This formula applies when blood flows in a streamline, laminar fashion, but it does not apply in the case of turbulent flow (*Reynold's formula* predicts the probability of turbulent flow).

Pulse

Each systolic contraction of the left ventricle forces more blood into the arteries and arterioles which are already filled with blood under diastolic pressure. This additional blood at each systole dilates the arteries. The wave of systolic pressure, which starts at the heart and spreads throughout the arterial network, is called the *pulse* or *pulse wave*. It can be felt in arteries near the surface of the body, particularly if the artery can be pressed against an underlying bone or other solid structure.

In large animals the pulse can be felt in the *facial artery* as it turns around the horizontal ramus of the mandible, or it can be felt in the *middle coccygeal artery* in the middle of the ventral surface of the tail. The *femoral artery*, on the medial side of the thigh, is readily accessible in the dog, cat, sheep, and goat.

Wave Velocity

Velocity of the pulse wave is much higher than the velocity of the blood traveling through the artery. In the aorta, the pulse wave travels at a rate of about 500 cm/sec, while the mean rate of blood flow is less than 60 cm/sec. As the arterial system branches, the walls become stiffer (less distensible) as their caliber is reduced with successive branches. For this reason the pulse velocity increases. In the smaller arteries it can be as high as 1000 to 1500 cm/sec.

The spurting of a cut artery is correlated with the pulse wave and consequently with systole of the heart. Actual average velocity of the blood is fastest in the arteries (370 mm/sec), slowest in the capillaries (0.5 mm/sec), and faster again in the veins (125 mm/sec). (See Fig. 17–6.)

Measurement of Blood Pressure

Since pressure of blood against the restricting vessel wall pushes in all directions, it can be experimentally measured conveniently by determining how high a column of fluid will rise if connected directly to an artery. The first recorded measurement of blood pressure was performed in 1733 by Stephen Hales, an English clergyman. He placed a brass tube in the carotid artery of a horse and connected it to a 12-foot, 9-inch glass tube with the trachea of a goose. The blood rose to a height of 12 feet, 6 inches in the tube and fluctuated with each heart beat.

The direct method used in experimental animals today is based on the same principle as Hale's, except that a cannula is inserted into the carotid artery and is connected to a pressurized vessel or electronic transducer, which in turn is electrically connected to an electronic amplifier and recorder. Pressure changes are then permanently recorded as a pen is caused to move on graph paper with changes in the transducer created by blood pressure changes. Blood pressure is conventionally measured in millimeters of mercury (mm Hg).

In man, blood pressure is determined indirectly with a sphygmomanometer, which measures the amount of pressure (in a cuff around the arm) necessary to stop blood flowing in the artery. This is determined by listening to the artery distal to the inflated cuff. The pressure indicated when blood first starts to flow through the artery, as pressure in the cuff is released, is the systolic pressure, and it represents the height of a column of mercury that could be lifted by systole of the heart. Systolic pressure, then, is taken as the manometer reading when one hears the first clear tapping sounds for at least two consecutive beats. This is phase I of five phase periods called *Korotkoff sounds*. As release of pressure continues, a point is reached at which the sound becomes abruptly muffled, producing a soft blowing quality. This is phase IV and is the best index of diastolic pressure. The fifth phase occurs when all sound disappears, and this should be recorded also. The recording of systolic, diastolic, and no sound pressures (e.g., 130/82/74) gives the most desirable data for diagnostic use. Indirect measure-

ment of blood pressure may not be completely accurate (since it depends on the listener's hearing acuity, among other things), but with trained persons the results are consistent.

NERVOUS CONTROL OF BLOOD FLOW

Primary control of blood flow depends on nervous control of the heart, because nearly all movement of blood ultimately depends on heart action. As mentioned previously, the heart has intrinsic nerve control in the form of the S–A node, A–V node, A–V bundle, and Purkinje network. In addition, the vagus nerves inhibit heart action by release of a chemical, *acetylcholine*, and sympathetic nerves stimulate heart action by release of the transmitter substance, *norepinephrine*.

Figure 17–7 shows the locations of the aortic bodies and carotid bodies in man, and Figure 17–8 shows the innervation of the heart.

Reflexes Involving the Heart

With the exception of the so-called *axon reflex*, which involves only part of one neuron, all reflex arcs require at least two neurons. In the axon reflex, one branch of a sensory nerve is located in the skin and another branch of the same nerve terminates near a blood vessel. Stimulation of the cutaneous (skin) branch causes the blood vessels at the terminal branch of the nerve to dilate, by causing histamine to be released.

A reflex arc, which is described in detail in Chapter 6, consists essentially of an afferent neuron (nerve cell), one or more internuncial neurons in the central nervous system, and an efferent neuron. When properly stimulated, the afferent neuron carries nerve impulses from the periphery or from some visceral organ to the central nervous system. The internuncial neuron sends the impulses to the appropriate efferent neuron. The efferent neuron carries the impulses to the proper organ, which is thus stimulated to

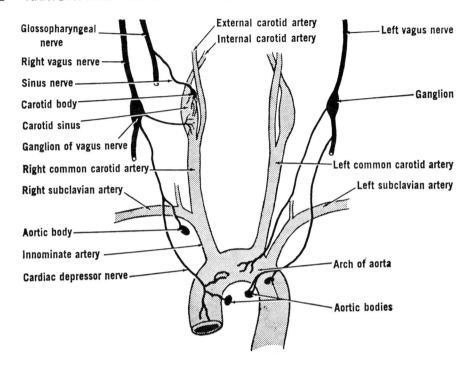

Glossopharyngeal nerve

Right vagus nerve

Sinus nerve

Carotid body

Carotid sinus

Ganglion of vagus nerve

Right common carotid artery

Right subclavian artery

Aortic body

Innominate artery

Cardiac depressor nerve

External carotid artery

Internal carotid artery

Left vagus nerve

Ganglion

Left common carotid artery

Left subclavian artery

Arch of aorta

Aortic bodies

Fig. 17–7.   Diagram showing location of aortic bodies and carotid bodies in man. (The innominate artery of man is equivalent to the brachiocephalic artery of the quadruped.) (DeCoursey, The Human Organism, courtesy of McGraw-Hill Book Co., Inc.)

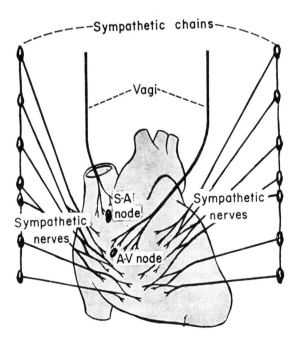

Sympathetic chains

Vagi

S-A node

Sympathetic nerves

Sympathetic nerves

A-V node

Fig. 17–8.   Innervation of the heart. (Guyton, Function of the Human Body, courtesy of W. B. Saunders Co.)

the appropriate activity. This reflex mechanism applies equally well to somatic reflexes, such as postural reflexes, and to reflexes that control the functioning of visceral structures, including those of the vascular system.

Simulation of many afferent (sensory) nerves may cause a change in the heart rate, but specific nerves that form the afferent side of well-known cardiac reflexes operate according to *Marey's law*, which states that heart rate is inversely related to arterial blood pressure; that is, when pressure rises, heart rate drops, and when pressure drops, heart rate increases.

The *Bainbridge reflex* is said to cause an increased heart rate whenever the blood volume and thus the pressure in the right atrium rise. Thus, during exercise, the heart rate increases because of the greater amount of blood returned to the right atrium by the active muscles. The purpose of the Bainbridge reflex was to explain the efficiency of cardiac pumping when venous return is increased. Both afferent and efferent fibers of the vagus nerve appear to be involved in the Bainbridge reflex.

The most widely accepted explanation of the heart's changing capabilities of handling varying amounts of blood at varying rates is *Starling's law of the heart*, which states that the greater the heart is filled during diastole, the greater will be the quantity of blood pumped out (within physiologic limits). The heart is able to do this simply because the increased incoming blood stretches the ventricular muscle more, which in turn causes the ventricles to contract with a greater force, pumping out the extra blood. This is referred to as *heterometric* or *intrinsic autoregulation* of output.

Both reflex slowing of the heart and vasodilation of peripheral vessels occur when stretch receptors in the aortic arch and carotid sinus are stimulated by increased arterial pressure, which stretches the aorta and carotid sinus. The *aortic nerve* is a branch of the vagus nerve known as the *cardiac depressor nerve*, and the nerve of the

carotid sinus is a small branch of the *glossopharyngeal nerve* that ramifies in the carotid sinus. The carotid sinus is a dilation of the terminal part of the *common carotid artery*.

In general, the afferent nerve fibers carry impulses to the cardioinhibitory centers in the *medulla oblongata* in the floor of the fourth ventricle of the brain. Vasodilator fibers pass to the smooth muscle in the walls of arterioles. Parasympathetic vasodilator fibers are carried by the facial, glossopharyngeal, vagus, and *pelvic nerves*. Some dorsal root fibers are believed to carry vasodilator impulses, either as efferent nerves or as antidromic impulses (conducted opposite to the usual direction of impulse propagation).

Electrocardiography

Cardiac muscle, as well as striated muscle, exhibits electrical activity preceding, during, and after contraction. These electric currents spread throughout the heart into surrounding tissues and can be recorded from the surface of the body by a sensitive instrument known as the electrocardiograph. The electrocardiograph is essentially a strong galvanometer whose fluctuations are recorded on a chart to produce the record called the electrocardiogram (also known as ECG or EKG) (Fig. 17–9). Major waves on the ECG are called *P, Q, R, S,* and *T*.

The *P wave* is caused by the spread of electrical activity from the S–A node, or pacemaker, throughout the atrial musculature. This wave of depolarization is associated with atrial systole; however, it slightly precedes atrial systole.

The *QRS waves* coincide with spread of the electrical impulse over the A–V bundle and its branches to the muscle of the ventricles (depolarization), which initiates ventricular systole.

The *T wave* is caused by repolarization of the ventricles (return to a state of receptivity

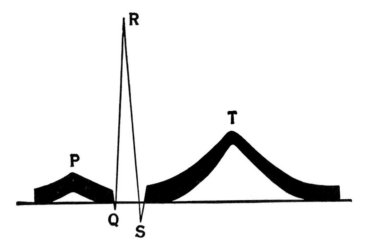

Fig. 17–9.   The waves of the electrocardiogram, enlarged and represented diagrammatically. (Best and Taylor, The Living Body, courtesy of Henry Holt and Co.)

to electrical stimulation) and marks the end of ventricular systole.

In summary, the *P wave* represents electrical activity of the atria, the QRS waves indicate ventricular electrical excitation, and the T wave coincides with repolarization of the ventricles. Disorders of the heart often cause abnormal electrocardiograms (Fig. 17–10).

VENOUS AND LYMPHATIC RETURN

In the systemic circulation, only a small amount of the arterial pressure carries through the capillary bed to assist the return of blood to the heart. Normally, only a small percentage of this pressure affects the return of lymph to the venous circulation. However, if there is an increase in arterial or venous pressure, the amount of fluid leaving the capillaries also increases. This increases both interstitial fluid volume and pressure, which in turn increase the amount of fluid entering the lymph vessels.

The factors that do aid the return of blood and lymph are based on the fact that both veins and lymph vessels are abundantly supplied with valves (Fig. 17–11) that permit movement of fluid in only one direction, toward the heart. Therefore, anything that

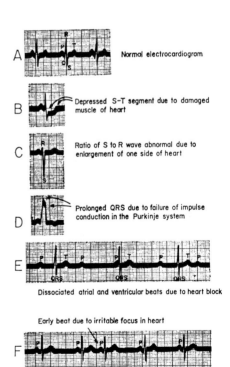

A   Normal electrocardiogram

B   Depressed S–T segment due to damaged muscle of heart

C   Ratio of S to R wave abnormal due to enlargement of one side of heart

D   Prolonged QRS due to failure of impulse conduction in the Purkinje system

E   Dissociated atrial and ventricular beats due to heart block

Early beat due to irritable focus in heart

F

Fig. 17–10.   The normal electrocardiogram and several abnormal ones. (Guyton, Functions of the Human Body, courtesy of W. B. Saunders Co.)

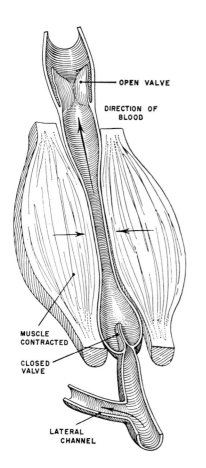

Fig. 17–11. Valves of a vein showing pumping action of adjacent muscles. (Grollman, The Human Body, courtesy of The Macmillan Co.)

applies intermittent pressure to a segment of a vein or lymph vessel acts as a pump and moves the fluid toward the heart.

Muscular activity puts pressure on adjacent veins and lymphatics, forcing the fluid out of that segment of the vessel. Since the valves prevent backflow to the periphery, the contents are moved toward the heart. *Stocking* (swelling) of the ankles and legs of horses kept several days in a tie stall shows a lack of muscular activity in the legs, as well as failure of the pumping action of the frog and hoof wall.

Even the pulsation of an artery can aid in moving blood and lymph out of tissues by causing intermittent pressure against accompanying veins and lymph vessels.

Contraction of the diaphragm during respiration aids movement of blood and lymph in two ways. First, it increases the negative pressure in the thorax, bringing air into the lungs, sucking blood into the atria and venae cavae, and bringing lymph from the *cysterna chyli* into the thoracic duct. Second, it complements this action by increasing the intra-abdominal pressure, which forces blood and lymph from the abdominal cavity into the thoracic cavity.

Peristalsis, or movement of the digestive tract, also acts as a positive force for movement of blood and lymph from the abdominal cavity.

Of course, gravity has a considerable effect on the movement of blood and lymph. It assists movement from parts located higher than (dorsal to) the heart, but inhibits movement of fluid from parts below (ventral to) the atria of the heart. Veins, however, do have smooth muscle in their walls which, upon nervous stimulation, can assist in propelling the blood. In the case of lymph vessels, prominent layers of smooth muscle cells often appear above each pair of valves, contraction of which could serve to propel the lymph.

SHOCK

Whenever the *effective* volume of blood circulated is insufficient to supply adequate nutrition to body tissues and to remove wastes, a condition of *shock* results. This lack of blood may be due to hemorrhage, dilation of visceral vessels, loss of fluid into tissues, failure of blood to return to the heart, or failure of the heart to pump sufficient blood. An animal in shock may lose consciousness, respiration may be altered, and the periphery becomes cold because of pooling of blood in the capillary beds of the viscera and a compensatory shut-down of the peripheral circulation by vessel constriction.

Shock may result if excess blood is lost from a cut or wound or if too much tissue is injured during surgery or by accidents. The

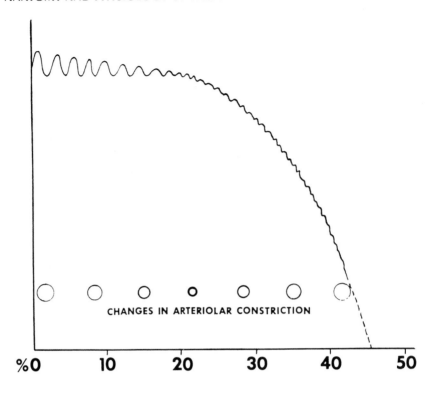

CHANGES IN ARTERIOLAR CONSTRICTION

%0   10   20   30   40   50

Fig. 17–12. Diagram showing changes in constriction of arterioles and decrease in blood pressure as blood is lost. Ordinates (along vertical line) indicate relative blood pressure. Abscissae (along horizontal line) indicate percentage of blood lost. Eventual inability to compensate for blood loss leads to a condition of shock. (After Guyton, Function of the Human Body, courtesy of W. B. Saunders Co.)

histamine released in *anaphylactic shock* (such as serum sickness or reaction to penicillin) or from damaged tissue causes vasodilation and subsequent shock from vascular pooling. Repeated injections of foreign protein material, such as serum or vaccines prepared from a different species, may sensitize an animal so that another injection of the same material at a later time can cause anaphylactic shock. Some animals become sensitive to antibiotics such as penicillin, or to the egg proteins in chick-embryo vaccines.

There are different physiologic responses to the various degrees of shock. First there is a *compensatory phase*, which is the early or mild stage of shock in which all arterioles except the coronary and cerebral vessels constrict in an effort to maintain arterial pressure and adequate circulation of fluid. Figure 17–12 shows the effect of loss of blood on arterial pressure and arteriolar size.

Severe shock, regardless of cause, becomes progressively worse and is called the *progressive phase* for several reasons. The heart cannot pump enough blood for adequate coronary circulation, further impairing the function of the heart by again decreasing coronary circulation, resulting in a vicious cycle that further decreases cardiac output. Lack of blood to the brain damages vasomotor and respiratory centers, causing more vasodilation. Capillary walls may also become weakened, permitting fluid to escape into the tissues, thus reducing the quantity of blood available for circulation and increasing the viscosity of available blood. This causes more venous pooling and diminished oxygenation of the blood. The ischemia and hypoxia cause more blood vessel dilation and more pooling, further impeding return flow of blood to the heart.

Early treatment of shock with rest, fluid replacement, heart stimulants, and vasoconstrictor drugs may reverse the course of the condition and save the patient's life. However, if the vicious cycles continue uninterrupted, a point is soon reached at which treatment is of no value because the heart damage is irreparable, the capillaries become too permeable, and the sluggish blood flow leads to intravascular clotting. When this state of damage is reached, it is called *irreversible shock*, and death results within a relatively short time.

Treatment of shock can often be helped also by giving a diuretic. Massive doses of glucocorticoids, to reduce capillary permeability and loss of vascular fluid, can be helpful. Glucocorticoids also prevent excessive vasoconstriction and capillary hypoxia.

Chapter *18*

The Respiratory System

The name *respiratory system* is perhaps better described by the name *pulmonary system*, because it is intended to refer only to those structures involved in the exchange of gases between the blood and the external system or environment. It should not be confused with cellular respiration (biochemical) at the cellular level of the body tissues.

Oxygen is one of the most vital requirements of animals. An animal may survive for days without water or for weeks without food, but life without oxygen is measured in minutes.

Supplying oxygen to the blood and removing carbon dioxide from the blood are the two major functions of the respiratory system. Secondary functions include assistance in the regulation of the acidity of the extracellular fluids of the body, assistance in temperature control, elimination of water, and *phonation* (voice production). The respiratory system consists essentially of the lungs and the passages that enable air to get into and out of the lungs. These passages include the nostrils, nasal cavity, pharynx, larynx, and trachea.

NOSTRILS

The *nares (nostrils)* are the external openings of the air passages (Fig. 18–1). They vary in size and shape from the soft, pliable, easily dilated nostrils of the horse to the rigid openings in the snout of a pig. The skin surrounding the nostril is continuous with and forms part of the muzzle. The muzzle of the horse, one of the chief organs of touch, may be used by the horse in the investigation of strange objects. The muzzle is covered with hair and contains both sebaceous and tubular (sweat) glands. The nonhaired areas *(planum nasale)* of the cow, sheep, and pig muzzles contain no sebaceous glands but do have numerous sweat glands. Longstanding

288

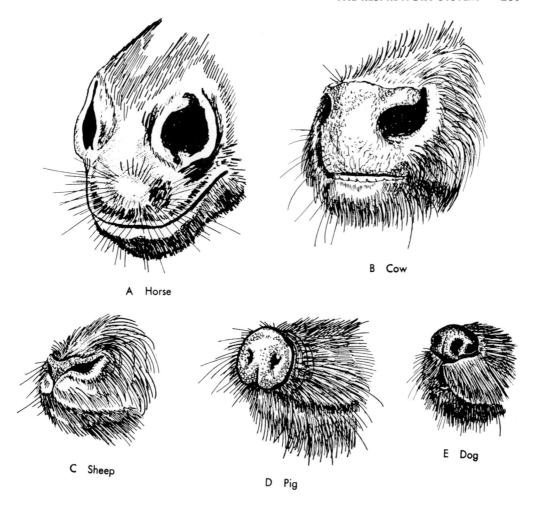

Fig. 18–1.   Planum nasale of domestic animals. *A*, horse; *B*, cow; *C*, sheep; *D*, pig; and *E*, dog. (After Nickel, Schummer, and Seiferle, Lehrbuch der Anatomie der Haustiere, Berlin, Paul Parey.)

fever in the cow may cause this area to become dry and scabby.

NASAL CAVITY

The nasal cavity is separated from the mouth by the hard and soft palates and separated into two halves by a median cartilaginous septum. Each half of the nasal cavity communicates with the nostril of the same side rostrally and with the pharynx caudally by way of the *posterior nares (choanae)*.

The nasal cavity is lined with mucous membrane, which covers a number of scroll-like *conchae (turbinate bones)* lo-cated on the lateral wall of the nasal cavity. There are two major conchae *(dorsal concha* and *ventral concha)* and a series of small *ethmoturbinate bones*. The vascular mucous membrane covering these turbinates helps to warm the inspired air. The mucous membrane in the caudal part of the nasal cavity contains the sensory endings of the *olfactory (I cranial) nerve*, which mediates the sense of smell.

The actual space of each half of the nasal cavity is subdivided in part by the dorsal and ventral turbinate bones into *nasal meatuses* (Fig. 18–2). The *dorsal nasal meatus* is lo-cated between the dorsal turbinate and the

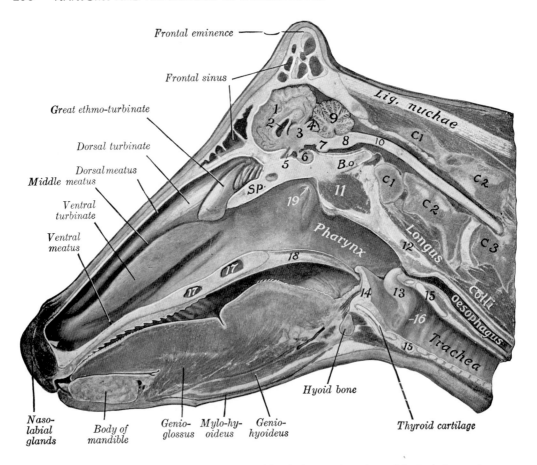

Fig. 18–2. Sagittal section of head of cow. *1*, Cerebral hemisphere; *2*, lateral ventricle; *3*, thalamus; *4*, corpora quadrigemina; *5*, optic chiasma; *6*, pituitary body; *7*, pons; *8*, medulla oblongata; *9*, cerebellum; *10*, spinal cord; *11*, ventral straight muscles; *12*, pharyngeal lymph nodes; *13*, arytenoid cartilage; *14*, epiglottis; *15*, cricoid cartilage; *16*, vocal cord; *17*, palatine sinus; *18*, soft palate; *19*, eustachian opening; *C1, C2, C3*, first, second, and third cervical vertebrae; *B.o.*, basioccipital; *Sp.*, presphenoid. (Sisson and Grossman, The Anatomy of Domestic Animals, courtesy of W. B. Saunders Co.)

roof of the nasal cavity. The *middle nasal meatus* is between the two turbinates. The *ventral nasal meatus* is between the ventral turbinate and the floor of the nasal cavity. The *common nasal meatus* is common to the first three meatuses. It is located between the nasal septum and the structures and spaces on the lateral side of the nasal cavity.

SINUSES

Passages from the *sinuses* (air-filled cavities) in certain cranial bones open into the nasal cavity. All farm animals have *maxillary, frontal, sphenoidal,* and *palatine sinuses* excavated in the bones of the same name. In the horse, the sphenoidal and palatine sinuses are fused to form one sinus, the sphenopalatine sinus. The cow and sheep have an additional sinus, the *lacrimal sinus,* excavated in each lacrimal bone. Several upper cheek teeth project into the maxillary sinus, which may become infected due to diseased teeth, particularly in horses. Dehorning mature cattle usually opens the frontal sinus, which is continued into the horn core. The opened sinus is susceptible to infection if foreign material gets into the opening; this infection is called *sinusitis*.

PHARYNX

The *pharynx* is a common passage for food and air, yet normally air cannot be inspired at the same time food is being swallowed. Openings into the pharynx include the two posterior nares (openings from the nasal cavity), two *eustachian (auditory) tubes* from the middle ears, the mouth, the larynx, and the esophagus. Each eustachian tube of the horse has a large ventral diverticulum known as the *guttural pouch*, which is located just lateral to the pharynx.

LARYNX

The larynx *(voice box)* controls inspiration and expiration of air, prevents inhalation of foreign objects, and is essential for voice production. Five large cartilages form the basis of the larynx in the horse and cow. Additional small cartilages may be found in other animals. The somewhat pitcher-shaped *epiglottic cartilage* is located just behind the base of the tongue. The *thyroid cartilage* consists of a body and two laminae. The body of the thyroid cartilage is the projection from the ventral aspect of the neck and in the human is known as the *Adam's apple*. The laminae, or wings, of the thyroid cartilage project backward and laterally, giving attachment to a number of muscles associated with swallowing and phonation.

The two *arytenoid cartilages* are irregular in shape and serve to close the glottis (opening into the larynx) and also act as levers for tightening or loosening the vocal cords, thus controlling the pitch of the voice.

The *cricoid cartilage* is shaped like a signet ring, with the expanded portion located dorsally. The cricoid cartilage aids in maintaining the shape of the larynx so air may pass through; it gives attachment to many of the intrinsic laryngeal muscles, and also attaches to the first ring of the trachea.

Roaring. Paralysis of the muscles that abduct the arytenoid cartilages results in a condition in horses called "roaring." A horse that is a roarer cannot dilate the larynx adequately, and consequently has difficulty bringing sufficient air into the lungs when exercising. Roaring usually is due to damage to the *left recurrent laryngeal nerve,* a branch of the vagus nerve that passes down the neck, into the thorax, around the arch of the aorta, and back up the neck, to supply most of the intrinsic muscles on the left side of the larynx. The course of the left recurrent nerve is considerably longer than the course of the *right recurrent laryngeal nerve*, so that damage to the left nerve occurs more frequently than damage to the right nerve.

TRACHEA

The larynx is continued by the trachea, which consists of a noncollapsible tube formed by a series of adjacent cartilage rings, which are incomplete dorsally. The trachea passes caudad as far as the base of the heart, where it divides into two chief *bronchi*, one for each lung. These bronchi branch into smaller bronchi and finally form even smaller branches called *bronchioles* (see Fig. 18–3). The several orders of bronchioles are *intralobular bronchioles, terminal bronchioles,* and *respiratory bronchioles*. Each respiratory bronchiole branches into several *alveolar ducts* which terminate as *alveolar sacs* consisting of numerous *alveoli*, which are the final and smallest subdivisions of the air passages. The general arrangement of air passages can be compared to a bunch of grapes, with the alveoli represented by the grapes and the larger air passages represented by the various orders of branches from the grape stem.

Blood capillaries, which connect the finest subdivisions of the pulmonary arteries and veins, are intimately associated with the

LUNGS: RESPIRATORY SURFACES

The Trachea and the Bronchial 'Tree' conduct Air down to the RESPIRATORY SURFACES.

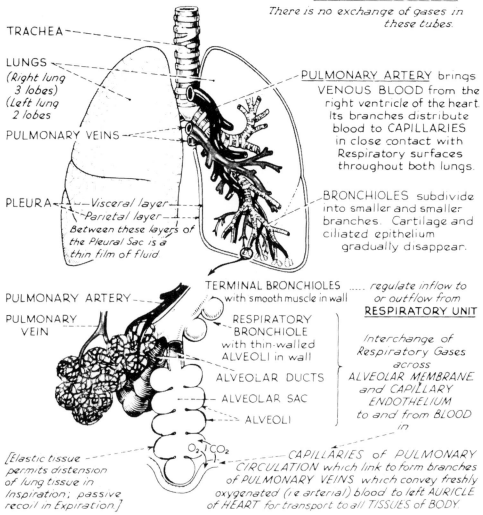

There is no exchange of gases in these tubes.

TRACHEA

LUNGS
(Right lung
3 lobes)
(Left lung
2 lobes

PULMONARY VEINS

PLEURA—Visceral layer—
—Parietal layer—
Between these layers of
the Pleural Sac is a
thin film of fluid

PULMONARY ARTERY brings
VENOUS BLOOD from the
right ventricle of the heart.
Its branches distribute
blood to CAPILLARIES
in close contact with
Respiratory surfaces
throughout both lungs.

BRONCHIOLES subdivide
into smaller and smaller
branches. Cartilage and
ciliated epithelium
gradually disappear.

PULMONARY ARTERY

PULMONARY
VEIN

TERMINAL BRONCHIOLES ..... regulate inflow to
with smooth muscle in wall   or outflow from
                               RESPIRATORY UNIT

RESPIRATORY
BRONCHIOLE
with thin-walled
ALVEOLI in wall

ALVEOLAR DUCTS

ALVEOLAR SAC

ALVEOLI

Interchange of
Respiratory Gases
across
ALVEOLAR MEMBRANE
and CAPILLARY
ENDOTHELIUM
to and from BLOOD
in

[Elastic tissue
permits distension
of lung tissue in
Inspiration; passive
recoil in Expiration.]

O_2 CO_2

CAPILLARIES of PULMONARY
CIRCULATION which link to form branches
of PULMONARY VEINS which convey freshly
oxygenated (ie arterial) blood to left AURICLE
of HEART for transport to all TISSUES of BODY.

Fig. 18–3. Lungs: respiratory surfaces. (McNaught and Callander, Illustrated Physiology, 3rd ed., 1975, courtesy of Churchill Livingstone, Edinburgh.)

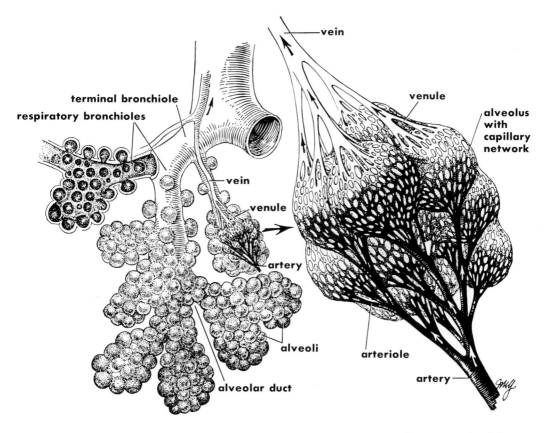

Fig. 18–4. Schematic representation of respiratory units of the lungs. (From Crouch, J. E.: Functional Human Anatomy. ed. 3. Philadelphia, Lea & Febiger, 1978.)

alveolar walls (Fig. 18–4). Thus blood is brought close enough to the inspired air that carbon dioxide in the blood may be exchanged for oxygen in the air.

LUNGS

The lungs are sometimes called "lights," indicating their low specific gravity, which is less than that of water. Each lung is a cone-shaped structure, with the base resting against the cranial side of the diaphragm and the apex within or close to the thoracic inlet. Because of the elasticity of the spongy, air-filled lung substance, the lungs completely fill the available space in the thoracic cavity regardless of whether the thorax is contracted in expiration or enlarged in inspiration. The hilus of each lung is located near the middle of the medial side, where the bronchus, pulmonary artery, and nerves enter the lung and the pulmonary veins and lymphatic vessels leave the lung. This is also the location where *mediastinal pleura* reflects onto the lung to become *visceral pleura*.

The lungs may be incompletely divided into lobes by deep fissures in the ventral part of the lung. In the cow, sheep, and pig, the left lung is divided into *apical (cranial)*, *cardiac (middle)*, and *diaphragmatic (caudal)* lobes. The right lung is these animals has an *intermediate* lobe in addition to the other three. The lungs of the horse have no subdivisions, except for the presence of an intermediate lobe of the right lung. (See Fig. 18–5.)

The lateral side of each lung is in contact

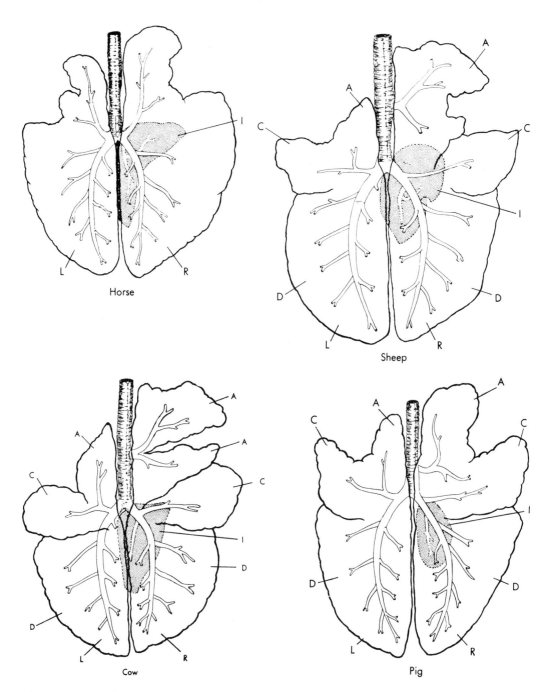

Fig. 18–5. Lungs of domestic animals (not to scale): horse, cow, sheep, and pig. *L*, left; *R*, right; *A*, apical (cranial); *C*, cardiac (middle); *D*, diaphragmatic (caudal); and *I*, intermediate. (After Nickel, Schummer, and Seiferle, Lehrbuch der Anatomie der Haustiere, Berlin, Paul Parey.)

with the thoracic wall, except at the *cardiac notch*, where the heart is against the thoracic wall instead.

After an animal has taken one breath, the lungs will never completely collapse, even if air is permitted to enter the pleural cavity, a condition known as *pneumothorax*. In the fetus, however, the lungs are nearly the consistency of liver, contain no air, and will sink in water. Whether the lungs will sink or float in water is a standard test to determine whether a newborn animal was born dead, in which case the lungs will sink, or if it drew at least one breath, in which case the lungs will float.

BONY THORAX

The bony thorax is bounded cranially by the first pair of ribs, the first thoracic vertebra, and the cranial part of the sternum; dorsally, by the thoracic vertebrae; laterally, by the ribs; ventrally, by the sternum; and in the living animal, caudally by the diaphragm.

PLEURA

Movement of the lungs within the thorax is facilitated by the presence of a smooth serous membrane, the *pleura*, which consists of a single layer of mesothelial cells on the surface of a connective tissue layer.

The pleura consists of two continuous serous sacs. One sac is reflected around each lung. The junction of the two sacs near the midline of the thorax forms a double layer of pleura called the *mediastinum* (Fig. 18–6). Whenever structures are interposed between these two layers of the mediastinum this area is called the mediastinal space. For example, the heart is located in the middle mediastinal space. The trachea, esophagus, lymph nodes, and most of the great vessels are located in the cranial mediastinal space and the esophagus and thoracic aorta are in the caudal mediastinal space. In other words, mediastinal pleura bounds both sides of these structures. The

caudal vena cava and right phrenic nerve are enclosed in a special fold of pleura, the *plica venae cavae*.

The pleura that lines the thorax is known as *parietal pleura*, while the pleura that covers the lungs is called *visceral pleura*. The three subdivisions of pleura (parietal, visceral, and mediastinal) are covered by one continuous sheet of simple squamous epithelium known as mesothelium. The *pleural sac*, or *pleural cavity*, is a potential space between parietal and visceral pleura and between mediastinal and visceral pleura. This pleural cavity contains nothing except a small amount of serous (watery) fluid, which acts as a lubricant to reduce friction between the lungs and other structures of the thorax.

MECHANICS OF RESPIRATION

The respiratory apparatus provides an open passageway for air from the exterior to reach the smallest subdivisions of the lung (the alveoli). The thin membranes of the alveolar wall and capillaries facilitate the movement of oxygen into the blood and movement of carbon dioxide into the alveolar air. This exchange constitutes external respiration, as contrasted with internal respiration, in which oxygen from the blood is diffused to the tissues for cellular oxidation and the resulting carbon dioxide diffuses into the blood.

External respiration depends on movement of air into and out of the lungs. Enlargement of the thoracic cavity reduces the already negative pressure (relative to atmospheric pressure) in the pleural cavity, causing the lungs to enlarge, which results in an inflow of air into the lungs, known as *inspiration*.

During relatively quiet respiration, contraction of the diaphragm enlarges the thorax sufficiently. The *diaphragm* is a dome-shaped structure, with the convexity directed craniad into the thorax. The central portion is largely tendinous, but the periphery consists of striated muscle, as do the two

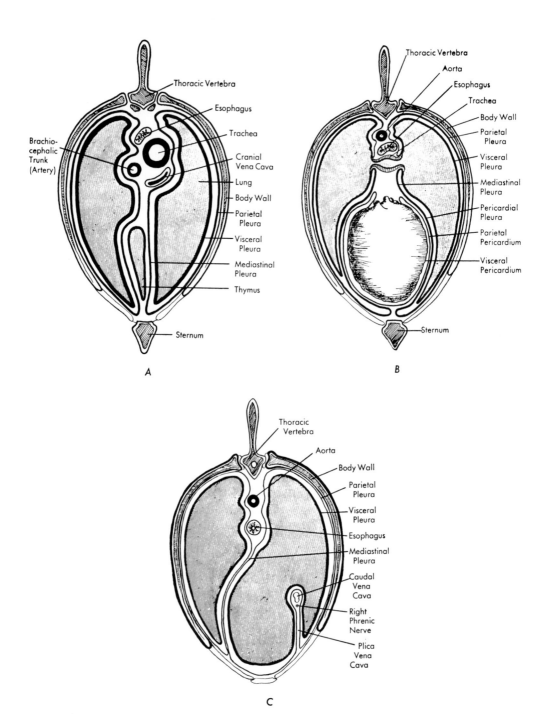

Fig. 18–6.   Cross sections of thorax showing serous membranes. Spaces are exaggerated for ease of visualization. *A*, Section cranial to the heart; *B*, section through the heart; and *C*, section caudal to the heart. (After Ellenberger, Handbuch der Vergleichenden Anatomie der Haustiere, Springer.)

crura (roots) of the diaphragm, which are attached ventral to the lumbar vertebrae. The *right* and *left phrenic nerves* supply the respective sides of the diaphragm. Contraction of the muscular portion of the diaphragm forces the abdominal contents caudad and also increases the length and volume of the thorax.

Muscles that extend from the *ribs* in a cranial direction to some other part of the body, such as the neck or forelimbs, may act as *muscles of inspiration* by rotating the ribs forward to increase the transverse diameter of the thorax. The ribs are curved so that the middle of the rib is caudal to the vertebral end and sternal end as well as being lateral to the ends of the rib. Thus, rotation of the ribs craniad increases the transverse diameter of the thorax, and rotation caudad decreases the transverse diameter of the thorax.

Some of the muscles that may act in inspiration in addition to the diaphragm include the *scalenes, pectorals, latissimus dorsi, serratus dorsalis cranialis, serratus ventralis,* and *intercostal muscles.*

Expiration is the movement of air out of the lungs. It results whenever the volume of the thorax is decreased. This decrease in volume is largely passive because of the tendency of elastic structures to return to their normal shape and location. Elasticity of the costal cartilages, lungs, and abdominal wall tends to return the thorax to a smaller volume without muscular effort during quiet respiration. However, *forced expiration* requires a considerable amount of muscular effort. The *abdominal muscles* press the viscera against the diaphragm, forcing it into the thorax as well as pulling the ribs caudad. Other muscles may decrease the volume of the thorax by pulling the ribs caudad. These muscles include the *transversus thoracis, retractor costae, serratus dorsalis caudalis,* and possibly the *intercostals.*

A strong expiratory effort made with the glottis (entrance to the larynx) closed, assists in emptying the abdomen of feces by defecation, urine by micturition, or a fetus at parturition.

RECORDING RESPIRATORY MOVEMENTS

Respiratory movements can be recorded by any apparatus that responds to changes in pressure in the pleural cavity or in the trachea.

A *pneumograph, stethograph,* or *plethysmograph* may be used to indicate changes in the circumference of the thorax and thus record respiratory movements. The pneumograph consists of a coil spring inside a rubber tube tied around the thorax. One end of the tube is closed; the other end is connected to an appropriate recording device. The stethograph consists of a cylinder with a rubber diaphragm at each end fastened to a cord around the thorax. The cylinder is connected to a recording device. In both the pneumograph and stethograph, inspiration decreases the pressure in the apparatus, and expiration increases the pressure. Translation of these pressures to a line of a pen recording instrument indicates respiratory movements.

The plethysmograph consists of a rubber bag filled with air, fixed between a metal sheath and the thorax. In this apparatus, inspiration increases the pressure in the bag, and expiration decreases the pressure.

TYPES OF BREATHING

The following terminology is used to characterize types of breathing.

Costal (thoracic)—involves considerable movement of the ribs; occurs when more air is needed than movement of the diaphragm produces.

Abdominal (diaphragmatic)—diaphragm contraction produces visible movement of the abdomen; occurs during ordinary quiet breathing.

Eupnea—normal quiet respiration.

Dyspnea—difficult breathing.

Apnea—absence or cessation of respiration.

Hyperpnea—increased depth or rate of breathing or both.

Polypnea—rapid, shallow breathing.

AIR VOLUMES AND CAPACITIES

The following terminology characterizes conventional descriptions of air volume (see also Fig. 18–7):

Tidal volume (TV)—the volume of air inspired or expired during normal respiration. It increases during excitement and activity.

Inspiratory reserve volume (IRV)—the amount of air that can be inspired above and beyond that which is inspired during a normal quiet inspiration.

Expiratory reserve volume (ERV)—the maximal amount of air that can be expired following a normal quiet expiration.

Residual volume (RV)—the amount of air remaining in the lung after a maximal expiratory effort.

The four conventional descriptions of lung capacity are as follows (see also Fig. 18–7):

Total lung capacity (TLC)—the amount of air contained in the lung at the end of maximal inspiration. TLC = IRV + TV + ERV + RV.

Vital capacity (VC)—the maximal amount of air that can be expired after a maximal inspiration. VC = IRC + TV + ERV.

Functional residual capacity (FRC)—the amount of air remaining in the lungs after a normal expiration. FRC = ERV + RV.

Inspiratory capacity (IC)—the maximal amount of air that can be inspired after a normal expiration. IC = IRV + TV.

DEAD SPACE

Dead space is the space occupied by air at the end of an expiration:

Anatomic dead space—the volume of air from the nose and mouth to the alveoli.

Physiologic dead space—includes the anatomic dead space, the volume of air in any nonfunctioning alveoli, and the volume of air in excess of the amount needed to convert O_2 content of capillary blood to that of arterial blood.

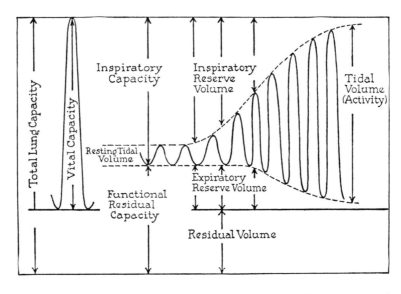

Fig. 18–7.   Subdivisions of lung air. (Ruch and Fulton, Medical Physics and Biophysics, courtesy of W. B. Saunders Co.)

PRESSURE RELATIONSHIPS

During normal respiration, the *intrapulmonic pressure* (pressure within the lung alveoli) is close to that of the atmosphere (760 mm Hg at sea level), because the external air has free access to the interior of the lungs. If the glottis is closed during either an inspiratory or expiratory movement, the pressure within the lungs may be considerably less or considerably more than atmospheric pressure. Forced maximal inspiration and expiration can cause possible variation of intrapulmonic pressure in man from -70 to $+100$ mm Hg variant from atmospheric.

Intrapleural pressure is the pressure in the intrapleural space that is required to maintain lung expansion (prevent collapse). It is measured within the pleural cavity and is always negative with respect to atmospheric pressure during normal respiration. This is true even at the end of the deepest expiration with the glottis open, because of the elasticity of the lungs and the intrapleural fluid pressure. Ranges of -2.5 to -20 mm Hg have been reported (Dukes).

If the glottis is closed during expiratory movements, the intrapleural pressure increases. The effect on organs in the thorax and abdomen may be great. Inspiratory efforts with a closed glottis aid the return of blood and lymph to the heart, help in belching and vomiting, and assist regurgitation of food for rechewing in the ruminant.

As previously mentioned, expiratory movements with a closed glottis are used in micturition, defecation, and parturition.

Average respiratory rates per minute at rest are horse, 12; pig, 12; fowl, 23; ox, 20; dog, 22; man, 12; dairy cow, 30; cat, 26; sheep, 19.

ARTIFICIAL RESPIRATION

Artificial respiration in animals may be applied by alternately compressing and releasing the thorax. The rate should approximate that of normal respiration. It should be started as soon as possible after breathing ceases and should be continued until normal breathing is again restored. Newborn animals, animals struck by lightning, and animals given an overdose of anesthetic or muscle relaxants may be helped by artificial respiration.

SURGERY

Surgery involving opening of the thorax permits the lungs to collapse. It requires the administration of oxygen or artificial respiration with air given under positive pressure to rhythmically inflate the lungs; otherwise, the resultant pneumothorax (air in pleural cavity) destroys the intrathoracic negative pressure, thus preventing respiration and the lungs collapse (atelectasis).

EXCHANGE OF GASES

Exchange of gases (oxygen and carbon dioxide) occurs in both external and internal respiration in accordance with the physical laws relating to behavior of gases and solutions. However, the presence of *hemoglobin* in *erythrocytes* greatly increases the efficiency of oxygen transport and oxygen exchange in blood. Pertinent laws relating to action of respiratory gases include the following:

Avogadro's principle states that the same volume of different gases at the same temperature and pressure will each contain the same number of molecules.

Dalton's law of partial pressures states that each gas in a mixture of gases acts as if it occupied the total volume alone, and its partial pressure is exerted independently of the other gases present. (Partial pressure is indicated by a capital letter P followed by the symbol for the gas, as a subscript, such as P_{O_2}, P_{CO_2}, P_{N_2}.)

Charles's law states that the volume of a gas is directly proportional to its absolute temperature if the pressure remains constant.

Boyle's law states that the pressure of a

gas is inversely proportional to its volume if the temperature and mass remain constant.

Henry's law of solubility of gases states that the amount of a gas physically dissolved in a liquid at a constant temperature is directly proportional to the partial pressure of the gas, and is not affected by molecules of the gas in chemical combination within the liquid.

Alveolar air is separated from blood in the pulmonary capillaries by a *respiratory membrane*, consisting of the endothelial lining of the capillaries, the capillary basement membrane, a thin interstitial fluid layer, the alveolar epithelium, a layer of alveolar fluid, and finally an alveolar layer of surfactant.

The alveolar air has a much higher partial pressure of oxygen and lower partial pressure of carbon dioxide than the blood entering the pulmonary capillaries. Diffusion of these gases across the membrane is so rapid that equilibrium between the air and blood is reached in less than one second. The rate of gas exchange is influenced by a number of factors, which include the permeability of the membrane, the area of surface in contact, the relative partial pressures of gases in blood and alveoli, and the volume of blood exposed to the alveoli.

The P_{O_2} (partial pressure of oxygen) is highest in the lung alveolar air—about 104 mm Hg in man; in the arterial blood it is about 95 mm Hg, having diffused across the respiratory membrane. When this blood reaches the tissue capillaries, where the P_{O_2} is hardly ever above 30 mm Hg in the cells, O_2 diffuses out of the blood, so that venous blood returning to the lung capillaries around the alveoli is down to a P_{O_2} of about 40 mm Hg. The P_{CO_2}, on the other hand, is highest at the tissue level as a waste product of cellular metabolism (about 45 mm Hg in venous blood), whereas the P_{CO_2} in alveolar air (intrapulmonic) is only about 40 mm Hg. These pressure differences naturally favor the loading of O_2 onto hemoglobin at the lung alveoli and the unloading of CO_2; whereas at the tissue level the opposite occurs (see Fig. 18–8).

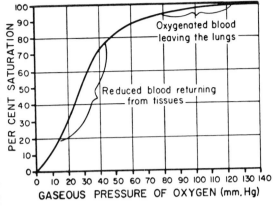

Fig. 18–8.   The oxygen-hemoglobin dissociation curve. (Guyton, Textbook of Medical Physiology, courtesy of W. B. Saunders Co.)

The gases are absorbed directly into blood plasma, but only a small fraction of the gases is carried in physical solution in the fluid. Most of the oxygen (97%) is carried in combination with the hemoglobin of the erythrocytes. The carbon dioxide is mostly carried in the bicarbonate ion form (HCO_3), while some is carried as carbonic acid and some (21 per cent) combines with the protein amino groups on hemoglobin as *carbamino hemoglobin*. If oxygen were carried only in physical solution, seventy-five times as much blood would be needed to supply adequate oxygen to the tissues as is needed with blood containing sufficient hemoglobin.

Each gram of hemoglobin (Hb) can combine with 1.34 ml of oxygen (O_2). Since blood contains a little less than 15 g of Hb/100 ml of blood, 100 ml of fully oxygenated blood contain about 20 ml of O_2. Blood leaving the lung capillaries is about 97% saturated with O_2. Complete saturation would require a P_{O_2} of 150 mm Hg.

The amount of O_2 that Hb can carry is decreased slightly by the increased presence of CO_2, increased acidity, a high temperature, elevated levels of diphosphoglyceride (2,3-DPG), and a low P_{O_2} of the surrounding medium. The dissociation curve of O_2 from Hb is somewhat sigmoid in shape (see Fig.

18–8). The curve illustrates the fact that the actual amount of O_2 combining with Hb is a function of the Po_2 (partial pressure). It shows the progressive increase in the quantity of O_2 that binds with Hb as the Po_2 increases, so it represents the percent-saturation of Hb with O_2. The curve is sigmoid in shape due to the progressive increase in the Hb affinity for O_2 after the first two molecules of O_2 are taken up, one at a time, by the hemes; the affinity increases somewhat for loading of the third and fourth hemes of Hb. Dissociation characteristics of HbO_2 (oxyhemoglobin) encourage saturation of the Hb while the blood is in contact with alveoli, yet permit O_2 to be given up to tissues with a low Po_2.

CO_2 produced by the tissues favors release of O_2 from HbO_2. The presence of CO_2 makes the blood more acid, and decreases the affinity of Hb for O_2. This is called the Bohr effect. Therefore the blood will hold less oxygen, and favors unloading of O_2 at the tissue level.

Higher temperature also favors release of O_2 from HbO_2. This is of value because rapidly metabolizing cells have a higher temperature and need more O_2 than inactive cells.

CO_2 from the tissues enters the systemic capillaries because the Pco_2 of tissue fluid is higher than the Pco_2 of the blood. At the same time, O_2 is diffusing across the capillary endothelium in the opposite direction. About one-fifth of the CO_2 is carried as carbamino compounds and mostly as carbaminohemoglobin. The CO_2 appears to be combined with an amino group (NH_2) in the form $Hb–NH–COOH$.

Carbonic anhydrase is an enzyme in erythrocytes that speeds the hydration of CO_2 to form carbonic acid and also the dehydration of carbonic acid to form CO_2 again for release into the alveoli.

CONTROL OF RESPIRATION

With the exception of smooth muscle in the walls of pulmonary blood vessels and in the walls of air passages, the respiratory system is controlled entirely by striated muscle. Although the striated muscles of respiration can be consciously controlled, as illustrated by voluntarily holding the breath, normal respiration is almost entirely reflex in nature.

The respiratory mechanism of the brain consists of at least three bilateral groups of nerve cells in the brainstem reticular substance; these have a definite effect on respiration when stimulated electrically. The three areas are: the *medullary rhythmicity* areas, located in the medulla just below the pons, the *apneustic area*, located about midway of the level of the pons, and the *pneumotaxic center*, located in the upper region of the pons (Fig. 18–9).

The medullary rhythmicity area consists mainly of an *inspiratory center*. Its neurons are tonically active, firing at an inherent rhythmic rate by regular variation of their

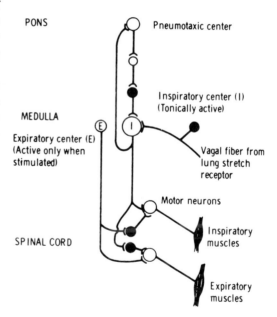

Fig. 18–9.   Hypothetic basic organization of the respiratory center (including the pneumataxic center). Neurons that exert excitatory effects are in white; those that exert inhibitory effects are in black. (Ganong, Review of Medical Physiology, courtesy of Lange Medical Publications.)

membrane potentials. Expiratory neurons are also located in this area; however, they do not discharge spontaneously and so are normally active only during a forced expiration.

Stimulation of the inspiratory center leads to the subsequent mechanical inspiration of air to the lung alveoli. This is because the impulses are transmitted down the spinal cord to the cervical segments, from which the phrenic nerves pass out and down to the diaphragm. Connections also stimulate the intercostal nerves going to the intercostal muscles of the ribs. The inspiratory musculature (diaphragmatic and intercostal) is therefore activated.

To bring about relaxation of these muscle contractions and allow for passive expiration, there is a feedback circuit between the inspiratory center and the pneumotaxic and apneustic area in the pons, by way of a recurrent collateral branch of the phrenic nerve. Stimulation of the pneumotaxic center by this nerve branch then inhibits the inspiratory center, and so the next inspiration cannot occur until this circuit is completed. This provides for regular intermittent rhythmic breathing at rates indicated earlier for each species (p. 299) during eupnea (normal quiet breathing).

Further regulating the inspiratory center and breathing rhythmicity is a reflex arc involving stretch receptors (visceroceptors) in the lung parenchyma, visceral pleura, and bronchioles. These receptors become stimulated as the lung inflates during inspiration, causing the firing of impulses up the afferent fibers of the vagus nerves into the brainstem and to the inspiratory center to inhibit the center from firing. This is the *Hering-Breuer reflex*, and it reinforces the action of the pneumotaxic center to stop inspiration and prevent overdistension of the lungs.

Rapid deep breathing (hyperpnea) is due to stimulation of the respiratory center to increase pulmonary ventilation and the exchange of the gases across the respiratory membrane. This is regulated by both neurogenic and humoro-chemical means involving collateral nerve inputs from the motor cortex of the brain, feedback from muscle and joint proprioceptors in exercise, and more importantly, the humoro-chemical factors of blood CO_2, H ion concentration, and under conditions of severe respiratory stress, the blood O_2 content.

The most important humoro-chemical factor influencing the activity of the respiratory center is the level of CO_2 in the blood. An increase in P_{CO_2} of arterial blood going to the center will increase activity of the center and, in turn, increase the ventilation rate. The next most important factor is the H^+ ion concentration of the blood, mediated by means of chemoreceptor cells in the medulla oblongata, which seem to monitor the H^+ ion concentration of the cerebrospinal fluid, since CO_2 easily crosses the blood-brain barrier and increases acidity. The net effect is an increased breathing rate from increased excitation of the respiratory center.

The third humoro-chemical regulator of respiratory activity is the O_2 concentration of arterial blood, which becomes a factor under conditions of pulmonary stress (hypoxia) when the P_{O_2} drops appreciably in arterial blood, thereby decreasing Hb saturation. This stimulates the chemoreceptors in the *carotid bodies* and *aortic bodies*, which send impulses up afferent nerves to stimulate the inspiratory center and thereby increase the rate of ventilation of the lungs until the major deficiency is made up. One carotid body is located near the termination of each common carotid artery. Fibers of the *carotid sinus nerves (nerves of Hering)* originate among the *epithelioid receptor cells* of the paired carotid bodies. These carotid nerves pass to the medulla by way of the *glossopharyngeal (IX cranial) nerves* to form the afferent side of the reflex originating in the carotid bodies.

In a somewhat similar manner the *right* and *left cardio-aortic nerves (nerves of Cyon)* originate in the aortic body and travel to the medulla in the respective vagus nerves. Therefore, reflex stimulation of respiration can be caused by increased P_{CO_2}, an increase in acidity of the blood, or a substantial P_{O_2} decrease.

PATHOLOGY OF
THE RESPIRATORY SYSTEM

All parts of the respiratory system are subject to inflammation and infection. As in other systems the suffix "itis" (meaning inflammation) is added to the root word that signifies the anatomic location of the inflammation.

Examination of the respiratory system of living animals, particularly the lungs, is facilitated by auscultation (listening) and percussion (striking) the area of the thorax. Auscultation usually is done with the aid of a stethoscope, although it may be done by placing the ear directly on the thoracic wall. Normal lungs produce a soft rustling sound called a *vesicular murmur*. Abnormal lungs may produce exaggerated sounds called *rales*, or they may not produce any sound at all, depending on the condition.

Percussion involves striking the thorax to determine the type of sound produced. If the thorax is normal the sound is clear and resonant, as produced by striking a drum. However, if the lungs are solid or the thorax is filled with fluid, the sound, or percussion, will be much duller.

Epistaxis (nose bleed) occasionally results in any animal because of the highly vascular nasal mucous membrane. Some race horses develop nose bleed during races, perhaps because of the high blood pressure involved.

Atrophic rhinitis (necrotic rhinitis) is an infectious disease of pigs, in which some of the structures lining the nasal cavity may be almost completely destroyed.

Calf diphtheria is an infectious laryngitis of cattle sometimes seen in feedlot cattle.

Pharyngitis (sore throat) is an inflammation of the pharynx and may involve the digestive system as well as the respiratory system, and may result in tonsillitis.

Bronchitis is an inflammation of the bronchi (bronchial tubes). It may be an extension of tracheitis (inflammation of the trachea) and can lead to pneumonia or pleuritis or both.

Pleuritis (pleurisy) is inflammation of the pleura. It usually is a complication of some other condition, such as pneumonia, shipping fever, or injury. Pleuritis may produce a rasping sound due to the roughened surfaces rubbing together. In severe cases adhesions may form between the parietal pleura and visceral pleura. *Hydrothorax* (fluid in the pleural sac) may also result from pleuritis.

Pneumonia is an inflammation of the lung substance itself. Noninfectious pneumonia is frequently caused by inhalation of feed, water, or improperly administered medicine. Infectious pneumonia may be caused by bacteria or viruses and rarely by other living organisms, including molds, yeasts, and parasites such as lung worms. One of the most common causes of pneumonia in cattle is *shipping fever* (also called *hemorrhagic septicemia*), which is probably caused by a combination of *Pasteurella bacteria* and one or more viruses.

Pulmonary emphysema (heaves) is due to enlargement of the alveoli of the lungs *(vesicular emphysema)* and, finally, rupture of some alveoli, with escape of air into the connective tissue between the alveoli *(interstitial emphysema)*.

Heaves is more common in horses than in any other animal, although it is described in cattle. In this disease inspiration is fairly normal, but expiration is difficult and usually requires a double bellows-like movement of the abdominal muscles. The strong contraction of the abdominal muscles produces a marked ridge at the location of the costal arch with each expiration effort. Dusty or moldy hay increases the severity of heaves and often results in a characteristic dry cough.

Some type of *cough* frequently is associated with inflammation of parts of the respiratory system from the larynx to the lungs, but is less frequently associated with inflammation of the nasal cavity, pharynx, or guttural pouches.

Chapter *19*

Anatomy of the Digestive System

The digestive system consists of a musculomembranous tube extending from the mouth to the anus. Its functions are ingestion, grinding, digestion and absorption of food, and elimination of solid wastes. The digestive system reduces the nutrients in the food to compounds that are simple enough to be absorbed and used for energy and building other compounds for metabolic use.

The digestive tract consists of a tube, lined with mucous membrane, that is continuous with the external skin at the mouth and at the anus. The four layers making up the wall of the digestive tract, from within outward, are (1) the *epithelium* (stratified squamous to the glandular part of the stomach and simple columnar from there on), (2) the *lamina propria* (including the muscularis mucosae and submucosa), (3) the muscles (striated into or through the esophagus, smooth the rest of the way—usually inner circular and outer longitudinal), and (4) caudal to the diaphragm, and covering most of the digestive tract, an outer serous covering, the *visceral peritoneum*.

Portions of the digestive tract are the mouth, pharynx, esophagus (forestomach in ruminants), glandular stomach, small intestine, large intestine, and the accessory glands, which are the salivary glands, the liver, and the pancreas.

MOUTH

The *mouth* is used primarily for grinding food and mixing it with saliva, but may also serve as a prehensile (grasping) mechanism and as a defensive and offensive weapon. The teeth and tongue are surrounded by lips, cheeks, and muscles to operate the jaws.

Functions of the oral cavity (mouth) and associated structures include prehension, mastication, insalivation, and bolus formation.

Teeth

Teeth develop from an invagination of the epithelium known as the *dental lamina*, which produces the *enamel organ*, a caplike covering of a connective-tissue elevation called the *dental papilla*. The connective tissue around the beginning tooth forms the *dental sac*. Both deciduous teeth and permanent teeth develop in the same manner from similar embryonic structures.

Figure 19–1 shows the structure of a tooth, and Figures 19–2 and 19–3 show the dentition of the horse, cow and pig.

The outer cells of the dental papilla eventually produce the *dentine* of the tooth, and the inner cells form the *pulp*, which is invaded by the vessels and nerves that will supply the tooth.

The *enamel* of the tooth is formed by the ameloblast layer of the enamel organ. It is the only part of the tooth derived from epithelium and is the hardest substance in the body.

The inner layer of the dental sac forms the *cementum*, and the outer layer of the dental sac forms the *periodontal membrane* that connects the tooth to the bone of the socket *(alveolus)*. It acts as a sling supporting the tooth.

Teeth are of the cutting or shearing type, such as the incisors of all animals, and of the grinding type, such as the premolars and molars, particularly of herbivorous animals. Teeth that have a short crown are called brachydont teeth, while those with a long crown are known as hypsodont teeth.

Dentine makes up the major portion of the tooth. It is produced by *odontoblasts*, cells that line the pulp cavity and send processes out through the dentine. It also contains collagenous fibrils and fine canaliculi.

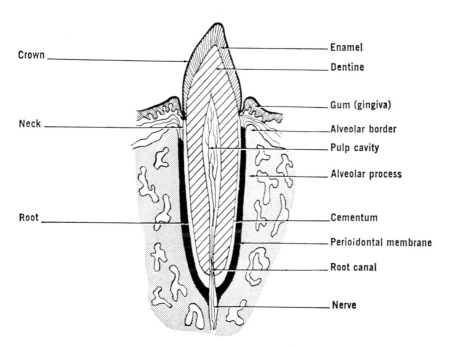

Fig. 19–1.   Structure of a tooth (longitudinal section). (De Coursey, The Human Organism, courtesy of McGraw-Hill Book Co.)

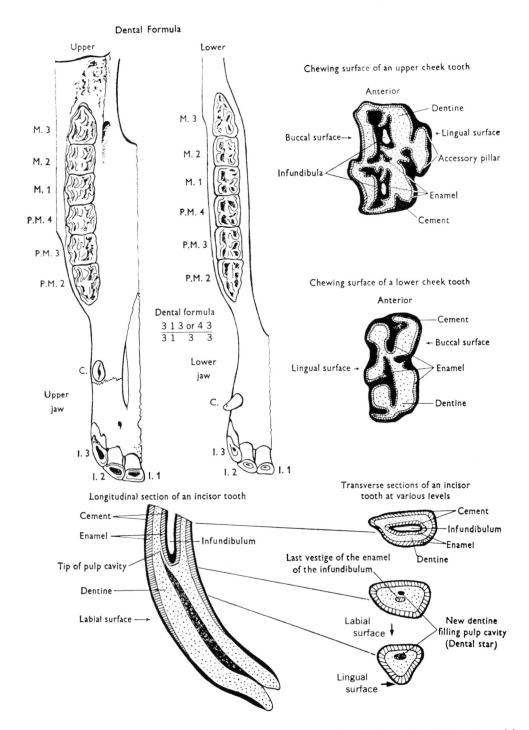

Fig. 19–2.   Dentition and dental characters of the teeth in the horse. (Taylor, Regional and Applied Anatomy of the Domestic Animals, courtesy of J. B. Lippincott Co.)

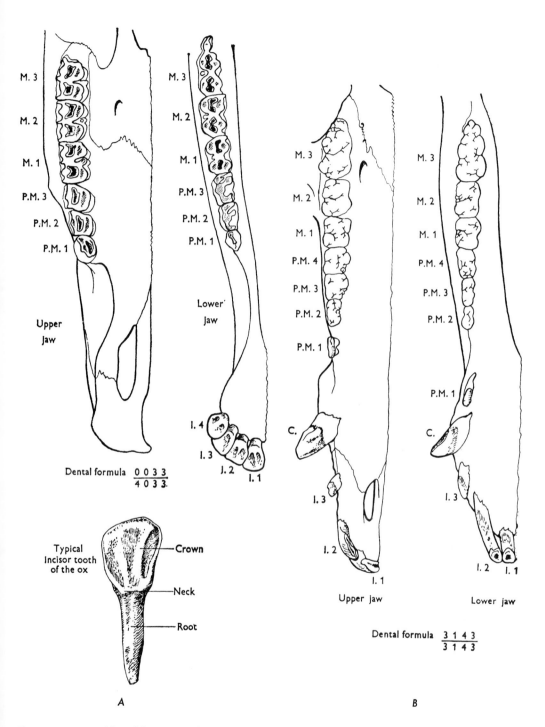

M. 3
M. 2
M. 1
P.M. 3
P.M. 2
P.M. 1

Upper
Jaw

Dental formula $\dfrac{0\ 0\ 3\ 3}{4\ 0\ 3\ 3}$

M. 3
M. 2
M. 1
P.M. 3
P.M. 2
P.M. 1

Lower
Jaw

I. 4
I. 3
I. 2   I. 1

Typical
Incisor tooth
of the ox

Crown

Neck

Root

A

M. 3
M. 2
M. 1
P.M. 4
P.M. 3
P.M. 2
P.M. 1

C.

I. 3

I. 2

I. 1

Upper jaw

M. 3
M. 2
M. 1
P.M. 4
P.M. 3
P.M. 2

P.M. 1

C.

I. 3

I. 2   I. 1

Lower jaw

Dental formula $\dfrac{3\ 1\ 4\ 3}{3\ 1\ 4\ 3}$

B

Fig. 19–3.   *A*, Dentition of the cow. *B*, Dentition of the pig. (Taylor, Regional and Applied Anatomy of the Domestic Animals, courtesy of J. B. Lippincott Co.)

Enamel covers the crown in *brachydont (short crown) teeth*. In *hypsodont (long crown) teeth* of herbivores, the enamel not only covers the crown but is invaginated into the longitudinal grooves and infundibula (cups) of the teeth.

Cementum is modified bone that covers the roots of brachydont teeth. In hypsodont teeth the cementum covers the root and crown and fills in the grooves and infundibula where the enamel is not in apposition with anything else.

Deciduous teeth (milk teeth) erupt first and are replaced by permanent teeth. This time of eruption or breaking through the gums by the teeth is probably the most accurate aid to determining the age of animals, when no accurate records are available.

The front teeth are called *incisors* and are designated by the letter I. The incisor teeth are numbered from the center of the mouth, or symphysis, laterally. The first pair of incisors is called I_1, or centrals, the next pair I_2 or first intermediates, next I_3, or second intermediates, and the last and most lateral pair of incisors is called I_4 or corners. In the nonruminants, only one pair of intermediate incisors is found.

Canine teeth are also called eye teeth, bridle teeth, tusks, and tushes (abbreviated C). Normally not more than one pair of canine teeth occur in each jaw at any given time, and canines may be completely absent in the mare, gelding, and ruminant.

Cheek teeth are called premolars, P, and molars, M. Deciduous cheek teeth are premolars and are numbered from front to back, P1, P2, P3, and P4. Molars appear caudal to the premolars and the numerical sequence is repeated, M1, M2, and M3.

The dental formula for deciduous teeth is indicated by a D preceding the key letter as DI, DC, and DP. There are no deciduous molars.

The dental formulas for cattle are

$$\text{Deciduous } 2 \ (DI\frac{0}{4}DC\frac{0}{0}DP\frac{3}{3})$$

and

$$\text{Permanent } 2 \ (I\frac{0}{4}C\frac{0}{0}P\frac{3}{3}M\frac{3}{3})$$

These formulas indicate the teeth found on one side of the mouth. The numerator of the fraction represents the teeth in the upper jaw, while the denominator indicates the teeth in the lower jaw. Obviously, this fraction must be doubled to include all the teeth in the mouth, as indicated by the Tables 19–1 and 19–2.

The permanent formula for cattle shows no incisors in the upper jaw and four on each side in the lower jaw. There are no canine teeth in either jaw. There are three premolars and three molars on each side in each jaw. Dental formulas and time of eruption of teeth for a number of domestic animals are indicated in Tables 19–1 and 19–2.

The gums consist of a nonglandular mucosa tightly adherent to the underlying bone.

Tongue

The tongue consists of a mass of muscle covered by mucous membrane. The *hyoglossus muscle* attaches to the *hyoid bone*, the *genioglossus muscle* attaches to the symphysis of the mandible (chin), and the *styloglossus muscle* attaches along the inside of the *great cornu* of the hyoid bone.

Cattle use the tongue as a prehensile organ as well as an aid to chewing and forming a bolus of the food. See Figures 19–4 and 19–5 for the structure of the tongue.

The tongue is covered with stratified squamous epithelium that presents a large number of papillae, particularly on the dorsal surface of the tongue. Filiform, fungiform, and circumvallate papillae are found in all domestic animals, and foliate papillae are present in the horse, pig, and dog, but not in the sheep and cow. The filiform papillae do not bear taste buds, but all other types of papillae do have taste buds.

The *filiform papillae* are somewhat hairlike in appearance. They consist of a connective-tissue core covered by a highly cornified epithelial layer. These papillae are shorter and softer in the horse than in other domestic animals, giving the tongue of the horse its velvety feel.

The *fungiform papillae* are assumed to

Table 19–1. Formulas and Eruption of Deciduous Teeth

	Horse	Cow	Sheep	Pig	Dog
	Deciduous Formulas				
	3 0 3	0 0 3	0 0 3	3 1 4	3 1 3
	2(DI–DC–DP–)	2(DI–DC–DP–)	2(DI–DC–DP–)	2(DI–DC–DP–)	2(DI–DC–DP–)
	3 0 3	4 0 3	4 0 3	3 1 4	3 1 3
	Deciduous Eruption				
Incisors					
DI 1	Birth to 1 wk	Birth to 2 wk	Birth to 1 wk	2–4 wk	4–5 wk
DI 2	4–6 wk	" " "	1–2 "	1½–3 mo	4–5 wk
DI 3	6–9 mo	" " "	2–3 "	Birth or before	4–6 wk
DI 4	——	" " "	3–4 "	——	——
Canines					
DCl	——	——	——	Before birth	3–4 wk
Premolars					
DP1	——	Birth to few da	2–6 "	5 mo	4–8 wk
DP2	Birth to 2 wk	" " "	2–6 "	5–7 wk	4–8 wk
DP3	" " "	" " "	2–6 "	U–4–8 da	4–8 wk
DP4	" " "	——	——	U–4–8 da	——
				L–2–4 wk	

Deciduous Incisors	DI		Day	da	Upper U
Deciduous Canines	DC		Week	wk	Lower L
Deciduous Premolars	DP		Month	mo	
			Year	yr	

(After Sisson and Grossman, Anatomy of the Domestic Animals. Courtesy of W. B. Saunders Co.)

Table 19–2. Formulas and Eruption of Permanent Teeth

	Horse	Cow	Sheep	Pig	Dog
	Permanent Formulas				
	3 1 3–4 3	0 0 3 3	0 0 3 3	3 1 4 3	3 1 4 2
	2(I–C–P——M–)	2(I–C–P–M–)	2(I–C–P–M–)	2(I–C–P–M–)	2(I–C–P–M–)
	3 1 3 3	4 0 3 3	4 0 3 3	3 1 4 3	3 1 4 3
	Permanent Eruption				
11	2½ yr	1½–2 yr	1–1½ yr	1 yr	3–5 mo
12	3½ yr	2–2½ yr	1½–2 yr	16–20 mo	3–5 mo
13	4½ yr	3 yr	2½–3 yr	8–10 mo	4–5 mo
14	——	3½–4 yr	3½–4 yr	——	——
Canines					
C	4–5 yr	——	——	9–10 mo	4–6 mo
Premolars					
P1	5–6 mo	2–2½ yr	1½–2 yr	12–15 mo	4–5 mo
P2	2½ yr	1½–2½ yr	1½–2 yr	12–15 mo	5–6 mo
P3	3 yr	2½–3 yr	1½–2 yr	12–15 mo	5–6 mo
P4	4 yr	——	——	12–15 mo	5–6 mo
Molars					
M1	9–12 mo	5–6 mo	3–5 mo	4–6 mo	5–6 mo
M2	2 yr	1–1½ yr	9–12 mo	8–12 mo	6–7 mo
M3	3½–4 yr	2–2½ yr	1½–2 yr	18–20 mo	6–7 mo

Incisors, I; Canines, C; Premolars, P; Molars, M; Day, da; Week, wk; Month, mo; Year, yr.
(After Sisson and Grossman, Anatomy of the Domestic Animals. Courtesy of W. B. Saunders Co.)

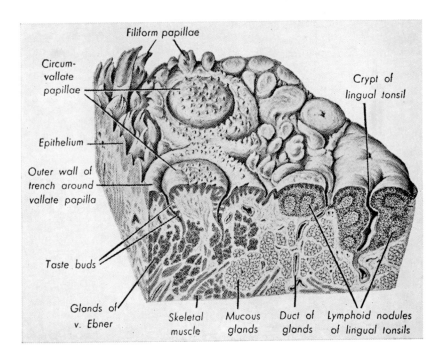

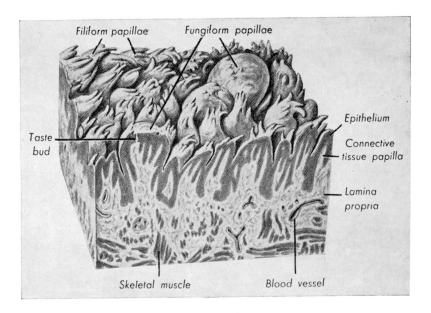

Fig. 19–4.   *A*, Drawing of the surface of the human tongue near the root. Magnification × 13. (Redrawn from Braus.) *B*, Drawing of the surface of the human tongue farther from the root. (Copenhaver, Bailey's Textbook of Histology, courtesy of Williams & Wilkins Co.)

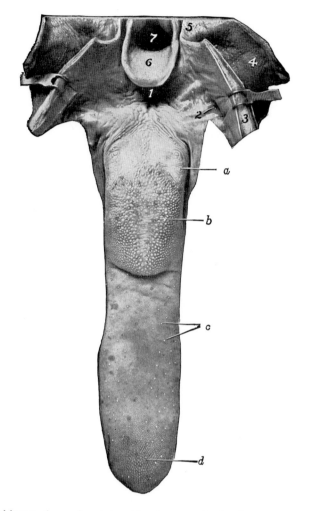

Fig. 19–5.   Tongue and fauces of cow; dorsal view. The pharynx and soft palate are cut dorsally and reflected. *a*, Vallate papillae; *b*, prominence of dorsum with broad, flattened papillae; *c*, fungiform papillae; *d*, filiform papillae of tip; *1*, glosso-epiglottic space; *2*, tonsillar sinus; *3*, cut surface of soft palate; *4*, pharynx; *5*, posterior pillar of soft palate; *6*, epiglottis; *7*, aditus laryngis; *8*, transverse groove. (Sisson and Grossman, The Anatomy of the Domestic Animals, courtesy of W. B. Saunders Co.)

resemble a fungus, or low toadstool. They contain taste buds in all animals.

Foliate papillae resemble the foliage or leaves of plants. They are found in the horse, pig, and dog, where they contain taste buds and serous glands. Mucous glands are also found in the foliate papillae of the horse and dog.

Vallate (circumvallate) papillae are large, circular projections surrounded by a deep groove. They contain taste buds and serous glands in all domestic animals and also contain mucous glands in the horse.

Taste buds are described in Chapter 7.

The tongue of the cow has a transverse groove in front of a dorsal prominence, which consists largely of a thickened mucosa.

Lips, Cheeks, Jaws, and Palates

Lips of sheep, goats, and horses are soft and flexible and aid in picking up food. Lips of cattle and hogs, being stiff and immobile, serve little more than to close the mouth.

Cheeks are muscular structures covered

with skin and lined with mucous membrane. They aid the tongue in positioning food between the teeth for chewing. The cow has numerous *conical papillae* lining the cheeks.

Jaws are closed by the powerful *masseter, temporal,* and *pterygoid muscles* and are opened by the *digastricus, occipito-mandibularis,* and *sterno-mandibularis muscles.* The pterygoid muscles contribute to grinding movements by protruding the jaw and moving it from side to side.

The *hard palate* forms the roof of the mouth and is continued caudally by the *soft palate,* which separates the mouth from the pharynx.

The lining of the oral cavity is stratified squamous epithelium that is thickened and highly cornified, particularly in areas exposed to considerable wear, such as the dental pad of ruminants, cheeks, hard palate, and the oral side of the soft palate. Glands are common in the submucosa of the mouth, except on the tip and body of the tongue, the hard palate, and the gums.

The *lips* are covered with skin externally and mucous membrane internally over a layer of muscle, connective tissue, and *labial glands.* As the skin joins the mucous membrane, the hair and skin glands disappear, and the labial glands begin. Relatively large conical papillae are found projecting inward on the mucosa of the lips of ruminants. The upper lip forms part of the *planum nasolabiale* of cattle and the *planum rostrale* of pigs (see Fig. 18–1). Serous glands are present on these areas as well as on the planum nasale of sheep, but not on the dog. (The moisture on a dog's nose comes from exhaled moisture or saliva from the tongue.) *Tactile hairs,* used as sensing probes, are present in the lips of some animals.

The cheeks have the same layers as the lips, with the skin externally, the mucous membrane internally, and the muscle, the connective tissue, and the *buccal (salivary) glands* between. The mucosa of the ruminant cheek bears rather large cornified papillae that may aid in mastication.

The hard palate contains transverse ridges formed by thickenings of the mucous membrane. A network of veins forming *cavernous tissue* underlies the mucosa. A condition called *"lampers"* in horses is an inflammation of the mucosa of the hard palate. An empiric treatment is incision of the palate with a sharp knife, which is dangerous because of the large arteries and venous plexus in the submucosa.

The oral side of the soft palate is covered with stratified squamous epithelium overlying mucous glands in the submucosa. The pharyngeal side of the soft palate is covered with pseudostratified columnar ciliated epithelium. The submucosa and lamina propria of the mucosa both contain glands.

TONSILS

The tonsils are more or less circumscribed masses of *lymphoid tissue,* named according to their location.

The *palatine tonsils* in man and the dog are paired oval bodies located in pockets on the lateral wall of the pharynx ventral to the soft palate and lateral to the base of the tongue. These are the structures commonly referred to as tonsils. In the horse, cow, and sheep these palatine tonsils are located in about the same relative position, but they are in the submucosa and are completely covered by mucous membrane except for the crypts or fissures over the tonsils. In other words, the tonsils do not project into the pharynx at all in these animals. In the pig the palatine tonsils are located in the substance of the soft palate.

The *lingual tonsils* consist of accumulations of lymph follicles on the base of the tongue. These tonsils are most prominent in the horse, cow, and pig.

The *pharyngeal tonsil* is an accumulation of lymphoid tissue in the submucosa of the dorsal pharyngeal wall of all domestic animals. Enlargement of the pharyngeal tonsil of man is called *adenoids.*

PHARYNX

The pharynx is a common passage for food and air, lined by mucous membrane and surrounded by muscles. Openings into the pharynx are the mouth, two posterior nares, two *eustachian (auditory)* tubes, the esophagus, and the larynx. Inspired air passing through the nasal cavity enters the posterior nares. The air then crosses the pharynx to enter the larynx.

Food, of course, enters the pharynx from the mouth and is forced into the esophagus by contraction of the pharyngeal muscles. During this period, the larynx is reflexly closed. Thus the paths of food and air must cross in the pharynx (Fig. 19–6).

The eustachian tubes provide free exchange of air from the pharynx to the middle ear, so that pressure is equalized on both sides of the tympanic membrane (ear drums).

The nasal portion of the pharynx is lined with pseudostratified columnar ciliated epithelium, and the oral portion is lined with stratified squamous epithelium. Mucous glands predominate in the oral portion, and mixed glands are found in the nasal part, with the serous type predominating.

The muscular wall of the pharynx is continuous with the muscle of the esophagus. Pharyngeal muscles are named according to the structure where each originates. These include the *pterygopharyngeus* (from the pterygoid bones), the *hyopharyngeus* (from the body of the hyoid bone), the *thyropharyngeus* (from the thyroid cartilage of the larynx), the *stylopharyngeus* (from the styloid process of the hyoid bone), and the *cricopharyngeus* (from the cricoid cartilage of the larynx). Most of these muscles insert on a fibrous raphe (band) on the midline at the dorsum of the pharynx.

During swallowing, the stylopharyngeus muscles shorten the pharynx, and the rest of the pharyngeal muscles (because of their circular arrangement), by contracting in series from cranial to caudal, force the bolus of food from the pharynx into the esophagus.

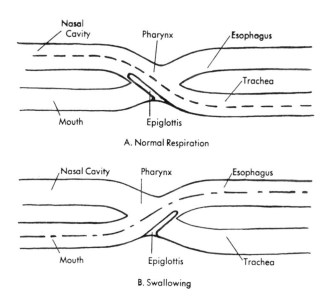

Fig. 19–6. Relationship of pharynx and mouth to larynx and esophagus during A, normal respiration; B, swallowing. (After Miller, Christensen, and Evans, Anatomy of the Dog, courtesy of W. B. Saunders Co.)

ESOPHAGUS

The esophagus, a direct continuation of the pharynx, is a muscular tube extending from the pharynx to the *cardia* of the stomach just caudal to the diaphragm.

From the pharynx the esophagus passes dorsal to the trachea and usually inclines somewhat to the left in the neck. It again passes dorsal to the trachea, where it enters the thorax and continues caudad between the trachea and the aorta at the diaphragm. The esophagus then passes through the *hiatus esophageus* and joins the stomach within the abdominal cavity at the *cardia*. The cardia, or *cardiac sphincter*, of the stomach is so named because of its proximity to the heart.

The muscular wall of the esophagus consists of two layers that cross obliquely, then spiral, and finally form an inner circular and an outer longitudinal layer. The muscle changes from striated to smooth in the caudal one-third of the esophagus in the horse and just in front of the diaphragm in the pig; it is striated throughout its entire length in the dog and ruminants.

NONRUMINANT STOMACH

In nonruminants the stomach is located just behind the left side of the diaphragm. The diaphragm is a dome-shaped muscular sheet that separates the thoracic and abdominal cavities.

Viewed from the exterior, the *stomach* is subdivided into the *cardia* (entrance), *fundus, body,* and *pylorus* (termination). The cardia and pylorus are sphincters which control the passage of food through the stomach.

The cardia and pylorus are quite close together, giving the stomach a shape somewhat like a bent pear. This arrangement produces a very short concave side between the cardia and pylorus, which is known as the *lesser curvature*, and a much longer convex side, known as the *greater curvature*. The large bulge near the cardia is called the fun-dus, but should not be confused with the fundic gland region of the interior of the stomach.

Immediately surrounding the cardia is an area of stratified squamous epithelium called the *esophageal region*. The size of the esophageal region varies with the species and is nonglandular. Other regions of the stomach are the *cardiac-gland region, fundic-gland region,* and *pyloric-gland region* (Fig. 19–7).

The glandular surface area of the stomach is increased many times by infolding of the epithelium into depressions called *gastric pits,* or *foveolae*.

The *lamina propria*, outside the epithelium, is thick. It is almost filled with glands that empty into the depths of the gastric pits. Three types of glands described are the *cardiac glands*, located closest to the cardia; the *pyloric glands*, located in the region of the pylorus; and the *fundic glands (gastric glands)*, found throughout the remainder of the stomach (Fig. 19–8).

The cardiac glands are simple or compound tubular glands that produce primarily, if not entirely, mucus. They are found in the cardiac-gland region of the mucous membrane lining the stomach, which should not be confused with the cardia of the stomach. The cardia is the location of a sphincter at the junction of the esophagus and stomach and in the ruminant is a great distance from the cardiac-gland region. The cardiac-gland region of the ruminant is poorly defined and contains cardiac, pyloric, and fundic glands.

The fundic-gland region occupies much more area than just the fundus of the stomach. It includes the entire area between the cardiac-gland region and the pyloric-gland region. A fundic gland is a simple tubular gland that consists of a mouth that opens into a gastric pit, a neck that is constricted, the main portion (called the body of the gland), and the blind extremity (called the fundus of the fundic gland). Several fundic glands may open into the same gastric pit.

The neck of the gland contains *mucous*

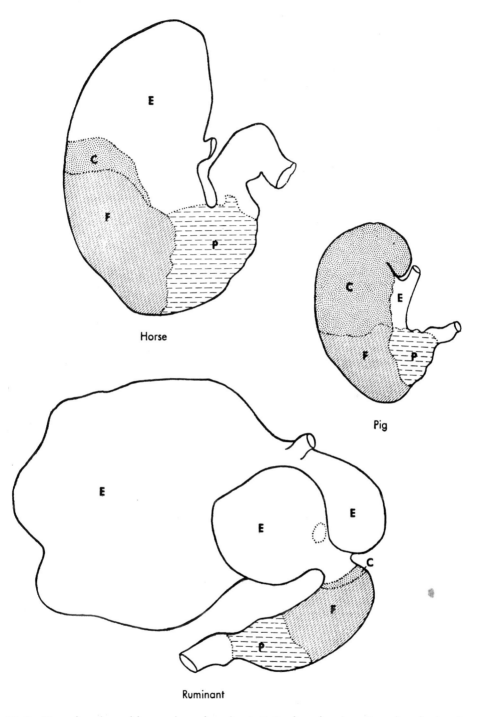

Fig. 19–7. Stomach regions of horse, pig, and ruminant. *E*, Esophageal region; *C*, cardiac-gland region; *F*, fundic-gland region; and *P*, pyloric-gland region.

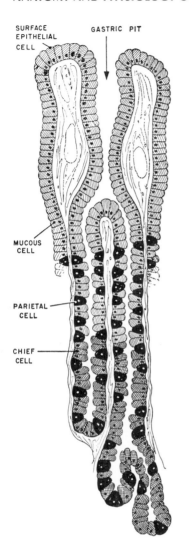

SURFACE EPITHELIAL CELL

GASTRIC PIT

MUCOUS CELL

PARIETAL CELL

CHIEF CELL

Fig. 19–8. Gastric glands from the fundus of the stomach. (Grollman, The Human Body, courtesy of the Macmillan Co.)

neck cells that produce mucus, and some *parietal cells* that are involved in the production of hydrochloric acid. Parietal cells are also found in the body, where they are the most numerous, and to a lesser extent in the fundus of the gland.

The *chief cells* contain an intracellular network of canaliculi which connect directly or indirectly with the lumen of the gland. The chief cells, also called *zymogen cells* because they produce enzymes or precursors of enzymes, are found mainly in the body and fundus of the fundic glands. The chief cells are located close to the lumen of the glands, where they appear to crowd the parietal cells out toward the periphery of the gland. *Pepsinogen* is produced by the chief cells. The pepsinogen is secreted and then split by HCl to form *pepsin*.

In the nonruminant stomach, the *esophageal region* compares to the forestomach of the ruminant, in that it is lined with nonglandular stratified squamous epithelium. The rest of the stomach can be more or less accurately divided into a cardiac-gland region, a fundic-gland region, and a pyloric-gland region.

The esophageal region is large in the horse, small in the pig, and practically absent in the dog. The cardiac-gland region is large in the pig but smaller in the horse, and the remainder of the nonruminant stomach is divided between fundic- and pyloric-gland regions.

RUMINANT STOMACH

The true (glandular) stomach in the ruminant is preceded by three divisions, or diverticula (lined with stratified squamous epithelium), where food is soaked and subjected to digestion by microorganisms before passing through the digestive tract.

The *rumen, reticulum,* and *omasum* of ruminants are collectively known as the forestomach. The cardia is located craniodorsally in the dome-shaped *atrium ventriculi,* which is common to both the rumen and reticulum. The *sulcus ruminoreticularis (esophageal groove),* which extends from the cardia to the omasum, is formed by two heavy muscular folds or lips, which can close to direct material from the esophagus into the omasum directly, or open and permit the material to enter the rumen and reticulum.

The stomach and viscera of cattle are shown in Figures 19–9 to 19–11.

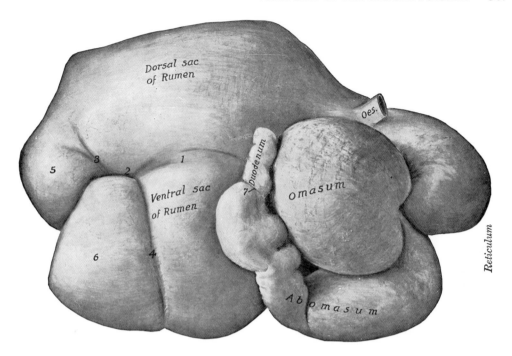

Fig. 19–9. Stomach of cow, right view. Oes, Esophagus; *1*, right longitudinal groove of rumen; *2*, caudal groove of rumen; *3, 4*, coronary grooves; *5, 6*, caudal blind sacs of rumen; *7*, pylorus. (Sisson and Grossman, The Anatomy of the Domestic Animals, courtesy of W. B. Saunders Co.)

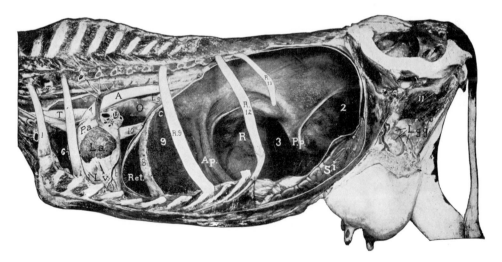

Fig. 19–10. Deep dissection of Holstein cow; left side. Ribs 9, 12, and 13 (rib thirteen had no costal cartilage) retained for landmarks on rumen.

A, Aorta; *A.p.*, cranial pillar of rumen; *C*, cardia; *L.a.*, left auricle; *L.g.*, caudal mediastinal lymph gland; *L.v.*, left ventricle; *O*, esophagus; *P.a.*, pulmonary artery; *P.p.*, caudal pillar of rumen; *R*, rumen; *Ret.*, reticulum; *R.9*, *R.12*, *R.13*, ribs 9, 12, and 13; *S.i.*, small intestine; *T*, trachea; *U*, left bronchus (opening of pulmonary artery to left of U); *1*, first rib (brachial vessels to left of 1); *2, 3*, caudal blind sacs of rumen; *4*, vagus nerve (recurrent branching off and passing over the ligamentum arteriosum below 4); *5*, thoracic duct; *6*, right auricle; *7*, pulmonary veins; *8*, lateral attachment of rumino-reticular fold; *9*, rumino-reticular opening; *10*, posterior vena cava; *11*, subpelvic tendon.

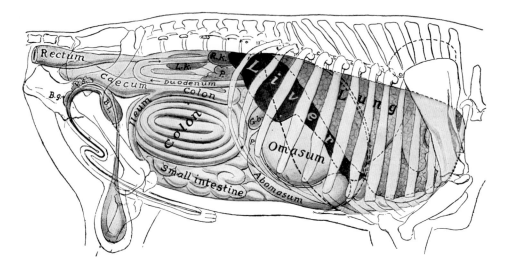

Fig. 19–11.   Projection of viscera of bull on body-wall; right side. *P.*, Pylorus; *G.b.*, gall bladder; *R.K.*, right kidney; *L.K.*, left kidney; *P.* (above duodenum), pancreas; *Bl.*, urinary bladder; *V.s.*, vesicula seminalis; *B.g.*, bulbo-urethral (Cowper's) gland. Costal attachment and median line of diaphragm are indicated by dotted lines. (Sisson and Grossman, The Anatomy of the Domestic Animals, courtesy of W. B. Saunders Co.)

Reticulum

The reticulum is the most cranial compartment. It is also called the honeycomb, and as the names imply, it is lined with mucous membrane containing many intersecting ridges which subdivide the surface into honeycomb-like compartments. The surface is stratified squamous epithelium. The location of the reticulum immediately behind the diaphragm places it almost in apposition to the heart, so any foreign objects such as wire or nails that may be swallowed tend to lodge in the reticulum, and are in a good position to penetrate into the heart.

Rumen

The rumen is a large muscular sac that extends from the diaphragm to the pelvis and almost entirely fills the left side of the abdominal cavity. The rumen is subdivided into sacs by muscular pillars, which appear from the exterior of the rumen as grooves. The *dorsal* and *ventral sacs* are separated by a nearly complete circle, which is formed on the frontal plane by the *right* and *left longitudinal pillars*, connected by the *cranial*

and *caudal pillars*. The dorsal sac is the largest compartment. The dorsal sac overlaps the ventral sac and is continuous cranially with the reticulum over the *ruminoreticular* fold, which separates the floor of the rumen from the floor of the reticulum.

Caudally the dorsal sac is further subdivided by the dorsal coronary pillars, which form an incomplete circle bounding the dorsal blind sac. The caudal part of the ventral sac is a diverticulum (ventral blind sac) separated from the rest of the ventral sac by the ventral coronary pillars.

The mucous membrane lining the rumen is glandless stratified squamous epithelium. The most ventral parts of both sacs of the rumen contain numerous papillae up to 1 cm in length, but papillae are almost entirely absent on the dorsal part of the rumen.

The smooth muscle of the wall of the rumen consists of two layers. The superficial layer runs largely cranio-caudad in direction and bridges most of the ruminal grooves. The fibers of the inner layer of muscle run more transversely and also make up most of the substance of the ruminal pillars.

The two muscle layers are continuous with the muscle of the esophagus. They run obliquely and cross at right angles. The wall of the esophageal groove consists largely of smooth muscle. Striated muscle from the esophagus predominates at the cardia but fades out rapidly in the groove. Both transverse and longitudinal smooth-muscle fibers are found in the floor of the groove. The lips contain mainly longitudinal fibers which form a loop around the cardia at the dorsal end of the groove and enter the sphincter of the reticulo-omasal orifice at the ventral end of the groove. Most of the transverse fibers enter the wall of the reticulum.

The mucous membrane of the esophageal groove resembles that of the reticulum in the ventral part and that of the rumen in the dorsal part. The lower part of the esophageal groove connects the atrium ventriculi with the omasum.

Omasum

The omasum is a spherical organ filled with muscular laminae that descend from the dorsum or roof. The mucous membrane covering the laminae is studded with short, blunt papillae that grind roughage before it enters the abomasum (true stomach). The omasum is located to the right of the rumen and reticulum just caudal to the liver. The omasum of the sheep and goat is much smaller than the omasum of the cow and normally is not in contact with the abdominal wall in these small ruminants.

The omasum is nearly filled with laminae, bearing pointed papillae arranged in such a manner that food is moved from the *reticulo-omasal* orifice, between the laminae, and on to the *omaso-abomasal* orifice. Each lamina contains three layers of muscle, including a central layer continuous with the muscle wall of the omasum, and a layer of muscularis mucosae on each side of the central muscle. The fibers of the *muscularis mucosae* run at right angles to the fibers of the central muscle.

The floor of the omasum as well as the leaves are covered with stratified squamous epithelium. At the junction of the omasum and abomasum is an arrangement of folds of mucous membrane, the *vela terminalia*, derived from the omasum in the cow, but from the abomasum in the sheep.

Abomasum

The abomasum (true stomach) is the first glandular portion of the ruminant digestive system. It is located ventral to the omasum and extends caudad on the right side of the rumen. The *pylorus* (terminal part of the abomasum) is a sphincter (thickening of circular smooth muscle fibers) at the junction of the stomach and small intestine.

The epithelium of the abomasum changes abruptly from the stratified squamous epithelium of the omasum to a tall simple columnar epithelium capable of producing mucus. Presumably the mucus covering the stomach epithelium prevents the digestive juices from digesting the stomach cells. In general, the gland regions of the abomasum correspond to the gland regions in the simple stomach of the nonruminant, and the fore-stomachs of the ruminant correspond to the esophageal region of the simple stomach.

SMALL INTESTINE

The small intestine is divided into three parts—duodenum, jejunum, and ileum—based in part on histologic or microscopic structural differences.

The *duodenum* is the first part of the small intestine. It is closely attached to the body wall by a short mesentery, the mesoduodenum. Ducts from the pancreas and liver enter the first part of the duodenum. The duodenum leaves the pylorus of the stomach and passes caudad on the right side toward the pelvic inlet. The duodenum then crosses to the left side behind the root of the great mesentery and turns forward to join the jejunum. The common bile duct from the liver and the pancreatic duct from the pancreas enter the duodenum a short distance behind the pylorus.

The *jejunum* is indistinctly separated from the duodenum. It begins approximately where the mesentery starts to become rather long. The jejunum and *ileum* are continuous, and there is no gross demarcation between them. The ileum is the last part of the small intestine. It enters the large intestine at the ileal opening.

It is impossible to give a definite location for the jejunum and ileum, but they tend to be located toward the left ventral portion of the abdominal cavity in nonruminants. The terminal part of the ileum, however, joins the cecum (horse), colon (dog), or cecum and colon (ruminant and pig) in the right caudal part of the abdominal cavity.

LARGE INTESTINE

The large intestine consists of the *cecum*, which is a blind sac, and the *colon*, which consists of ascending, transverse, and descending parts. The descending colon terminates as the *rectum* and *anus*.

There is considerably more variation in the large intestine (particularly the ascend-

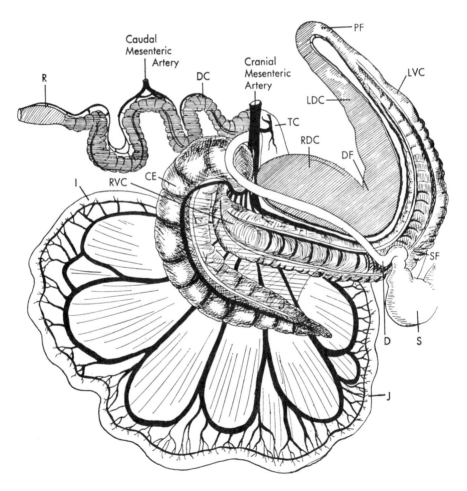

Fig. 19–12.   Gastrointestinal tract of the horse. *S*, Stomach; *D*, duodenum; *J*, jejunum; *I*, ileum; *CE*, cecum; *RVC*, right ventral colon; *SF*, sternal flexures; *LVC*, left ventral colon; *PF*, pelvic flexure; *LDC*, left dorsal colon; *DF*, diaphragmatic flexure; *RDC*, right dorsal colon; *TC*, transverse colon; *DC*, descending colon (small or floating colon); *R*, rectum. (After Nickel, Schummer, and Seiferle, Lehrbuch der Anatomie der Haustiere, Berlin, Paul Parey.)

ing colon) from one species to another than in the small intestine. Therefore, the large intestine will be described separately for each species.

Horse

The horse has the largest and most complex large intestine of any of the domestic animals (Figs. 19–12, 19–13).

The cecum in the horse is a comma-shaped structure extending from the right side of the pelvic inlet to the floor of the abdominal cavity just behind the diaphragm near the xiphoid cartilage of the sternum. The base of the cecum usually is located in the dorsal part of the right flank, and may

project craniad as far as the middle of the fifteenth rib, while the apex usually is located over the caudal part of the sternum.

The ileum enters the concave side, or lesser curvature, of the cecum near the base, at a sphincter called the *ileo-cecal valve*, or orifice.

The first part of the large colon leaves the cecum and passes craniad along the right ventral abdominal wall toward the sternal part of the diaphragm, where it turns sharply to the left and proceeds caudad along the left ventral abdominal wall toward the pelvic inlet. These first parts of the *large colon* are known respectively as the *right ventral colon*, the *sternal flexure*, and the *left ventral colon*. They are arranged like a horse-

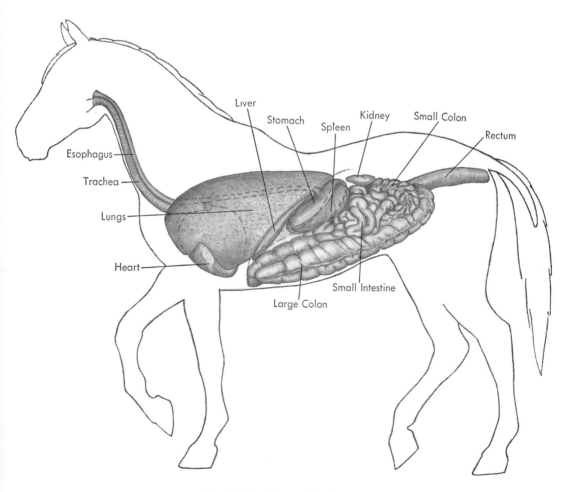

Fig. 19–13.   Viscera of the horse.

shoe, with the toe forward and the branches directed caudally on either side of the apex of the cecum.

The left ventral colon turns sharply dorsad at the pelvic inlet to form the *pelvic flexure*. The colon then continues craniad as the *left dorsal colon*, located just dorsal to the left ventral colon. At the *diaphragmatic flexure* it continues a short distance caudad as the *right dorsal colon*. The right dorsal colon turns again to the left and crosses the midline in front of the root of the great mesentery as the *transverse colon*.

The *small*, or *floating, colon* in the horse is the direct continuation of the transverse colon. The small colon is arranged in loops within the mesocolon, much like the small intestine in the mesentery. The small colon, however, is somewhat larger in diameter than the small intestine. The small colon is usually located near the middle of the caudal part of the abdominal cavity.

The *rectum*, the relatively straight portion of the large intestine found mainly within the pelvic cavity, is readily dilated for storage of feces.

The junction of the terminal part of the digestive tract and the skin is the *anus*. The anus is closed by both smooth and striated sphincter muscles.

Pig

The large intestine of the pig begins with the cecum (Fig. 19–14). The blind end of the cecum projects forward and ventrally near the midline. The dorsal end of the cecum is continuous with the colon at the ilio-ceco-colic junction, where the entrance of the ileum marks the division between the cecum and colon.

The ascending colon of the pig presents a spiral arrangement of coils, giving a somewhat cone-shaped appearance. When the colon leaves this spiral, it passes forward and crosses to the left as transverse colon and then continues caudad as descending colon to the rectum. As in other animals, the rectum terminates at the anus.

Dog

The large intestine of the dog is the shortest and simplest of all domestic animals, consisting of a short irregular cecum, a short ascending colon, a transverse colon, a descending colon, a rectum, and an anus.

Ruminants

In the ruminant the large intestine consists of the cecum, colon, and rectum (Fig. 19–15). The cecum has one blind end that projects caudad. Cranially, it is continuous with the colon. This junction is marked by the entrance of the ileum at the ileal orifice.

The ascending colon passes forward, apparently between the two layers of mesentery that support the small intestine. The proximal loop *(ansa proximalis)* is located between the cecum and the coiled colon *(ansa spiralis)*. The ansa spiralis is arranged in coils. The first portion spirals toward the center of the coils (centripetally) and the next part spirals away from the center (centrifugally). The last part of the ascending colon, the *ansa distalis*, connects the ansa spiralis with the transverse colon. The transverse colon crosses from right to left and continues caudad to the rectum and the anus, the terminal part of the digestive tract.

The arrangement of the intestinal tract of the sheep and goat is similar to that of the cow, as illustrated in Figure 19–15. However, the last centrifugal gyrus (loop) of the ansa spiralis is outside the cranial mesenteric artery and mesenteric lymph nodes, and is much closer to the jejunum than in the cow.

GENERAL ARRANGEMENT OF THE DIGESTIVE TRACT

The entire digestive tract is sometimes described as a tube within a tube. This concept seems most logical when considering the embryo, although the same general arrangement persists throughout life. The body wall is essentially a tube consisting,

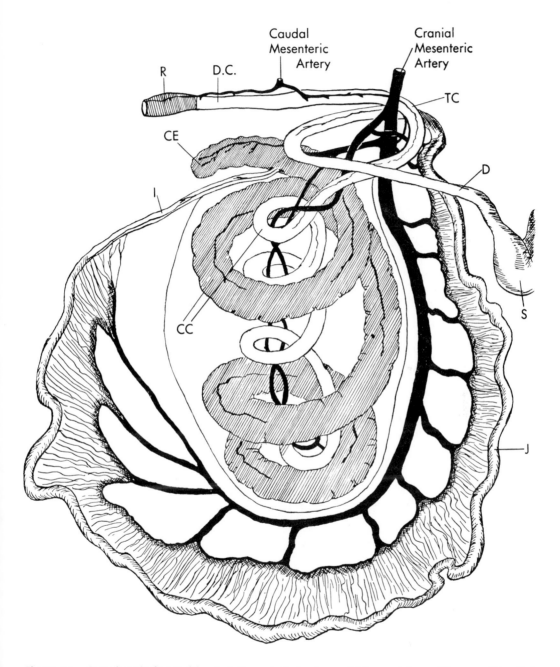

Fig. 19–14. Gastrointestinal tract of the pig. *S*, Stomach; *D*, duodenum; *J*, jejunum; *I*, ileum; *CE*, cecum; *CC*, coiled colon; *TC*, transverse colon; *DC*, descending colon; *R*, rectum. (After Nickel, Schummer, and Seiferle, Lehrbuch der Anatomie der Haustiere, Berlin, Paul Parey.)

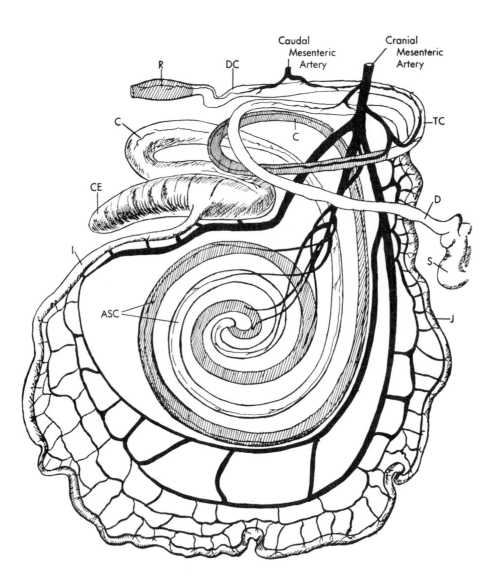

Fig. 19–15.   Gastrointestinal tract of the cow. *S*, Stomach—Abomasum (fore-stomach not shown); *D*, duodenum; *J*, jejunum; *I*, ileum; *CE*, cecum; *C*, colon; *ASC*, ansa spiralis (coiled colon); *TC*, transverse colon; *DC*, descending colon; *R*, rectum. (After Nickel, Schummer, and Seiferle, Lehrbuch der Anatomie der Haustiere, Berlin, Paul Parey.)

from without inward (or superficial to deep), of (1) epithelial covering (the epidermis), (2) a connective-tissue layer (the dermis and superficial fascia), (3) muscle (skeletal muscles), and (4) a serous membrane lining (parietal peritoneum). (See Fig. 1–12.)

The abdominal portion of the digestive tract presents the same layers but in reverse order. From without inward the layers are (1) serosa (visceral peritoneum), (2) muscle (mostly smooth muscle), (3) submucosa (connective tissue), and finally (4) the epithelial lining of the tube (mucous membrane).

The *peritoneum* consists of a continuous layer of simple squamous epithelial cells called *mesothelium* supported by a variable amount of connective tissue. The peritoneum is a serous membrane that lines the entire abdominal cavity and covers all visceral organs within the abdomen. The peritoneum lining the abdominal cavity is called *parietal peritoneum*, since it covers the wall (*parietal* refers to wall). The peritoneum covering the organs is called *visceral peritoneum*, since it covers the viscera. All peritoneum is continuous, so the parietal peritoneum is connected with visceral peritoneum by double folds of peritoneum that are named according to the organs each supports.

The *mesentery* is a double fold of peritoneum that supports the intestine and attaches it to the dorsal abdominal wall. The mesentery may be subdivided into *mesoduodenum, mesojejunum, mesoileum*, and *mesocolon*, depending on which part of the intestine it supports. The mesoduodenum, or that portion of the mesentery that supports the duodenum, is relatively short, so movement of the duodenum is restricted. The remainder of the mesentery of the small intestine is much longer and permits the jejunum and ileum to move freely into any area of the abdominal cavity not occupied by other viscera.

Omentum refers to peritoneum connecting the stomach with other structures.

Ligaments are folds of peritoneum (other than omentum or mesentery) which connect abdominal organs with each other or with the parietal peritoneum of the body wall. These ligaments are also named according to the structures they connect, such as hepatoduodenal or gastrosplenic ligaments.

Blood vessels, nerves, and lymph vessels reach the various abdominal organs by passing between the two layers of the various double folds of peritoneum.

OTHER STRUCTURES

Throughout the intestine (both large and small), small tubular depressions, called *crypts of Lieberkühn*, are found between the villi. These crypts are directed toward the periphery of the intestine into the lamina propria. The lining cells are continuous with the epithelium covering the mucous membrane and produce a considerable amount of mucus. In the small intestine, the crypts of Lieberkühn also secrete the enzyme *enterokinase*, which activates the pancreatic secretion *trypsinogen*, and a small amount of the enzyme *amylase*, which assists in starch breakdown.

Duodenal glands, also called *Brunner's glands*, are branched tubulo-alveolar glands located in the submucosa and/or lamina propria of the first part of the duodenum. The duodenal-gland zone extends a variable distance from the pylorus, depending on the animal. Its length is about 1.5 to 2 cm in carnivores, 60 to 70 cm in sheep, 3 to 5 m in pigs, 4 to 5 m in cows, and 5 to 6 m in horses. These glands secrete mucus.

Lymph nodules are also found both in the submucosa and in the lamina propria throughout the intestine. Aggregations of lymph nodules, termed *Peyer's patches*, are commonly described in the ileum, but may be found in other parts of the intestine.

The intestinal wall consists of the serosa (visceral peritoneum) superficially, the muscularis next, then the submucosa, and the mucosa deepest. These layers sometimes are called tunics, and the prefix "tunica" is used with the Latin forms.

The *serosa* is a layer of simple squamous epithelium (mesothelium) supported by a thin layer of connective tissue. This forms a smooth covering for the intestine that reduces friction of the intestine against other structures in the abdomen.

The *muscularis* in most areas of the intestine is made up of an outer longitudinal layer of smooth muscle fibers and an inner circular layer of smooth muscle fibers. Coordinated contractions and relaxations of both sets of muscles move the ingesta through the intestine by a process called *peristalsis*. These contractions also mix the contents to facilitate absorption.

The *submucosa* is a loose connective tissue layer between the inner circular muscle layer (of the muscularis) and the *muscularis mucosae* of the mucous membrane. Fairly large blood vessels travel in the submucosa, and a network of unmyelinated nerve fibers called *Meissner's plexus* or the *submucous plexus* is also located in the submucosa. Along with *Auerbach's plexus* or the *myenteric plexus* located between the circular and longitudinal layers of smooth muscle, they form the *intramural plexus* found throughout the length of the GI tract from esophagus to anus. Nerve fibers from both the sympathetic and parasympathetic divisions of the autonomic nervous system enter the tract wall and parasympathetic fibers synapse with neurons of the plexuses, thereby exerting their effect on the glands and smooth muscle. The myenteric plexus is more extensive than the submucosal plexus.

The most superficial layer of the mucous membrane is the *muscularis mucosae*, which like the muscularis externa consists of an inner circular layer and an outer longitudinal layer. The muscularis mucosae, however, is much thinner than the muscularis externa.

The *lamina propria* is the thick middle layer of connective tissue that forms the basis of the mucous membrane. It forms fingerlike projections, the villi, which protrude into the lumen of the intestine. Blood capillaries, lymph capillaries (lacteals), and smooth muscle fibers are found in the lamina propria, including the lamina propria of the villi.

The entire inner surface of the mucous membrane consists of columnar epithelial cells, some of which are modified to form goblet cells for the production of mucus. The rest of the columnar cells have a striated border of microvilli on the free surface, which increase the cell surface tremendously and increase the absorptive function of the cell.

Surface area of the mucous membrane lining the intestine is increased by circular folds and by villi, both of which project into the lumen of the intestine.

ACCESSORY DIGESTIVE ORGANS

There is much similarity from one species to another in the glands that aid digestion. In addition to the numerous small glands located in the walls of the stomach and intestine, accessory glands include the salivary glands, the liver, and the pancreas.

Salivary Glands

The salivary glands consist of three pairs of well-defined glands as well as scattered lobules of salivary tissue (minor salivary glands). The chief salivary glands are the *parotid, mandibular,* and *sublingual.* The minor salivary glands include labial, buccal, lingual, and palatine glands. The dog also has a zygomatic salivary gland near the eye. The *parotid salivary gland* is located ventral to the ear in relation to the caudal border of the mandible. In most animals the parotid salivary duct, along with the facial vessels, passes ventrad and craniad on the deep face of the caudal part of the mandible, and crosses the cheek superficially just cranial to the masseter muscle (the large muscle that closes the jaw). The duct then passes dorsad to penetrate the mucous membrane of the cheek near the upper third or fourth cheek

Table 19–3.   Character of the Salivary Glands

Serous Glands	Mucous Glands	Mixed Glands
Parotid (contains mucous endpieces in young carnivores and lambs)	Labial glands of sheep, goats, and carnivores	Mandibular gland
Ventral buccal gland of cattle and its ventral portion in sheep and goats	Lingual glands, except those listed elsewhere	Sublingual gland
Ebner's glands under the circumvallate and foliate papillae	Middle and dorsal buccal glands of cattle	Marginal glands of the tongue of the horse
	Ventral buccal gland of carnivores, and its dorsal portion in sheep and goats	Glandula frenularis of sheep and goat
		Glands of the root of the tongue in horse and ox
		Buccal glands of horses and swine
		All glands not mentioned under mucous or serous glands

(Trautmann and Fiebiger: Fundamentals of the Histology of Domestic Animals, courtesy of Comstock Publishing Associates, 1957.)

tooth. The parotid duct of the dog crosses the lateral face of the jaw directly and does not follow the contour of the mandible.

The *mandibular, or submaxillary, salivary gland* is usually located ventral to the parotid gland just caudal to the mandible. The mandibular gland may be deep to part of the parotid gland and mandible. The mandibular salivary duct passes forward medial to the mandible to open ventral to the tongue on a little papilla located slightly anterolateral to the *frenulum linguae* (fold that holds the tongue to the floor of the mouth).

The *sublingual salivary gland* is located deep to the mucous membrane along the ventral side of the lateral surface of the tongue near the floor of the mouth. Numerous ducts pass directly dorsad from the sublingual salivary gland to open into the floor of the mouth just ventrolateral to the tongue (Fig. 19–16). With the exception of the horse, the sublingual salivary gland has a monostomatic portion that empties onto the floor of the mouth by way of the major sublingual duct.

The salivary glands are classified as serous, mucous, or mixed. Serous means "wheylike." *Serous glands* secrete a watery clear fluid, as compared with *mucous glands*, which secrete mucus, a viscid, tenacious material that acts as a protective covering for the surface of mucous mem-

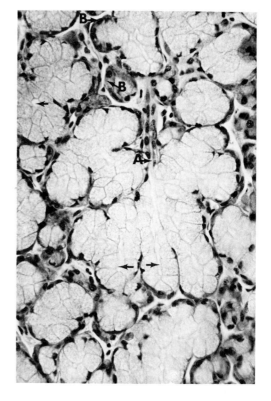

Fig. 19–16.   Sublingual salivary gland, dog. Mucous acini with lumina (arrows) emptying into intercalated duct *(A)*; serous demilunes *(B)*. H & E. ×280. (From Dellmann, H-D., and Brown, E. M.: Textbook of Veterinary Histology. Philadelphia, Lea & Febiger, 1976.)

branes. A mixed gland produces both mucous and serous fluids.

The cells of a serous secretory unit are somewhat pyramidal in shape (sections are wedge-shaped like a piece of pie), with the apex pointing toward the lumen of the *alveolus* (terminal unit of gland). The nucleus is round and located close to the base of the cell. Zymogen (secretion) granules are found between the nucleus and the apex of the cell, near the Golgi apparatus, and chromidial material is found near the base. There is some evidence that the cells are apocrine in nature, and some cytoplasm may be lost when the granules leave the cells.

Cells of mucous secretory units have flattened nuclei almost against the base of the cell. There are no zymogen granules or chromidial substance in the mucous cells, as found in serous cells. Instead there are a number of mucigen droplets, which may appear as holes (vacuoles) in the usual stained section. The mucigen droplets, after leaving the cells as *mucin,* combine with water to form mucus.

Some glands contain both serous and mucous cells. They usually have mucous units associated with crescent-shaped groups of serous cells called *demilunes.* These serous cells probably secrete into the lumen of the mucous alveolus through small canals between the mucous cells.

The parotid glands are compound tubulo-alveolar serous glands enclosed in connective tissue capsules.

The submandibular (submaxillary) glands are mixed compound tubulo-alveolar glands, predominantly serous in type. The capsule is well defined.

The sublingual glands are not encapsulated. They are located deep to the mucous membrane on the floor of the mouth, lateral to the tongue.

The small glands embedded in the submucosa are branched tubulo-alveolar glands, and the larger salivary glands are true compound tubulo-alveolar glands, connected with the oral cavity by one or more excretory ducts.

The secretion of mucous cells is basophilic and stains blue with common stains, such as hematoxylin and eosin (H & E). The cytoplasm of serous cells, particularly the secretory granules, stains red, being acidophilic.

The pressure of the contents of mucous cells flattens the nuclei against the bases of the cells. Droplets of extruded *mucin* swell in water to form mucus.

Lobules of salivary glands contain intercalated ducts which join, while still in the lobule, to form striated tubules (salivary ducts), which continue as interlobular excretory ducts. The ducts to this level are lined by simple columnar epithelium, but larger excretory ducts are lined by two-layered columnar epithelium and then stratified columnar and finally by stratified squamous epithelium at the junction with the oral mucosa. Most if not all levels of ducts are believed to be secretory.

Pancreas

The *pancreas* is a compound tubulo-alveolar gland that has both endocrine and exocrine portions (Fig. 19–17). The exocrine portion of the pancreas produces $NaHCO_3$ and digestive enzymes, which pass through the pancreatic duct to empty into the duodenum close to the opening of the bile duct.

The endocrine portion of the pancreas consists of isolated groups of pale-staining cells scattered throughout the connective tissue stroma of the gland. These vascular areas are called the *islets of Langerhans.* They produce the hormones *insulin* and *glucagon,* which pass directly into the bloodstream.

The pancreas appears grossly as an irregularly lobulated organ which is always related to the first portion of the duodenum and frequently to the caudal vena cava and caudal part of the liver as well. The pancreas appears to be formed of aggregated nodules which are loosely connected to form an elongated gland lying along the duodenum.

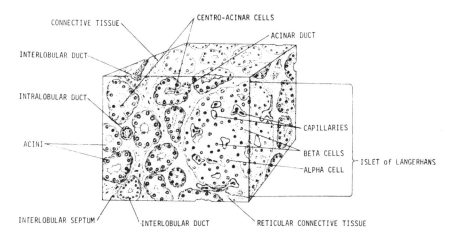

CONNECTIVE TISSUE

CENTRO-ACINAR CELLS

ACINAR DUCT

INTERLOBULAR DUCT

INTRALOBULAR DUCT

CAPILLARIES

ACINI

BETA CELLS

ISLET of LANGERHANS

ALPHA CELL

INTERLOBULAR SEPTUM

INTERLOBULAR DUCT

RETICULAR CONNECTIVE TISSUE

Fig. 19–17. Section of pancreas; H.P. (From Bradley, J. V.: Elementary Microstudies of Human Tissue, 1972. Courtesy of Charles C Thomas, Publisher, Springfield, Ill.)

The main pancreatic duct enters the first part of the duodenum with the common bile duct.

The exocrine portion is the major part of the pancreas. It resembles the parotid salivary gland in microscopic appearance. The main *pancreatic duct (duct of Wirsung)* opens into the duodenum with or close to the common bile duct from the liver. An *accessory pancreatic duct (duct of Santorini)* may also open into the duodenum a short distance from the main duct. The first branches of these ducts are interlobular ducts because they run between lobules of the pancreas. Interlobular ducts branch into intralobular ducts that enter lobules and give rise to intercalated ducts, which enter the alveoli (acini).

The alveolus is the secretory unit of the pancreas. It is a grape-like aggregation of pyramidal cells surrounding the beginning of an intercalated duct. The nuclei of the secretory cells are close to their bases. Acidophilic zymogen granules are found in the cytoplasm between the nuclei and apex cells, particularly during fasting, when they accumulate. These granules are discharged into the ducts during digestion and diminish in number as secretion continues. The basal portions of the cell stain darkly because of the presence of that chromidial substance which is associated with synthesis of the zymogen granules.

Liver

The liver varies somewhat in number of lobes and exact location from one species to another. However, the liver is always located immediately behind the diaphragm and tends to be located on the right side, particularly in ruminants, in which the large stomach arrangement pushes everything else to the right.

The liver receives nutrient blood from the hepatic artery, a branch of the celiac artery, that enters the porta of the liver. The portal vein also enters the area of the liver called the porta. The portal vein carries blood to the liver from the stomach, spleen, pancreas, and intestines. This portal blood is detoxified and modified within the sinusoids (capillaries) of the liver and then leaves the liver by way of the short hepatic veins that empty into the caudal vena cava.

All domestic animals except the horse have a gallbladder for storage of bile. Bile leaves the liver through the *hepatic duct*, which joins the cystic duct from the

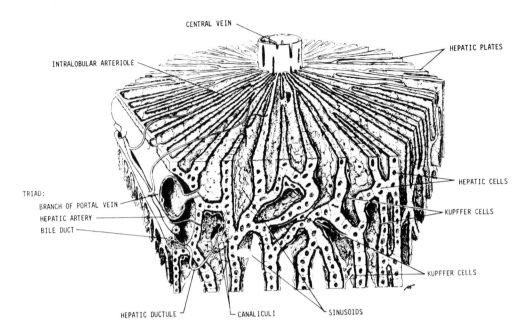

CENTRAL VEIN

HEPATIC PLATES

INTRALOBULAR ARTERIOLE

HEPATIC CELLS

TRIAD:
BRANCH OF PORTAL VEIN
HEPATIC ARTERY
BILE DUCT

KUPFFER CELLS

KUPFFER CELLS

HEPATIC DUCTULE   CANALICULI   SINUSOIDS

Fig. 19–18. Simplified drawing showing the basic cellular arrangement of a liver lobule. (From Bradley, J. V.: Elementary Microstudies of Human Tissue, 1972. Courtesy of Charles C Thomas, Publisher, Springfield, Ill.)

gallbladder to form the *common bile duct*, which then passes to the first part of the duodenum.

The liver is classified as a compound tubular gland, although the arrangement of liver cells appears more like cords or plates than like tubules. Between adjacent rows of liver cells is a tiny bile canaliculus, which is little more than a tube formed by grooves in the surfaces of the apposed liver cells. The lining of the canaliculus is formed by the cell membranes of the liver cells. The liver cords are arranged in a radial manner within lobules, the units of structure of the liver. In the center of the lobule is the central vein, the smallest tributary of an hepatic vein (Fig. 19–18). The cords radiate outward from the central vein to the periphery of the liver lobule, and the bile is carried in this direction by the bile canaliculi to the small bile ducts located at the periphery of the liver lobule, where several lobules meet. The liver

sinusoids are large spaces within the liver lobule that empty into the central vein. These sinusoids bring blood from branches of the portal vein and from branches of the hepatic artery into contact with the epithelial cells of the liver cords. Blood from both the portal vein and from the hepatic artery travels from the periphery of the lobule toward the central vein of the lobule. The arterial blood mainly supplies the connective tissue of the liver (stroma), while the blood from the portal vein is subjected to action by the parenchyma (epithelial cells) of the liver. Branches of the portal vein, branches of the hepatic artery, and small bile ducts travel together in the connective tissue at the junction of several liver lobules. This grouping of vessels is sometimes referred to as a *portal trinity* or *triad*. The sinusoids are lined by large *macrophage* cells known as *Kupffer's cells*. These cells represent the largest part of the *reticuloendothelial system* that functions in phagocytizing foreign material and as scavengers of tissue debris, including worn-out red cells destroyed in the liver by Kupffer's cells.

Liver lobules of the pig are surrounded by rather heavy connective tissue septa (or laminae), which give a lobulated appearance to the surface of the liver of the pig. Other animals and man have much less interlobular connective tissue than the pig, so lobules are not so easy to see grossly.

Lymphatic vessels are found in the connective tissue capsule, interlobular connective tissue, connective tissue around portal veins, and connective tissue around hepatic veins.

Chapter 20

Foods and Their Basic Chemistry

One of the important functions of food is replacement of tissue in mature animals and building of new tissue in young animals and pregnant animals. Therefore, the composition of the animal body is pertinent to consider first.

The major constituents of the animal body are water, protein, fat, minerals, and a small amount of carbohydrate. Proportions of each vary with species, age, sex, and condition of the animal. Approximate percentage composition of several different animals, without the contents of the digestive tract, ranges from 50 to 60% water, 15 to 20% protein, 17 to 25% fat, and 3 to 5% mineral matter and less than 1% carbohydrate.

Water content decreases in cattle from a high of 95% in the early embryo to a low between 50 and 60% at maturity. At a given age, fat is the most variable constituent of the animal body, and variations in fat content influence the percentage figures of the other body substances.

In addition to building or rebuilding tissue, food is essential as the primary source of energy and as a source of the material secreted by glands. Foods may be classified either as proper foods (carbohydrates, proteins, and fats), which supply energy, or as accessory foods (water, inorganic salts, and vitamins), which are essential for life but do not supply energy.

Food for animals comes from plants, directly in the case of *herbivorous* (plant-eating) *animals* and indirectly in the case of *carnivorous* (flesh-eating) *animals*. Those plants that contain chlorophyll have the ability to synthesize carbohydrates from carbon dioxide and water, by using sunlight as their source of energy.

The green plant, like the animal body, contains more water than anything else. Here the similarity ceases, since the plant contains a large amount of carbohydrate and smaller amounts of protein, fat, and mineral matter. On the other hand, the animal body contains a small amount of carbohydrate and much larger amounts of protein, fat, and mineral matter.

CARBOHYDRATES

Carbohydrates include sugar, starch, cellulose, gums, and similar substances. As the

Table 20–1. Classification of Carbohydrates

I. Monosaccharides	III. Trisaccharides, $C_{18}H_{32}O_{16}$
1. Pentoses, $C_5H_{10}O_5$	Raffinose
Arabinose	IV. Polysaccharides
Xylose	1. Pentosans, $(C_5H_8O_4)x$
Ribose	Araban
2. Hexoses, $C_6H_{12}O_6$	Xylan
Glucose	2. Hexosans, $(C_6H_{10}O_5)x$
Fructose	Dextrin
Galactose	Starch
Mannose	Cellulose
II. Disaccharides, $C_{12}H_{22}O_{11}$	Glycogen
Sucrose	Inulin
Maltose	3. Mixed polysaccharides
Lactose	Gums
Cellobiose	Mucilages

(Maynard and Loosli, *Animal Nutrition*, 5th ed., courtesy of McGraw-Hill Book Co., Inc.)

complexity of these substances increases, the ease of digestion decreases. *Cellulose*, the principal structural carbohydrate, is the main constituent of crude fiber in feeds. Those feeds that contain a high percentage of cellulose, such as hay, silage, and straw, are called *roughages* and have a low digestibility. Seeds of plants and most of their by-products are low in cellulose. They are highly digestible and are called *concentrates*.

Table 20–1 gives a classification of major nutritional carbohydrates, in order of increasing complexity. Carbohydrates, as the name implies, contain carbon combined with hydrogen and oxygen. The hydrogen and oxygen usually are in the same ratio as they are in water (H_2O).

Monosaccharides. Important monosaccharides, simple *sugars*, include pentoses (5-carbon-atom sugars) and hexoses (6-carbon-atom sugars). (See Fig. 20–1.) *Pentoses* occur free in nature in small amounts. They can be produced by *hydrolysis* of the *pentosans* in wood, corn cobs, oat hulls, hay, and gums. *Hexoses* are more common and more important in animal nutrition than other monosaccharides. *Fructose (levulose)* is found free in ripe fruit and honey. *Glucose (dextrose)* is also found in fruits and honey, and is the sugar found in the blood. *Galactose* (itself a monosaccharide) occurs in combination with glucose to form *lactose* (milk sugar), a disaccharide.

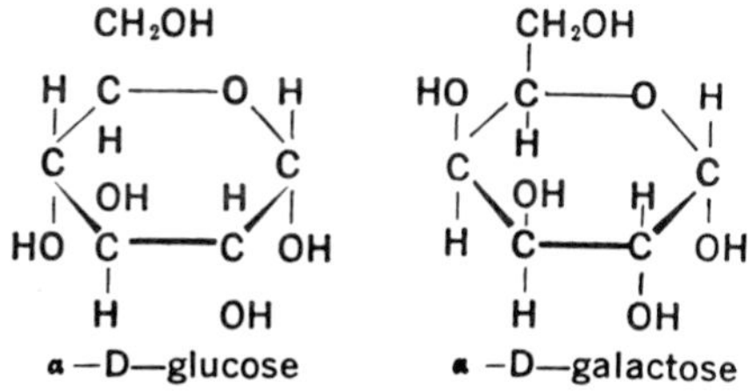

Disaccharides. Disaccharides are formed by the chemical combination of two molecules of monosaccharides with the elimination of one molecule of water (Fig. 20–2). Sucrose, maltose, and lactose are the most common disaccharides. *Sucrose* (table sugar), a combination of glucose and fructose, is found in cane sugar, beet sugar, and maple sugar. *Maltose* consists of two molecules of glucose. It is formed by hydrolysis of starch. Lactose *(milk sugar)* is a combination of glucose and galactose. *Cellobiose* is a saccharide that is formed from cellulose by the action of *cellulase* from microorganisms.

Trisaccharides. The trisaccharide *raffinose* consists of one molecule each of glucose, galactose, and fructose. It occurs to some extent in sugar beets and cottonseed.

Fig. 20–1. Structure of monosaccharides.

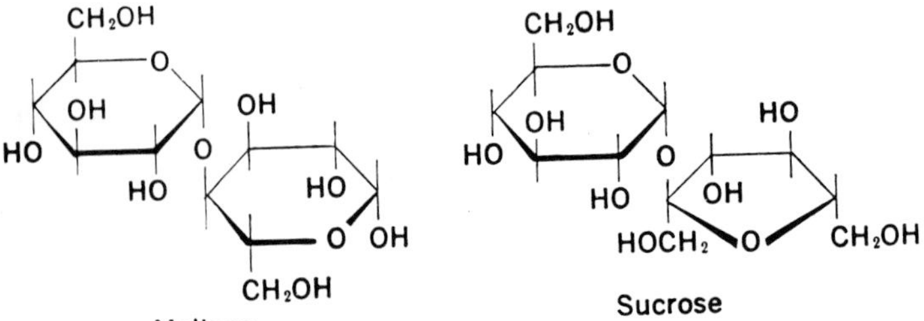

Fig. 20–2. Structure of disaccharides.

Polysaccharides. Polysaccharides are made up of numerous molecules of simple sugars. Most polysaccharides are formed from hexoses, but a few, the pentosans, are composed of pentose sugars.

Pentosans are found in the woody portions and seed coats of many plants, including legume and nonlegume hays, wheat bran, cottonseed hulls, and some root crops. They are digested in a manner similar to the digestion of cellulose and are approximately as useful for livestock feed.

The hexose polysaccharides form a major amount of nutrients of plant origin. *Starch*, the chief food reserve of most plants, hydrolyzes into *dextrin*, then maltose, and finally glucose. It is an excellent source of energy for farm animals. Cellulose, which forms much of the structural part of plants, is more complex and more resistant to hydrolysis than starch. It is digested by enzymes of cellulose-splitting microorganisms that function mainly in herbivorous animals. The rumen and reticulum are the chief sites for action in the ruminant, while the cecum and colon of nonruminant herbivorous animals provide a suitable environment for these microorganisms.

Most of the carbohydrate reserve in animals exists as *glycogen* in the liver and in muscles. It is soluble in water, and starch is not; otherwise glycogen resembles starch. Both yield glucose as the final end product of hydrolysis, and both are forms for storage of sugar.

Inulin, a polysaccharide that yields fructose upon hydrolysis, is stored by the Jerusalem artichoke in place of starch. *Chitin* is a mixed polysaccharide found in the exoskeleton (hard outer covering) of many insects.

PROTEINS

Proteins, as described in Chapter 3, are complex, high-molecular-weight, large colloidal molecules comprised primarily of amino acids that are polymerized (joined) into polypeptide chains. (See Fig. 20–3.) The union of amino acids within a protein molecule is by way of the *peptide linkage*, a union between the amino (NH_2) group of one acid and the carboxyl ($COOH$) group of another acid, with the elimination of a molecule of water. Several amino acids con-

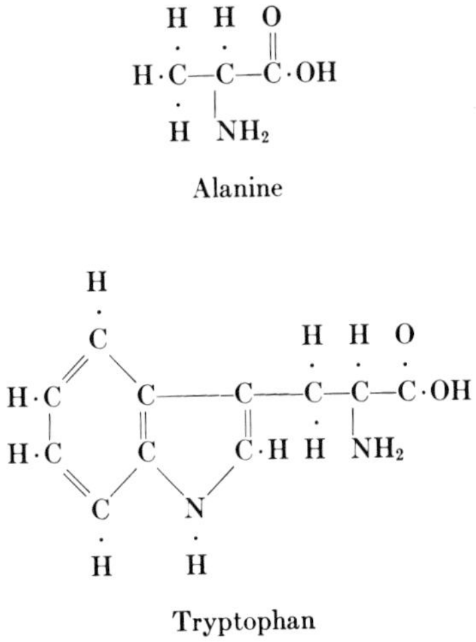

Fig. 20–3. Examples of amino acid structure.

nected by the peptide linkage form a compound called a *polypeptide*.

Proteins contain *carbon, hydrogen, oxygen,* and *nitrogen*. Some also contain such components as *sulfur, phosphorus,* or *iron*. In addition to the classification given in Chapter 3, proteins may also be classified as simple (both fibrous and globular), conjugated, and derived.

Simple proteins yield only amino acids or their derivatives upon hydrolysis. The simple proteins, and examples of each, are as follows:

1. albumins (plasma albumin, milk lactalbumin)
2. globulins (plasma globulins, globulins in plant seeds)
3. protamines (in sperm cells)
4. prolamines (zein of corn, gliadin of wheat)
5. histones (with nucleoproteins of somatic cells)
6. albuminoids (collagen and elastin of connective tissue)

Conjugated proteins consist of simple proteins combined with a nonprotein or nonamino acid component called a *prosthetic group*. The conjugated proteins, and examples of each, are:

1. glycoproteins–includes mucopolysaccharides and oligosaccharides as the carbohydrate prosthetic group (in connective tissue and salivary mucus)
2. lipoproteins–prosthetic group is lipid (in blood plasma and egg yolk)
3. nucleoproteins–nucleic acid prosthetic group (in cell nuclei, chromosomes, and viruses)
4. chromoproteins–Fe-porphyrin prosthetic group (hemoglobin, cytochromes)
5. metalloproteins–contain Fe, Zn, or Cu (blood transferrin, ferritin, carbonic anhydrase)
6. phosphoproteins–phosphate prosthetic group (casein in milk, vitellin in eggs)

Derived proteins are breakdown products of naturally occurring proteins. In order of decreasing complexity, they include *primary protein derivatives, proteins, metaproteins, coagulated proteins, secondary protein derivatives, proteoses, peptones,* and *peptides*.

Amino Acids

Amino acids consist largely of carbon, hydrogen, and oxygen in various configurations, plus one or two amino groups (NH_2). They have been called the building blocks of protein because they are arranged in various ways to produce different proteins, just as the letters of the alphabet are arranged in a variety of ways to form different words.

About ten of the amino acids either cannot be synthesized at all or cannot be synthesized rapidly enough by the animal body to permit normal growth. These are known as the *essential amino acids*. The remainder of

Table 20–2.   Classification of Amino Acids with Respect to Their Growth Effects in the Rat*

Essential	Nonessential
Lysine	Glycine
Tryptophan	Alanine
Histidine	Serine
Phenylalanine	Cystine†
Leucine	Tyrosine‡
Isoleucine	Aspartic acid
Threonine	Glutamic acid§
Methionine	Proline§
Valine	Hydroxyproline
Arginine‖	Citrulline

* W. C. Rose et al., J. Biol. Chem., *176*, 753, 1948.

† Cystine can replace about one-sixth of the methionine requirement but has no growth effect in the absence of methionine.

‡ Tyrosine can replace about one-half of the phenylalanine requirement but has no growth effect in the absence of phenylalanine.

§ Glutamic acid and proline can serve individually as rather ineffective substitutes for arginine in the diet. This property is not shared by hydroxyproline.

‖ Arginine can be synthesized by the rat, but not at a sufficiently rapid rate to meet the demands of maximum growth. Its classification, therefore, as essential or nonessential is purely a matter of definition.

the amino acids are called *nonessential* because the body can synthesize them in sufficient quantities to ensure normal growth. Table 20–2 lists the essential and nonessential amino acids.

Protein Quality

Biologic value and *protein quality* are synonymous terms referring to the relative proportions of essential amino acids in a protein when compared with the needs of the animal for those amino acids. A protein of the highest quality (greatest biologic value) would provide all the essential amino acids needed by a given animal in the exact proportions required by that animal. A protein of lower quality might contain all the essential amino acids, but contain some in excess of the animal's needs and contain less than the animal's needs of other essential amino acids. A still lower quality protein might completely lack one or more of the essential amino acids. For example, when *zein*, the protein of corn, is used as the sole protein for rats, it will not produce normal growth unless *tryptophan* and *lysine* are added to the ration.

A protein that lacks any of the essential amino acids is a poor-quality protein. A protein that provides all the essential amino acids in proper proportions is a good-quality protein.

LIPIDS

Lipids include fats and related substances. The lipids are soluble in fat solvents, including ether, chloroform, and xylene, but they are insoluble in water. Lipids may be classified as simple lipids, compound lipids, and derived lipids.

Simple lipids are esters of fatty acids and alcohols and include fats (esters of fatty acids and glycerol) and waxes (esters of fatty acids and alcohols other than glycerol). *Compound lipids* contain some group besides alcohol and fatty acids, such as phosphoric acid, nitrogen, or carbohydrate. *Derived lipids* are compounds resulting from hydrolysis of simple or compound lipids.

Saturated fatty acids have twice as many hydrogen atoms as carbon atoms, and each molecule of fatty acid contains two atoms of oxygen (Fig. 20–4). Fatty acids, like other organic acids, contain the configuration COOH. Saturated fatty acids contain all the hydrogens possible, and adjacent carbon atoms are connected by single valence bonds. *Unsaturated fatty acids* contain less than twice as many hydrogen atoms as carbon atoms, and one or more pairs of adjacent carbon atoms are connected by double bonds (Fig. 20–4). If several pairs of adjacent carbon atoms contain double bonds, the term *polyunsaturated* is used. Table 20–3 lists some of the common saturated and unsaturated fatty acids.

$$CH_3-CH_2-CH_2-CH_2-CH_2-CH_2-CH_2-CH_2-CH_2-CH_2-CH_2-CH_2-CH_2-CH_2-CH_2-COOH$$

$$C_{15}H_{31}-COOH$$

Palmitic acid

$$CH_3-CH_2-CH_2-CH_2-CH_2-CH_2-CH_2-CH_2-CH=CH-CH_2-CH_2-CH_2-CH_2-CH_2-CH_2-CH_2-COOH$$

$$C_{17}H_{33}-COOH$$

Oleic acid; 9-octadecenoic acid

Fig. 20–4. Palmitic acid is a saturated fatty acid; oleic acid is an unsaturated fatty acid.

Table 20–3.   Fatty Acids Commonly Found in Lipids

Acids	Formula	Melting Point °C
Saturated acids:		
Butyric (butanoic)	$C_4H_8O_2$	Liquid
Caproic (hexanoic)	$C_6H_{12}O_2$	Liquid
Caprylic (octanoic)	$C_8H_{16}O_2$	16
Capric (decanoic)	$C_{10}H_{20}O_2$	31
Lauric (dodecanoic)	$C_{12}H_{24}O_2$	44
Myristic (tetradecanoic)	$C_{14}H_{28}O_2$	54
Palmitic (hexadecanoic)	$C_{16}H_{32}O_2$	63
Stearic (octadecanoic)α	$C_{18}H_{36}O_2$	70
Arachidic (eicosanoic)α	$C_{20}H_{40}O_2$	76
Lignoceric (tetracosanoic)	$C_{24}H_{48}O_2$	86
Unsaturated acids:		
Palmitoleic (hexadecenoic)	$C_{16}H_{30}O_2$	Liquid
Oleic (octadecenoic)	$C_{18}H_{34}O_2$	Liquid
Linoleic (octadecadienoic)	$C_{18}H_{32}O_2$	Liquid
Linolenic (octadecatrienoic)	$C_{18}H_{30}O_2$	Liquid
Arachidonic (eicosatetraenoic)	$C_{20}H_{32}O_2$	Liquid
Clupanodonic (docosapentaenoic)	$C_{22}H_{34}O_2$	Liquid

(Maynard and Loosli, *Animal Nutrition,* 5th ed., courtesy of McGraw-Hill Book Co., Inc.)

A *neutral fat* (triglyceride) is an ester of three molecules of fatty acids (all may be the same acid or may be different acids) combined with one molecule of glycerol. If R-COOH is used as the formula for any fatty acid, the following equation illustrates the formation of a typical neutral fat.

$$
\begin{array}{lll}
CH_2OH & HOOC\text{–}R & CH_2\text{–}OOC\text{–}R \\
| & | & | \\
CHOH + HOOC\text{–}R & \longrightarrow & CH\text{–}OOC\text{–}R + 3H_2O \\
| & | & | \\
CH_2OH & HOOC\text{–}R & CH_2\text{–}OOC\text{–}R
\end{array}
$$

glycerol   fatty acids   fat

Saturated fatty acids have a higher melting point than unsaturated acids of the same number of carbon atoms. As shown in Table 20–3, the longer chains of saturated fatty acids have higher melting points than acids with shorter chains. In general the same statements are true of fats as for the fatty acids.

All *triglycerides* of fatty acids are called fats, but those that are liquid below 20°C. are sometimes called oils. Table 20–4 shows the fatty acid content of several common fats.

The *iodine number* is a measure of unsaturation of a fat, because two atoms of iodine are absorbed at each double bond when a fat is treated with iodine. The higher the iodine number, the more double bonds in the fat and consequently the greater degree of unsaturation.

Length of the carbon chain is indicated by the *saponification number*. When a fat is treated with an alkali, a soap is formed, in a process called saponification. Since one molecule of alkali combines with one molecule of fatty acid, the larger the amount of alkali absorbed for a given quantity of fat, the more fatty acids present, and therefore the shorter the fatty-acid chains. If long-chain fatty acids make up the fat, there will be fewer acids and consequently a lower saponification number.

Unsaturated fats can be artificially saturated by adding hydrogen and breaking the double bonds. Some type of catalyst is needed for this reaction, called *hydrogenation*. Hydrogenated fats have a higher melting point and better keeping qualities than unsaturated fats of the same chain length.

Table 20–4.   Fatty Acids as a Percentage of Total Fatty Acids* and Physical Constants of Some Common Fats

	Butterfat	Lard	Coconut Fat	Soybean Fat	Corn Fat	Cottonseed Fat
I. Saturated acids:						
Butyric	3.2					
Caproic	1.8	—	0.2			
Caprylic	0.8	—	8.2			
Capric	1.4	—	7.4			
Lauric	3.8	—	47.5			
Myristic	8.3	—	18.0	—	—	2.0
Palmitic	27.0	32.2	8.0	8.5	7.0	19.0
Stearic	12.5	7.8	2.8	3.5	2.4	2.0
Total saturated	58.8	40.0	92.8	21.1	9.4	24.4
II. Unsaturated acids:						
Oleic	35.0	48.0	5.6	17.0	45.6	20.1
Linoleic	3.0	11.0	1.6	54.4	45.0	55.5
Linolenic	0.8	0.6	—	7.1		
Melting point, °C.	28 to 36	35 to 45	20 to 35	Liquid at ordinary temperature		
Iodine No.	26 to 38	40 to 70	8 to 10	130 to 137	105 to 125	100 to 115
Saponification No.	220 to 241	193 to 220	250 to 260	190 to 194	87 to 93	190 to 200
Reichert-Meissl No.	23 to 33	—	6 to 8			

* Most of these data were taken from a compilation prepared by Verz R. Goddard and Louise Goodall, issued by the Agriculture Research Service, U. S. Department of Agriculture, May 1959. (Maynard and Loosli, *Animal Nutrition,* 5th ed., courtesy of McGraw-Hill Book Co., Inc.)

There is some evidence that vascular disease in man may be related to a diet high in saturated fats.

Waxes consist of a fatty acid combined with a monohydroxy alcohol (only one OH group). They are difficult to saponify and have a higher melting point than most fats.

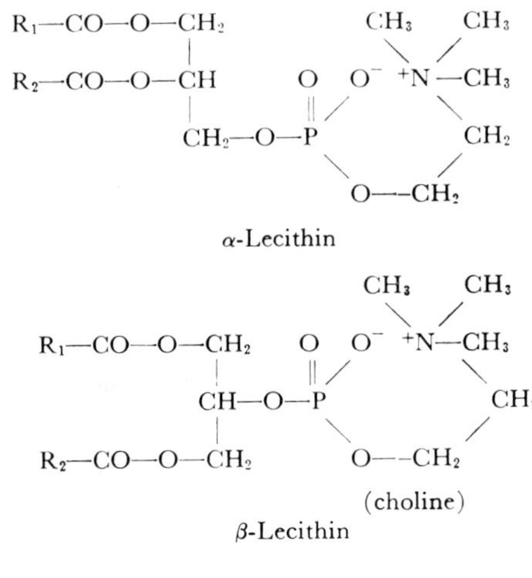

R$_1$—CO—O—CH$_2$

R$_2$—CO—O—CH

CH$_2$—O—P ... O   O$^-$ $^+$N—CH$_3$ ... CH$_3$ CH$_3$ ... CH$_2$ ... O—CH$_2$

α-Lecithin

R$_1$—CO—O—CH$_2$

CH—O—P ... O   O$^-$ $^+$N—CH$_3$ ... CH$_3$ CH$_3$ ... CH$_2$

R$_2$—CO—O—CH$_2$ ... O—CH$_2$

(choline)

β-Lecithin

Fig. 20–5.   Structures of *α*- and *β*-lecithin.

The *phospholipids* contain phosphorus in addition to the lipid portion. They include such compounds as *lecithin, cephalins, sphingomyelins,* and *cerebrosides* (see Fig. 20–5).

Sterols are unsaponifiable high-molecular-weight alcohols. They may occur free or as esters of fatty acids. *Cholesterol,* the best-known example of a sterol, has the formula $C_{27}H_{45}OH$. Plant sterols are called *phytosterols. Ergosterol,* found in both plants and animals, is transformed into vitamin D when it is irradiated by ultraviolet light.

MINERAL MATTER

Total mineral matter (the inorganic constituents) of plants (feed) is determined by burning a sample of feed until the ash formed contains no carbon. Although this process gives an indication of total mineral matter, it does not indicate what elements or how much of each make up the ash. Structural

Table 20–5.   Classification of Minerals in the Animal Body

Major or Macro	% Body Weight	Micro or Trace
Calcium (Ca)	1.33	Chromium (Cr)
Phosphorus (P)	0.74	Cobalt (Co)
Potassium (K)	0.19	Fluorine (F)
Sodium (Na)	0.16	Iodine (I)
Chlorine (Cl)	0.11	Iron (Fe)
Magnesium (Mg)	0.04	Manganese (Mn)
		Molybdenum (Mo)
		Selenium (Se)
		Silicon (Si)
		Zinc (Zn)

Adapted from Ensminger and Olentine: Feeds and Nutrition. Clovis, Ensminger Publishing Co., 1978.

parts of plants, the leaves and stems, are higher in ash than is the grain portion.

Virtually all minerals have been reported to be present in the animal body. The minerals believed to be essential include the macrominerals, which are needed in relatively large quantities, and the microminerals or trace minerals, which are needed by the animal only in minute amounts. Some minerals that are essential in small amounts may become toxic if ingested in large quantities.

Authorities differ in the classification of minerals and disagree about which minerals should be included in each category. Undoubtedly, there are species differences as well. The classification of minerals by Ensminger and Olentine appears in Table 20–5.

Minerals known to be toxic in relatively large amounts include: selenium, flourine, arsenic, lead, copper, and molybdenum. However, some of these may be essential in relatively small amounts.

Minerals, particularly calcium and phosphorus, function in the teeth and skeleton and in muscle contraction. Other functions of minerals include biochemical processes, such as maintaining osmotic gradients and ionic exchange, all surface electrical activity, storage of energy (ATP and ADP), and metabolic functions, including acting as cofactors in enzyme systems.

VITAMINS

Vitamins include a large number of organic compounds that are, in general, chemically unrelated. They are essential for normal metabolism, but most cannot be produced by the body. However, some vitamins are formed by microorganisms in the digestive tract.

Fat-soluble vitamins are either soluble in fat or absorbed with fat. Vitamins A, D, E, and K are the common fat-soluble vitamins.

Water-soluble vitamins are either soluble in water or absorbed with water. Common water-soluble vitamins are B_1, B_2, B_{12}, C, *niacin*, and *folic acid*.

Specific dietary vitamin requirements vary considerably from species to species, depending in part on the ability of the animal to synthesize the particular vitamin and also on the presence of microorganisms in the digestive tract that may synthesize some of the vitamins.

Water-Soluble Vitamins

The water-soluble vitamins function as enzymes in certain metabolic reactions.

Thiamine. Thiamine (*vitamin B_1*) functions widely as a coenzyme in *decarboxylation reactions*. Combined with ATP, thiamine forms *cocarboxylase*, which is a coenzyme for oxidative decarboxylation of pyruvic acid and other keto acids.

Deficiencies of thiamine cause *beriberi* in man and *polyneuritis* in birds. Ruminants and most other mammals do not ordinarily need additional thiamine in the diet because microorganisms in the digestive tract synthesize more thiamine than needed by the host animal.

Accumulation of pyruvic acid and *lactic acid* in blood and tissues due to thiamine deficiency causes irritability, loss of appetite, fatigue, degeneration of myelin sheaths of nerve fibers, weakened heart muscle, and gastrointestinal disorders. Thiamine is present in meat (especially pork), whole grains, nuts and yeast.

Cobalamin (B₁₂). Cobalamin *(vitamin B₁₂)* is a vitamin containing cobalt that is frequently seen as the cyanide derivative, *cyanocobalamin.* Vitamin B_{12} may function in protein synthesis and in metabolism of nucleic acid and compounds containing one carbon atom. Deficiency of cobalamin causes an *anemia* because of failure of red blood cells to mature. Deficiency also causes demyelination and irreversible degeneration of the spinal cord. Vitamin B_{12} can be found in most animal products such as milk, meat, and organ tissues.

Biotin. Biotin is involved in the synthesis of *oxaloacetate,* in the formation of urea, fatty acids, and purines. In fact it acts as a coenzyme prosthetic group that combines CO_2 with organic compounds, as in the examples just cited. Intestinal bacteria synthesize biotin, and egg yolk is a good source of biotin. Raw egg white contains an antibiotin factor (a protein called *avidin*), which inactivates the vitamin.

Deficiency of biotin causes loss of hair, loss of weight, and, in chickens, high chick mortality rates and skeletal changes in the baby chicks.

Riboflavin (B₂). Riboflavin *(vitamin B₂)* forms the *prosthetic group* for *flavoprotein coenzymes* that are necessary for oxidation reactions in normal cellular metabolism. Intestinal and ruminal microorganisms synthesize riboflavin in adequate amounts for most animals. Calves will show deficiency symptoms if ruminal organisms are absent.

Deficiency symptoms for riboflavin include loss of hair, skin lesions, vomiting, diarrhea, and eye disorders. Yeast, milk products, liver, fish, and green vegetables are sources of riboflavin.

Niacin. Niacin (nicotinic acid) forms a part of NAD (nicotinamide adenine dinucleotide), also known as *coenzyme I.* It also forms a part of the NADP molecule, which is also known as *coenzyme II.* The coenzymes act with the flavoproteins in cellular respiration (metabolism).

Niacin plays a role in carbohydrate absorption and metabolism. *Tryptophan* is used in the synthesis of niacin by both mammals and microorganisms. Calves synthesize niacin even in the absence of ruminal organisms.

"Black tongue" in dogs and *pellagra* in man result from deficiency of niacin. All body functions decrease for lack of ATP formation. Gastrointestinal problems and muscle weakness are early signs, along with swollen tongue and dermatitis.

Pyridoxine (B₆). Pyridoxine *(vitamin B₆)* is important in protein metabolism where *pyridoxal phosphate* is a coenzyme for several different chemical reactions relating to amino acid and protein metabolism, such as transamination and decarboxylation. Pyridoxine is synthesized by intestinal and ruminal microorganisms.

Deficiency of pyridoxine may result in retarded growth, *dermatitis,* and *anemia.*

Pantothenic Acid. Pantothenic acid forms a part of coenzyme A, which acts in transfer of acetyl groups. This occurs in acetylation of choline to form *acetylcholine,* and in the acetylation of decarboxylated pyruvate to form acetylcoenzyme A for use in the Krebs cycle. Coenzyme A also takes part in the degradation of fatty acids to acetyl-CoA. Pantothenic acid is synthesized by rumen and intestinal microorganisms.

Deficiencies of pantothenic acid are associated with dermatitis, depressed growth, loss of hair, graying of hair, and lesions of various organs, all a result of poor carbohydrate and fat oxidation.

Folic Acid. Folic acid *(pteroylglutamic acid)* functions in nucleoprotein metabolism through the synthesis of *purines* and *thymine.* Folic acid appears to be synthesized by intestinal microorganisms (Fig. 20–6). Deficiency of folic acid is associated with problems in blood formation, as well as cellular reproduction. Drugs such as *sulfonamides,* which inhibit intestinal bacteria, may cause folic-acid deficiency symptoms indirectly. Growth retardation and anemia are the major effects of deficiency. Parasites

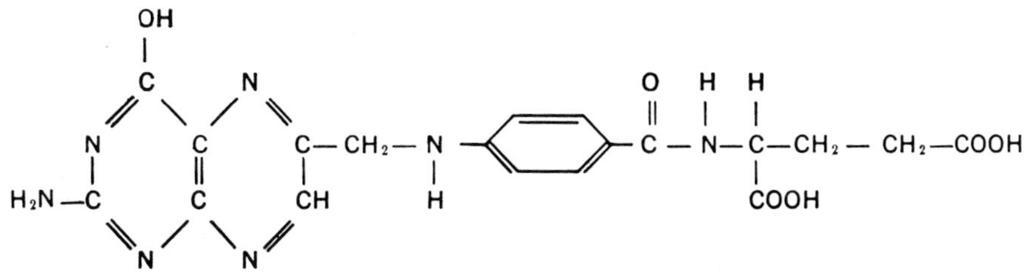

Fig. 20–6. Folic acid.

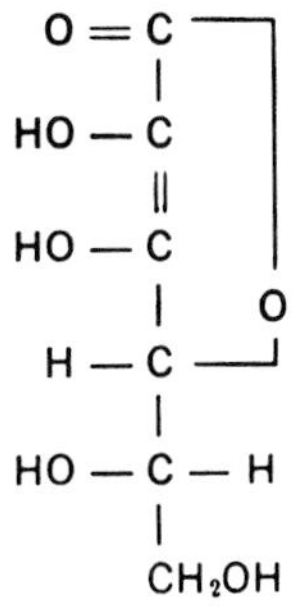

Fig. 20–7. Ascorbic acid.

keys, and man, however, must receive their ascorbic acid in the diet. Vitamin C occurs naturally in fresh vegetables and fruits.

Deficiency of ascorbic acid causes *scurvy*. The symptoms are related to the need of this vitamin C for collagen synthesis. Therefore, the pathology involves weakened blood vessels and capillary beds (which causes a tendency to hemorrhage), ulceration and poor healing of wounds, and changes in the teeth and gums. Bone growth is deficient and fractures heal poorly.

in the body can decrease folic acid absorption. Meats and vegetables, especially green leaves, are sources of folic acid.

Ascorbic Acid. Ascorbic acid *(vitamin C)* is not part of any known coenzyme (Fig. 20–7). Instead, it is involved in the synthesis of collagen, which is the structural protein of connective tissue. It may also take part in several reduction-oxidation reactions. Many plants and vertebrate animals can synthesize ascorbic acid. Guinea pigs, mon-

Fat-Soluble Vitamins

The fat-soluble vitamins, A, D, E, and K, appear to be required by all farm animals.

Vitamin A. Vitamin A *(antixerophthalmic vitamin)* is a biochemical alcohol, *retinol*, and occurs as vitamin A_1, in higher vertebrates (Fig. 20–8) and salt-water fishes, and *vitamin A_2* occurs chiefly in fresh-water fishes. Several plant pigments *(alpha, beta,* and *gamma carotene,* and *cryptoxanthin)*

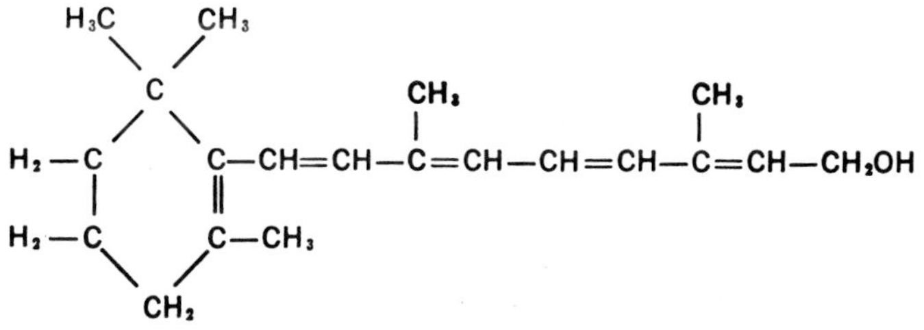

Fig. 20–8. Vitamin A_1.

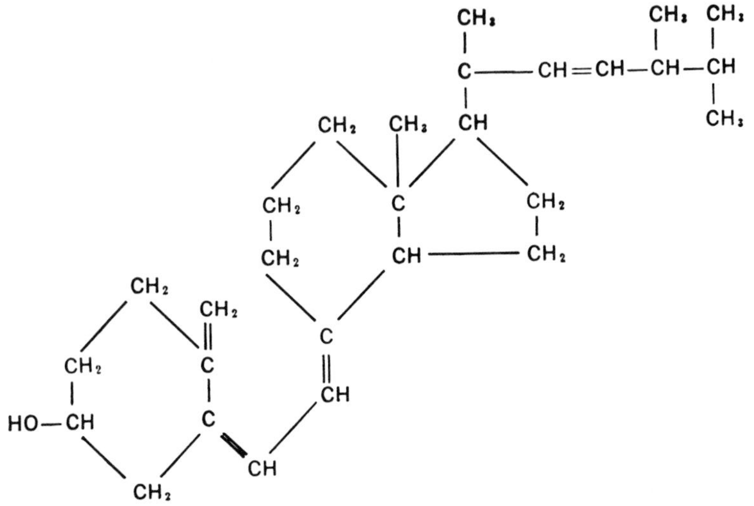

Fig. 20–9.   Vitamin D.

are precursors for vitamin A. The precursors are yellow in color, but vitamin A carotenoid is colorless, so no correlation can be made between the yellow color of milk or cream and its vitamin A content. Precursors of vitamin A are converted to vitamin A in the intestine and in the liver, and the resulting vitamin A is stored both in the *liver* and in the *retina*.

Vitamin A is essential for the formation of retinal pigments needed for vision. Vitamin A is also needed for normal growth, particularly of epithelial and osseous tissues. Deficiency of vitamin A results in *night blindness* (nyctalopia), degeneration of epithelia, excessive cornification of stratified squamous epithelium, and increased susceptibility to infections because of abnormal function of the adrenal cortex.

Vitamin D. Vitamin D *(antirachitic vitamin)* consists mainly of vitamin D_2 and vitamin D_3 (Fig. 20–9).

Vitamin D_2 (ergocalciferol) is a plant product formed by ultraviolet irradiation of plant *ergosterol*. *Vitamin D_3 (cholecal-* ciferol) is synthesized in the skin from the irradiation of *7-dehydrocholesterol* by ultraviolet light. Since this irradiation occurs from the action of sunlight on the exposed skin, vitamin D is sometimes called the "sunshine vitamin." Cholecalciferol (vitamin D_3) can also be ingested in the food if the diet includes particularly fish liver oils.

Vitamin D has three primary effects: (1) it increases absorption of calcium from the small intestine; (2) it can cause the resorption of calcium from the bones; and (3) it increases the excretion of phosphate from the kidneys. Together with *parathyroid hormone,* the result of vitamin D activity is an increase in blood levels of calcium.

Before the cholecalciferol can be effective, however, it must be activated. It is partially activated in the liver by conversion to *25-hydroxycholecalciferol* (by hydroxylation). This is then transported to the kidneys, where further hydroxylation to the 1,25 form occurs to make it fully active. In the blood, the active form then acts on the cells of the intestinal mucosa to cause syn-

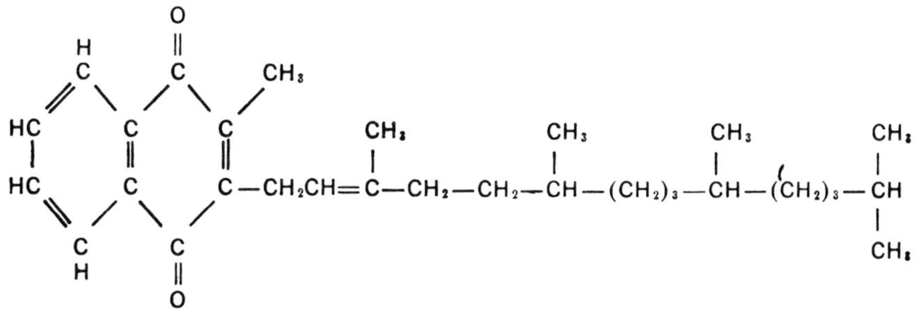

Fig. 20–10.   Vitamin K₁ is 2-methyl-3-phytyl-1,4-naphthoquinone.

thesis of a specific mRNA. The mRNA, in turn, causes a calcium-carrier protein to be produced, which increases the absorption of calcium from the intestine. Therefore, vitamin D facilitates calcium absorption and, in turn, can facilitate calcification of bones.

A deficiency of vitamin D results in *rickets*, which affects the bones because of insufficient calcium. It can therefore cause knock-knees, enlarged joints, and bowlegs. Like vitamin A, vitamin D is only slowly excreted from the body, by way of bile; hence, it is possible to produce toxicity if too much is ingested. Such high blood levels of vitamin D affect calcium metabolism, resulting in neurologic problems and deposition of calcium in soft tissues of the body if continued for a long time.

Vitamin E. Vitamin E *(tocopherol)* may function as a cofactor for *cytochrome reductase* in heart muscle and skeletal muscle. In some species, at least, vitamin E is necessary for normal reproduction of both the male and female, but this apparently is not true for the horse, cow, or man. It seems to also act as an antioxidant, preventing autooxidation of unsaturated fatty acids and to inhibit peroxidation of cell membrane lipids. Deficiency of vitamin E can result in degeneration of germinal epithelium in the male and resorption of embryos in the female of those mammalian species that are dependent on vitamin E. The vitamin occurs naturally in animal and plant fats and oils, especially wheat germ.

Vitamin K. Vitamin K is necessary for the formation of *prothrombin* and factors VII, IX, and X (essential for blood clotting). Vitamin K in the *farnoquinone* form is formed by microorganisms in the digestive tract; it is found in green plants in the *phylloquinone* form. Deficiency of vitamin K results in *hemorrhages* because of the failure of the blood to clot.

Other Substances

Other substances that function in metabolism include *hematin* (a part of cytochrome) and nitrogenous acids including *carnosine, anserine,* and *carnitine.* These may all be likened to vitamins for some species, as could also the essential amino acids and fatty acids.

Table 20–6 lists vitamins and other substances essential to health; Table 20–7 shows a classification of nutrients by analysis.

Table 20–6.   Vitamins

Class	Chemical Nature	Effect of Lack on Vertebrates	Cellular Function
A	Carotenoid	Growth interference, night blindness	Part of visual purple in retina; growth
D	Sterol	Bone defects	Not known; mobilizes salts in gut
E	Tocopherol	In rat, defective implantation and testis development	Unknown
B_1	Thiamine	Beriberi	Coenzyme for pyruvate metabolism
B_2	Riboflavin	Cataract	Prosthetic group of flavoprotein enzyme
Niacin	Nicotinic acid amide	Pellagra	Part of dehydrogenase coenzyme
Pantothen	Pantothenic acid	Dermatitis and spectacle eye	Part of coenzyme A
B_6	Pyridoxine	Need not demonstrated	Coenzyme for amino acid conversions
H	Biotin	Need not demonstrated	Coenzyme in CO_2 fixation in C_4 acids
Inositol	Cyclic Compound	Need not demonstrated	Unknown
Folic acid	Pteroylglutamic acid	Anemia	Coenzyme functioning in "one" carbon metabolism
B_{12}	Cyanocobalamin (tetrapyrrole with cobalt in center)	Anemia	Coenzyme of an enzyme involved in methyl transfer and nucleic acid metabolism
Protogen	Thioctic acid	Need not demonstrated	Coenzyme in pyruvate oxidation
C	Ascorbic acid	Scurvy	Maintains optimal oxidation-reduction potential
K	1,4-naphthoquinone acetate	Hemorrhage	Prothrombin formation in blood
P	A mixture of substances*	Capillary fragility	Maintains cement of capillary walls
Essential amino acids	Essential amino acids†	Failure in growth or normal function Wasting of tissue	Structure of cells, etc.
Essential fatty acids	Linoleic, linolenic and arachidonic	Failure in growth or functioning	Structure of cells, etc.
Methyl compounds	Choline, methionine	Failure in growth, etc.	Structure of cells, etc.
Sulfhydryl-containing compounds	Cysteine, glutathione	Failure in growth, etc.	Structure of cells, etc.

* Eriodictin, hesperidin, rutin.

† Tryptophan, phenylalanine, lysine, histidine, leucine, isoleucine, threonine, methionine, valine and arginine are required by the rat. The requirement is not always the same for all types of animals. (Giese, Cell Physiology, 4th ed., 1973, courtesy of W. B. Saunders Co.)

Table 20-7. Classification of Nutrients by Analysis

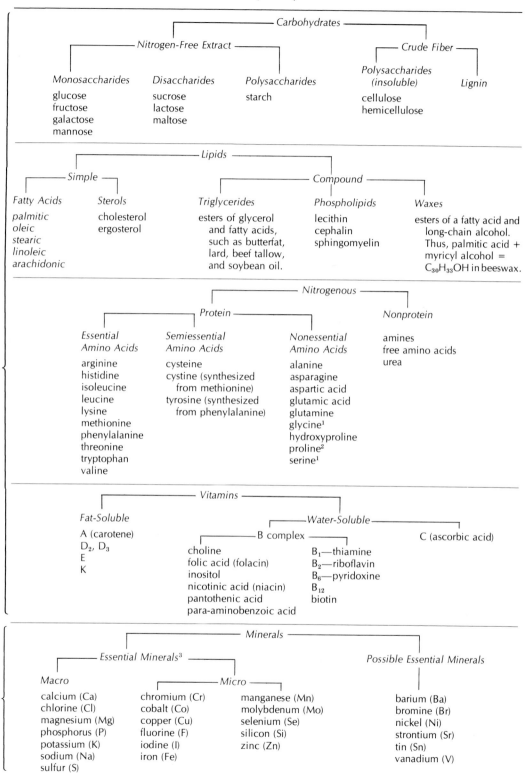

ORGANIC

Carbohydrates

Nitrogen-Free Extract

Monosaccharides
glucose
fructose
galactose
mannose

Disaccharides
sucrose
lactose
maltose

Polysaccharides
starch

Crude Fiber

Polysaccharides (insoluble)
cellulose
hemicellulose

Lignin

Lipids

Simple

Fatty Acids
palmitic
oleic
stearic
linoleic
arachidonic

Sterols
cholesterol
ergosterol

Compound

Triglycerides
esters of glycerol
and fatty acids,
such as butterfat,
lard, beef tallow,
and soybean oil.

Phospholipids
lecithin
cephalin
sphingomyelin

Waxes
esters of a fatty acid and
long-chain alcohol.
Thus, palmitic acid +
myricyl alcohol =
$C_{30}H_{33}OH$ in beeswax.

Nitrogenous

Protein

Essential Amino Acids
arginine
histidine
isoleucine
leucine
lysine
methionine
phenylalanine
threonine
tryptophan
valine

Semiessential Amino Acids
cysteine
cystine (synthesized
   from methionine)
tyrosine (synthesized
   from phenylalanine)

Nonessential Amino Acids
alanine
asparagine
aspartic acid
glutamic acid
glutamine
glycine[1]
hydroxyproline
proline[2]
serine[1]

Nonprotein
amines
free amino acids
urea

Vitamins

Fat-Soluble
A (carotene)
D_2, D_3
E
K

Water-Soluble

B complex
choline
folic acid (folacin)
inositol
nicotinic acid (niacin)
pantothenic acid
para-aminobenzoic acid

B_1—thiamine
B_2—riboflavin
B_6—pyridoxine
B_{12}
biotin

C (ascorbic acid)

INORGANIC

Minerals

Essential Minerals[3]

Macro
calcium (Ca)
chlorine (Cl)
magnesium (Mg)
phosphorus (P)
potassium (K)
sodium (Na)
sulfur (S)

Micro
chromium (Cr)
cobalt (Co)
copper (Cu)
fluorine (F)
iodine (I)
iron (Fe)

manganese (Mn)
molybdenum (Mo)
selenium (Se)
silicon (Si)
zinc (Zn)

Possible Essential Minerals
barium (Ba)
bromine (Br)
nickel (Ni)
strontium (Sr)
tin (Sn)
vanadium (V)

[1] Under some conditions, glycine or serine synthesis may not be sufficient for most rapid growth; either glycine or serine may need to be supplied in the diet.

[2] When diets composed of crystalline amino acids are used, proline may be necessary to achieve maximum growth.

[3] Required by at least one animal species.

(From Ensminger and Olentine: Feeds and Nutrition. By permission of the Ensminger Publishing Co., Clovis, Calif., 1978.)

Chapter *21*

Physical Factors in Digestion

PREHENSION AND CHEWING

The act of bringing food into the mouth is called *prehension*. The teeth, lips, and tongue are used as prehensile organs by domestic animals. The lips of the horse, the tongue of the cow and sheep, and the snout of the pig are used extensively in obtaining food.

Mastication (chewing) usually follows prehension immediately. The type of teeth, arrangement of jaws, and chewing habits vary with the species and class of food ingested. Carnivorous animals have simple teeth and tear their food but do little grinding. Herbivorous animals have at least some hypsodont teeth, the upper jaw is wider than the lower jaw, and chewing of the food is thorough. The folding of enamel, dentine, and cementum results in a ridged surface of the teeth due to differential rates of wear of the different substances. Enamel, being the hardest substance in the teeth, forms ridges and also may form sharp points. The points are on the buccal (cheek) side of the upper teeth and the lingual (tongue) side of the lower teeth. These sharp points may inter-fere with chewing, and in horses may make the mouth sensitive to the bridle.

The *medial pterygoid, masseter,* and *temporal muscles* close the jaws; the *lateral pterygoid muscles* produce a grinding action; and the *digastricus* and *sternomandibularis muscles* open the jaws.

Mastication can be controlled voluntarily, but the presence of food in the mouth will cause reflex chewing.

SALIVARY GLANDS

Sympathetic nerves go to the salivary glands by way of the cervical sympathetic trunk to the cranial cervical ganglion, where synapses occur. The postganglionic sympathetic fibers pass from the *cranial cervical ganglion* to the salivary glands with the arteries that supply the glands.

The *parotid salivary gland* receives parasympathetic nerve fibers from the *glossopharyngeal nerve*, which accompany the auriculo-temporal branch of the trigeminal nerve.

The *mandibular* and *sublingual salivary glands* receive parasympathetic nerve fibers

346

from the *chorda tympani* branch of the *facial nerve* that joins the lingual branch of the trigeminal nerve. The nuclei of origin of these nerves are located in the medulla oblongata.

Parasympathetic stimulation of both mandibular and parotid salivary glands increases blood supply to the glands and causes secretion of generous amounts of rather thin *saliva*. Sympathetic stimulation, on the other hand, decreases blood supply, inhibits flow of saliva, and causes secretion of a thick mucous type of saliva.

The facts that saliva contains mucus not found as such in blood, that metabolic activity of the gland is high during secretion, and that pressure in a salivary duct caused by secretion can exceed arterial blood pressure all support the hypothesis that saliva is a true secretion that is actively produced and not merely a fluid transudate that passively crosses the cell membrane.

Secretion of *saliva* is a reflex act that normally is stimulated by the presence of food in the mouth. When dry food is in the mouth, the saliva is watery and copious. When food is moist, only enough mucous saliva is secreted to lubricate the food during swallowing.

It is well known that the sight of food may cause the mouth to water. This is called a *psychic reflex* because it involves connection with the cerebrum. It is also a good example of a *conditioned reflex* as studied by Pavlov, the Russian scientist who did much of the initial work on conditioned reflexes. The sight, smell, or even thought of food can initiate reflex salivation. The type of saliva produced corresponds to the dryness of the food, just as occurs when a stimulus comes from food in the mouth. Psychic reflex salivation in domestic animals is absent or limited in the horse and ruminants. It has been demonstrated in the dog and pig.

Mechanical stimulation of the ruminant cardia evokes reflex salivation. The afferent impulse is carried by way of the *vagus nerves*.

The saliva of domestic animals contains little or no *amylase* (also called *ptyalin*), the enzyme of saliva that hydrolyzes starch to maltose. Small amounts have been reported in the saliva of the dog and pig. In the ruminant, saliva functions to maintain the fluid consistency of the rumen contents, helps neutralize acids formed by rumen organisms, and may help prevent frothing.

SWALLOWING

Deglutition, the act of swallowing, is arbitrarily divided into three stages. The first stage involves passage through the mouth, the second involves passage through the pharynx, and the third consists of passage through the esophagus into the stomach.

The first stage of swallowing is under voluntary control. After the food is chewed and mixed with saliva, a bolus is formed which is placed on the upper surface of the tongue. The tongue then is raised, tip first, against the hard palate, moving the bolus toward the pharynx. At the same time the soft palate is raised, closing the posterior nares. The base of the tongue then acts as a plunger, forcing the bolus into the pharynx.

As the *bolus* enters the pharynx it stimulates pressure receptors in the walls, which reflexly initiates the second stage, passage of the bolus through the pharynx. Respiration is reflexly inhibited, and the larynx is reflexly closed and pulled upward and forward. The base of the tongue folds the epiglottis over the laryngeal opening as it moves back. The pharynx is shortened, and a peristaltic (milking) action of the pharyngeal muscles forces the bolus into the esophagus.

The third stage of deglutition consists of reflex peristalsis of the esophagus, initiated by the presence of food in the esophagus. *Peristalsis* consists of alternate relaxation and contraction of rings of smooth muscle in the wall coupled with regional contraction of longitudinal muscles in the area of the bolus (Fig. 21–1).

Solid and semisolid food is carried

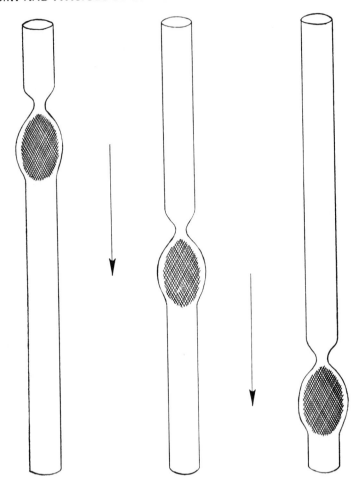

Fig. 21–1. Diagram of peristalsis in the esophagus. A wave of relaxation precedes the bolus and a wave of constriction follows the bolus. (After Carlson and Cavert, The Machinery of the Body, The University of Chicago Press.)

through the esophagus of the horse by peristalsis at a rate of 35 to 40 cm/sec. Liquids are carried about five times as fast by a squirting action of the mouth and the pharynx.

GASTRIC MOVEMENTS

Simple Stomach

Relaxation of the cardia is essential for food to enter the stomach. In the simple stomach as found in man, pig, horse, and dog, the first food consumed when the stomach is empty travels to the pyloric end of the stomach. Food subsequently swallowed tends to become stratified (form layers) as the stomach fills. Experiments with differentially colored foods in the horse have shown this to be correct.

Movements in the stomach are most vigorous in the pyloric antrum region, where most of the mixing of food occurs. The stomach regularly produces recurring peristaltic contraction-waves, beginning in the region of the cardia and increasing in force as they travel over the stomach to the pyloric antrum. This serves to mix the food and to force some through the pyloric sphincter into the duodenum. While the sphincter opens slightly to allow some food to pass into the duodenum, much of the food will be reflected back, which allows for more mixing of the food. (See Fig. 21–2.)

Factors that control gastric emptying through the pyloric sphincter include the volume of food in the stomach (usually faster with higher volume), the fluidity of the food mixture (depends partly on the degree of mastication and the degree of digestion by the stomach enzymes and acid), and the receptivity of the duodenum (depends on the chemical composition of the food content and amount of chyme in the duodenum).

With the duodenum empty, as soon as the food in the pyloric end of the stomach causes persistaltic contraction waves of sufficient intensity in the antrum, small amounts of material are forced through the pyloric sphincter and into the duodenum. This material, called *chyme* (different from chyle in the lymphatics), is a mushy, semisolid mixture of food, water, and gastric juice. The pyloric sphincter remains closed until the duodenum is receptive to more chyme. This receptivity is determined by the amount of chyme already present in the duodenum, the type of food comprising the chyme, its acidity, and its tonicity. These factors control the activity of the pylorus by means of the *enterogastric reflex* and the hormone *cholecystokinin*.

The length of time food remains in the stomach varies with the type and consistency of the food and with the species.

Water may pass through a full stomach without diluting the contents to any great extent (under 10% in the horse). Water ingested when the stomach is nearly empty will mix more readily with the stomach contents than if the stomach is full. The more fluid the consistency of the food, the sooner it leaves the stomach.

The stomach of carnivores will empty within a few hours, usually before the next meal. On the other hand, other animals require many hours to empty the stomach. Both the horse and pig require a full day's fast (24 hours) to empty a full stomach.

In addition to the typical pattern of stomach contraction when food is present, a series of rhythmic oscillations of the membrane potential of the smooth muscle cells occur when the stomach is empty. These are initiated by pacemaker cells in the stomach cardiac region near the entry of the esophagus. It is referred to as the the *basic electrical rhythm*. Occasionally these oscillations of potential produce an action poten-

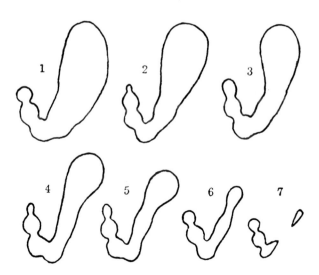

Fig. 21–2. Changes in the shape of the stomach of a cat at intervals of an hour during the digestion of a meal, as revealed by tracing of the shadow cast on the fluorescent screen. (From Alvarez, The Mechanics of the Digestive Tract, Paul B. Hoeber, Inc.)

tial depolarization and a wave of peristaltic contraction over the stomach as a slight ripple.

In prolonged fasting, the magnitude of the contractions becomes greater. These are apparently mediated by adding parasympathetic inputs from brain centers during hunger, which increases stimulation of the smooth muscle cells well above the basic electrical rhythm, and so we have hunger contractions. These reach maximum intensity in man after about three days without food, and progressively get weaker thereafter. In the horse, hunger contractions may begin as early as five hours after eating, when the stomach still contains quite a bit of food. The level of blood sugar is related to the intensity of hunger contractions. As the blood-sugar level decreases, the intensity of hunger contractions increases, along with the need for more food by the animal.

Ruminant Stomach

The rumen and reticulum of the adult cow normally undergo a fairly complicated sequence of contractions, which are repeated at varying frequencies up to several times per minute. First the reticulum contracts sharply, forcing fluid material into the rumen. This first contraction is followed immediately by a second reticular contraction. The cranial pillar of the rumen starts to contract before the second reticular contraction is completed, thus shunting much of the material expelled from the reticulum into the cranial dorsal sac of the rumen.

The ruminal contraction, started at the cranial pillar, passes back along the longitudinal pillars, caudal pillar, dorsal coronary pillars, and adjacent rumen wall of the dorsal sac. The ventral coronary pillars and ventral sac of the rumen contract as soon as the dorsal sac and associated pillars relax. The entire rumen contraction, starting with the cranial pillar, is then repeated, before the reticulum contracts again to initiate a whole new cycle.

Variations of the preceding pattern are common. Frequency of rumen contractions has been reported in cows at rest as 1.8/min, cows ruminating as 2.3/min, and cows eating as 2.8/min. Rumen contraction can be felt by forcing the fist into the upper left flank (paralumbar fossa). Pathologic conditions of the rumen usually result in a decreased rate or complete cessation of rumen movements.

Hyperglycemia (an increase in blood sugar level) produced by glucose injection inhibits rumen activity. *Hypoglycemia* (decreased blood sugar level) due to insulin injection stimulates rumen activity.

Rumination is a process that permits an animal to forage and ingest food rapidly, then complete the chewing at a later time. It involves regurgitation of the food (returning it to the mouth), remastication (rechewing), reinsalivation (mixing with saliva), and finally reswallowing of the food.

Regurgitation is the only step of rumination that differs markedly from the initial mastication, insalivation, and swallowing of the food. Regurgitation is preceded by contraction of the reticulum, which presumably brings some of the heavier ingesta into proximity to the cardia. This is followed immediately by an inspiratory movement with the glottis closed. The negative pressure produced in the thorax by this movement is transmitted to the relatively thin-walled esophagus, causing the thoracic esophagus and cardia to dilate. The lower pressure in the esophagus as compared to the rumen causes a quantity of material (semifluid ingesta) to pass through the cardia into the esophagus and up to the mouth, where excess liquid is squeezed out and swallowed.

The speed of regurgitation suggests that striated muscle rather than smooth muscle provides the active force. Apparently contractions of the esophageal groove between the cardia and the reticulo-omasal orifice, the rumen, the reticulum, and the abdominal muscles play little if any part in the actual process of regurgitation. Any opening into the trachea or thorax that interferes with the production of a negative pressure in the thorax does inhibit regurgitation.

Remastication occurs in a more leisurely manner than the initial chewing. Jaw movements of about 55/min during remastication compare with 94/min while eating grain and silage, and 78/min while eating hay. Mandibular (submaxillary) salivary glands are less active during the reinsalivation than initially.

The bolus formed after regurgitation and rechewing is swallowed just as any other bolus, and apparently enters the rumen rather than passing into the omasum or abomasum (true stomach), as was once believed. The regurgitated material consists largely of roughage and fluid with little if any concentrate. It is well known that whole kernels of corn may pass through the entire digestive tract with little change in physical appearance.

Cattle average about eight hours a day ruminating, with periods of activity scattered throughout the entire day. One rumination cycle requires about one minute, of which three to four seconds is utilized for both regurgitation and reswallowing.

Rumination appears to be largely reflex in nature, although the process can be interrupted or stopped voluntarily. Both afferent and efferent portions of the reflex probably are carried in the vagus nerves. Contact of roughage with the reticulum and more particularly near the cardia likely is the major stimulus for rumination.

Closure of the Esophageal Groove. Closure of the esophageal groove is of importance in young ruminants. Nursing appears to reflexly stimulate closure of the groove, which causes the milk to bypass the rumen and reticulum and pass through the omasal groove directly to the abomasum. The paunchiness of bucket-fed calves usually is attributed to milk entering the rumen, where it is not properly digested. The use of buckets with nipples tends to prevent appreciable amounts of milk from entering the rumen. After weaning, fluid drunk from open containers largely passes into the rumen and reticulum. This has been called a thirst pattern as opposed to a nursing pattern that involves reflex closing of the esophageal groove in young nursing calves.

Reflex closure of the *esophageal groove* has been produced with sodium salts in cattle less than two years old. *Copper sulfate* initiates reflex closure of the esophageal groove in sheep within 8 sec after it is given. The groove remains closed from 1 to 11 sec.

The pharynx appears to be the location where the stimulus is effective. The afferent side of the reflex is by way of the *cranial laryngeal nerve,* and the main part of the vagus nerve carries the efferent side of the reflex.

Eventually food that has soaked enough and been finely divided enough finds its way through the reticulo-omasal orifice. It may pass directly into the abomasum by way of the omasal groove or stop in the omasum for further processing. The factors responsible for this passage are not well understood.

Omasum. The omasum is nearly always found packed tightly with rather dry roughage in animals examined after death. The appearance of the omasal leaves, studded with short horny papillae, suggests a burr type of grinder. Becker et al. found that the omasal leaves restrict the entrance of large particles of feed into the reticulo-omasal orifice and reduce the particle size of material that passes through the omasum.

Movement of the leaves seems limited and not caused by stimulation of the vagus nerve. The omasal wall undergoes strong contractions when the vagus nerve is stimulated. Some peristaltic-type contractions of the omasum have been described. Omasal contractions presumably squeeze fluid out of the ingesta, grind the solids to some extent, and move it on into the abomasum.

Abomasum. Movements of the abomasum resemble movements described for the simple stomach. Activity in the area of the fundus is limited. Contractions of the body are more marked, and peristaltic waves are seen in the pyloric portion. Activity of the abomasum depends to some extent on the contents of the duodenum. Abomasal activity is inhibited by weak hydrochloric acid and fat emulsion, but activity is stimulated by hypertonic saline solutions and emptying of the duodenum.

SMALL INTESTINE

Movement of the intestine is similar in nonruminant and ruminant animals.

Reflex movements of the intestine are initiated by the stimulus of material within the lumen, stretching the intestinal wall. Intestinal movements not only propel the ingesta through the gut, but also mix it with digestive juices, bring it into contact with the intestinal wall and villi for absorption, and aid circulation of blood and lymph.

Rhythmic segmentation is a type of intestinal movement that does not move the contents along the intestine, but merely mixes it (Fig. 21–3). Intermittent contractions of circular muscle fibers divide the ingesta into bead-like segments. In a few seconds the next series of contractions occurs in the muscle fibers near the middle of each of the

segments, dividing it in two and thus uniting adjacent halves to form new segments. Rhythmic segmentation facilitates absorption by bringing the ingesta into contact with the villi and by stimulating the flow of blood and lymph in the intestinal wall.

Peristalsis refers to movement that tends to propel the ingesta along the intestine in a direction toward the anus. This is an inherent property of any tube of syncytial smooth muscle and is normally initiated by distension. The presence of material in the intestine stimulates contraction of the circular muscle fibers on the oral side (in front) of the material, and relaxation of the muscle fibers in the region of the material and a segment beyond the material. Some researchers have been unable to find evidence of relaxation of the intestinal wall and believe the ingesta are forced into succeeding segments by contraction of appropriate circular muscles on the oral side. The peristaltic wave (whether contraction alone or contraction and relaxation) moves along the intestine at a rate averaging

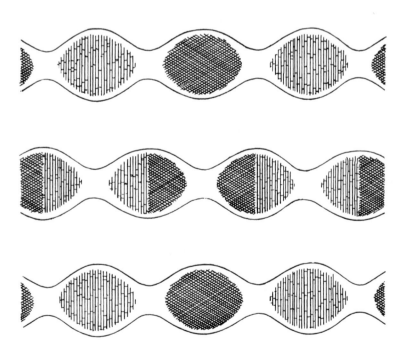

Fig. 21–3.   Diagram of rhythmic segmentation in the small intestine. Three stages in mixing of small masses of food are shown. (After Carlson and Cavert, The Machinery of the Body, The University of Chicago Press.)

between one-half and one inch per minute. The intramural plexus (Auerbach's and Meissner's) is important in peristalsis, and the rate is in turn increased or decreased by stimulation of autonomic nerves and hormone secretions.

The normal direction of peristalsis is from oral to aboral, or from the pylorus toward the ilio-cecal junction. Reverse peristalsis, also called antiperistalsis, is a movement in the opposite direction (aboral to oral) but this wave dies out quickly, so the net peristalsis is all aboral.

Segments of small intestine have been completely isolated and placed in appropriate fluids for study. Each segment exhibits a rhythmic contraction that is fastest near the pylorus and decreases in rate as distance from the pylorus increases. Isolated segments of intestine also exhibit inherent electrical activity that can be recorded.

The villi of the intestinal wall undergo movements, as a result of peristaltic smooth muscle contractions and intrinsic adjustment to the contents, which increase contact with the ingesta and assist in the circulation of blood and lymph in the villi.

LARGE INTESTINE

Isolated segments of large intestine show less tendency for automatic rhythmic contractions than do isolated segments of the small intestine.

Movements of the colon are normally sluggish, but still consist of mixing movements and propulsive movements. In the same manner that segmentation movements (mixing) occur in the small intestine, large circular constrictions occur in the large intestine. Combined contractions of the circular and linear smooth muscle at various points along the colon cause bulging into sacs called *haustrations* or *sacculations* which last about 90 sec and then occur at other points, progressing in such a way as to turn over the contents in a mixing action and to increase absorption by greater contact with the mucosa.

The typical, slow peristaltic waves that occur in the small intestine are almost absent in the large intestine. Instead, *mass movements* propel the fecal contents toward the anus. These mass movements usually occur only a few times a day. They are initiated at a distended or stimulated point of the colon, by a contraction that progresses for some length distal to the constriction, forcing the contents of the entire segment *en masse* down the colon. Such mass movements can occur in all parts of the colon, and when they have forced a mass of feces into the rectum, distending it, the defecation reflex is triggered.

Chapter 22

Absorption of Food and Enzymes of Digestion

ABSORPTION

No food is absorbed before it reaches the stomach, and little of the food in the stomach is absorbed there even after stomach digestion. Proteins and carbohydrates are only partially digested in the stomach, and fats are only slightly hydrolyzed before the food passes into the intestine. Most absorption occurs in the small intestines of all animals, particularly carnivores and omnivores.

Absorption in the large intestine is most important in simple-stomach herbivorous animals, since much digestion takes place in the colon, and these substances obviously cannot be absorbed before they are digested. Small amounts of water are absorbed from the large intestines of all animals, and mucus is secreted from the goblet cells for lubrication and protection of the mucosa. The water is absorbed osmotically as the result of active reabsorption of salts, especially sodium, from the colon. In fact, when constipation develops in an animal and

the feces remain in the colon, more and more water will be absorbed from it, the feces will progressively become drier and harder, and defecation becomes more difficult.

The *forestomach* of ruminants (rumen, reticulum, and omasum) has been shown to absorb a number of drugs, salts of sodium and potassium, carbonates and chlorides of various substances, and end-products of digestion, including glucose and short-chain fatty acids (acetic, propionic, and butyric).

The mucosa of the intestine cannot absorb to any extent large molecules of carbohydrates, proteins, or fats. The end-products (simple sugars, amino acids, fatty acids, and glycerol) of digestion of these substances, however, pass readily through the mucosa and into the blood or lymph vessels.

Amino Acids and Simple Sugars

In general, the *amino acids* and *simple sugars* enter those blood vessels that are tributaries to the portal vein. The *portal vein* carries these substances to the liver sinusoids, where they may be acted upon by the liver epithelial cells. Blood from the liver sinusoids then passes into the general circulation by way of the central veins of the liver to the hepatic veins, and thence into the caudal vena cava.

Fats

Most dietary fat is neutral fat (triglycerides), with the remainder being phospholipids and cholesterol. The bile salts emulsify the large fat droplets into smaller droplets, which pancreatic lipase degrades to diglycerides, monoglycerides, free fatty acids (FFA), and glycerol. The bile salts then promote aggregation of the FFA, monoglycerides and cholesterol into *micelles*, each containing hundreds of molecules. The micelles are water-soluble and can enter the intestinal absorptive cells.

Once inside the epithelial cells, resynthesis to triglycerides occurs, and these are released into the lymphatic lacteals by emiocytosis (reverse pinocytosis). The lacteals are capillary-like lymph vessels in the intestinal villi. The triglycerides enter the lacteals as tiny droplets called *chylomicrons*, which also contain small amounts of phospholipid, cholesterol, FFA, and protein. This is carried as *chyle* to larger lymph vessels, which eventually empty into the *cysterna chyli* between the two crura of the diaphragm. From the cysterna chyli, the chyle (lymph-containing fat) passes by way of the thoracic duct to the cranial vena cava or to the jugular veins near their entrance into the vena cava and enters the venous circulation in this manner.

Evidence gained biochemically and with the electron microscope indicates that small droplets of emulsified fat can be absorbed pinocytotically by the epithelial cells of the intestine and pass into the lacteals in the same form.

About 10% of the fatty acids are not reconstituted to triglycerides in the epithelial absorptive cells, but instead pass directly into the portal blood along with glycerol. The glycerol can then enter the scheme of glycolysis by the action of ATP and the enzyme glycerokinase to form 3-P-glyceric acid. The fatty acids meanwhile can be broken down by successive removal of two carbon atoms at a time to form acetyl-coenzyme A used in the Krebs cycle.

Mechanisms of Absorption

Contractions of the smooth muscle of the intestinal wall (lamina muscularis) and of the muscularis mucosa aid digestion and absorption by churning the intestinal contents and by pumping fluid (blood and lymph) from the intestinal capillaries and lacteals.

The mechanism of *absorption* involves more than the usual physical and chemical forces of filtration, osmosis, diffusion, adsorption, and pinocytosis, although these are important factors in absorption.

The fact that much absorption is an active process rather than merely being passive is indicated by the ability of epithelial cells to absorb selectively materials such as glucose, galactose, and fructose in unequal concentrations. Glucose is absorbed faster than galactose and galactose faster than fructose, as long as the epithelium is alive and undamaged. However, after death the three sugars pass through the mucosa at equal rates, because only passive absorption by physical forces is then involved. During absorption, the epithelial cells increase their metabolic activity, as shown by increased oxygen consumption.

Absorption of vitamins occurs essentially in two ways. Most cross the intestinal mucosa by simple diffusion down concentration gradients and thereby enter the blood capillaries that supply the mucosa. However, vitamins A, D, E, and K are fat-soluble, and they become part of the micelles before being absorbed. Therefore, their absorption rate depends upon the presence and action of bile.

ENZYMES OF DIGESTION

Salivary Glands

Secretion of *saliva* is an active process that can occur against pressure in the salivary duct that is greater than carotid arterial pressure. Material such as mucin is found in saliva but not in the blood; the consumption of oxygen and glucose by the glands also indicate that a metabolic activity is occurring during secretion, rather than simply a transudate crossing the cell membrane.

Saliva of the dog and pig contains some *amylase* capable of digesting starch. Saliva in the cow, sheep, and goat does not contain amylase, but the saliva of the horse may contain small amounts of amylase.

Stomach Glands and Secretions

Stomach glands include cardiac glands, fundic glands, and pyloric glands.

Cardiac glands and pyloric glands produce little if anything besides mucus. The mucus functions as a protective coating over the epithelial cells to act as a barrier against the effects of stomach acid.

Fundic glands contain specialized cells called body chief cells, neck chief cells, and parietal cells. The body chief cells synthesize and secrete the enzyme precursor called *pepsinogen*. Once in the stomach lumen, the pepsinogen is acted on by hydrochloric acid (HCl) to form the active enzyme *pepsin*. Pepsin then acts on proteins in the stomach to degrade them to peptides. At the same time, the pepsin has an autocatalytic effect on more pepsinogen being secreted; that is, the pepsin can directly convert pepsinogen to pepsin. There are three forms of pepsin—pepsin I, II, and III—with form II being most abundant.

The neck chief cells are mucous cells that resemble the cardiac gland cells and pyloric

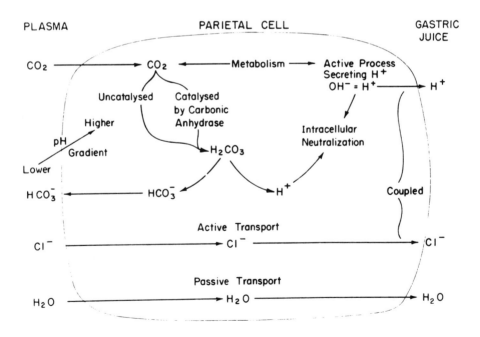

Fig. 22–1.   Secretion of acid by the gastric mucosa. (Reproduced with permission from Davenport, H.W.: Physiology of the Digestive Tract. ed. 4. Copyright © 1977 by Year Book Medical Publishers, Inc., Chicago.)

gland cells. The *parietal cells* produce HCl and secrete it into the stomach against a large concentration and electrical gradient, since the stomach is highly acid—the H^+ concentration of the stomach is about three million times greater than that in the blood (150 mEq/L compared to 0.00004 mEq/L). In the stomach, the HCl dissociates to H^+ and Cl^- ions. How the parietal cells derive the HCl is shown in Figure 22–1.

While this mechanism of synthesis has not been irrefutably determined, studies have shown that the cell's smooth endoplasmic reticulum, modified into canaliculi, is the site of the HCl formation for secretion. Hydrochloric acid is present in the stomach of all domestic animals, and it is, of course, the major factor in lowering the pH of the stomach contents, thus making them more acidic. It also protects the body by killing most foreign bacteria ingested with food.

The parietal cells apparently also secrete *intrinsic factor*. This is a glycoprotein that is essential for life. It combines with vitamin B_{12} for pinocytotic absorption from the ileum into the body.

The term *gastric juice* is often used to refer to all the substances contributed to the stomach lumen by the mucosal cells. This then includes water, cations, anions, HCl, intrinsic factor, and the enzymes pepsinogen, rennin, gastric lipase, amylase, urease, and gastrin.

The pepsin from pepsinogen begins the hydrolysis (digestion) of ingested proteins in the stomach. The most favorable pH range for this is 1.3 to 5 (highly acidic), depending on the form of protein. Protein digestion is completed in the small intestine.

Rennin is the enzyme of young ruminants which causes milk to coagulate in the presence of calcium ions. Dukes (1977) gives the following reaction: "Casein + rennin → paracasein (soluble). Paracasein + Ca → calcium paracaseinate (coagulum)." The precipitate thus formed tends to remain in the stomach longer than does the same substance in the liquid form.

Gastric lipase can hydrolyze fats that contain short or medium length fatty acid chains. Most fat digestion occurs in the small intestine. Carnivores have the most gastric lipase; herbivorous animals have much less.

Gastrin is synthesized and released by the "G" cells of the antral mucosa in response to the amount of protein in the stomach contents. The gastrin, in turn, stimulates the secretion of more HCl from the parietal cells.

Stimulation of gastric-juice secretion may result from the sight, smell, thought, or taste of food (the cephalic phase), the presence of food in the stomach (the gastric phase), or in the duodenum (the intestinal phase).

The *cephalic phase of gastric-juice secretion* occurs even though the food may not enter the stomach, as in experimental animals that have had the esophagus severed. Stimuli reach the stomach by way of the *vagus nerves* to the myenteric plexus. Herbivorous animals do not appear to have a cephalic phase of gastric stimulation.

The *gastric phase* accounts for about 75% of the total gastric juice secretion and occurs when food reaches the stomach. Gastric-juice secretion increases for a period up to several hours. Mechanical stimulation of the stomach mucous membrane increases the flow of gastric juice reflexly by distention. In fact, stomach distention is the most potent stimulator of the myenteric plexus activity (the nerve network of the stomach wall), which increases the peristaltic contractions.

Chemically, the greatest effect is produced by the amount of peptide fragments resulting from the breakdown of proteins in the stomach by the action of pepsin. Fats and carbohydrates in the stomach have little effect on gastric secretion, and therefore, the enzymes gastric lipase, amylase, and urease have little effect.

The greater the amount of protein in the food, the more peptide fragments are formed and the more gastrin is released from pyloric (antral) mucosa cells. The gastrin in turn stimulates the parietal cells to increase hydrochloric acid secretion; to a lesser degree, it also stimulates the chief cells of the gastric glands.

The *intestinal phase of gastric secretion* involves small amounts of gastric juice that continue to be secreted as long as chyme remains in the small intestine, even though no food remains in the stomach.

The control of gastric secretion and motility (see Fig. 22–2) depends on both neural and hormonal mechanisms that feed back from the duodenum to the stomach, directly and indirectly. The stimulation of these feedback mechanisms depends on the distention of the duodenum, the fluidity of the chyme in the duodenum, and the concentration of amino acids, fatty acids, and chyme acidity in the duodenum.

As any of these substances increase in the duodenum, the myenteric neural plexus is stimulated, sending nerve signals back to the stomach. This is the *enterogastric reflex*, caused by stimulation of pressoreceptor cells in the duodenal wall, which results in a decreased rate of emptying of the stomach by decreasing the motility of the stomach wall. It also decreases the release of gastrin from the G cells in the antral region, which in turn decreases the HCl secretion from the parietal cells. The purpose of all this is to slow down digestion in the stomach and the

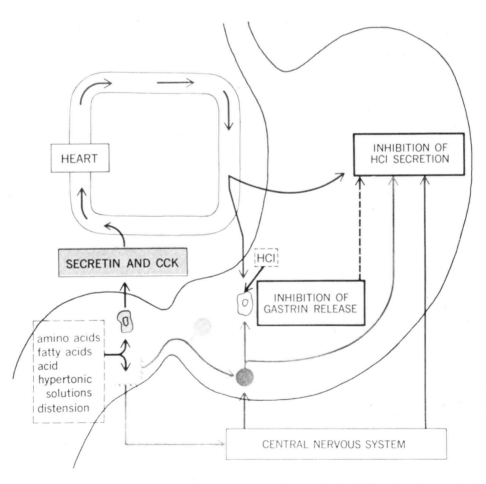

Fig. 22–2. Summary of pathways controlling gastric secretion. All except the local effect of HCl on gastrin release are involved in the intestinal phase of gastric secretion. Inhibition of gastrin release decreases HCl secretion. (From Vander, A. J., et al.: Human Physiology. ed. 2. New York, McGraw-Hill, 1975.)

rate of chyme passing into the duodenum, until the contents of the duodenum can be adjusted to the proper pH, volume, and digested state.

The enterogastric reflex is not the only mechanism operating to control the rate of gastric emptying. Afferent sensory fibers of the vagus nerve are also stimulated, which in turn stimulate sympathetic fibers of the autonomic nervous system, and these affect the stomach by decreasing the motility of the stomach, increasing the contraction state of the sphincter, and inhibiting the release of HCl. So, there is an extrinsic neural control, by way of the central nervous system, as well as an intrinsic feedback by way of the myenteric plexus enterogastric reflex.

A third factor is involved in this control of gastric secretions; it involves the two hormones *secretin* and *cholecystokinin*. These represent the *humoral* (hormonal) response or control of gastric secretion. At first, cholecystokinin (CCK) was believed to be different from the hormone *pancreozymin*, but has since been determined to be one and the same. Therefore it is sometimes abbreviated as CCKPZ, to include the two names as one.

Secretin and cholecystokinin are synthesized by and secreted from mucosal cells in the duodenum in response to the same stimuli that cause the enterogastric reflex and CNS response (i.e., chyme, pH, digestive state, fluidity, and volume in the duodenum). These hormones are secreted directly into the blood and are carried back to the stomach by the vascular system. In the stomach they decrease motility of the stomach, inhibit the release of gastrin, and inhibit release of HCl. It is through these three control feedback mechanisms, then, that the rate at which the stomach processes and empties the food is regulated by the duodenum being receptive to more chyme, as illustrated in Figure 22–2. The stomach has a direct mechanism also, when the pH becomes low due to a high HCl concentration. This will inhibit the release of gastrin from the antral G cells, which in turn will inhibit the further secretion of HCl from the parietal cells.

Pancreatic Secretions and Controls

The pancreas is a mixed endocrine-exocrine gland. The hormones *insulin* and *glucagon* are secreted from the endocrine cells (to be discussed in Chapter 32). It is the exocrine function of the pancreas that we are concerned with in this chapter on the digestive processes.

The exocrine cells produce and secrete two types of solution. One consists primarily of enzymes, and is secreted from the acinar cells, as illustrated in Figure 22–3. The other solution consists of a high concentration of sodium bicarbonate, secreted from the cells that line the ducts. The ducts empty into one or two pancreatic ducts, which empty into the duodenum. The essential purpose of these pancreatic secretions is to break down or hydrolyze the proteins, fats, and carbohydrates that are in the chyme received from the stomach, and to neutralize or effectively raise the pH (to increase the alkalinity) of the chyme from its acid content to a pH acceptable for transport through the small intestine.

The sodium bicarbonate secretion represents a strong alkaline solution. In the cellular synthesis of it, an equivalent amount of acid is produced and enters the blood. This is exactly opposite to what happened in the stomach, where the parietal cells secreted HCl and produced an equivalent amount of bicarbonate, which entered the blood. So, while the blood leaving the stomach is high in bicarbonate and therefore more alkaline, the blood leaving the pancreas is more acidic. This means that normally there will be no net change in blood pH, because the one will tend to balance the other. It is the acidity of the chyme entering the duodenum that acts as a strong stimulant for the pancreatic secretion of the bicarbonate solution.

The major enzymes secreted from the pancreatic acinar cells are mostly secreted

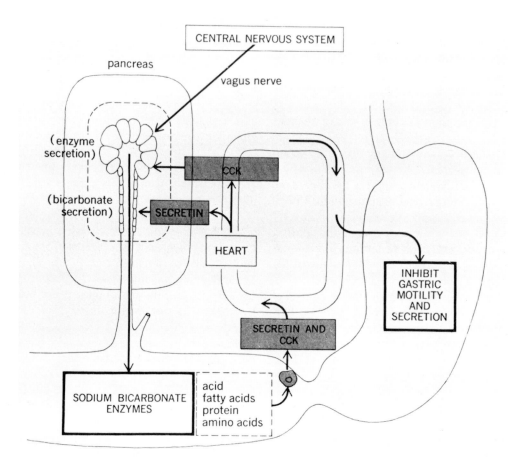

Fig. 22–3. Pathways regulating pancreatic secretion. (From Vander, A. J., et al.: Human Physiology. ed. 2. New York, McGraw-Hill, 1975.)

in an inactive form. This prevents the enzymes from breaking down (digesting) the acinar cells in which they are synthesized, just as occurs in the stomach, where the enzyme pepsin is secreted in the inactive pepsinogen form. Upon entering the duodenum, the pancreatic enzymes are converted to their active forms.

The enzymes ribonuclease and deoxyribonuclease act on RNA and DNA, respectively, to degrade these nucleic acids into nucleotides.

Proteolytic enzymes include *trypsin* and *chymotrypsin* (which are secreted as inactive precursors, *trypsinogen* and *chymo-*

trypsinogen), and the enzyme carboxypolypeptidase, which acts on peptides.

Trypsinogen is activated by a substance called *enterokinase*, which is released by the intestinal mucosa. Chymotrypsinogen is activated by trypsin.

These enzymes usually continue protein digestion that was started by pepsin in the gastric juice, although they can attack undigested proteins. The end-products of protein digestion are amino acids, but the pancreatic proteolytic enzymes may stop digestion when the peptides reach a length of two or more amino acids. If this occurs, intestinal peptidases complete hydrolysis of the peptides to individual amino acids. Trypsin and chymotrypsin split whole proteins; carboxypolypeptidase splits off terminal amino acids.

Pancreatic amylase can convert starch to the disaccharide sugar maltose. *Maltase*, also found in pancreatic juice, hydrolyzes maltose to glucose (Fig. 22–4).

Pancreatic lipase (steapsin) hydrolyzes fats into fatty acids and glycerol. This action is most effective after the fats have been emulsified by bile. A pH near 8 is optimum for the action of lipase in fat hydrolysis and for trypsin in protein hydrolysis. Control of pancreatic exocrine secretion depends on the relative stimulation of the vagal autonomic nerves that innervate the pancreas, plus the degree of secretion of three hormones; namely, cholecystokinin (CCK) and secretin from the duodenal cells, and gastrin from the stomach cells.

The neural control, by way of stimulation of the vagus nerves, occurs mostly in the *cephalic phase* as a result of seeing or smelling food, or taking food into the mouth. This increases enzyme secretion from the pancreas through the vagal nerve impulses. Gastrin is released from the stomach during the *gastric phase* when food enters the stomach, and this in turn increases secretion of the bicarbonate solution from the pancreatic duct cells.

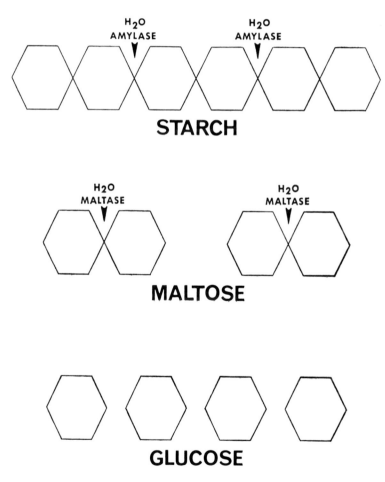

Fig. 22–4.   The hydrolysis of starch to glucose. Amylase hydrolyzes starch into maltose molecules. Maltase then hydrolyzes each maltose molecule into two glucose molecules.

The greatest amount of pancreatic exocrine secretion occurs in the *intestinal phase* when the acid chyme and food components in the duodenum stimulate the release of CCK and secretin from the mucosal cells of the duodenum. The CCK, circulating in the blood that travels through the pancreas, causes increased release of pancreatic enzymes to degrade the protein, lipids, and other food constituents in the duodenum. The secretin in the circulation of the pancreas stimulates the increased release of bicarbonate solution from the duct cells, to decrease the acidity of the chyme in the duodenum. These two duodenal hormones also feed back to the stomach, as explained earlier, to decrease secretions in the stomach and slow down the activity and emptying of the stomach until the duodenal chyme has been degraded by the enzymes and adjusted in pH by the pancreatic bicarbonate.

All of these factors, then, operate as regulatory feedback mechanisms to control the specific activities of the stomach, duodenum, and pancreas, so that food can be broken down to the point where it can be optimally absorbed from the small intestine into the blood, and utilized ultimately for energy and synthesis of cell substances for the benefit of the animal.

Intestinal Enzymes

Succus entericus, intestinal juice, is derived from intestinal glands in the *crypts* of *Lieberkühn*, scattered throughout the entire small intestine, and mucus is contributed by *Brunner's glands (duodenal glands)*, found only in the duodenum. Secretion by these intestinal crypt glands is stimulated by the presence of food in the intestine. Presumably this is a reflex stimulation of a local nature.

In addition to water, salts, and mucus, intestinal cells secrete a number of enzymes. These include the following:

1. *enterokinase*—activates trypsinogen
2. inverting enzymes
   a. *maltase*—hydrolyzes maltose to glucose
   b. *sucrase*—hydrolyzes sucrose to glucose and fructose (levulose)
   c. *lactase*—hydrolyzes lactose to glucose and galactose
3. *peptidase*—hydrolyzes peptides to amino acids
4. *ribonuclease*—hydrolyzes ribonucleic acids
5. *deoxyribonuclease*—hydrolyzes deoxyribonucleic acids

Bile

Secretion of *bile* occurs in the hepatic cells of the liver. In all farm animals except the horse, bile is stored in the *gallbladder*. Since the horse has no gallbladder, the bile passes directly from the liver to the duodenum by way of the bile duct and its tributaries at a fairly continuous rate. The gallbladder not only stores bile for intermittent discharge into the duodenum, but also concentrates the bile, adds mucus to the bile, and serves as a relief mechanism to prevent excessive pressure in the hepatic ducts coming from the liver substance.

Bile is a greenish-yellow salt solution consisting primarily of bile salts, cholesterol, the phospholipid *lecithin*, and bile pigments. The bile salts (sodium and potassium salts of glycocholic and taurocholic acids) are the most important constituents of bile, since it is these salts that assist in digestion and absorption of the fats. The triglycerides in the duodenal chyme tend to clump together as long-chain fatty acid groups that are essentially insoluble with water. The bile breaks down these groups (the process is called emulsification) into small droplets, which can then be absorbed from the duodenum and small intestine. Bile also aids in the absorption of fat-soluble vitamins, and it assists the action of pancreatic lipase. The bile salts are basic salts, and so they also aid in producing a more alkaline pH in the intestinal chyme for optimal absorption to take place.

The *cholesterol* component of bile is both formed in the liver and supplied by foods eaten. Cholesterol is insoluble in water, but the bile salts and lecithin normally change it to a soluble form so that it can exist in the bile. However, sometimes cholesterol precipitates from the bile in the gallbladder or bile ducts, forming *gallstones*. This occurs if there is a deficiency of the bile salts or lecithin. In man, excess cholesterol circulating in the blood has been implicated in subsequent disease of the blood vessels (atherosclerotic plaques and arteriosclerosis).

The regulatory mechanisms for the secretion of bile include (1) the hormones secretin, cholecystokinin, and gastrin, (2) the plasma level of bile salts, and (3) stimulation by the vagus nerves (Fig. 22–5). Cholecystokinin (pancreozymin) acts preferentially on the gallbladder, along with neural stimulation by increased vagal nerve stimulation. Together they contract the gallbladder to force the stored bile out and down the duct into the duodenum, where the bile can then emulsify the fat content of the chyme. Bile secretion can also be increased exogenously by giving the animal drugs classified as *choleretics* (the process of bile secretion is called choleresis).

The secretion of the bile salts from the

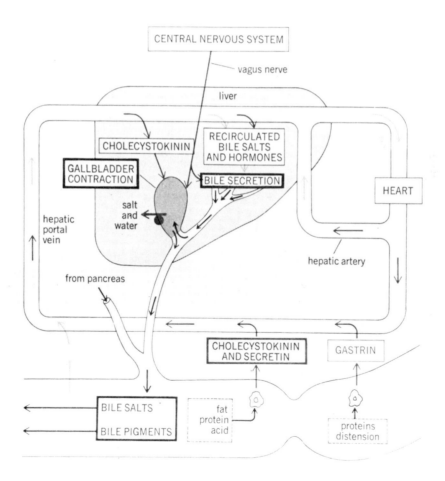

Fig. 22–5.   Pathways regulating bile secretion and release from the gallbladder. (From Vander, A.J., et al.: Human Physiology. ed. 2. New York, McGraw-Hill, 1975.)

liver depends mostly on the concentration of bile salts in the blood passing through the liver. As the plasma concentration of bile salts rises, which happens during digestion (because the bile salts are reabsorbed from the small intestine into the hepatic portal vein going back to the liver), then the rate of bile secretion from the liver increases. The bile salts directly stimulate the secretory cells.

Secretion of the alkaline solution of the bile depends on the secretion of gastrin from the antral region of the stomach, and on the rate of secretion of cholecystokinin and secretin from the duodenal mucosal cells. As these secretions circulate in the blood through the liver during the digestion of foods, they increase the output of bile solution from the liver. Secretin is especially effective in increasing this output.

No mammal is able to digest cellulose or hemicellulose directly because mammals do not produce the enzyme cellulase, which is necessary to breach the glucopyronosyl bonds between glucose units. Ruminant mammals are able to utilize cellulose because the forestomach provides an excellent environment for the growth of bacteria, protozoa, and possibly other microbes that do produce cellulase. Microbial byproducts as well as the microbes themselves are utilized by the animal as sources of energy, high quality protein, and many water soluble vitamins. These microbes are able to utilize nonprotein nitrogen (NPN) sources such as urea and ammonia and convert it into protein by incorporating it into their own protoplasm.

The contents of the rumen and reticulum, while constantly being processed, tend to become stratified in three layers. The lowest (most ventral) layer consists mostly of liquid containing partially digested food, including grains. The middle layer includes food particles that have most recently entered the rumen and are not completely soaked. The most dorsal layer consists mainly of carbon dioxide and methane, which are produced continuously by the microbes.

Saliva, up to 200 L/day, helps keep the rumen contents liquid and near a neutral pH by neutralizing the organic acids formed during anaerobic fermentation of carbohydrates. Acetic acid is one of the volatile fatty acids absorbed through the rumen wall. It is utilized by muscle and the mammary gland as an energy source. Acetic acid is also used in the production of fatty acids for the mammary gland and fat deposits, as well as a part of the acetyl-coenzyme A.

Cellulose digestion in the large intestine of the horse is similar to cellulose digestion in the rumen of the ox. However, other nutrients in the diet, including soluble carbohydrates, proteins, and fats, have been largely digested and absorbed before the cellulose enters the cecum or colon. Therefore, there is relatively little if any loss of nutrients from fermentation as seen in the ruminant.

The volatile fatty acids produced in the large intestine of the horse are absorbed and utilized, but there is some question about the use of the microbes themselves and the ability of the horse to use nonprotein nitrogen as a protein source.

Chapter 23

Metabolism and Energy

A tank of gasoline under certain conditions may explode (combine with oxygen rapidly and violently) almost instantly, producing a great deal of heat (energy) through oxidation of the hydrogen and carbon to water and carbon dioxide respectively. The same gasoline (hydrogen and carbon), when burned under controlled conditions in an engine or gasoline stove, will be of much more value.

In a similar way a stack of hay or a bin full of grain may burn in a matter of hours, with a complete waste of the energy resulting from rapid oxidation of the carbon and hydrogen in the carbohydrate, fats, and proteins of the feed. However, if this same material is fed to livestock, the stepwise-controlled degradation, oxidation, and phosphorylation (*catabolism*) will provide enough energy in the proper amounts to maintain a herd of livestock over a period of time.

Energy relationships within the animal body are studied under the broad classification of metabolism. The process that results in building and maintaining body tissues and storing energy is classified as *anabolism*. That in which substances are broken down,

with the concurrent release of energy, is classified as *catabolism*.

All energy available to the animal ultimately is derived from the sun. (See Fig. 23–1.) Plants utilize this energy in *photosynthesis* to combine CO_2 and H_2O in the formation of plant tissue and consequent storage of energy. Strictly herbivorous animals obtain this energy directly from plants; omnivores receive some energy directly from plants and some second-hand by eating flesh of other animals; and strict carnivores receive all of their energy second- or third-hand by consuming only other animals. However, most so-called carnivores do eat plant materials. Most commercial dog foods contain a large amount of grain products and even wild animals such as coyotes and wolves eat the digestive contents of the herbivores they kill.

Catabolism of the three major classes of foods—carbohydrates, fats, and proteins—provides the energy for all vital processes in the animal body. This energy is temporarily stored in the form of so-called "high-energy bonds," which link phosphorus and oxygen atoms in *ATP (adenosine triphosphate)*.

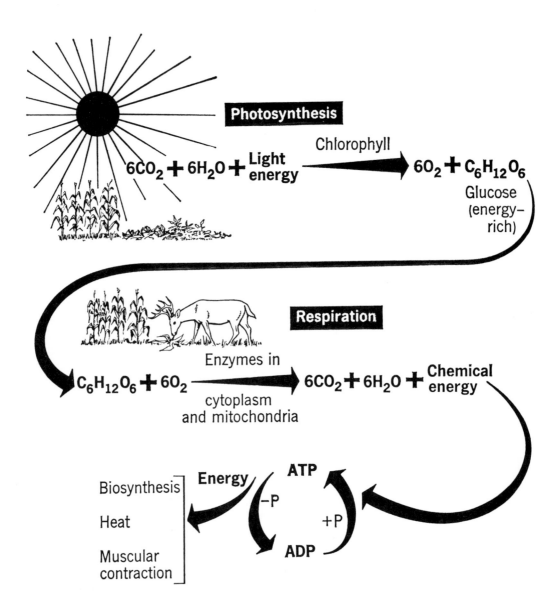

Fig. 23–1.   Energy relationships in life. (Biological Science: An Inquiry Into Life, courtesy of Harcourt, Brace & World, Inc. and American Institute of Biological Sciences.)

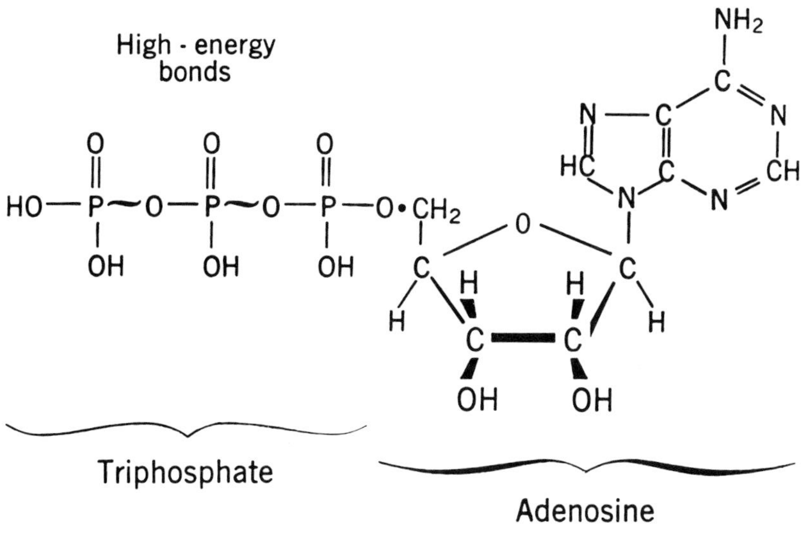

Fig. 23–2. A diagram of a molecule of adenosine triphosphate (ATP), the substance that supplies most of the energy for the chemical reactions of a cell. Energy derived from the oxidation of foods is stored in ATP until needed for the cell's work.

(See Fig. 23–2.) In the presence of the appropriate enzyme *(ATPase)*, one phosphate radical splits off in a transphosphorylation with the release of available energy. The resulting compound, *ADP (adenosine diphosphate)* can be readily reconverted to ATP by the addition of phosphate and energy.

CELLULAR BREAKDOWN OF FOODS

Initial stages of chemical breakdown vary with the different foods, but the products of each enter the *tricarboxylic acid cycle (Krebs cycle or citric acid cycle)* at some point for the final common method of energy formation breakdown of foods (see Fig. 23–3).

As carbohydrate is broken down to *pyruvic acid*, about 10% of its potential energy is released, which leaves 90% of the energy to be released by oxidation of pyruvic acid by the citric acid cycle. Fats are hydrolyzed into *glycerol* and *fatty acids*. The glycerol is transformed into *triose*

phosphate, then into *phosphoglyceric acid*, and finally into pyruvic acid, which enters the citric acid cycle for oxidation.

The fatty acids are broken down, two carbon atoms at a time (β oxidation), and form acetyl-coenzyme A, which is then used in the initial step of the citric acid cycle.

Breakdown of protein is somewhat more complicated because the *amino acids* resulting from protein digestion must be deaminated or transaminated (NH_2 groups removed or exchanged) before further conversion can occur. Amino acids that go to pyruvic acid and then form carbohydrate are called *glycogenic*. Those that form acetoacetic acid and acetyl-coenzyme A are called *ketogenic*. The glycogenic amino acids enter the glycolysis scheme and work back up to glucose (gluconeogenesis) and glycogen. The ketogenic amino acids enter into the citric acid cycle.

Oxidation involves the addition of oxygen, removal of hydrogen, and the loss of electrons. Reduction is the opposite of oxidation. Since one cannot occur without the other, we usually speak of *redox reactions*.

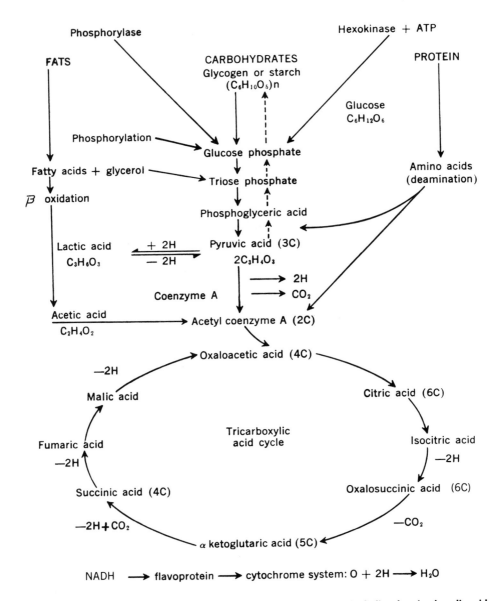

Fig. 23–3.   A simplified diagram of some of the phases of cellular metabolism, including the tricarboxylic acid cycle (Krebs cycle). (DeCoursey, The Human Organism, courtesy of McGraw-Hill Book Co., Inc.)

CARBOHYDRATE METABOLISM

Carbohydrate metabolism involves chemical reactions and energy relationships in the utilization of *polysaccharides, disaccharides,* and *monosaccharides* within the cells.

Starch, glycogen, and disaccharides are hydrolyzed to monosaccharides by enzymes in the digestive tract of simple-stomach animals. More complex carbohydrates, such as *cellulose* and *pentosans,* must be digested by the organisms in the digestive tract to be of any value to the animal. This occurs to a marked degree only in herbivorous animals, where the carbohydrates are converted to fatty acids rather than to monosaccharides. In the ruminant, much of the starch and sugar is also converted to fatty acids by the organisms in the rumen. These fatty acids, including acetic, *propionic,* and *butyric acid,* are absorbed, at least to some extent, through the rumen wall.

The overall effect of carbohydrate catabolism within cells is a release of a large amount of energy by the time the end-products of CO_2 and H_2O are reached. However, just as combustion of ordinary fuel requires an initial flame, the cellular process, termed *glycolysis,* requires energy also. This energy is supplied by the cell in the form of ATP, which has been produced in the mitochondria of the cell.

Referring to Figure 23–3, glycolysis is the step-wise reactions for changing glucose to pyruvic acid. Although it utilizes ATP energy, it yields a net gain of more ATP energy than is used. Glycolysis is carried on in the cell cytoplasm, requiring enzymes to catalyze each step, but not requiring oxygen to do so; therefore, it is an *anaerobic* process (meaning without O_2).

More specifically, the process of glycolysis begins with the entry of glucose from the blood into the cell. Here it reacts with ATP in the presence of the enzyme *glucokinase (hexokinase)* to phosphorylate the glucose to *glucose-6-phosphate,* leaving ADP. The glucose-6-phosphate is then en-zymatically changed to fructose-6-phosphate, and this reacts with another ATP to form *fructose-1,6-diphosphate,* leaving another ADP.

Fructose-1,6-diphosphate, in the presence of an aldolase enzyme, is split into two triose phosphates: *3, glyceraldehyde phosphate* and *dihydroxyacetone phosphate.* After a series of further reactions catalyzed by different enzymes, these three-carbon phosphates yield *pyruvic acid,* plus a net gain of two ATP (total four, but two were used in the glycolysis process). Then the pyruvic acid is converted by taking one of six directions:

1. it can enter the mitochondria and thereby go through the tricarboxylic acid cycle (citric acid cycle, Krebs cycle) for oxidation and subsequent phosphorylation of ADP to form more ATP in the cytochrome system (this is the most frequent pathway of pyruvic acid)

2. it can be reversibly reduced to form lactic acid

3. it can be converted back to carbohydrate by glycogenesis (reverse glycolysis)

4. it can be reduced to malic acid and enter the tricarboxylic acid cycle

5. it can be oxidized to oxaloacetic acid for the tricarboxylic acid cycle

6. it can be converted to the amino acid alanine by transamination

These are all possible pathways for pyruvic acid; which pathway it takes depends on each cell's metabolic needs at the time. During the process of glycolysis, each mole of glucose (180 gm) forms two moles of pyruvic acid (pyruvate) and yields a net gain of two moles of ATP by phosphorylation of ADP, all of which occurs in the cell cytoplasm.

The tricarboxylic acid cycle (as illustrated in Fig. 23–3) occurs in the mitochondria and requires oxygen to function; thus it is the *aerobic* component of cellular catabolism, which cannot function without the animal taking O_2 into its lungs, from where it is then carried to all the tissues cells by the blood.

The pyruvic acid from glycolysis, upon entry into the mitochondria, is converted to acetyl-coenzyme A. Then, as the oxidation steps proceed in the tricarboxylic acid cycle, pairs of hydrogen atoms (2H) are released, along with CO_2. These hydrogen atoms provide the hydrogen ions or protons (H^+) and electrons which then enter the *mitochondrial electron transport* system. The hydrogen ions and electrons are picked up by a molecule of NAD^+ *(nicotinamide adenine dinucleotide)*, reducing the NAD^+ to NADH. The NADH is the principal intermediary between the tricarboxylic acid cycle and the enzymes in the inner membrane of the mitochondria that will carry the electrons through the *cytochrome system* of the respiratory chain.

The NADH transfers its proton and electrons to FMN *(flavin mononucleotide)*. Then, according to the chemiosmotic theory proposed by P. Mitchell, which is widely accepted, the following steps occur. FMN takes another proton from the inside of the membrane, becoming reduced to $FMNH_2$. It then gives up its 2H, which are transferred to the exterior of the mitochondrial membrane and released as protons (H^+). At the same time, the two electrons go to a molecule called *ubiquinone* or *coenzyme Q*, which in turn picks up H atoms. It then gives up one electron to cytochrome C_1 and the other to cytochrome b of the mitochondrial membrane. The electrons are then transferred to cytochromes a and a_3, from which the electrons combine with an oxygen atom and two protons (H^+) to form water.

In this sequence of oxidation-reduction reactions, occurring in and across the mitochondrial membrane, every two protons that pass inward across the membrane will, because of differences in electric potential, cause an inorganic phosphate to attach to an ADP in a high energy state, forming ATP. The speed of the reaction is apparently increased by an enzyme system.

The net result of the tricarboxylic acid cycle and the cytochrome transport system is to produce three more ATP from ADP for *each* pair of H atoms released during the tricarboxylic acid cycle; this occurs through *oxidative phosphorylation*. Three molecules of CO_2 and three molecules of H_2O also result.

Since there are two moles of pyruvate formed for each mole of glucose, the tricarboxylic acid cycle operates twice for each glucose degraded. Therefore, we get essentially four pairs of hydrogen atoms released on each cycle. The two cycles yield $8 \times 3 =$ 24 ATP, and two ATP net during glycolysis, plus four more ATP from the generation of reduced flavin-adenine dinucleotide during the tricarboxylic acid cycle, and two more from substrate level phosphorylation in the cycle equals 32 ATP. Six more are possible from glycolytic generation of $NADH_2$.

All told, it is possible to produce 38 moles of ATP from the degradation of one mole of glucose. The ATP thus formed is a ready source of energy for any biologic work, including muscle contraction, glandular secretion, nerve conduction, active absorption, and membrane transport.

Pyruvate, in the presence of NADH, H^+, and the enzyme *lactic dehydrogenase*, forms *lactate* and NAD. By enzymatic reversal of this, the lactate can later be reconverted to pyruvate and then enter the tricarboxylic acid cycle to be completely oxidized as described previously, the end-products always being $CO_2 + H_2O$ + available energy in the form of ATP.

Some of the glucose that enters cells does not become catabolized to pyruvate by glycolysis; instead, it forms *glycogen* anabolically by the process called *glycogenesis*, so that glucose can be temporarily stored in the cell. This process is later followed by the opposite process (glycogenolysis), whereby the glycogen store is broken down to glucose-6-phosphate in some cells, or to glucose itself in other cells, such as in the liver.

Glucose does not always have to enter the cell from the blood capillaries. Some cells, mostly in the liver, are capable of producing glucose from substrates other than carbohydrate. That is, the liver cells use fats or proteins to synthesize new glucose for the blood, and the process is called *gluco-neogenesis*. This occurs essentially when blood glucose levels are low, or when insufficient glucose is entering the cells and the glycogen stores are depleted.

FAT METABOLISM

Fats are found mostly in adipose tissue as a storage form of potential energy. They are synthesized by the anabolic cellular process called *lipogenesis*. When such energy stores are needed by the animal's body, the fats are broken down by hydrolysis to *fatty acids* and *glycerol*. The fatty acids are then degraded by beta-oxidation to acetoacetic acid, which is a *ketone body* from which beta-hydroxybutyric acid and acetone can also be formed. All three are ketones, and the catabolic process is therefore called *ketogenesis*.

Most of this fat degradation occurs in the liver cells, from which the ketones and glycerol leave and enter the circulation. Upon delivery to all other body cells, the glycerol can enter the scheme of glycolysis-to-pyruvate, and the ketones can be converted to acetyl-CoA for entering the tricarboxylic acid cycle. The regulation of both fat anabolism and catabolism depends on the body's needs, and is accomplished through hormonal activity related to the state of carbohydrate metabolism in the animal at any one time.

Fatty acids are oxidized through a series of reactions involving *coenzyme A* to acetyl-coenzyme A, which can enter the tricarboxylic acid cycle.

PROTEIN METABOLISM

The metabolism of protein is not directly involved in producing energy. Rather protein metabolism is involved with producing primarily enzymes, hormones, structural components, and blood proteins of the body cells and tissues. Cell *synthesis* of the proteins is accomplished by utilizing the amino acids available to form the polypeptides, through the translation process described in Chapter 3.

The degradation of protein (catabolism) yields amino acids again. The amino acid then has an NH_2 amino group removed by oxidative *deamination* in the liver cells, leaving a keto-acid. The keto-acid then can enter the tricarboxylic acid cycle for energy formation when carbohydrate stores are depleted, or it can form pyruvate and ultimately glucose by gluconeogenesis, or it can enter the lipogenesis process for forming fats. As a result of deamination in the liver cells, ammonia is also formed (NH_3), and this is then contributed to the formation of urea. As in the case of fat and carbohydrate metabolism, protein metabolism is governed by the relative activity of several hormones.

SYNTHESIS OF GLYCOGEN, FATS, AND PROTEINS

Synthesis of *glycogen, fats,* and *proteins* may start at nearly any stage in the respective catabolic cycle. This anabolic process (synthesis) occurs wherever tissue is increased, as in growth, or when energy is stored in the form of fat or glycogen. The energy for synthesizing these compounds is derived from hydrolysis of ATP.

METABOLISM AND HEAT

In the late 1700s Lavoisier found that in a ten-hour period a guinea pig produced about the same amount of heat as produced by burning 3.3 gm of carbon, and that the carbon dioxide produced in the ten-hour period was the same volume as produced by burning 3.3 gm of carbon. Crawford had previously demonstrated the same relationship between oxygen consumption and heat production, regardless of whether carbon was burned inside the body or outside of it.

Lavoisier used an *ice calorimeter* to measure body heat produced by a guinea pig. This consisted of a chamber for the guinea pig, surrounded by another chamber filled with ice. The amount of heat produced was determined indirectly by measuring the amount of ice melted during a given period.

Metabolism of 1 gm of fat yields 9.3 Calories of heat, about the same as produced by burning 1 gm of fat outside the body. One gram of carbohydrate yields about 4.1 Calories when burned either outside or inside the body. Protein, however, yields 5.3 Calories when burned outside the body but only 4.1 Calories when metabolized. This difference in heat production by protein is due to the excretion of nitrogenous waste products from protein metabolism. The difference practically disappears when the heat equivalent of the urine and feces is added to the metabolic figure for protein.

Heat production measured by direct calorimetry (placing the animal in a calorimeter) agrees within 1% with heat production calculated by indirect calorimetry (measurement of O_2 consumption and CO_2 production).

ENERGY VALUE OF FOODS

The energy value of food can be determined by the use of a *bomb calorimeter*, which consists of a metal chamber surrounded by water. The chamber is loaded with a known sample of dried food and an excess of oxygen. The sample is ignited with an electric fuse and the heat produced is calculated from the rise in temperature of the water surrounding the chamber.

In physiologic work, the unit of heat is the large calorie (Calorie, or Cal, or Kc for Kilocalorie). This is the amount of heat necessary to raise the temperature of 1 kg of water from 15° to 16° (1°C). This is 1000 times as much heat as the small calorie (calorie or cal), which is the heat required to raise the temperature of 1 gm of water 1°C.

Basal metabolic rate refers to the amount of calories needed to maintain a subject at complete rest 12 to 14 hours after eating a light meal. Surface area is a more important factor than weight in influencing basal metabolism, so in man the basal metabolic rate is related to the calculated surface area of the individual. Basal metabolism, then, refers to the number of Calories required to maintain the body in metabolic equilibrium. The rate (BMR) is measured by spirometry, and the results are adjusted for age and sex.

RESPIRATORY QUOTIENT

Respiratory quotient *(RQ)* is the ratio of the volume of CO_2 expired divided by O_2 inspired. The *RQ* of glucose is 1, since one molecule of CO_2 is produced for each molecule of O_2 used. This is generally true of any carbohydrate, because the hydrogen and oxygen in the molecule are in the same proportion as in water, which leaves the carbon as the only element to be oxidized.

Neither the carbon nor the hydrogen in fats is completely oxidized, so more molecules of O_2 are required than molecules of CO_2 produced. Some of the O_2 is used to oxidize a portion of the hydrogen to H_2O. This gives the RQ in the neighborhood of 0.71. Proteins give an RQ of about 0.80.

The RQ is supposed to afford an indication of the type of food being metabolized. In animals fattened on carbohydrates, the RQ may be greater than 1, because a relatively oxygen-rich material (carbohydrate) is being converted to an oxygen-poor material (fat).

Chapter 24

The Urinary System

The urinary system consists of two kidneys, two ureters, the bladder, and the urethra.

ANATOMY OF THE KIDNEYS

The kidneys are organs that filter plasma and plasma constituents from the blood, and then selectively reabsorb water and useful constituents back from the filtrate, ultimately excreting excesses and plasma waste products. Figures 24–1 to 24–3 show the structure of the kidneys. With the exception of the lobulated kidneys of the cow and the heart-shaped right kidney of the horse, most domestic animals have somewhat bean-shaped kidneys.

The kidneys are located in the dorsal part of the abdominal cavity on each side of the aorta and vena cava just ventral to the first few lumbar vertebrae. In the cow, sheep, and goat, particularly with a full rumen, the left kidney may be pushed to the right as far as the median plane or beyond. In these

animals the left kidney may be much more loosely attached to the body wall than the right kidney, and consequently the left renal artery and vein are longer than the right vessels. Like other abdominal organs, the kidneys are *retroperitoneal*, that is, they are located outside of the peritoneal cavity. However, the kidneys are more closely attached to the abdominal wall by fascia, vessels, and peritoneum than are other organs.

The medial border of the kidney is usually concave and has a depression, the *renal hilus*, where blood vessels and nerves enter and the ureter and lymphatic vessels leave. The expanded origin of the ureter within the kidney is called the *renal pelvis*. It receives urine from the collecting tubules of the kidney. The cavity within the kidney that contains the pelvis is called the *renal sinus*. The renal pelvis has no relationship to the bony pelvis described as a part of the skeleton.

In the horse, sheep, and dog, the collecting tubules empty onto a longitudinal ridge that projects into the renal pelvis. This ridge

373

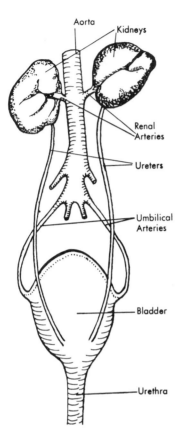

Aorta

Kidneys

Renal
Arteries

Ureters

Umbilical
Arteries

Bladder

Urethra

Fig. 24–1.   Dorsal view of the urinary organs of the horse. (After Sisson and Grossman, The Anatomy of the Domestic Animals, 4th ed., W. B. Saunders Co.)

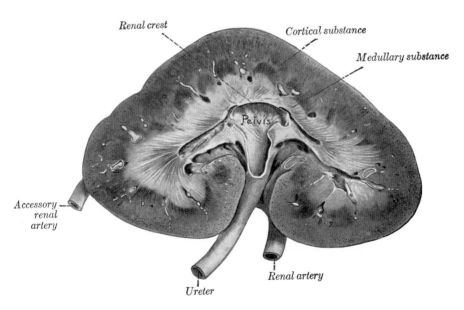

Renal crest

Cortical substance

Medullary substance

Pelvis

Accessory
renal
artery

Renal artery

Ureter

Fig. 24–2.   Frontal (horizontal) section of kidney of horse. The renal vein is removed. A large accessory renal artery entered the caudal pole. Sections of arteries in limiting layer between cortical and medullary substances are white in figure. (Sisson and Grossman, The Anatomy of the Domestic Animals, 4th ed., W. B. Saunders Co.)

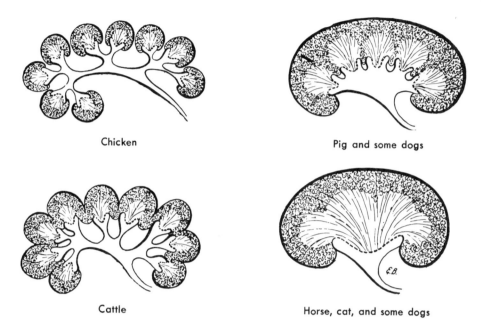

Chicken

Pig and some dogs

Cattle

Horse, cat, and some dogs

Fig. 24–3. Lobulation of the kidney. (Elias and Pauly, Human Microanatomy, 2nd ed., courtesy of Da Vinci Publishing Co.)

is called the *renal crest*. In the kidney of the cow and pig, individual pyramids project into minor calyces, which in turn empty into major calyces. These major calyces in the pig kidney empty into the renal pelvis and thence into the ureter. The kidney of the cow has no pelvis, so the major calyces empty into the ureter directly.

The portion of the kidney immediately surrounding the renal pelvis is the *medulla*, which appears striated because of the radially arranged collecting tubules. These tubules form the basis for the renal pyramids, which have their apices at the renal pelvis and their bases covered by the cortex. In addition to collecting tubules, the medulla also contains some *loops of Henle*. The *cortex*, located between the medulla and the thin, connective-tissue capsule, has a granular appearance because of the large number of *glomeruli*. Proximal convoluted tubules and distal convoluted tubules are also located in the cortex in fairly close relation to the glomeruli and many loops of Henle.

Blood and Nerve Supply

The blood supply to the kidney is much more extensive than the size of the organ would suggest. The two *renal arteries* may carry as much as one-fourth of the total circulating blood. The renal artery enters the hilus of the kidney and divides into a number of relatively large branches, the *interlobar arteries*. These pass peripherally between pyramids almost to the cortex, where they bend abruptly and travel in an arched manner, suggesting the name *arciform or arcuate arteries*.

Each arcuate artery gives off a number of interlobular arteries, which in turn give rise to the afferent arterioles. Each afferent arteriole branches to form a capillary network called the *glomerulus*. An efferent arteriole leaves each glomerulus. Leaving the glomeruli, most of the efferent arterioles break up into a capillary network that surrounds the rest of the *nephron*. Those arterioles that leave glomeruli close to the medulla send branches directly into the medulla as *arteriae rectae*, where they form capillary networks around the collecting tubules and loops of Henle.

Arcuate veins drain blood from both the cortex and medulla, pass through the medulla as interlobar veins, and enter the renal vein. Lymph drains from the kidney to the renal lymph nodes.

The kidneys of reptiles, birds, and amphibians receive a portion of their blood from veins that drain the body wall or hind legs. This system, the *renal portal system*, is not found as such in mammals. The pampiniform plexus of veins, which drains the mammalian testicle, is believed to be a remnant of the more primitive renal portal system.

The kidneys are supplied with *sympathetic nerves* from the renal plexus, which follow blood vessels and terminate largely on glomerular arterioles. Branches of the *vagus nerve* may also supply the kidneys. Both *vasoconstrictor* and *vasodilator* nerves are found in the kidney.

URETERS, BLADDER, AND URETHRA

The ureter is a muscular tube that conveys urine from the pelvis of the kidney to the bladder. Each ureter passes caudad to empty into the bladder near its neck at an area known as the *trigone*. The manner in which the ureter passes obliquely through the wall of the bladder forms an effective valve to prevent return flow of urine to the kidney.

The *urinary bladder* is a hollow muscular organ that varies in size and position with the amount of urine it contains. The empty contracted bladder is a thick-walled, pear-shaped structure located on the floor of the pelvis. As the bladder fills with urine, the wall becomes thinner, and most of the bladder is displaced craniad toward or into the abdominal cavity. Peritoneum covers a variable amount of the cranial portion of the bladder, depending on its fullness. The caudal part of the bladder is covered with pelvic fascia.

The neck of the bladder is continuous with the urethra caudally, and the muscle of the bladder wall is arranged in a circular manner at the neck of the bladder, forming a sphincter that controls passage of urine into the urethra.

The *pelvis, ureter, bladder,* and *urethra* are all lined with transitional epithelium. This epithelial lining is useful in these areas, where considerable distention of the lumen may occur. When these organs are empty, the lumen is small, the walls are thick, and the lining epithelial cells are piled deeply to form a many-layered stratification. However, when the organs are distended, the

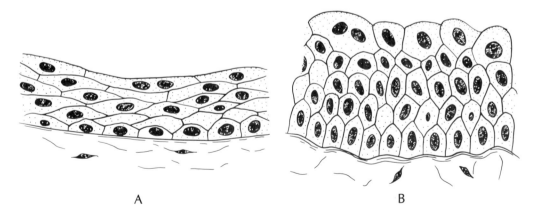

A   B

Fig. 24–4. Transitional epithelium. *A*, Bladder full —wall distended; *B*, bladder empty—wall relaxed.

lumen is enlarged, the walls are thinner, and a transition to a much lower stratification of the lining occurs. Hence the name transitional epithelium.

Between the lining epithelium and the smooth muscle of the organ wall is a variable amount of connective tissue called the *lamina propria*. More connective tissue is found superficial to the longitudinal and circular fibers of smooth muscle. This outer layer of connective tissue, called the *adventitia*, is covered by peritoneum on the apex and body of the bladder.

The pelvic *urethra* extends from the bladder to the *ischial arch*. In the male it receives the *ductus deferens* and ducts from the accessory sex glands. It is surrounded by the striated urethral muscle, which is somewhat continuous with the *bulbospongiosus muscle*, which partially surrounds the *pars spongiosa* around the *penile urethra*. A plexus of veins forms cavernous tissue between the lining epithelium and the surrounding muscle. Around the penile urethra this cavernous tissue is well developed and is called the *corpus spongiosum penis (corpus cavernosum urethrae)*. With the exception of the *urethral bulb*, the cavernous tissue surrounding the urethra is supplied with blood from veins. The urethral bulb, located between the *crura* (roots) of the penis, receives blood from the artery of the bulb.

MICTURITION

Micturition is the term for expulsion of urine from the bladder. It normally is a reflex activity stimulated by distention of the bladder from the constant inflow of urine by way of the ureters. The bladder adjusts to a gradual inflow of urine until the pressure becomes high enough to stimulate reflex centers in the spinal cord, which in turn cause contraction of the muscle wall of the bladder by way of sacral parasympathetic nerves. However, reflex emptying of the bladder can be prevented by voluntary control of the external sphincter surrounding the neck of the bladder.

MICROANATOMY AND PHYSIOLOGY OF THE NEPHRON

The *nephron* is the unit of structure and function of the kidney. It includes the glomerulus, *glomerular capsule (Bowman's capsule)*, proximal convoluted tubule, loop of Henle, and distal convoluted tubule (which is continued by the collecting tubule).

The glomerulus is a tuft of capillaries interposed on the course of an arteriole (small artery). The *glomerular capsule (Bowman's capsule)* is the expanded blind end of the tubule, which is evaginated around the glomerulus and almost entirely surrounds it. The visceral (inner) layer of the glomerular capsule closely surrounds the capillaries, and the parietal (outer) layer of the glomerular capsule is continuous with the proximal convoluted tubule. This complex of glomerulus and inner and outer layers of the glomerular capsule is called a *renal (Malpighian) corpuscle*. The space between the inner and outer layers of the glomerular capsule communicates with the lumen of the proximal tubule.

The renal corpuscle is the major site for filtration of fluid from the blood. Approximately 100 times as much fluid passes through this filter as is eventually excreted as urine. In order that the filter might operate effectively, blood pressure within the capillaries of the glomerulus must remain relatively high. This condition is ensured by the capillaries being on the course of an artery rather than between an artery and a vein, as in most capillary beds. Both the afferent arteriole entering the glomerulus and the efferent arteriole leaving the glomerulus are equipped with smooth muscle, so the amount of blood entering the glomerulus and the pressure within the glomerulus can be controlled by constricting either the afferent arteriole or the efferent arteriole or both. (See Fig. 24–5.)

As the afferent arteriole approaches the glomerulus, it is surrounded by a cuff of myoepithelial cells that have some charac-

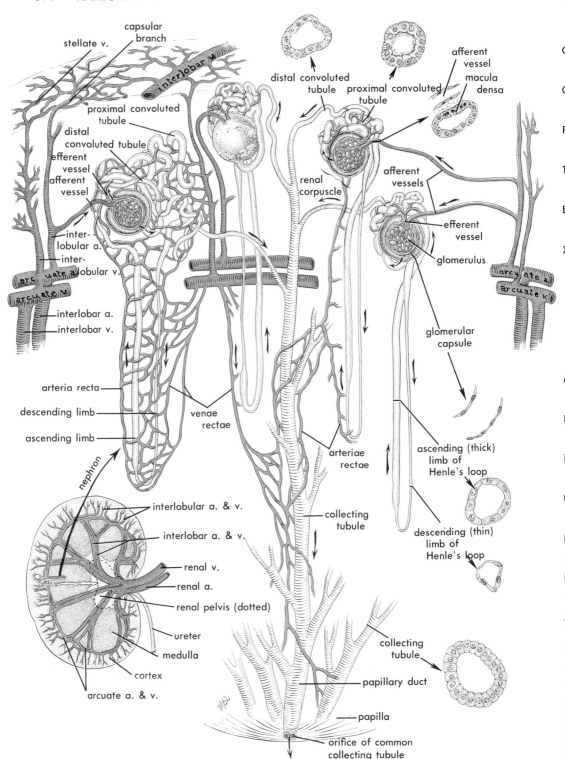

Fig. 24–5. Schematic representation of cat kidney tubules and their relationship to the blood vessels. (Crouch, J. E.: Functional Human Anatomy. ed. 3. Philadelphia, Lea & Febiger, 1978.)

teristics of smooth muscle and some characteristics of epithelium. These cells surrounding the arteriole are called the *juxtaglomerular cells*. They are the site of production of *renin* (not to be confused with rennin), which is secreted into the blood when the blood pressure in the afferent arterioles falls, when the sodium concentration of the plasma decreases, when the distal tubular osmolality decreases, or when sympathetic nerve fibers innervating the afferent arteriole are stimulated. In the blood, renin acts on an alpha globulin, *angiotensinogen*, to produce *angiotensin*, which acts as a vasoconstrictor to increase blood pressure, and which also acts on the adrenal gland to secrete aldosterone. Aldosterone in turn acts on the kidney to conserve Na^+ ions.

Each human kidney contains approximately one million nephrons. Under normal conditions only about one-fourth of the nephrons of the kidneys function at a given time. Whether or not a specific nephron is functioning depends largely on the relative constriction of afferent and efferent arterioles.

In addition to the renal corpuscle, the nephron consists of the proximal convoluted tubule, Henle's loop, and the distal convoluted tubule. The capillaries supplying this portion are derived from the efferent arteriole. Since the blood in the efferent arteriole has lost about 20% of its water, it is more concentrated (has a higher potential osmotic pressure) and therefore is better able to reabsorb water from the tubules.

The *proximal convoluted tubule* may connect directly with the parietal layer of the glomerular capsule, or a short neck may be interposed. In any event, the proximal convoluted tubule is the longest and most winding portion of the nephron. It forms much of the tissue of the renal cortex. The cells lining the proximal segment of the tubule are columnar or cuboidal in shape and present a striated luminal border, the so called *brush border*, on the free surface of the cell. The free surface is directed toward the lumen of the tubule. The brush border is similar to

that of the absorptive cells of the small intestine.

The proximal tubule reabsorbs most of the constituents of the glomerular filtrate that are needed by the animal body, including about seven-eighths of the sodium chloride and water. This action is facilitated by the more concentrated blood which the capillaries around the tubule receive from the efferent arteriole of the glomerulus. In addition to selective reabsorption from the glomerular filtrate, cells of the proximal segment are able to secrete waste products from the blood into the fluid passing through the lumen of the tubule.

Henle's loop is interposed between the proximal convoluted tubule and the distal convoluted tubule. It is a U-shaped tube that begins near the glomerulus as a continuation of the proximal tubule. The descending limb, which is thin, extends a variable distance into the medulla, where it turns back upon itself as the thick, ascending limb of Henle's loop. The thin, descending limb is lined by simple squamous epithelial cells, and the thick, ascending limb is lined by cuboidal epithelial cells.

The loop of Henle usually contains the most concentrated fluid, with the highest concentration at the lowest part of the loop close to or within the medulla, due to the *countercurrent mechanism*.

The distal convoluted tubule is shorter and less twisted than the proximal convoluted tubule. It extends from the termination of the ascending limb of Henle's loop to the collecting tubule.

The initial *collecting tubules*, called *arched tubules*, empty into the *straight collecting tubules* in the cortex of the kidney. Each straight tubule receives several arched tubules before entering the medulla. The straight tubules unite to form papillary ducts (in the inner zone of the medulla), which empty into the pelvis of the kidney. Lining cells of the collecting ducts gradually change from cuboidal epithelium in the arched tubules to columnar epithelium in the papillary ducts.

FUNCTION OF THE KIDNEY

The urinary system is responsible for excretion of many waste products of the body. It is also an important factor in maintenance of *homeokinesis (homeostasis)*, the relatively constant condition of the internal environment of the body. This includes regulation of such diverse factors as water balance, pH, osmotic pressure, electrolyte levels, and concentration of many plasma substances. This control is obtained by filtering a large quantity of plasma and small molecules through the glomerulus. Varying amounts of each substance are then reabsorbed, either passively by such forces as osmosis and diffusion, or actively by tubular cell transport.

The major factors affecting actions of the kidneys include composition of the blood, arterial blood pressure, hormones, and the autonomic nervous system.

Composition of the blood includes the relative concentration of plasma proteins. Dilution of plasma proteins generally causes *diuresis* (increased excretion of urine), including greater excretion of water, sodium, chloride, and bicarbonate. The low osmotic pressure of dilute blood inhibits the release of ADH (the antidiuretic hormone of the *neurohypophysis*). A high osmotic pressure of the blood usually results in decreased excretion of a more concentrated urine because of the release of ADH as well as other factors. (This is discussed later in this chapter.)

The metabolic production of a substance or its injection or ingestion into the body usually is followed by increased urinary excretion of that substance or its metabolites, which maintains a relatively constant composition of the blood. In other words, an increase in the concentration of a substance in the blood tends to increase the excretion of that substance. A large increase in excretion of a substance dissolved in the blood generally will cause an increase in the volume of urine. This type of volume increase is called *osmotic diuresis* and may also result in loss of electrolytes.

Much experimental work has been done with various substances administered to animals in order to determine how the kidneys respond to them. Dramatic results may be obtained when large quantities of materials are given, but in the normal animal, small excesses of any substance usually result in little more than simple excretion of the excess.

Arteriolar pressure determines glomerular pressure, which is a factor in determining quantity of fluid filtered from the blood. As discussed later, when glomerular osmotic (colloidal osmotic) pressure of the plasma and intracapsular pressure are subtracted from glomerular hydrostatic pressure, the result is the *effective filtration pressure*.

ADH and Aldosterone

ADH (the *antidiuretic hormone* from the neurohypophysis) and *aldosterone* (the Na ion-conserving hormone from the adrenal zona glomerulosa) are the two hormones that normally have the greatest effect on the kidney. ADH acts on the collecting ducts; aldosterone acts on all parts of the tubules, the ADH increasing the reabsorption of water, and aldosterone increasing the reabsorption of sodium ions. Increased reabsorption of water is due to increased permeability to water in the collecting ducts, while increased reabsorption of sodium ions takes place by active transport across the cell membranes.

The reabsorption of water by the proximal tubules is essentially *passive* or *obligatory*, and accounts for reabsorption of about 80% of the glomerular filtrate. Another 5% is reabsorbed from Henle's loop. The remaining 15% of the glomerular filtrate can be influenced by ADH and aldosterone.

Osmoreceptors in the *hypothalamus* cause the release of ADH from the posterior pituitary gland whenever the osmotic pressure of blood in the internal carotid artery increases. This mechanism aids conservation of water by causing increased reabsorption of water, resulting in a more concentrated urine.

Stress and certain drugs also stimulate the release of ADH from the neurohypophysis. These drugs include *acetylcholine, nicotine, adrenaline,* and *barbiturates.*

Glomerular Filtrate

The glomerular filtrate is the fluid and fluid constituents that pass from the blood in the glomerulus through the glomerular capillary endothelium and the simple squamous epithelium, forming the visceral layer of the glomerular capsule into the lumen of the glomerular capsule. The *glomerular membrane* is a composite membrane that consists of (1) the capillary endothelium of the glomerulus—endothelial cells having fenestrations between them, (2) a basement membrane, which has no pores, and (3) a layer of *podocytes* (foot-cells) with slit-like pores between them. Podocytes are the epithelial cells that form the visceral layer of the glomerular capsule.

In spite of these three layers, the permeability of the glomerular membrane is about 100 times greater than the permeability of any other capillaries in the animal's body. This greater permeability is due to the fenestrations between the capillary endothelial cells, the slit-pores between the podocytes, and the large surface area of the glomerulus. Therefore, the whole membrane acts much like a sieve, and all substances up to a size of about 70 Å or a molecular weight of 65,000 readily pass across from the plasma and become filtrate. Actually, the ease with which each plasma substance filters across the membrane will vary, of course, not only with its size but also its electrical charge and the charge of the capillary wall.

Water and most molecules smaller than colloidal size may be filtered from the blood plasma to form the glomerular filtrate. Blood cells, colloidal proteins, and fats normally do not pass through the membrane. The filtrate, then, has essentially the same composition and osmolality as the blood plasma, except that it should contain no erythrocytes and little protein (only 0.03%). The filtrate includes those plasma constituents that readily cross the membrane, and these are in the same concentration as they were in the plasma. These constituents include glucose, amino acids, urea, uric acid, creatinine, and the ions Na^+, Cl^-, and H^+ and K^+.

Glomerular filtration occurs as a result of the operation of the same hemodynamics of capillary filtration as anywhere in the body, except that the glomerulus is a *high-pressure* capillary bed. The quantity of glomerular filtrate produced depends on filtration pressure, which is a result of differences in hydrostatic pressure (fluid pressure) and osmotic pressure in the glomerular capillaries as compared with the same types of pressures in the lumen of the glomerular capsule. In man, hydrostatic pressure in the glomerular capillaries normally is about 60 mm Hg, while the pressure in the glomerular capsule is about 18 mm Hg. Colloidal osmotic pressure in the capillaries is about 32 mm Hg, because the large molecules (mostly proteins) will not pass through the glomerular membrane. Colloidal osmotic pressure in the glomerular capsule is close to zero because colloids normally do not enter the glomerular capsule. Any osmotic pressure due to smaller molecules that pass freely through the glomerular membrane will essentially be the same in the capillaries as in the glomerular capsule, so *this* osmotic pressure does not enter into calculations of filtration pressure.

Blood (hydrostatic) pressure in the glomerulus (60 mm Hg for example) tends to force fluid from the glomerulus into the glomerular capsule. Colloidal osmotic pressure in the glomerulus (32 mm Hg) and the blood (hydrostatic) pressure in the glomerular capsule (18 mm Hg) both tend to resist the flow of fluid from the glomerulus into the glomerular capsule. The net difference in pressure (60 mm Hg minus the sum of 32 and 18 mm Hg) equals 10 mm Hg, and this is the net filtration pressure forcing fluid from the glomerulus into the glomerular capsule.

The amount of glomerular filtrate is directly proportional to the filtration pressure. Any change that results in a different filtration pressure automatically affects the quantity of filtrate. An increase in general blood pressure can cause an increase in glomerular pressure and consequently increased filtration. An increase in glomerular pressure also occurs when the efferent arteriole is constricted and the afferent arteriole is not. Excess water intake dilutes the blood and lowers its osmotic pressure. A reduced glomerular colloidal osmotic pressure in effect increases filtration pressure, resulting in more glomerular filtrate.

Conversely, a decrease in general blood pressure, constriction of the afferent arteriole, and dehydration (resulting in increased osmotic pressure of the blood) decrease filtration pressure, resulting in less glomerular filtrate.

Glomerular Filtration Rate (GFR). The *rate* at which the fluid and constituents leave the blood and become filtrate is called the *glomerular filtration rate* (GFR). The GFR is directly proportional to the filtration pressure; so, whatever changes filtration pressure will also change GFR.

If there is constriction of the *afferent* arteriole, there will be a decrease in the rate of blood flow into the glomerulus and therefore a decrease in the glomerular pressure and decreased GFR. Conversely, dilation of the afferent arteriole will increase blood flow, increasing glomerular pressure and GFR. In the case of the *efferent* arteriole, constriction will increase resistance to the flow of blood out of the glomerulus. That will increase glomerular pressure, which increases GFR, up to the point where the flow becomes sluggish and large amounts of plasma have been lost. This increases the effect of the colloidal osmotic pressure in the blood and therefore will decrease GFR.

Such constriction effects occur because of strong *sympathetic* stimulation in total-body emergencies, such as hemorrhage, shock, or severe hypoxia. Such emergencies cause stimulation of the vasomotor baroreceptor and chemoreceptor responses, which in turn cause sympathetic vasoconstriction. The smooth muscle of the kidney blood vessels is well innervated by the sympathetic nerves, and so renal function and GFR will be reduced, sometimes to the point of almost complete shutdown. This is a reasonable response, because the animal can better afford the loss of renal function for a few hours than it can the loss of brain, heart, or liver function—the blood is preferentially shunted to these organs during such emergencies. If the kidneys essentially lose their blood supply (ischemia) over a protracted period of time, degeneration of the tissues can produce *renal failure* and tubular cell *necrosis* (death).

Besides sympathetic constriction affecting GFR, the afferent arterioles have an *autoregulatory* mechanism that helps to prevent GFR from greatly increasing and rupturing the glomerulus; i.e., they will *reflexly* constrict whenever the systemic blood pressure increases and stretches the smooth muscle of the arteriole. So, even though systemic blood pressure may increase greatly, the glomerular pressure and GFR will increase only to about 15%.

Of course, anything that effectively increases or decreases the plasma protein concentration will affect the GFR, because of the change in colloid osmotic (oncotic) pressure: the higher the oncotic pressure, the less is the GFR; the lower the oncotic pressure, the greater is the GFR. Therefore, if too much water is taken in, the blood is diluted, the oncotic pressure decreases, and GFR increases because the net filtration pressure increases. Conversely, if the animal becomes dehydrated, the oncotic pressure increases because of a relative increased protein concentration, which then decreases net filtration pressure (FP) and GFR.

Plasma Clearance

Plasma clearance expresses the degree to which any substance is removed from the plasma by the kidneys and excreted in the urine. The concept is an excellent measure of kidney function. To accurately measure it, one must infuse a substance into the blood at a constant rate and then take serial samples of blood and urine (by catheterizing the animal). Because this is generally too time-consuming, meticulous, and costly, the clearance of *creatinine* is used most commonly clinically because nothing has to be infused. Creatinine is the normal endogenous end-product of creatine phosphate metabolism in the muscles of the animal. The creatinine filters freely across the glomerular membrane. It is not reabsorbed from the filtrate, and only a small additional amount is secreted into the tubules of the nephrons. Its plasma concentration and the total daily excretion remain constant even with changes of diet. Therefore it is convenient and usually adequate for most clinical purposes. Pathologically, when renal disease decreases the number of functional nephrons, the clearance of creatinine decreases and its plasma concentration increases. The formula for calculating the plasma clearance of any substance is:

to supply a substance at the rate it is actually excreted in the urine.

Chemical Balance

The *proximal tubules* reabsorb about 80% of the water, sodium, chloride, and bicarbonate electrolytes. Also, all of the glucose and all of the amino acids are normally reabsorbed. The fluid leaving the proximal tubules has a pH of about 7.4. It contains sodium, chloride, and bicarbonate in about the same concentrations as in the plasma. This fluid, therefore, is approximately isotonic with the blood plasma.

Although glucose can pass through the glomerular membrane, normally the concentration of glucose in the blood is restored by complete reabsorption. In fact, the presence of glucose in the urine is usually abnormal. An active transport of glucose from the lumen of the tubule back to the blood accounts for the reabsorption. The active transport is apparently dependent on sodium transport, which in turn depends on the amount of glucose present; one enhances the other.

Glucose reabsorption takes place in the proximal tubules, and glucose is normally completely reabsorbed. If the transport capacity is exceeded by the glucose load in the

$$\frac{\text{mg/ml of substance in urine} \times \text{ml urine/min}}{\text{mg/ml of substance in plasma}} = \text{plasma clearance of substance}$$

Clearance is expressed in ml/min of plasma that is *completely* cleared of the substance by ending up in the urine. However, this is a *virtual* figure, not the *actual* amount of plasma. For example, assume that 650 ml of plasma are flowing through the kidneys each minute. We know that only 20% of the plasma normally becomes filtrate. Now, if the clearance of urea, for example, is found to be 70 ml/min, then only 70 ml of plasma, out of the total 650 ml, are being *totally* cleared each minute. Clearance, then, is the minimum volume of plasma that would be needed each minute, if *cleared completely*,

filtrate, then the *tubular maximum* is exceeded and the excess remains in the urine, as in diabetes mellitus. Sodium reabsorption occurs in all tubules and in the collecting duct. In the distal tubules and collecting ducts, Na ions are often exchanged for hydrogen, potassium, or ammonium ions. Whenever a sodium ion is reabsorbed it must be accompanied by an anion (negative ion) or exchanged for another cation (positive ion).

The ionic exchange of sodium for hydrogen or ammonium to form acid urine occurs in the proximal tubule and distal part of the nephron. Concentration of *hypertonic urine* occurs in the distal tubules and in the collecting tubules and ducts.

The final *pH* of *urine* is dependent on the quantities of various ions in the urine. An increase of bicarbonate causes greater alkalinity of the urine. Acid urine may be produced by exchange of sodium for hydrogen and ammonium ions, which are excreted in the form of monobasic Na-phosphate or ammonium chloride.

In an *acid urine* with a pH of less than 6, titratable acid is present, ammonium ions are present, and bicarbonate ions are absent. The renal tubule cells have the ability to form ammonia (NH_3) from deamination of amino acids. This ammonia diffuses into the tubules and immediately reacts with hydrogen ions to form ammonium ions (NH_4^+) which are then excreted into the urine in combination with chloride or other anions. This is a means of removing hydrogen ions and chloride as the neutral salt, ammonium chloride, to help maintain the normal pH of the filtrate. The reabsorption of bicarbonate and Na^+ ions into the blood plasma is an important means of controlling body acid-base balance.

Alkaline urine with a pH over 7 contains bicarbonate, but no titratable acid or ammonium. It also contains sodium and potassium.

Diuresis is simply an increase in the quantity of urine produced. It may be caused by a raised plasma level of one or more urinary components, including water. Water diuresis occurs whenever the osmotic pressure of the plasma is reduced to a level that will not stimulate release of ADH. Excess substances other than water must be kept in solution or they cannot be excreted. This produces an osmotic diuresis. The water necessary to act as a solvent produces the increased urine volume.

Reabsorption and Secretion

The kidneys directly control the volume and composition of the extracellular fluid of the body and indirectly control the intracellular fluid composition. Even with a wide range of intake of water and solutes (dissolved substances), the composition and volume of body fluids are kept constant. Transporting water and these substances across the tubular cells is a basic functional mechanism of the kidney. If the materials are carried from the lumen of the tubule to the interstitial fluid, the process is called *reabsorption*. If they are carried to the tubular lumen, the process is called *secretion* or *excretion*. The transport may be passive when caused by such forces as diffusion or osmosis. Active transport utilizes energy supplied by the tubular cells to link the substances with carrier molecules and thereby effect transport across the cells during either reabsorption or secretion.

Usually, filtered substances of further use to the body are returned to the circulation, but excess amounts of these substances, and substances that are not useful, are excreted in the urine and are not reabsorbed.

Substances that normally are found in the blood in definite percentages have limits regarding how much can be reabsorbed or secreted at a time by the tubular cells, based on the cellular capacity to actively transport them. Therefore, there is a *tubular maximum* (Tm) for reabsorption or secretion of a substance. Essentially, each substance has a threshold, and the excess of a reabsorbable substance above threshold remains in the filtrate to be excreted in the urine. All of these substances found in the glomerular filtrate, up to the threshold value, are reabsorbed by the tubules; only the amounts over the threshold are excreted.

Regulation of Na^+ and K^+

Another function that the kidneys perform for the animal's body is maintaining the proper concentration of ions in the extracellular fluids of the whole body.

The kidney regulation of sodium ions (Na^+) is based on excreting the same amount of sodium that is ingested daily in the diet, as long as the animal's sodium concentration is in equilibrium. Regulation mostly occurs by the action of the hormone *aldosterone* (a mineralocorticoid) secreted from the cortex of the adrenal gland whenever: (1) plasma sodium concentration decreases, (2) plasma potassium concentration increases, or (3) plasma volume or cardiac output decreases, and stimulates the sympathetic nervous system.

Aldosterone secretion apparently occurs by two means. One is that changes in the plasma concentration of Na^+ or K^+ have a *direct* effect on the secretory cells of the zona glomerulosa of the adrenal cortex as the blood flows through the adrenal gland. A low plasma Na^+ or high plasma K^+ concentration stimulates aldosterone secretion into the blood.

The other mechanism occurs in the kidney when the Na^+ concentration is deficient in either the plasma or in the distal convoluted tubule at the level of the *juxtaglomerular apparatus*, or when the blood pressure is decreased and causes a decrease in the blood flow through the renal arterioles. Any of these events affect the juxtaglomerular cells in the afferent arterioles and cause the release of *renin* from these cells into the blood. Renin secretion is also stimulated when the sympathetic division of the autonomic nervous system is stimulated (as in the case of low blood pressure). The sympathetic nerve fibers that innervate the juxtaglomerular cells stimulate the beta-adrenergic receptors of these cells, causing them to secrete renin into the blood of the arterioles, while at the same time constricting the arterioles.

Renin is a proteolytic enzyme, and once in the blood it catalyzes the conversion of an inactive globulin, called *angiotensinogen*, which is normally present, to *angiotensin I*, which is also inactive. Angiotensin I is then converted by another enzyme to the active form, *angiotensin II*. This hormone acts on the cells of the adrenal cortex to release the hormone, aldosterone, and it causes the arterioles of the circulatory system to constrict, thereby helping to increase blood pressure by increasing resistance to blood flow.

Once aldosterone is released into the blood, it acts on all parts of the kidney tubules to cause an increase in the reabsorption of sodium-salts, to correct the deficiency in the blood that first triggered the response. Also, increased sodium-salt reabsorption means that more water is osmotically reabsorbed as well, which helps somewhat in restoring blood volume.

When Na^+ is being reabsorbed in this way, K^+ ions are being lost from the blood by exchange and excretion into the urine. So, when K^+ concentration is high relative to the Na^+ concentration, aldosterone causes reabsorption of the one and excretion of the other in order to reestablish the normal sodium-to-potassium ratio in the extracellular fluid of the animal. The balance between these major cations is critical to maintaining normal body functions, such as nerve conduction and stimulation, muscle contraction, and heart function.

REGULATION OF ACID-BASE BALANCE

Large amounts of intermediary organic acids are produced continuously in all cells of the animal's body as a result of metabolism. In addition, a great variety of potential acids come from the animal's diet. However, in spite of all this acid formation, the pH of the blood plasma and the other body fluids is kept constant. It is important to maintain this constancy, because enzyme activity and metabolic processes require control of pH within narrow limits for optimal function.

The normal average pH of arterial blood is 7.4. Venous blood is normally 7.35, because of the extra CO_2 being carried from the tissue cells back to the lungs to be exhaled. The pH within cells in the body varies from 4.5 (highly acid) to 8.0 (highly alkaline), depending on the type of cell. The average is 7.0 (neutral pH).

If the pH of the arterial blood should fall below 6.8, the animal usually dies in coma because the high CO_2 concentration (acidosis) depresses the CNS neurons. On the other hand, if it reaches about 7.8, death can occur from tetany of the respiratory muscles, because the high pH (alkalosis) overexcites the CNS nerves, producing spasms and tetany. To prevent these abnormal pH developments, the animal's body controls pH by the triple action of: (1) the buffer systems—bicarbonate, phosphate, and proteins; (2) breathing—pulmonary ventilation; and (3) the kidneys—excreting alkaline or acid urine as needed.

Buffer Systems and Ventilation

Bicarbonate Buffer System. The bicarbonate buffer system is quantitatively the most important buffer in the *blood plasma*. It is the combination of carbonic acid $[H_2CO_3]$ and a salt of bicarbonate $[HCO_3^-]$ (the conjugate base of the acid). The pH is affected by the ratio of one to the other in the plasma. However, the acid is actually represented by the amount of $[CO_2]$ present, so the ratio of $[HCO_3^-]$ to $[CO_2]$ determines the pH (the brackets refer to *concentration*). If the $[HCO_3^-]$ increases, then the pH increases. If the $[CO_2]$ increases, the pH decreases. If pH increases it is more alkaline; if it decreases, it is more acidic. Clinically, the pH and $[CO_2]$ of the blood can be readily measured, and the $[HCO_3^-]$ level can then be calculated.

The $[HCO_3^-]$ level tells whether there is a *base excess* or a *base deficit* in the blood. So an animal in acidosis has a base deficit, and would be given some form of bicarbonate $[HCO_3^-]$ to increase the pH back toward normal. Conversely, an animal in alkalosis (a base excess) would be given an acid such as NH_4Cl to increase the $[H^+]$, which, in effect, increases plasma CO_2 and decreases pH back toward normal.

Normally, the animal can regulate the amounts of CO_2 in the blood by increasing or decreasing its breathing rate (pulmonary ventilation rate), which is automatically controlled by the respiratory center in the brain. The $[HCO_3^-]$ is controlled by the kidneys.

Phosphate Buffer System. The phosphate buffer system is most important in controlling the pH of the cells of the body, because the major concentration of phosphate is intracellular. However, it does assist pH regulation in the extracellular fluid also, mainly in the kidney tubules. Its mechanism of action is the same as the bicarbonate system, but it is the ratio of

$$\frac{[HPO_4^=]}{[H_2PO_4^-]}.$$

Protein Buffer System. The protein buffer system also operates mostly within cells. This includes the hemoglobin (Hb) proteins within the red blood cells throughout the circulation. It is the ratio of

$$\frac{[Hb^-]\ base}{[HHb]\ acid} \text{ and } \frac{[HbO_2^-]}{[HHbO_2]}.$$

Therefore, Hb is an important component in tying up H^+ ions to reduce acidity, and giving up H^+ ions to increase acidity, as needed.

Ventilation. The lungs participate in controlling acid-base balance by controlling the $[CO_2]$ level of the body fluids, because they eliminate the CO_2 delivered to the lungs by the blood. Whether CO_2 is eliminated by increasing the breathing rate (hyperventilation) when the animal is acidotic, or whether CO_2 is retained more by hypoventilation when the animal is alkalotic, is dictated by the degree of activation of the *respiratory center* in the brain. Its activity, in turn, depends on the degree of stimulation of the chemoreceptors in the aortic and carotid bodies, and in the medulla of the brain, as was explained in Chapter 18.

Kidney Regulation

The kidneys participate in acid-base regulation of the body fluids by controlling the $[HCO_3^-]$. The normal pH of the urine is about 6, but it can range from about 4.5 to 8 in compensating for acidosis and alkalosis.

A. NORMAL MECHANISM

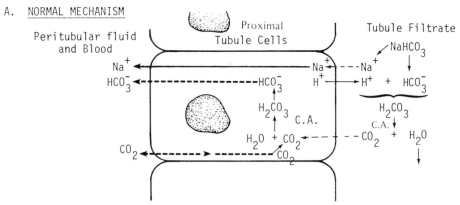

B. COMPENSATION OF ACIDOSIS (Acid excretion and retention of alkaline buffer).

1. Excretion of NaH_2PO_4 (monobasic Na-phosphate)

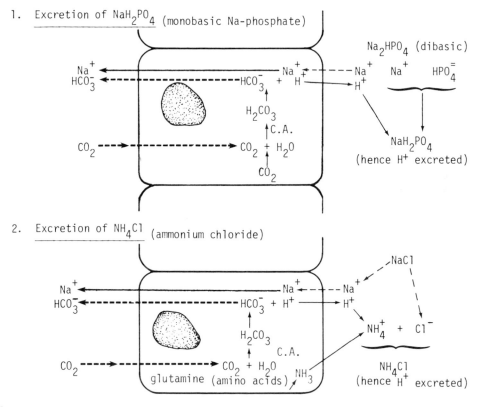

2. Excretion of NH_4Cl (ammonium chloride)

C. IN ALKALOSIS, the above 2 systems are relatively inoperable. The excess $NaHCO_3$ in the glomerular filtrate is not reabsorbed. Its excretion forms an alkaline urine.

Dotted lines represent passive transport
Solid lines represent active transport

Fig. 24–6. Kidney mechanisms for maintenance of acid-base (pH) balance.

Function in Normal States. Normally, H ions are secreted into the filtrate by the epithelial cells of the proximal and distal tubules and collecting ducts. This is the result of the metabolically produced CO_2 and H_2O forming the acid H_2CO_3, which then dissociates into HCO_3^- and H^+. About 85% of this H^+ ion secretion, and recovery of HCO_3^-, occurs in the proximal tubules, where the H^+ is secreted in exchange for Na^+ from the filtrate. So Na^+ is reabsorbed and H^+ is eliminated to prevent acid accumulation.

The secreted H^+ links up to form H_2CO_3 in the tubular fluid, but then dissociates to CO_2 and H_2O. The CO_2 diffuses back into the cells, and the excess then diffuses to the blood, where it can be blown off when it reaches the lungs. Meanwhile, the HCO_3^- formed in the cells, and the Na^+ reabsorbed from the filtrate are returned to the blood to maintain the proper ratio of $HCO_3:CO_2$ (see Fig. 24–6).

Function in Alkalosis and Acidosis. When an animal develops *alkalosis*, the bicarbonate ion concentration $[HCO_3^-]$ has been increased relative to the $[CO_2]$; that means the pH of the body fluids has increased. So, the kidneys will filter more HCO_3^- than H^+ ions secreted into the tubules. The excess HCO_3^- will combine with positive ions and be excreted in the urine. This makes the urine more alkaline, and it decreases the HCO_3^- portion of the $HCO_3:CO_2$ buffer system. That, in turn, decreases the pH of the body fluids back toward normal.

In *acidosis*, there is a relative rise in $[CO_2]$ and, therefore, a relative decrease in $[HCO_3^-]$. In effect, this means that more acid is present, represented by hydrogen ions $[H^+]$. The kidney compensates by secreting more H^+ into the filtrate than HCO_3^- is filtered. The increased H^+ secretion occurs because excess CO_2 in the peritubular capillaries diffuses into the tubular cells, where it forms H_2CO_3, which dissociates into new HCO_3^- and H^+. The new HCO_3^- diffuses back to the blood to increase that part of the buffer system, and Na^+ is also reabsorbed in exchange for the H^+ secreted.

(See Fig. 24–6.) The net effect, then, is an increase in blood $[HCO_3^-]$ and a decrease in blood $[CO_2]$. That increases the pH of the extracellular fluid back toward normal.

The H^+ secreted into the fluid of the tubules is excreted in one of two ways. It may combine with a Na^+ and $HPO_4^=$ and form *monobasic sodium-phosphate*, which is excreted. More often, it combines with ammonia (NH_3) to form the ammonium ion (NH_4^+), which then can combine with chloride or sulfate ions and be excreted in the urine, especially as *ammonium chloride*. In either case, the net effect is to eliminate hydrogen ions, which come indirectly from the excess CO_2, and to produce more HCO_3^- for the blood to elevate the pH.

Classification of Alkalosis and Acidosis

Alkalosis and acidosis are classified as being either *metabolic* or *respiratory*, to indicate the cause of the imbalance. The term *metabolic* refers to an acid-base imbalance due to any cause except CO_2 excess or deficiency.

Metabolic alkalosis is a primary *excess* of HCO_3^-. It is caused by excess ingestion of alkaline salts of organic acids, or by gastric vomiting, which causes loss of HCl. The body compensates for metabolic alkalosis by hypoventilation to increase CO_2 retention, and by kidney excretion of bicarbonate salt in the urine.

Metabolic acidosis is a primary *deficit* of HCO_3^- in the plasma. It can be caused by an excessive loss of HCO_3^-, as occurs in calf scours (severe diarrhea in neonatal enteritis). It can also be caused by excessive acid formation in the animal's body, as occurs (1) during starvation, when body fats are being degraded, (2) in diabetes mellitus, (3) in renal failure, because H^+ ions are not adequately excreted, (4) in lactic acidosis, and (5) from the ingestion of acidifying salts or acids. The body compensates for metabolic acidosis by hyperventilation, to blow off CO_2, and by kidney excretion of ammonium chloride and monobasic sodium-phosphate.

Respiratory acidosis represents *hyper-capnia*—the abnormal retention of CO_2. The term "respiratory" refers to an abnormality of pulmonary ventilation. Respiratory acidosis, then, represents a primary CO_2 excess, which can be caused by such things as partial obstruction of the trachea, pneumonia, pulmonary fibrosis, acute pulmonary edema, or breathing air laden with CO_2. The body compensates for respiratory acidosis by (1) kidney excretion of acid, (2) buffering the blood H^+ ions with hemoglobin, and (3) increased formation of new HCO_3^- in the tubular cells, which utilizes blood CO_2 and gives back HCO_3^- to the blood.

Respiratory alkalosis represents *hypo-capnia*, which is a primary deficit of CO_2 in the blood. Most commonly, it is caused by (1) going to higher altitude, where the O_2 tension is lower and causes overbreathing; (2) a high fever, which causes hyperventilation; (3) encephalitis, which stimulates the respiratory center in the brain, and (4) a brain tumor that stimulates the respiratory center. In compensation, the kidneys excrete HCO_3^- in an alkaline urine.

Often, these four forms of acid-base imbalance are *mixed disturbances,* involving both metabolic and respiratory pathways simultaneously. These pathways must be plotted from laboratory results of blood and urine tests to establish the *primary* causes in diagnosis for proper treatment.

PATHOLOGY OF THE URINARY SYSTEM

Nephritis is a general term for inflammation of the kidneys. All or any part of the nephrons, the connective tissue, or the renal vessels may be affected. The course of nephritis may be acute (rapid), or chronic (of long duration).

Nephrosis refers to noninflammatory kidney disease. Nephrosis frequently involves degeneration of the tubules, resulting in lowered albumin in the blood, albumin in the urine *(albuminuria)*, and edema (excess fluid in the tissues). Nephrosis may be due to damage caused by toxins such as salts of heavy metals.

Uremia (urine in the blood) may occur in kidney disease if the kidneys are unable to remove from the blood enough of the usual constituents of urine. An animal suffering from uremia develops a urinous odor of the breath and skin. Uremia involves acidosis, and retention in the blood of urea, uric acid, and creatinine (azotemia).

Urinary calculi, also called *urolithiasis* or simply stones, are concretions found in any part of the urinary system. They may originate in the pelvis of the kidney and obstruct passage of urine through the ureter, or they may develop in the bladder and interfere with passage of urine through the urethra. Animals with a sigmoid flexure of the penis (ruminants and swine) are particularly susceptible to trouble with urinary calculi, because the calculi have a tendency to lodge in one of the sharp curves of the urethra as it follows the S shape of the penis.

Many factors have been incriminated as causes of urinary calculi. Some of these are high mineral intake in feed or water, low vitamin A level, and low water intake (as is sometimes seen in cold weather).

Acute cases of urolithiasis (also called water belly) may be treated surgically by providing a new exit from the urethra to the exterior. This operation, of course, makes an animal useless for breeding. Often this is not a problem, since more castrates are seen with calculi lodged in the urethra than unneutered animals.

Obstruction of a urinary passage results in *hydronephrosis* (destruction of the kidney substance and dilation of the pelvis) if maintained for a considerable period of time.

Inflammation of the bladder is called *cystitis*; inflammation of the renal pelvis is *pyelitis*; and inflammation of the pelvis and kidney is *pyelonephritis*. These inflammations usually are caused by infections, which may be carried by the blood stream or may ascend from the exterior by way of the urethra.

Chapter 25

Anatomy of the Female Reproductive System

Ovaries
Uterine Tubes
Uterus

Vagina
Vulva
Blood and Nerve Supply of the Female Genitalia

Reproduction in the female is a complex process that involves the entire animal body. The reproductive system itself includes the two ovaries, two uterine (Fallopian) tubes, the uterus, the vagina, and the vulva. The ovum (or egg) is expelled from the ovary and received by the infundibulum and carried to the uterine tube, where fertilization normally occurs during passage of the ovum from the ovary to the uterus. Within the uterus the fertilized ovum develops into an embryo and then into a fetus, and finally passes out of the uterus through the vagina and vulva as a newborn animal.

OVARIES

The ovaries are the primary (or essential) organs of reproduction in the female, just as the testes are in the male. The ovaries may be considered to be both endocrine and cytogenic (cell producing) in nature, since they produce hormones, which are absorbed directly into the bloodstream, and also ova, which are expelled from the gland.

The ovaries are paired glands consisting of a right ovary located behind the right kidney, and a left ovary located behind the left kidney. The distance of each ovary from the respective kidney varies with the species.

In most species, the ovaries are somewhat almond-shaped structures (Fig. 25–1). However, in the mare the ovaries have a bean shape due to the presence of a definite *fossa ovarii (ovulation fossa)*, an indentation in the attached border of the ovary. Ovaries of the sow usually appear lobulated because of the presence of numerous *follicles, corpora lutea*, or both.

When palpated through the wall of the rectum, an ovary feels solid because of the large amount of connective tissue that makes up the stroma of the gland. Irregularities in the surface may be cystlike follicles about to rupture or the more substantial corpora lutea, which form after ovulation.

Normal size of the ovary varies considerably from species to species, and even within a species there is some variation. For

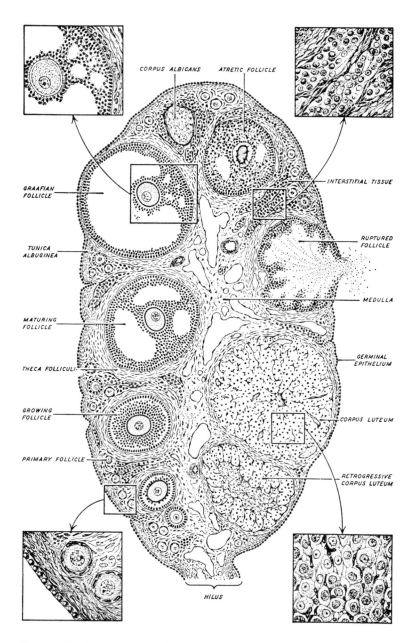

Fig. 25–1.   A diagram of a composite mammalian ovary. Progressive stages in the differentiation of a Graafian follicle are indicated on the left. The mature follicle may become atretic *(top)* or ovulate and undergo luteinization *(right)*. (Turner, General Endocrinology, courtesy of W. B. Saunders Co.)

example, the ovary of a young mare may be less than 1 inch in diameter when no cysts are present, or as large as 4 inches in diameter with the presence of numerous cysts.

The medulla, or central portion *(zona vasculosa)*, of the ovary is the most vascular part, while the majority of the cortex or outer portion *(zona parenchymatosa)* consists of dense irregular connective tissue interspersed with parenchymal epithelial cells that have migrated from the surface. The outer layer of cortex is a dense connective tissue capsule, the *tunica albuginea*. The outermost surface consists, in the fetus, of a single layer of germinal epithelium, the primary sex cells.

Cords of germinal epithelial cells invade the stroma of the ovary and eventually form isolated clumps of cells known as *primary follicles*. One large cell in each follicle is an *oocyte* or *ovum* surrounded by a single layer of follicular cells.

Ova in primary follicles increase in size, and the follicular cells multiply into several layers, forming *maturing follicles* (Fig. 25–2). A thick membrane, the *zona pellucida*, appears between the ovum and the inner layer of follicular cells of the *maturing follicle*. As soon as a fluid-filled cavity, the *antrum*, appears within the mass of follicular cells, the follicle may be called a *Graafian follicle* or a *vesicular follicle*, and the layer of follicular cells is called the *stratum granulosum*. [A double layer of cells from the stroma of the ovary surrounds the stratum granulosum, forming the theca folliculi. The *tunica interna (theca interna)* is a layer of irregularly shaped cells resembling epithelial cells. It is believed to be the source of *estrogens* (female sex hormones) found in the follicular fluid. The *tunica externa (theca externa)* is a layer of connective tissue cells that blends, on its inner surface, with the theca interna, and on its outer surface, with the stroma of the ovary.]

Some of the membrana granulosa cells form a mound surrounding the ovum. This mound is called the *cumulus oophorus*

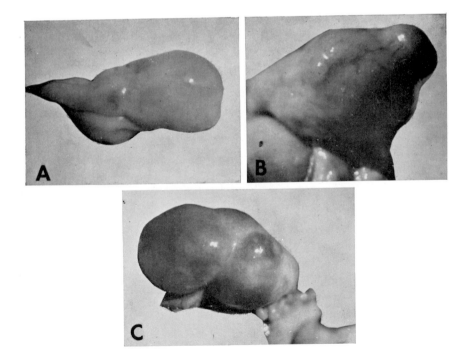

Fig. 25–2.   Bovine ovaries. *A*, Normal ovary with maturing follicle; *B*, normal ovary with well developed corpus luteum; and *C*, abnormal ovary with cystic follicles. (Belling, courtesy of Veterinary Medicine.)

(germ hill or *discus proligerus)*. Its inner-most layer, the *corona radiata*, consists of cylindrical follicular cells arranged in a radial manner over the entire surface of the zona pellucida. Cells of the corona radiata send processes through the zona pellucida to the *vitelline membrane* (cell membrane) of the ovum and presumably supply yolk material to the egg. The *vesicular (Graafian)* follicle, as it is called, after an appreciable amount of fluid forms, continues to increase in size and pushes toward the surface of the ovary, where in some species it can be palpated or observed as a cyst-like bulge.

Monotocous animals, animals not bearing litters, such as the horse and cow, normally have only one offspring per gestation. At each heat period, one follicle usually develops more rapidly than the others, so that when it ruptures, only one ovum or egg is released, and the rest of the follicles then regress and form *atretic follicles.*

Polytocous animals, such as carnivores and swine, which normally produce two or more offspring per gestation, usually have several follicles rupture at approximately the same time. The ova may all come from one ovary, or some may come from each ovary.

The immediate cause of rupture of the follicle at ovulation is not known. In most species it appears to occur as a slow oozing process that may result from local *ischemia* (lack of blood supply), followed by death of cells in the follicular wall.

Immediately following ovulation, the follicular cavity fills with a variable amount of blood and lymph, forming a structure called the *corpus hemorrhagicum*. It is relatively larger in swine than in sheep and cattle. The corpus hemorrhagicum is gradually reabsorbed and replaced by a corpus luteum.

Granulosa (follicular) cells multiply rapidly to form the major part of the *corpus luteum*, but some cells are derived from the theca interna. The corpus luteum has a yellow color in the mare, cow, and carnivores, but is grayish white or flesh-colored in the ewe and sow. The corpus luteum decreases in size and eventually leaves a whitish scar, the *corpus albicans*, as a remnant on the surface of the ovary.

UTERINE TUBES

The uterine tubes (also called *oviducts* or *Fallopian tubes*) are paired, convoluted tubes that conduct the ova from each ovary

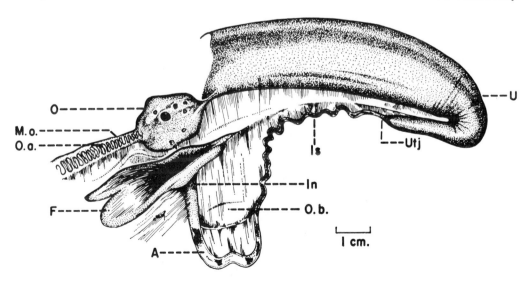

Fig. 25–3. Anatomic relationship between the ovary and the oviduct in the ewe. *A*, Ampulla; *F*, fimbriae; *In*, infundibulum; *Is*, isthmus; *M.o.*, mesovarium; *O*, ovary; *O.a.*, ovarian artery; *O.b.*, ovarian bursa; *U*, uterus; *Utj*, uterotubal junction. Note the suspended loop to which the ovarian bursa is attached. The oviduct in the ewe is pigmented. (From Hafez, E. S. E.: Reproduction in Farm Animals. ed. 3. Philadelphia, Lea & Febiger, 1974.)

to the respective horn of the uterus (Fig. 25–3), and also serve as the usual site for *fertilization* of ova by *spermatozoa*. The portion of the uterine tube adjacent to the ovary is expanded to form a funnel-like structure called the *infundibulum*. The fringe-like margin of the infundibulum is called the *fimbria*. The fimbria appears to take an active part in ovulation, at least to the extent of partially or completely enclosing the ovary and directing the ovum into the abdominal opening of the uterine tube.

The lining of the uterine tube is a highly folded mucous membrane that is covered mainly with simple columnar ciliated epithelium. During heat and before parturition, the nonciliated cells become actively secretory. The rest of the wall of the uterine tube includes a connective tissue submucosa, an inner circular smooth muscle layer, an outer longitudinal smooth muscle layer, and superficially, a layer of connective tissue covered with peritoneum. Both the cilia and muscles function in the movement of

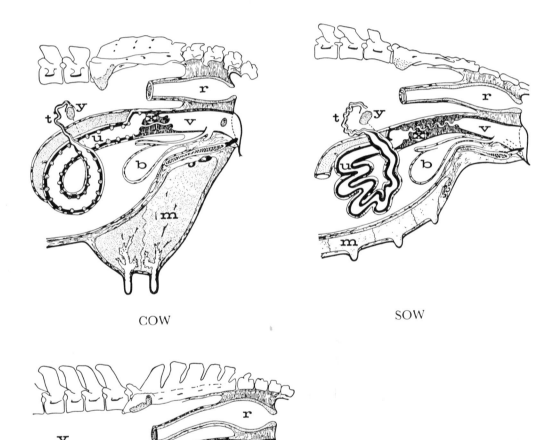

COW

SOW

MARE

Fig. 25–4. Comparative anatomy of the reproductive organs in the female. *b*, Bladder; *m*, mammary gland; *r*, rectum; *t*, oviduct; *u*, uterus; *v*, vagina; *x*, cervix; *y*, ovary. Note species differences in anatomy of cervix, uterus and mammary gland. (From Hafez, E. S. E.: Reproduction in Farm Animals. ed. 3. Philadelphia, Lea & Febiger, 1974.)

ova and possibly in the movement of spermatozoa.

UTERUS

The *uterus* of the domestic mammal consists of a corpus (body), a cervix (neck), and two horns, or cornua (Figs. 25–4, 25–5). The relative proportions of each vary considerably with the species, as do the shape and arrangement of the horns. The *corpus (body) of the uterus* is largest in the mare, less extensive in the cow and sheep, and small in the pig and dog. Superficially, the body of the uterus of the cow appears relatively larger than it actually is because the caudal parts of the horns are bound together by the intercornual ligament.

Like most other hollow internal organs, the uterine wall consists of a lining of mucous membrane, an intermediate smooth muscle layer, and an outer serous layer (peritoneum).

The mucous membrane lining the uterus is a highly glandular structure, the *tunica mucosa (endometrium)*. It varies in thickness

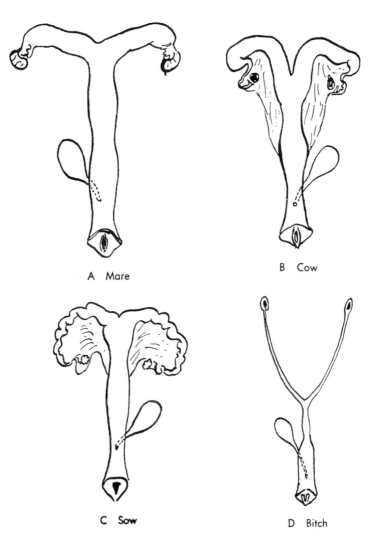

A Mare

B Cow

C Sow

D Bitch

Fig. 25–5. Uteri of farm animals.

and vascularity with hormonal changes in the ovary and with pregnancy. The epithelial covering of the mucous membrane is of the simple columnar type in the horse and dog, but is stratified columnar epithelium in the pig and ruminants.

The uterine glands are simple, branched, tubular glands that exhibit considerable coiling. These glands are scattered throughout the entire endometrium of the uterus, except in ruminants, in which the caruncles are nonglandular. (Caruncles are mushroom-like projections from the inner surface of the uteri of ruminants that give attachment to the fetal membranes.)

The cervix, or neck, of the uterus projects caudally into the vagina. In reality the cervix is a heavy, smooth-muscle sphincter that is tightly closed except during estrus (heat) or at parturition. At the time of estrus the cervix relaxes slightly, permitting spermatozoa to enter the uterus. At this time it is not uncommon for some mucus to be discharged from the cervix and to be expelled from the vulva. An increased amount of mucus is also produced by the goblet cells of the cervix during pregnancy, preventing infective material from entering the uterus from the vagina. In ruminants and to some extent in swine, the inner surface of the cervix is arranged in a series of circular ridges or rings, sometimes called annular folds (Fig. 25–6). The cervix of the mare is relatively smooth, but projects quite a distance caudally into the vagina.

Tunica muscularis (myometrium) is the muscular portion of the wall of the uterus. It consists of a thick, inner, circular layer of smooth muscle and a thinner, outer, longitudinal layer of smooth muscle, separated from each other by a vascular layer (blood vessels in connective tissue). During pregnancy, the amount of muscle in the uterine wall increases immensely, both by increase in cell size and by increase in cell numbers.

The tunica serosa (the serous covering of the uterus) is continuous with the peritoneum known as the broad ligament, which supports the internal genitalia. The broad ligament is composed of the mesovarium, which supports the ovary; the mesosalpinx, which supports the oviduct; and the mesometrium, which supports the uterus. In most nonruminants, the broad ligament is continuous with the parietal peritoneum in the sublumbar region, in such a manner that the uterine horns, oviducts, and ovaries are held in two lines parallel to the median plane, with each ovary located just behind the respective kidney. However, in the ruminant, the attachment of the broad ligament is dorsolateral, in the region of the ilium, resulting in the uterus being arranged like a ram's horns, with the convexity dorsal, then cranial, and then ventral, with the ovaries located near the brim of the pelvis.

VAGINA

The vagina is that portion of the birth canal that is located within the pelvis between the uterus cranially and the vulva caudally. The vagina also serves as a sheath for acceptance of the penis of the male during copulation, the act of breeding or service.

The mucous membrane of the vagina is glandless, stratified squamous epithelium, except in the cow, in which there are some mucous cells in the cranial part of the vagina next to the cervix. In this part of the vagina of the cow, the surface fails to cornify, probably because of low levels of circulating estrogens. The submucosa is loose and the muscular layers consist of an inner circular layer of smooth muscle and an outer longitudinal layer of smooth muscle. The serosa (peritoneum) is present only on the cranial part of the vagina. The caudal portion of the vagina is covered by pelvic fascia (connective tissue).

The fornix of the vagina is the angle, or reflection, formed by the projection of the cervix into the vagina. The fornix may form a complete circle around the cervix, as in the mare, or may be completely absent, as in the pig, in which the caudal end of the cervix is continuous with the vagina. In the cow,

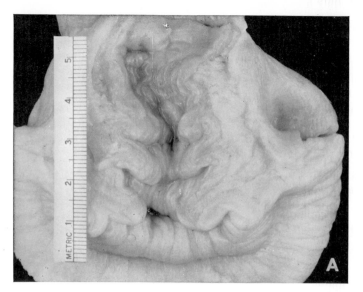

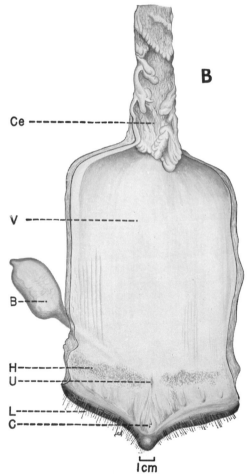

Fig. 25–6. *A*, Cervix (cut open) of a heifer 4 days after estrus. Note the annular folds around the cervical canal. *B*, Cervix, vagina and external genitalia in a non-pregnant ewe. Note the annular folds in the cervix. *B*, urinary bladder; *Ce*, cervix; *C*, clitoris; *H*, hymen; *L*, labia; *U*, external urethral opening; *V*, vagina. (Hafez, Reproduction in Farm Animals, Lea & Febiger, 1974.)

sheep, and goat, only a dorsal fornix is well marked.

VULVA

The *vulva (pudendum femininum)* is the external portion of the genitalia of the female that extends from the vagina to the exterior. The junction of the vagina and vulva is marked by the *external urethral orifice* and frequently also by a ridge just cranial to the external urethral orifice, the vestigial *hymen*. Occasionally the hymen may be complete enough to interfere with copulation.

The *vestibule of the vagina* is the tubular portion of the reproductive tract between the vagina and the labia of the vulva. Commonly the vestibule has been considered a part of the vulva, but the N. A. V. (Nomina Anatomica Veterinaria) lists it separately from both the vagina and vulva.

In domestic animals, the *labia*, or lips, of the vulva are simple, rather than consisting of major and minor labia as in the human. The ventral commissure (lowest part) of the vulva conceals the *clitoris*, which has the same embryonic origin as the *penis* in the male. The clitoris consists of two crura, or roots, a body, and a glans. It is made up of erectile tissue covered by stratified squamous epithelium and is well supplied with sensory nerve endings.

BLOOD AND NERVE SUPPLY OF THE FEMALE GENITALIA

In most domestic animals, the uterus receives blood from the paired cranial uterine arteries, middle uterine arteries, and caudal uterine arteries.

The *ramus uterinus (cranial uterine) artery* is a branch of the *ovarian artery* that supplies blood to the ovary and to the anterior extremity of the uterine horn by the cranial uterine artery. The oviduct also receives its blood supply from the ovarian artery. In most species of farm animals (except the mare), the ovarian artery and the uterine vein run in close proximity, providing a venoarterial pathway for substances from the uterus to reach the ovary on the same side (Fig. 25–7). If the substance (luteolysin)

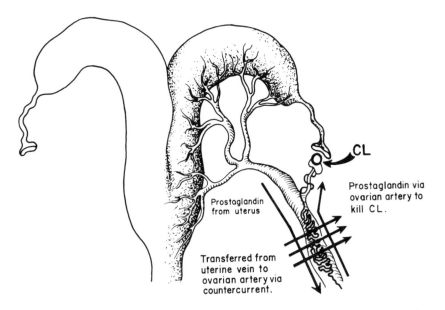

Fig. 25–7. Prostaglandin transfer from uterus to uterine vein, then countercurrent transfer to ovarian artery and thence to corpus luteum (CL), in the ewe and possibly other species. (From McDonald, L. E.: Veterinary Endocrinology and Reproduction. ed. 2. Philadelphia, Lea & Febiger, 1975.)

Table 25–1.   Comparative Anatomy of the Reproductive Tract in the Adult Nonpregnant Female of Farm Mammals

	Animal			
Organ	Cow	Ewe	Sow	Mare
Oviduct				
Length (cm)	25	15–19	15–30	20–30
Uterus				
Type	Bipartite	Bipartite	Bicornuate	Bipartite
Length of horn (cm)	35–40	10–12	40–65	15–25
Length of body (cm)	2–4	1–2	5	15–20
Surface lining of endometrium	70–120 caruncles	88–96 caruncles	Slight longitudinal folds	Conspicious longitudinal folds
Cervix				
Length (cm)	8–10	4–10	10	7–8
Outside diameter (cm)	3–4	2–3	2–3	3.5–4
Cervical lumen				
Shape	2–5 annular rings	Annular rings	Corkscrewlike	Conspicuous folds
Os Uteri				
Shape	Small and protruding	Small and protruding	Ill-defined	Clearly-defined
Anterior Vagina				
Length (cm)	25–30	10–14	10–15	20–35
Hymen	Ill-defined	Well-developed	Ill-defined	Well-developed
Vestibule				
Length (cm)	10–12	2.5–3	6–8	10–12

The dimensions included in this table vary with age, breed, parity and plane of nutrition.
(From Hafez, E. S. E.: Reproduction in Farm Animals, ed. 3. Philadelphia, Lea & Febiger, 1974.)

comes from a nongravid uterus, it may stimulate resorption of the corpus luteum. If the substance (luteotropin) comes from a gravid uterus or possibly an infected uterus, it may stimulate retention of the corpus luteum.

The *uterine (middle uterine) artery* is a branch of either the *internal iliac artery* or *external iliac artery*, and frequently it is derived from a common trunk with the *umbilical artery*. The uterine artery is the chief blood supply to the uterus in the region of the developing fetus, and, consequently, it enlarges greatly as pregnancy progresses.

One of the signs of pregnancy in cattle is the definite buzzing or vibration of this artery, which can be palpated through the rectum.

The *ramus uterinus (caudal uterine) artery* is a branch of the *vaginal artery* (formerly called urogenital artery). The *internal pudendal artery* supplies blood to the vagina, vulva, and anus.

The nerve supply to the ovary, oviduct, and uterus is primarily by autonomic nerves. The *pudendal nerve* supplies sensory fibers as well as parasympathetic fibers to the vagina, vulva, and clitoris.

Chapter 26

Physiology of Female Reproduction

PUBERTY

Puberty is the period during which reproductive organs first become functional. Sexual maturity in this sense differs among the different species. Mares usually reach puberty by the second year, whereas heifers reach this point at seven to fifteen months of age. Ewes, sows, and bitches may breed as young as six months of age. Great variations can be found within a single species, depending on climatic conditions, level of nutrition, heredity, and levels of hormones released.

Ovarian developments associated with sexual maturity include oogenesis (the development of the ovum from a primary sex cell), ovulation, and formation of corpora lutea. These events in turn affect other parts of the reproductive system in a cyclic manner, producing the estrous cycle.

OOGENESIS

In contrast to the male sex cells, which form four spermatozoa from each primary sex cell, the maturation of the female primary sex cell results in only one mature *ovum* (or *ootid*) and three rudimentary cells, called *polar bodies* or *polocytes*. Usually, the division that produces the first polar body is *meiotic* in nature; that is, it is a reduction division in which the chromosome number is reduced to one-half the original number. The ovum then undergoes *mitotic division* to split off the second polar body. The first polar body may also divide mitotically or amitotically before the polar bodies degenerate. In most animals, the first polar body is given off in the ovary. The second polar body is given off after ovulation occurs.

OVULATION AND CORPUS LUTEUM FORMATION

As the ovarian follicle increases in size, due primarily to the large amount of fluid produced, it exerts pressure on the *tunica albuginea* of the ovary, resulting in a definite bulging and consequent thinning of the sur-

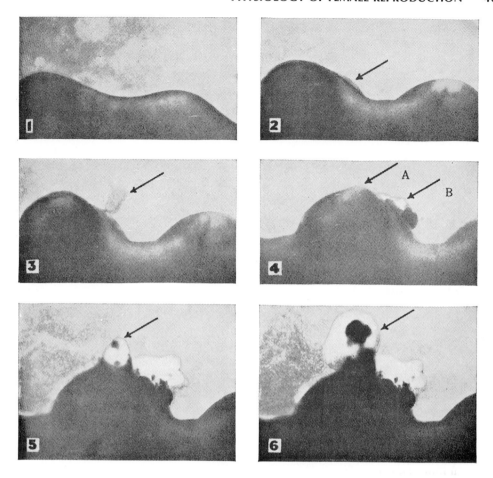

Fig. 26–1.   Enlargements of single frames of a time-lapse motion picture showing ovulation in the rabbit. *1*, Profile view of two follicles about 1½ hours before rupture. *2*, Same follicles about ½ hour before rupture. *3*, Exudation of clear fluid in early phases of rupture. *4*, At arrow *A*, a new follicle becomes conical as the time of its rupture approaches. At arrow *B*, the exudate from the follicle shown starting to rupture in *3* has become more abundant and contains some blood (dark). *5*, The follicle indicated by arrow *A* in *4* is now beginning to rupture. The blood-tinged exudate from the follicle which started to rupture in *3*, and showed more vigorous exudation in *4* (arrow *B*), can be seen partly behind the more recently rupturing follicle. *6*, The rupture of the follicle is indicated by the arrow in *5*. Time elapsed between the photographs shown in *5* and *6* is 8 seconds. The ovum is carried out with this final gush of fluid from the ruptured follicle. (Hill, Allen, and Kramer, courtesy of Anatomical Record.)

face of the ovary, in much the same way an abscess "points" toward the surface of the body and eventually ruptures (Fig. 26–1). The follicular fluid and *ovum* are expelled into the peritoneal cavity in the vicinity of the *infundibulum* of the *oviduct* or *uterine tube*, thus completing the process of *ovulation*. In most mammals, ovulation is closely associated with heat, or *estrus*, because of absorption into the blood stream of large amounts of estrogen just prior to ovulation.

Sometimes during ovulation a small blood vessel may rupture, and the cavity of the follicle then fills with a blood clot which is called a *corpus hemorrhagicum*. Whether or not a corpus hemorrhagicum forms, the epithelial cells lining the empty follicular cavity begin to multiply under the influence of *LH (luteinizing hormone)* from the anterior lobe of the pituitary gland, to form a *corpus luteum*, or *yellow body*. In most species, the corpus luteum projects from the surface of the ovary, much as the original ovarian follicle did. Each follicle that ruptures normally is replaced by a corpus luteum.

Although the follicle and corpus luteum are about the same size, they can be differentiated by sight or palpation. The follicle is a sac filled with fluid which has the appearance and feel of a blister, while the corpus luteum looks and feels solid.

If the ovum is not fertilized, the corpus luteum, which is called a corpus luteum of estrus, regresses and disappears, leaving only a scar called a *corpus albicans*. If the ovum is fertilized and pregnancy ensues, the corpus luteum may last throughout the gestation period as a corpus luteum of pregnancy. The corpus luteum is, in reality, an endocrine gland that produces progesterone, a hormone essential for maintenance of pregnancy. Occasionally a corpus luteum of estrus fails to regress and the animal does not come in season, thus giving the false appearance of being pregnant. This type of corpus luteum is called a *retained corpus luteum* and is an important cause of temporary infertility in dairy cattle.

Sterility may also be caused by an abnormally large number of follicles developing at the same time without rupturing or regressing. This is a cystic condition of the ovary, and in the cow and horse these cysts, or abnormal follicles, can be palpated through the rectum. An animal suffering from cystic ovaries may be called a *nymphomaniac* because she appears to be in heat much of the time.

ESTROUS CYCLE

Domestic females come into heat at fairly regular intervals that differ rather widely between species. This interval from the beginning of one heat period to the beginning of the next is called the estrous cycle. It is controlled directly by hormones from the ovary and indirectly by hormones from the anterior lobe of the pituitary gland. The basic pattern of the estrous cycle is the same, but species differences are found in different parts of the cycle (Fig. 26–2). The estrous cycle is divided into several well-marked phases called proestrus, estrus, metestrus, and diestrus.

Proestrus

Under stimulation of *FSH (follicle-stimulating hormone)*, from the anterior lobe of the pituitary, and some LH *(luteinizing hormone)*, the ovary produces increasing quantities of estrogens, which cause increased development of the uterus, vagina, oviducts, and ovarian follicles. This first phase (proestrus) of the estrous cycle is referred to as the "building up" phase. It is during this phase that the ovarian follicle, with its enclosed ovum, increases in size primarily by increasing the follicular fluid, which contains estrogenic hormones.

Estrogens absorbed from the follicles into the blood stream stimulate increased vascularity and cell growth of the tubular genitalia, in preparation for estrus and subsequent pregnancy.

Estrus

Estrus is the period of sexual receptivity in the female, which is determined largely by circulating estrogen level. During or shortly after this time, ovulation occurs. This is brought about by a decrease in the FSH levels in the blood and an increase in LH levels. Just before ovulation, the follicle is large and turgid, and the enclosed ovum undergoes maturation changes. Estrus terminates about the time when rupture of the ovarian follicle, or *ovulation*, occurs. At this time the ovum is expelled from the follicle to pass into the upper part of the uterine tube.

Follicular rupture occurs spontaneously in most animal species. However, in the cat, rabbit, mink, ferret, and a few other animals, rupture is possible only if coitus occurs. Since, in these animals, ovulation is caused by a delayed neuroendocrine reflex involving hormone release from the pituitary, re-

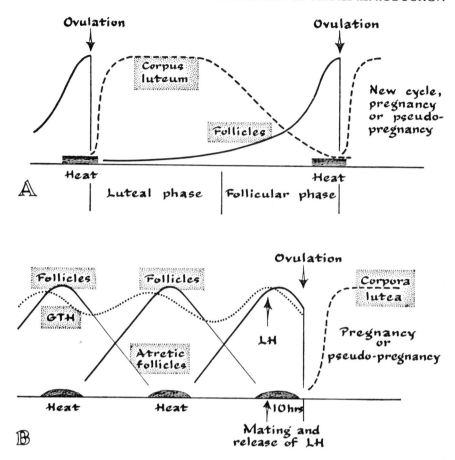

Fig. 26–2.   Comparison of estrous cycles in: *A*, Females with spontaneous ovulation and, *B*, females with induced ovulation. (Reproductive Physiology, by A. V. Nalbandov, courtesy of W. H. Freeman and Co., copyright 1958.)

sulting from stimulation by the act of coitus, they are called *reflex-ovulators*. If coitus does not occur in these animals, the follicle with enclosed ovum regresses. A sterile mating frequently is followed by pseudopregnancy in reflex ovulators.

Metestrus

Metestrus is the postovulatory phase during which the corpus luteum functions. The length of metestrus may depend on the length of time LTH *(luteotrophic hormone)* is secreted by the anterior pituitary. During this period there is a decrease in estrogen and an increase in progesterone formed by the ovary.

During metestrus, the cavity left by the rupturing of the follicle begins to reorganize. The lining of the ruptured follicle begins to grow inward as the blood vascular supply increases within the cavity. The cells lining the cavity that have not been expelled increase in size, multiply, and become laden with fat droplets. This newly reorganized structure is called the corpus luteum, or yellow body. Progesterone secreted by the corpus luteum prevents further development of follicles and hence prevents the occurrence of further estrous periods. Estrus does not occur so long as an active corpus luteum is present. If pregnancy occurs, secretions from a functional corpus luteum are necessary for proper implantation of the fertilized ovum in the uterus, subsequent nourishment of the developing embryo, and development of the alveoli of the mammary gland.

Diestrus and Anestrus

Diestrus is a relatively short period of quiescence between estrous cycles in polyestrous animals. *Anestrus* is a longer period of quiescence between the breeding seasons.

A fully developed corpus luteum has a notable influence on the uterus. The endometrial lining of the uterus thickens, uterine glands increase in size, and uterine muscles also show increased development. All the reactions are directed toward supplying a bed for nourishment of the embryo. If pregnancy occurs, these phenomena are prolonged throughout gestation, and the corpus luteum remains intact for all or most of the period.

If the ovum is not fertilized and pregnancy does not come about, the corpus luteum regresses. During the breeding season in some species, such as the cow and the ewe, regression of the corpus luteum is followed by a new wave of ovarian follicles, which initiates a new proestrous period. At the end of the breeding season, the ovaries of nonpregnant ewes become quiescent (anestrus), and the other sexual organs, such as the oviducts, uterus, and vagina, deprived of hormonal influence, tend to atrophy. When another breeding season comes about, the ovary is again activated, and a new cycle is started. In the bitch, even though unmated, the corpus luteum persists throughout a period equal to the normal gestation period.

SUMMARY OF ESTROUS CYCLES

The estrous cycle may be summarized as follows:

A. proestrus—period of build-up during which follicles increase in size, vaginal wall thickens, and uterine vascularity increases.
B. estrus—period of heat and greatest receptivity to male; rupture of ovarian follicles in most farm animals.
C. metestrus—formation of the corpus luteum, changes in vaginal wall and uterus.

Alternatives that may follow metestrus:

1. diestrus—short period of inactivity before the next proestrous period during the breeding season of polyestrous animals.
2. pregnancy—period of gestation
3. pseudopregnancy—changes similar to pregnancy, but no embryo or fetus is present.
4. anestrus—long period of inactivity between sexual seasons.

Animals that have only one estrous cycle per year are called *monestrous* animals, while those that have several estrous cycles per year are called *polyestrous animals*. The period of successive estrous cycles is known as the *breeding season*, or, perhaps more properly, the *sexual season*, since the term "breeding season" may be used to include pregnancy and even lactation. The relatively long period of inactivity between sexual seasons in some animals is called anestrus and is not properly a part of the sexual cycle. The period of anestrus, at least in some animals, appears to be determined by seasonal changes in length of day, ultimately affecting the *hypothalamus*, which in turn affects the release of hormones from the pituitary gland *(hypophysis)*.

There are two phases to the sexual cycle proper. The estrogenic phase, or follicular phase, includes proestrus and estrus. The luteal phase includes metestrus and diestrus, although there is hormonal overlap in both phases.

The nonbreeding period, or anestrus, may occupy the greater part of the year in some species, such as the sheep and dog. It is followed by the breeding season, when one or more estrous cycles occur.

This sequence, the estrous cycle, is repeated a number of times each sexual season in polyestrous animals if conception does not occur. If conception occurs during estrus, the next step is gestation rather than metestrus and diestrus. Gestation in turn may be followed by proestrus, initiating another sexual cycle, or by anestrus.

Pseudopregnancy, or *false pregnancy*, is a condition that may follow estrus in some species of carnivora and rodents if conception does not occur. The bitch may become pseudopregnant whether a sterile mating occurs or not, but several rodents require coitus or else artificial stimulation of the cervix to induce pseudopregnancy. Corpora lutea remain in the ovary, and changes in the uterus resemble those in pregnancy. The mammary glands become active and may secrete milk at the end of the pseudopregnancy, which is approximately equal in length to a normal gestation, or somewhat shorter.

Estrous Cycle of the Mare

Puberty begins between 10 and 24 months, with an average onset at about 18 months.

Length of Estrous Cycle. The length of time elapsed from the beginning of one estrous period to the beginning of the next has been reported to vary in the mare from 7 to 124 days (Fig. 26–3). However, the average figure reported by all investigators has been close to 21 or 22 days. The abnormally long cycles undoubtedly include a number of skipped periods or cycles.

Length of Estrus. The average length of the estrous period in the mare is approximately six days, but wide variations are possible. Trum (1950) reported that thoroughbred mares at Fort Robinson, Nebraska, showed estrous periods as follows: 11%, 2 to 3 days; 61%, 4 to 6 days; 28%, 7 to 9 days; and 5%, over 10 days.

Heat periods tend to become shorter from spring to midsummer. The shorter heat periods appear to be correlated with increased fertility. Early in the breeding season, through March and April, heat periods tend to be irregular and long, frequently with no ovulation occurring. From May to July the periods become shorter and more regular, with ovulation as a normal part of the cycle. Ovulation usually occurs from one to two days before the end of estrus.

Time of Breeding. Fertility rises during estrus to a peak two days before the end of estrus, then falls off abruptly. Mares with heat periods of one to three days should be bred on the first day. Mares with longer heat periods should be bred on the third or fourth day and again 48 to 72 hours later. If heat is longer than eight to ten days, it is better to wait until the next heat period. Mares with regular, short heat periods throughout the

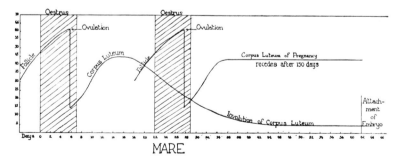

Fig. 26–3.   The estrous cycle in the mare. (Dukes, The Physiology of Domestic Animals, courtesy of Comstock Publishing Co.)

year can be successfully bred at any time of the year.

Early in the breeding season, some mares show intense sexual desire during long heat periods but do not ovulate. These mares probably will not conceive until their heat periods become shorter and more regular. Other mares may have only "silent heat" periods in which ovulation occurs but no sexual desire is evident. Many of these mares will conceive if the heat period is identified by rectal palpation and appearance of the vulva, vagina, and cervix.

Histologic changes of the genitalia of the mare during the estrous cycle approximate the general pattern found in all mammals. However, these changes are not distinctive enough to make a vaginal smear useful in determining the stage of the estrous cycle.

Estrous Cycle of the Cow

In cattle, puberty varies considerably with the breed and level of nutrition. Holstein heifers showed first estrus at an average of 37 weeks of age on a high level of nutrition, 49 weeks on a medium level, and 72 weeks on a low level of feeding. Puberty appears to occur when the heifer is about two-thirds of its adult body size, measured by height and length rather than weight.

Length of Estrous Cycle. The estrous cycle length averages 20 days for heifers and 21 to 22 days for mature cows (Fig. 26–4).

Length of Estrus. The estrous period in the cow may be defined as the time she will stand when mounted by another cow or bull. This period averages about 18 hours in both dairy and beef cows, and is somewhat shorter in heifers. The normal range is 12 to 24 hours.

Time of Ovulation. Ovulation normally occurs about 10 to 15 hours following the end of estrus in the cow (Fig. 26–5).

Time of Breeding. Conception has occurred in cattle bred as early as 34 hours before ovulation and as late as 14 hours after ovulation. It has been suggested that bull spermatozoa must be present for at least six hours in the uterus or oviduct of the cow before they are capable of fertilizing an ovum.

For artificial insemination, cows that come into "*standing heat*" in the morning are bred the same afternoon, and cows that come into "*standing heat*" in the afternoon

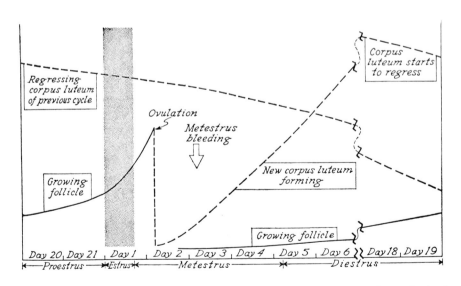

Fig. 26–4. The estrous cycle in the cow. (From Physiology of Reproduction and Artifical Insemination by G. W. Salisbury and H. L. VanDemark. Copyright by W. H. Freeman and Company, 1961.)

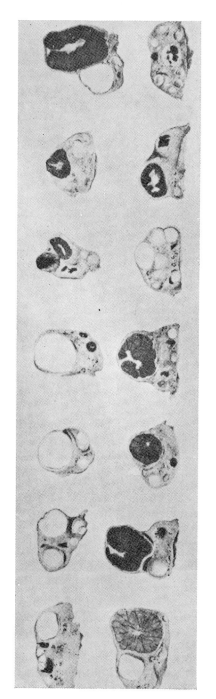

Fig. 26–5.   Ovaries of cows at different stages of the estrous cycle. The two ovaries of the animal are shown one above the other. In the top row the ripening follicle is seen; it ruptures between 24 and 48 hours after the beginning of heat and forms the new corpus luteum, which at first is dark from a blood clot and later in the process of reorganization becomes a paler body, in the meantime increasing in size. In the bottom row, which shows the ovary with the old corpus luteum of the previous heat period, the stages of its degeneration are seen. (Hammond, Physiology of Reproduction in the Cow, 1927; reproduced by permission of the Cambridge University Press.)

are bred the next morning. A cow in "standing heat" stands for mounting by a bull, a steer, or another cow.

Bleeding from the vulva occurs in a high percentage of heifers and cows one to three days following the end of estrus. This phenomenon is called metestrous bleeding, and, if breeding is done at this time, conception seldom follows. However, if breeding takes place at the proper time, fertility and conception are not impaired because of metestrous bleeding.

Estrous Cycle of the Ewe

Puberty usually occurs the first fall at four to 12 months of age if the ewes are well fed.

Breeding Season. The ewe is probably the best example of a seasonally polyestrous animal, with a long period of anestrus followed by a breeding season that may vary from 1 to 20 consecutive estrous cycles. The length of breeding season appears to be related to the severity of climatic conditions under which the breed developed. In severe climates, a suitable lambing period is restricted and, consequently, the breeding, or sexual, season is likewise restricted, so that lambing occurs only during the favorable time (Scotch Black Face is an example of such a breed). Breeds developed in milder climates may lamb successfully over a longer period, so the breeding or sexual season is also extended (example: Merino sheep).

Length of Estrous Cycle. The average estrous cycle in the ewe is between 16.5 and 17.5 days. Unusually long or unusually short cycles tend to appear during the early and later parts of the sexual season, rather than during the middle part.

Length of Estrus. Duration of estrus averages about 30 hours. It has been reported to range from 3 hours to 84 hours, but most ewes will accept a ram during a period of 24 to 48 hours. The ram may be attracted both during proestrus and metestrus as well as estrus, but the ewe will accept him only during the actual estrous period.

Time of Ovulation. Ovulation occurs near the termination of estrus, when two or three ovulations may occur in the same estrous period.

Time of Breeding. The best time for breeding ewes is from the middle of estrus to the latter part of estrus. However, since estrus usually is short, the question of optimum time of breeding is not practical.

Estrous Cycle of the Sow

Sexual maturity in the gilt usually occurs about seven months of age. As in other species, it is delayed by an inadequate diet.

Length of Estrous Cycle. The average estrous cycle in swine is about 21 days, with a reported range from 11 to 41 days. A range from 18 to 24 days is considered normal.

Length of Estrus. The estrous period may range from 15 to 96 hours, with an average duration between 40 and 46 hours. The first estrus after weaning is usually longer and may average 65 hours; it occurs about 7 to 9 days after weaning of the pigs.

Many sows exhibit a nonfertile estrus one to three days following parturition. In nearly all of these animals, ovulation does not occur. It has been suggested that this heat may be caused by estrogen from some source other than the ovary.

Time of Ovulation. Ovulation occurs during the latter part of estrus about the second day of the cycle. At each period, 10 to 25 ova are shed, with an average of 16.4.

Estrous Cycle of the Bitch

The appearance of the first estrus varies considerably between breeds and also between individuals within a breed. The smaller breeds may attain puberty as early as 6 to 8 months, while larger breeds may be 1½ to 2 years old before the first heat.

Length of Estrous Cycle. The dog is a monestrous animal with a variable period of anestrus between estrous periods. While the bitch is commonly considered to come in season twice a year with approximately 6

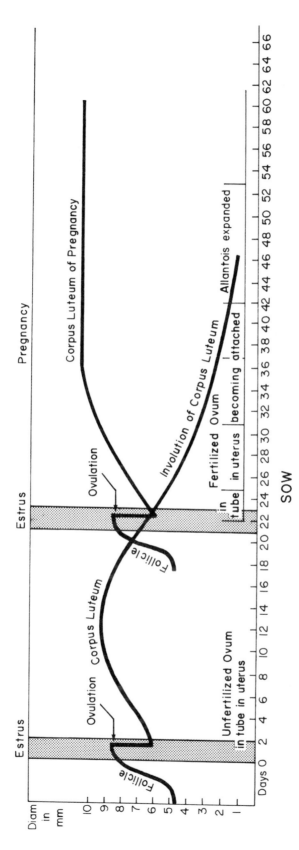

Fig. 26–6. The estrous cycle of the sow. (Slightly modified from Corner.) (Dukes, The Physiology of Domestic Animals, courtesy of Comstock Publishing Co.)

409

months between heat periods, the interval averages between 7 and 8 months. The length of the anestrous period may vary from 4 months in small breeds to 8 months or more in large breeds. The estrous cycle itself is much less variable, with an average proestrus of 9 days, estrus of 9 days, and metestrus of 80 to 90 days. Some authorities consider metestrus to be limited to the early luteal phase, while the bitch is still receptive to the male. They consider diestrus to continue from the loss of sexual receptivity.

Length of Estrus. Estrus may range from 5 to 19 days, with a higher conception rate occurring in bitches with estrous periods that last from 5 to 10 days and a much lower conception rate in those extending from 17 to 19 days.

Time of Ovulation. The bitch appears to ovulate spontaneously during the first three or four days of true estrus. It is not known whether all follicles ovulate at one time or whether ovulation is a continuing process during the early part of estrus.

Time of Breeding. During proestrus the vulva swells considerably, and a more or less moderate flow of blood occurs. The advent of estrus can be definitely determined by the willingness of the female to accept a male. At this time, the flow of blood de-

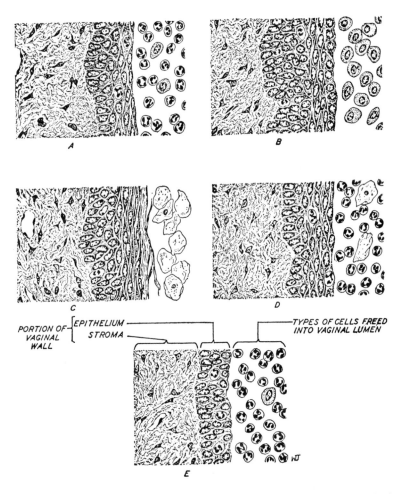

Fig. 26–7. Sections through the vaginal wall of the rat during different stages of the estrous cycle showing types of cells that appear in vaginal smears. A, Diestrus; B, proestrus; C, estrus; D, metestrus; and E, adult animal spayed for six months. (Turner, General Endocrinology, courtesy of W. B. Saunders Co.)

creases considerably, and the turgidity of the vulva may decrease. The bitch assumes a typical stance with the back extended (swayed), tail head elevated, and tail raised and often held to one side. She may assume this position during the latter part of proestrus, but she will not permit copulation until estrus actually begins.

Breeding should occur during the first four days of estrus. If only two matings are permitted, the first day of acceptance and the third days of estrus are probably the most desirable. In other words, breed as soon as the bitch will accept the male, skip the next day, then breed again on the third day.

A vaginal smear may be utilized as an aid in determining the stage of the estrous cycle (Fig. 26–7), but it may not be as accurate an indication of when to breed as is the willingness of the bitch to accept the male. The vaginal smear during proestrus is marked by an abundance of erythrocytes. The onset of estrus may not be clearly defined in a vaginal smear, but cornified epithelial cells with small nuclei are abundant during true estrus. Leukocytes begin to appear during late estrus and are abundant during metestrus.

Pseudopregnancy. During pseudopregnancy, which is not uncommon in the bitch, many of the signs of pregnancy are present even though the bitch has not conceived. The uterine horns increase in diameter during the fifth week after estrus and may be confused with pregnancy on palpation. Mammary glands develop, and in extreme cases lactation, nest building, and adoption of objects or other animals may occur.

HORMONES OF FEMALE REPRODUCTION

Hormones produced in the ovary include estrogens from the follicles and progesterone from the corpora lutea. Secretory activity of the ovary is under control of the *gonadotrophic hormones* of the anterior lobe of the pituitary gland, and these in turn are at least partially controlled by the ovarian hormones through the classic feedback

mechanism described in Chapter 32, page 475.

Estrogens

The term *estrogen* refers to any of a group of compounds that act as female sex hormones and stimulate female accessory sex glands. *Estrone, estradiol,* and *estriol* are natural estrogens produced by the mammalian ovary or placenta. *Diethylstilbestrol* is the most common of a group of synthetic estrogens. It is used in hormonal treatments, to produce abortion in some domestic animals (bitches and feed-lot heifers) and, until banned by the Food and Drug Administration, as a feed additive for fattening animals. A number of plants also produce substances that have estrogenic activity. In addition to the ovary, the *adrenal cortex, testes,* and *placenta* are natural sources of estrogens in the mammal.

The action of estrogens on accessory sex organs usually can be correlated fairly well with behavior typical of estrus (heat). Estrogens stimulate muscular activity of the uterine tubes and uterus and sensitize both of these organs for the action of progesterone. Other uterine changes stimulated by estrogen include increases in cellular water content, *DNA (deoxyribonucleic acid), RNA (ribonucleic acid),* protein synthesis, and enzyme activity.

The epithelium lining the vagina and vulva is stimulated by estrogens and in some species becomes cornified during estrus. An increasing level of estrogen is undoubtedly an important factor in the development of *libido,* the sex drive associated with receptivity to the male by the female in heat.

Estrogens also sensitize the pregnant uterus to the action of *oxytocin* from the posterior lobe of the pituitary gland.

Secondary sex characteristics associated with femininity to a large extent result from the actions of estrogens. In domestic mammals, secondary female sex characteristics are associated with growth and development of the mammary gland ducts, and a less mas-

Table 26–1. Female Reproduction[1]

Animal	Onset of Puberty	Av. Age First Service	Length Estrous Cycle	Length Estrus	Gestation Period
Mare	18 mo (10 to 24 mo)	2 to 3 yrs	21 days (19 to 21 days)	5 days (4½ to 7½ days)	336 days (323 to 341 days)
Cow	4 to 24 mo	14 to 22 mo	21 days (18 to 24 days)	18 hrs (12 to 28 hrs)	282 days (274 to 291 days)
Ewe	4 to 12 mo (1st fall)	12 to 18 mo	16½ days (14 to 20 days)	24 to 48 hrs	150 days (140 to 160 days)
Sow	3 to 7 mo	8 to 10 mo	21 days (18 to 24 days)	2 days (1 to 5 days)	114 days (110 to 116 days)
Bitch	6 to 24 mo	12 to 18 mo	6 to 12 mo	9 days (5 to 19 days)	63 days (60 to 65 days)

Animal	Time of Ovulation	Optimum Time for Service	Advisable Time to Breed after Parturition
Mare	1 to 2 days before end of estrus	3 to 4 days before end of estrus or the second or third day of estrus	About 25 to 35 days or second estrus. About 9 days or first estrus only if normal in every way
Cow	10 to 15 hours after the end of estrus	Just before the middle of estrus to the end of estrus	60 to 90 days
Ewe	12 to 24 hours before the end of estrus	18 to 24 hours after the onset of estrus	Usually the following fall
Sow	30 to 36 hours after the onset of estrus	12 to 30 hours after the onset of estrus	First estrus 3 to 9 days after weaning pigs
Bitch	1 to 2 days after the onset of true estrus	2 to 3 days after onset of true estrus; or 10 to 14 days after onset of proestrous bleeding	Usually the first estrus or 2 to months after weaning pups

[1] Data compiled from standard references, including Dukes, Payne, Roberts, and Spector.

sive skeleton and lighter muscling than males. In the human, distribution of hair and fat and the pitch of the voice are observable secondary sex characteristics.

Progesterone

Progesterone is produced mainly by the corpus luteum, but is also found in the adrenal cortex, placenta, and testes. In general, progesterone acts on tissues that have been primed (prepared) by estrogen, although it may act synergistically (at the same time as estrogens); in large quantities, progesterone and estrogens may be antagonistic in their actions.

Progesterone is known as the hormone of pregnancy because it causes thickening of the endometrium and development of the uterine glands prior to implantation of the fertilized ovum. It inhibits excessive uterine motility during the period of implantation and during the period of gestation. Apparently, a change in ratio of estrogen and progesterone may sensitize the uterus to oxytocin and possibly trigger parturition. The initiating cause of parturition, however, is still in doubt. The importance of progesterone in maintaining pregnancy is suggested by the fact that spontaneous abortion occurs in some animals if the ovaries are removed during the gestation period, with the consequent reduction in progesterone.

During pregnancy, progesterone suspends ovulation, by a feedback inhibition of FSH and LH from the anterior pituitary. FSH plays a major role in maturation of the follicle, whereas LH plays the major role in ovulation.

Progesterone acts on the mammary gland, which has previously been primed by estrogens. It promotes complete development of the alveoli of the mammary gland. Progesterone also tends to raise the body temperature, and this fact is used in the human as an indicator to determine the time of ovulation. A temperature rise is correlated with ovulation and the release of progesterone from the corpus luteum.

Other Hormones

Relaxin is a water-soluble, nonsteroid polypeptide hormone that is formed by the ovaries. It can be extracted from corpora lutea and the endometrium, and the placenta in some species. Relaxin causes relaxation of the pelvic ligaments, and is believed to be a factor in relaxation of the cervix at parturition.

Both the pituitary gland and the ovaries appear to be essential in all species for the events leading to conception and implantation (see Figs. 26–8, 26–9). There is considerable species variation in the need for the pituitary gland and ovaries in later stages of pregnancy. Some animals abort immediately if either the pituitary gland or ovaries are removed, but others appear to tolerate either or both operations without fetal loss. In these latter animals, the placenta secretes sufficient gonadotrophins, estrogens, and progesterone to maintain pregnancy.

Chorionic gonadotrophin is a glycoprotein hormone secreted by the trophoblastic cells of the implanted developing zygote membranes; it functions much like luteinizing hormone in the human. It is found in *pregnant mare serum* (PMS), where it functions more like FSH, and in the urine of pregnant women, where it is called *human chorionic gonadotrophin (HCG)*. These gonadotrophins are the basis for pregnancy tests in the mare and the human.

By the last third of pregnancy, estrogens and progesterones have stimulated essentially complete mammary gland development of the arborized duct system and milk alveoli. At the time of parturition, a factor believed to be present in the hypothalamus, called *prolactin inhibiting factor* (PIF), is released from its inhibitive action on *prolactin* hormone in the adenohypophysis (anterior pituitary), allowing prolactin to enter

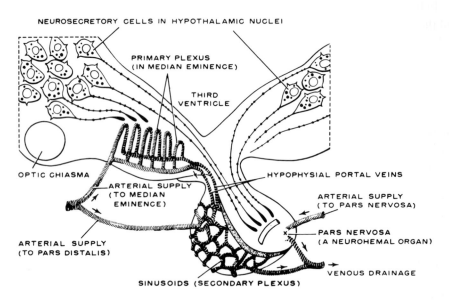

NEUROSECRETORY CELLS IN HYPOTHALAMIC NUCLEI

PRIMARY PLEXUS
(IN MEDIAN EMINENCE)

THIRD
VENTRICLE

OPTIC CHIASMA

ARTERIAL SUPPLY
(TO MEDIAN
EMINENCE)

HYPOPHYSIAL PORTAL VEINS

ARTERIAL SUPPLY
(TO PARS NERVOSA)

PARS NERVOSA
(A NEUROHEMAL ORGAN)

ARTERIAL SUPPLY
(TO PARS DISTALIS)

VENOUS DRAINAGE

SINUSOIDS (SECONDARY PLEXUS)

Fig. 26–8. Diagram of the anatomic connections between the hypothalamus and the pituitary gland. Neurosecretory cells are present in certain hypothalamic nuclei: Some of the secretory axons pass down the infundibular stalk and terminate near blood vessels in the pars nervosa; others terminate in close proximity to the capillary loops of the median eminence. The hormones of the neurohypophysis (vasopressin and oxytocin)are the products of hypothalamic neurosecretory cells and are stored and released from the pars nervosa (a neurohemal organ). The hypophysial portal venules start as the primary plexus of the median eminence and convey blood downward to the sinusoids of the anterior lobe. There are strong indications that the hypothalamic axons of the median eminence liberate multiple releasing factors (probably peptide in nature) into the portal vessels and that these neural factors are concerned with the regulation of anterior pituitary functions. It is apparent that the whole pituitary gland is predominantly subservient to and has partly evolved from the hypothalamic portion of the brain. (Turner and Bagnara, General Endocrinology, courtesy of W. B. Saunders Co.)

the blood in quantity. Its effect is to stimulate lactation to fill the mammary glands with milk. The inhibition during pregnancy is probably due to the circulating blood levels of progesterone.

The suckling by the newborn reflexly stimulates the release of oxytocin from the neurohypophysis (posterior pituitary, pars nervosa), which releases the milk to the nipples or teats by way of the mammary ducts and by contraction of the myoepithelial cells surrounding the mammary alveoli. (The process is sometimes called milk *letdown*.) Nursing also continues to cause the release of prolactin, to replenish the milk supply as needed. Release of prolactin and oxytocin is therefore sustained by sensory impulses during nursing, which are carried to the hypothalamus, bringing about pituitary release of the hormones.

The primordial follicle apparently can develop in the absence of pituitary hormones, but maturation of the follicle, including the development of the *thecae* and *antrum*, requires a combination of FSH and LH, with the proper balance and timing of each. As the follicle releases increasing amounts of estrogen, FSH is inhibited by this estrogen, which simultaneously, by blood-level feedback to the hypothalamic *releasing factors*, decreases FSH and increases LH secretion from the pituitary. When the correct ratio of FSH and LH is reached, ovulation occurs.

In some animals (rat, mouse, and sheep), LTH (luteotrophic hormone or prolactin) is reported to maintain the corpus luteum and cause secretion of progesterone. A luteotrophic effect by chorionic gonadotrophin from the placenta may also stimulate secretion of progesterone by the corpus luteum.

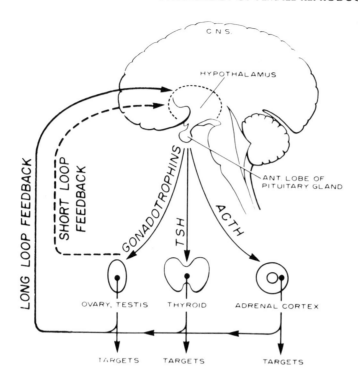

Fig. 26-9.   Diagram illustrating the reciprocal relationships among the central nervous system and certain endocrine organs. Ovarian, testicular, thyroidal and adrenocortical hormones in the blood act back upon the hypothalamus, a major integrative center in the brain, to adjust the output of pituitary hormones in accordance with the needs of the organism. This forms a self-balancing system, often referred to as the "long loop" feedback (solid line). It is possible that the trophic hormones themselves may affect the hypothalamus in a similar manner over a "short loop" system (broken line). (Turner and Bagnara, General Endocrinology, courtesy of W. B. Saunders Co.)

The control of hormones associated with reproduction is complex and not completely understood. The classic feedback mechanism undoubtedly is an important means of hormonal control, in which the level of a circulating hormone either stimulates or inhibits further release of the same hormone.

In addition to the control of endocrine glands by other hormones, the nervous system is involved in control of some endocrine glands by serving as the afferent limb of a neurohormonal reflex. In most instances, the nerve impulses eventually reach the hypothalamus, ultimately causing the release of pituitary hormones, and in this manner they indirectly control the release of other hormones. Ovulation following coitus in the rabbit and cat and the release of prolactin and oxytocin during nursing are examples of this neuroendocrine reflex mechanism.

Chapter 27

Pregnancy and Parturition

PREGNANCY

Pregnancy refers to the condition of a female while young are developing within her uterus. This interval, the gestation period, extends from fertilization of the ovum to the birth of the offspring. It includes fertilization, or union of the ovum and sperm; nidation, or implantation of the embryo in the uterine wall; placentation, or the development of fetal membranes; and continued growth of the fetus.

Normal *gestation periods* vary greatly from species to species, and there is considerable variation between individuals within each species. Average gestation periods are: mare, 336 days, about 11 months; cow, 282 days, a little over 9 months; ewe, 150 days, about 5 months; sow, 114 days, or 3 months, 3 weeks, and 3 days; and bitch, 63 days, about 2 months. If the young are carried throughout a normal gestation period, it is a full-term pregnancy. Abnormally early termination of pregnancy is called abortion, or premature birth. In domestic animals, premature birth is nearly always fatal to the fetus.

Penetration of the ovum by the *spermatozoon* stimulates formation of the *second polar body* (see Chapter 26, p. 400) and also contributes one-half of the chromosomes of the new individual. Physical or chemical stimuli can also stimulate division of the ovum. The mechanism of sperm penetration is still in doubt, as is the reason why only one sperm usually penetrates the ovum. However, occasionally several spermatozoa are found in the perivitelline space (between vitelline membrane and zona pellucida), and sometimes more than one is found inside the ovum. Penetration by more than one sperm is abnormal.

Time of *fertilization* appears to be important. Sperm must remain in the female reproductive tract, the uterus, or the *uterine tube*, for a certain period in order to fertilize ova effectively. This is called *capacitation of the spermatozoa*. Capacitation involves a partial breakdown of the outer acrosome and plasma membranes, so that acrosomal enzymes can be released. The enzymes, in turn, can penetrate the zona pellucida. Capacitation also activates the metabolic activity of the sperm cell by increasing the cell's rate of glycolysis and increasing its oxidative metabolism. Capacitation begins in the uterus and is complete in the oviduct.

Both ciliary action and muscular contractions are involved in movement of the fertilized ova through the uterine tubes into the uterus.

Polytocous animals, those giving birth to several offspring at one time, have a definite spacing of the *blastocysts* (developing embryos) in the uterus. It has been suggested that the implantation of one blastocyst in some way produces a surrounding refractory area in the *endometrium* that inhibits further implantation in the immediate vicinity. There is some evidence that the embryos near the uterine tubes are slightly more advanced in development than those near the cervix. Blastocysts of the rabbit are evenly distributed in the uterus by seven days after mating. Uterine contractions probably are involved in movement of the blastocysts, as there is no evidence that they move in any but a passive manner.

Fertilization

The fimbria of the oviduct are in close association with the ovary, and upon ovulation, the ovum enters the infundibulum of the uterine tube. The ovum is then transported down the oviduct into the uterus by the combined action of the cilia on the mucosal surface of the epithelial cells, and by contractions occurring in the muscular walls of the uterine tube. The contractions, in turn, are influenced by (1) the ratio of the hormones, estrogen and progesterone (high estrogen levels increase contractions), (2) the level of prostaglandins present, and (3) the degree of stimulation of the oviduct by the sympathetic division of the autonomic nervous system. The ova remain viable in the oviduct for about 12 hours. During this time fertilization can occur, and it normally takes place in the ampulla of the oviduct.

Following ovulation, pregnancy cannot occur normally without penetration of the ovum by a spermatozoon, within the time period that the ovum remains viable. Ova in unmated animals gradually lose their covering of cells and begin to disintegrate as they pass down the uterine tube. Ova that stay in the uterine tubes too long before exposure to spermatozoa may have lowered fertility and possibly result in a high percentage of abnormal embryos and birth defects.

In the mare and the bitch, the ova enter the oviduct as primary oocytes and then mature in the oviduct. On the other hand, in the cow, ewe, and sow, the ovum has already formed the *first polar body* and is in metaphase of the second maturational division at the time of ovulation. The polar body may be found in the perivitelline space between the ovum and the zona pellucida until it disintegrates. The second division occurs after fertilization by a spermatozoon.

Immediately following ovulation, the ovum within the *vitelline membrane* (cell membrane of ovum) is surrounded by a heavy mucopolysaccharide membrane, the *zona pellucida*, and by a variable amount of granulosa cells that make up the *corona radiata* outside the zona pellucida. The zona pellucida is believed to be a product of the innermost layer of granulosa cells (corona radiata), which was a part of the *cumulus oophorous* of the follicle. Microvilli from the vitelline membrane of the ovum penetrate into the zona pellucida, as do processes from the follicular cells. The zona pellucida is believed to be a semipermeable membrane that helps protect the ovum. In some instances a coat of mucus is applied to the ovum outside the zona pellucida as it travels down the oviduct. This may aid attachment of the ovum to the uterine wall later.

There is a great variation in the amount of cumulus cells surrounding the zona pellucida in different animals. A well-defined corona radiata has been described in the dog and some other animals, but is absent in the cow, sheep, pig, and horse.

Following capacitation and contact with the ovum, the spermatozoon can penetrate the zona pellucida. The cumulus surrounding the ovum has already broken down shortly after ovulation in the cow, mare, ewe, and sow. Penetration by the sperm is accomplished by the acrosomal enzymes, *acrosin*, which is a trypsin-like enzyme, and *hyaluronidase*, which breaks down the hyaluronic acid-protein matrix of the zona membrane.

The spermatozoon, upon penetration, then attaches to the vitelline membrane. This stimulates the second meiosis of the ovum to proceed, and results in the formation of the *second polar body*, at which time the ovum chromosomes form the *pronucleus* (Fig. 27–1). The head of the sperm then enlarges, becoming the male pronucleus. The two pronuclei then come together and fuse membranes, forming one cell, with the chromosomal genetic DNA material of both male and female now combined in it. The new cell is ready for cleavage and formation of the blastocyst.

Only one sperm usually succeeds in penetrating the ovum. After that, others are prevented from entering by changes in the zona pellucida that resist *polyspermia*. The osmosis that follows inward, tends to force the zona away from the ovum, which makes it more difficult for another sperm to enter. More sperm will attach to the outer zona surface, and some sperm are occasionally found in the perivitelline space (between the vitelline membrane and zona pellucida), but they usually cannot penetrate into the ovum. It is not yet known specifically what makes the membrane impenetrable once one spermatozoon has entered, but it is obviously beneficial to reproduction, because the extra genetic input would otherwise destroy the new zygote.

Implantation

Following fertilization, the new zygote is transported down the oviduct into the uterus, as the blastocyst is being formed. In the cow and ewe, the new embryo reaches the uterus four days postestrus. Entry occurs slightly sooner in the sow, and slightly later in the bitch. The rate of transport varies with the levels of endocrine secretions, particularly the estrogen-progesterone ratio. In the cow, it takes about eight days to reach

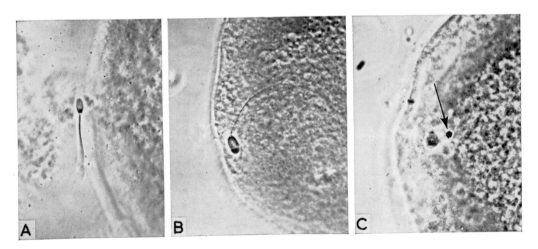

Fig. 27–1. Different regions of a single pig ovum, 8 hours *post coitum*. (× 450). *A* shows a nonfertilizing sperm in the zona pellucida; *B* shows the penetrating sperm which has entered the vitellus (note its swollen head); *C* shows the nuclear apparatus of the ovum, with the recently formed nucleus of the second polar body to the left, and the presumptive female pronucleus (arrowed) to the right. (Hafez, Reproduction in Farm Animals, Lea & Febiger.)

the blastocyst stage, whereas it is only about six days in the sow, ewe, and goat.

Implantation (nidation) is the process whereby the new embryo becomes established at a developmental site on the *endometrium* in the uterus, where it will then develop and become a *fetus*. Until implantation occurs, the cell divisions and growth are provided with necessary nutrients by the ovum yolk and by secretions from the uterus. Upon implantation, the nutrients are supplied henceforth through the placenta.

The zona pellucida is shed by the blastocyst prior to implantation, and the uterine endometrium proliferates and becomes more vascular and secretory in preparation for nourishing and accepting the embryo. Both physical and chemical factors are involved in this stimulation of the uterus to accept the embryo. The connective tissue beneath the endometrium appears to respond first to the presence of the blastocyst, even before the endometrium does.

After fertilization, implantation occurs in the sow about 11 days, in the bitch about 15 days, in the ewe about 16 days, in the cow about 35 days, and in the mare about 55 days.

The relationship between the endometrium and the developing fetal membranes is complex and varies from one species to another. Some of these differences are discussed on page 421.

Failures of Reproduction

Casida (1953) estimates reproductive failures in domestic animals from fertilization failure and embryonic death at approximately 50% of the potential production of bred animals. Results reported with a group of normal sows were: loss due to fertilization failure and tubal obstruction, 2.3%; loss from no apparent reason, 9.5%; embryonic death, 32.4%; and young born at term (no loss), 55.8%. A group of repeat breeding cows, those that did not conceive on the first service, showed a much poorer survival percentage: ovulation failure and tubal obstruction, 6.0%; no apparent reason, 39.3%; embryonic death, 32.5%; and normal embryos at 34 days, 22.2%. In cattle, chances of successful conception decrease rapidly with each rebreeding. Possible causes of embryonic death include inherited lethal factors, infections, nutritional deficiencies, disturbance of endocrine functions, and defects in the egg or sperm before fertilization.

Placentation

As the embryo increases in size, the process of diffusion, which nourishes the zygote, becomes inadequate to maintain life and continued growth. The extra-embryonic membranes, or *placenta*, develop as a means of meeting this increasing need for more nutrition. This process is known as placentation.

The placenta consists of an arrangement of membranes such that nutrition from the dam can reach the fetus, and in turn, waste products from the fetus can be excreted by the dam. In domestic animals, the terms fetal membranes and placenta are used interchangeably, although technically the fetal membranes are known as the fetal placenta. In some species a portion of the endometrium is shed at parturition. This is called the maternal placenta, or *decidua*. The fetal placenta includes the chorion, allantois, amnion, and vestigial yolk sac (Fig. 27–2).

The *chorion*, the outermost membrane, is in contact with the maternal uterus. The *amnion* is the innermost membrane, closest to the fetus. The *allantoic* sac, a space formed by two layers of *allantois*, located between the amnion and chorion, is sometimes called the first water bag. It is continuous with the anterior extremity of the bladder by way of the *urachus*, which passes through the umbilical cord. The outer layer of allantois is fused to the chorion by connective tissue, and the inner layer of allantois is fused to the amnion. The *amniotic sac*, which immediately surrounds the fetus, is sometimes called the second water bag.

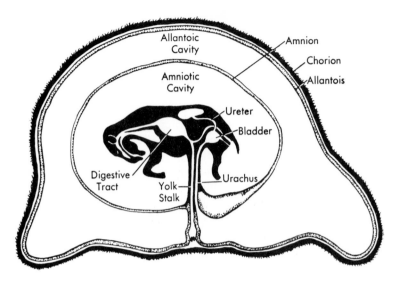

Fig. 27–2. Fetus of horse within the placenta. The chorion and allantois make up the chorioallantois, often called the chorion. (After Witschi, Development of Vertebrates, W. B. Saunders Co.)

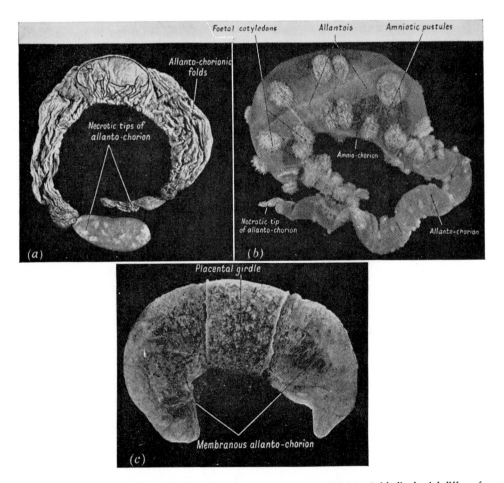

Fig. 27–3. Types of placentas. (By permission of Professor E. C. Amoroso, F.R.S.) a, Epitheliochorial-diffuse, from a sow; b, epitheliochorial-cotyledonary, from a cow; c, hemochorial-zonary, from a cat. (Nalbandov, Reproductive Physiology, courtesy of W. H. Freeman and Co.)

The terms "first" and "second" water bags refer to fetal membranes at the time of parturition, when the allantoic sac is expelled first and the amniotic sac, second.

Branches of the *umbilical arteries* and veins are located in the connective tissue between the allantois and chorion. These vessels are an important part of the fetal circulation. The umbilical arteries and their branches carry unoxygenated blood from the fetus to the placenta, and tributaries of the *umbilical vein* carry oxygenated blood from the placenta to the fetus.

As a general principle, blood from the fetus never mixes with blood from the dam. However, the two circulations are close enough at the junction of chorion and endometrium so that oxygen and nutrients pass from the maternal blood to the blood of the fetus, and waste products pass from the fetal blood into the blood stream of the dam. The exact relationship of the blood vessels of the fetus to the blood vessels of the dam depends on the species and the type of placenta involved. (Figures 27–3 and 27–4 show various types of placentas.)

In some rodents, the blood vessels of the fetus enter pools of maternal blood, so that only the endothelium of the fetal blood vessels separates the two circulations. This type of placental arrangement is called *hemoendothelial.* (See Table 27–1.)

The *hemochorial* type of placenta is found in man and certain lower types of rodents. Here not only the fetal vessels but also the chorion of the fetal placenta is invaginated into pools of maternal blood. Both hemochorial and hemoendothelial placentas are usually attached to the uterus in a disk-shaped area only. Hence the term *discoidal* is used to describe their general area of attachment.

Carnivorous animals such as the cat and dog have the chorion of the fetal placenta in contact with the endothelium of the blood vessels of the dam. This type is known as *endotheliochorial* and is attached in a girdle-like band, so the attachment is known as *zonary.*

Both the discoidal and zonary types of placental attachment are *deciduate* in nature, since a portion of the maternal endometrium, or maternal placenta, is shed at the time of parturition.

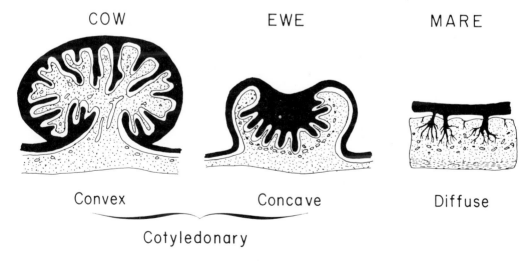

COW EWE MARE

Convex Concave Diffuse

Cotyledonary

Fig. 27–4. Epitheliochorial placenta of cow (left), ewe (middle) and mare (right). Villi from chorioallantois (black) invade crypts in maternal uterine epithelium (stippled). The apposition of maternal and fetal tissues is diffuse (mare) or localized as placentomes (cow and ewe). Each placentome is composed of fetal cotyledon and maternal caruncle. (Adapted from Mossman, 1937.) (From Hafez, E. S. E.: Reproduction in Farm Animals. ed. 3. Philadelphia, Lea & Febiger, 1974.)

Table 27–1. Classification of Mammalian Placenta Based on Tissue Layers Separating Maternal and Fetal Blood

	Placental Microscopic Structure			
Type	Maternal Tissue	Fetal Tissue	Gross Form	Species
Epitheliochorial			Diffuse	Pig, horse
			Cotyledonary or multiplex	Sheep, goat, cow*
Endotheliochorial			Zonary	Dog, cat
Hemochorial			Discoid	Man, mouse, rat guinea pig, rabbit
Hemoendothelial			Discoid	Rabbit

* A syncytium is present between trophoblast and maternal connective tissue as observed under the electron microscope. The placentas of sheep, goats and cows are therefore classified as epitheliochorial rather than syndesmochorial (Bjorkman, 1965, J. Anat. 99, p. 283).

(Adapted from Amoroso, 1952, In Parkes, A. S. (ed.) Marshall's Physiology of Reproduction. New York, Longman.)

(From Hafez, E.S.E.: Reproduction in Farm Animals, ed. 3, Philadelphia, Lea & Febiger, 1974.)

The rest of the domestic animals have *indeciduate* placentas, in which little or no maternal tissue is lost at parturition.

The placental attachment of ruminants is known as the *epitheliochorial* type, and the area of attachment is cotyledonary in nature. In this type, the chorion of the fetus is in direct contact with the epithelium of the uterus of the dam. This relationship, however, is localized in mushroom-like areas of attachment known as *caruncles*. These caruncles project inward from the surface of the uterus approximately ½ inch and vary in size from ½ to 4 or more inches in diameter. The term *cotyledon* is used correctly in reference to the portion of the fetal placenta that attaches to the caruncle. *Placentome* refers to the combination of maternal caruncle and fetal cotyledon.

The size of caruncles increases as pregnancy progresses, and the caruncles are larger in the gravid (pregnant) horn than in the nongravid horn. The epithelial surface of the caruncle is covered with crypts into which the villi of the fetal placenta project. The area between the caruncles is completely devoid of any attachment between the fetal placenta and the maternal uterus. The shape of the caruncles in the sheep is slightly different from those of the cow. In the sheep, the elevations contain a rather large central depression, which is the only portion of the caruncle to contain crypts for the attachment of the chorionic villi.

The placental attachment in both the horse and pig is diffuse, or villous, in nature. Chorionic villi, which cover much of the fetal placenta, project into crypts scattered over the entire endometrium of the uterus. The histologic arrangement is *epitheliochorial*, in which the chorion of the fetal placenta is in contact with the epithelium of the endometrium of the uterus.

Pregnancy Diagnosis

The knowledge of whether a breeding female is pregnant or not is important to a livestock breeder. There are criteria that may help to determine whether a female is pregnant and how long she has been pregnant. These criteria include absence of estrus (heat), change of contour of the abdominal wall, palpation of the internal genitalia through the rectum, ballottement (palpation) of fetus through the abdominal wall, x-ray pictures, and biologic tests.

Absence of Estrus. If accurate records of estrus periods and breeding dates are kept, the earliest indication of pregnancy in most animals is the failure to come in season at the time of the next expected heat period. Such an absence of estrus, however, is not absolute proof of pregnancy. A nonpregnant animal may not show estrus because of failure of the corpus luteum to regress normally (retained corpus luteum) or because of disease or other abnormality of the genitalia. Another possible reason for an animal to miss one or two heat periods following breeding is conception followed by early abortion. If such is the case, the female may then show a fairly normal season following the abortion.

Although there are exceptions, as noted, the fact that a female misses one or more estrous periods following breeding is good evidence that she has conceived.

Change of Contour of Abdomen. As pregnancy advances in any female, a definite dropping of the abdominal wall occurs, as well as a widening of the abdomen. This increase in size of the abdomen is commonly called "bellying down." It is due not only to the increase in size of the fetus, but also to increase in fetal fluids and enlargement of the uterus.

Palpation per Rectum and Ballottement. A skilled veterinarian can diagnose pregnancy with a high degree of accuracy by rectal palpation in cattle and horses. The diagnosis of pregnancy and estimation of stage of pregnancy are based on a knowledge of the rate of development of the fetus and changes in the genitalia and associated structures of the dam (Fig. 27–5).

In the cow, the presence of a corpus luteum in the ovary and a slight enlargement of one horn of the uterus as compared to the other is suggestive of early pregnancy.

At about three months, fetal membranes may be felt slipping between the fingers and very small caruncles are palpable in the uterine wall. The middle uterine artery on the pregnant side will be slightly larger than on the nonpregnant side, and a "buzzing" or *"fremitus"* becomes noticeable in the artery. Both the fetus and caruncles are definitely palpable in the cow by four months of pregnancy.

At 5 to 7 months of pregnancy, the uterus drops over the brim of the pelvis and stretches the cervix taut. Ovaries and fetus become difficult to palpate, but the caruncles on the uterus are definite and large. From this stage onward the calf can usually be bumped in the right flank. This technique, known as ballottement, is accomplished by gently forcing the fist into the lower right flank of the cow in a reciprocating manner so

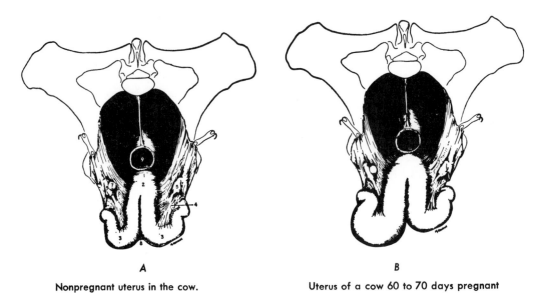

A

Nonpregnant uterus in the cow.

B

Uterus of a cow 60 to 70 days pregnant

1, Cervix; 2, body of uterus; 3, horn of uterus; 4, oviduct; 5, ovaries; 7, corpus luteum; 8, intercornual ligament; 9, rectum.

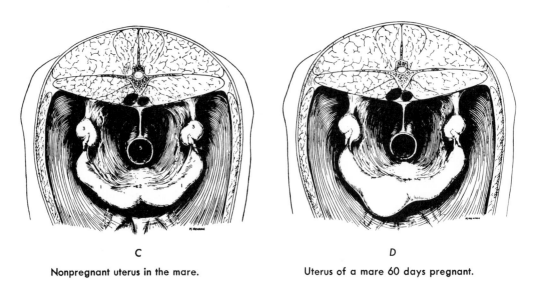

C

Nonpregnant uterus in the mare.

D

Uterus of a mare 60 days pregnant.

1, Uterine horns; 2, body of uterus; 3, ovary; 4, ovarian ventricle; 5, rectum.

Fig. 27–5.   *A*, Nonpregnant uterus in the cow. *B*, Uterus of a cow 60 to 70 days pregnant. 1, Cervix; 2, body of uterus; 3, horn of uterus; 4, oviduct; 5, ovaries; 7, corpus luteum; 8, intercornual ligament; 9, rectum. *C*, Nonpregnant uterus in the mare. *D*, Uterus of a mare 60 days pregnant. 1, Uterine horns; 2, body of uterus; 3, ovary; 4, ovarian ventricle; 5, rectum. (From Roberts, Veterinary Obstetrics and Genital Diseases, courtesy of Edward Brothers.)

that the fetus rocks from side to side. Then the fist is forced into the flank and held until the calf bumps into the fist. The calf is the only solid object that can be palpated through the right flank of a pregnant cow. From 8 to 9 months, the fetus can again be palpated through the rectum and various parts of the fetus may be identified.

In the mare, pregnancy diagnosis by rectal palpation is more difficult than in the cow. The bulge of the amniotic sac surrounding the fetus is the earliest diagnostic feature. It increases in size approximately as shown in Table 27–2.

Most pregnant bitches can be successfully palpated through the abdominal wall at three to four weeks of pregnancy. One hand with the fingers extended may be placed on each side of the dorsal flank region of the standing bitch. The hands are brought as close together as possible and gently moved ventrad till the gravid uterus is felt.

Use of X-ray Studies. Diagnosis of pregnancy with x-ray film is of limited value in domestic animals. Horses, cattle, and sheep are too large for satisfactory abdominal x-ray procedure. In dogs and cats, x-ray pictures may be used effectively to determine pregnancy after the fetal bones have begun to calcify.

Biologic Tests. The discovery of pituitary-like *gonadotrophins*, hormones that stimulate the ovaries and the testes and are secreted by the placenta during pregnancy, has led to a means of diagnosing pregnancy in several species. In mares, at about 50 to 84 days of pregnancy, gonadotrophic substance is found in the blood. The test is conducted by using 10 ml of blood

serum collected from a mare between 50 and 84 days after breeding. The serum is injected into the ear vein of a mature, nonpregnant female rabbit that has been isolated from all male rabbits for at least 30 days. A positive test showing that the mare is pregnant is indicated by dark red follicles, *corpora hemorrhagica,* in the ovaries of the rabbit 48 hours after the injection. The ovaries of the rabbit may be examined during a surgical exploratory operation, and the rabbit may then be saved for future use, or the rabbit may be butchered and the ovaries examined at that time.

Although placental gonadotrophins probably are secreted by all domestic animals during pregnancy, the quantities are insufficient—except in the mare—to produce a reaction in the ovaries of test animals.

In the human, other tests for pregnancy depend upon the fact that the placenta also produces appreciable quantities of estrogenic hormones and chorionic gonadotrophin, the metabolites or end-products of which are excreted in the urine. The *estrogen* output by the placenta is highest in the latter part of pregnancy, when progesterone levels fall off.

When urine containing the estrogens is injected into ovariectomized rats, there is cornification of the test animal's vaginal epithelium. A smear of the vaginal wall is made and the cellular changes observed with the aid of a microscope. However, newer simpler methods of pregnancy testing are now used.

PARTURITION

Parturition, or labor, which is the act of giving birth to young, marks the termination of pregnancy. It is customary to divide the act of parturition into three stages. The *first stage* consists of uterine contractions that gradually force the water bags against the uterine side of the cervix, causing it to dilate. This stage lasts 2 to 6 hours in the cow and ewe, 1 to 4 hours in the mare, and 2 to 12 hours in the sow and bitch.

Table 27–2. Pregnancy Diagnosis by Rectal Palpation in Mare

Days of Pregnancy	Size of Bulge (in inches)
30	2 diameter by 3 length
45	3 diameter by 4½ length
60	5 to 6 length
90	5–6 diameter by 8–9 length
100–150	Fetus palpable

In the *second stage*, actual delivery of the fetus occurs. Passage of parts of the fetus through the cervix into the vagina along with rupture of one or both water bags reflexly initiates actual straining or contraction of the abdominal muscles. The combination of uterine contraction and abdominal contraction forces the fetus through the birth canal.

The *third stage* of *parturition* consists of delivery of the placenta, which normally follows the fetus almost immediately.

Several factors appear to be involved complexly in the initiation of parturition, particularly changes in hormone levels, as measured in the maternal blood plasma. In the cow, progesterone levels decline rapidly in the last 48 hours prior to delivery. At the same time, the estrogen levels are rising, but just prior to parturition, they decline rapidly. The corticosteroid levels follow the estrogen pattern, first rising and then falling abruptly just before parturition. Prolactin levels essentially do the same, whereas LH levels remain relatively unaltered.

In the case of the mare, progesterone levels increase during the last 30 days of pregnancy and then abruptly decline the day after delivery. Meanwhile, estrogen levels slowly decrease in the last 30 days, and then abruptly drop at the time of delivery.

The ewe shows a slow decrease in the blood level of progesterone, as does the cow, but the decrease begins several days before it occurs in the cow, and the level does not fall as much as in the cow. Estrogen levels and corticosteroids increase greatly during the last 24 hours, whereas the prolactin level rises on the last day of pregnancy.

Plasma levels in the sow show an abrupt decrease in progesterone concentration in the last 48 hours, preceded by a gradual, progressive decrease 2 to 3 days earlier. Meanwhile, estrogen levels increase for a week before farrowing, and corticosteroids increase during the last 2 days.

Both estrogen and progesterone plasma levels in the bitch decrease two to four days before delivery.

What causes the changes in hormone levels and starts the uterine contractions is still uncertain. However, evidence to-date implicates an increase in the amount of ACTH being released from the hypophysis of the fetus. That, in turn, increases secretion of adrenal gland steroids. Increasing the corticosteroid levels in the fetus causes an increase in the release of a prostaglandin ($PGF_2\alpha$) from the maternal uterine wall. The prostaglandin may then start the myometrial contractions, after the progesterone levels have decreased and the estrogen levels have increased.

The prostaglandin may also stimulate the release of *oxytocin*. It is well known that the *oxytocin* secreted from the posterior pituitary gland causes uterine muscle to contract. In fact, extract of the posterior pituitary is used extensively to stimulate contractions of the fatigued uterus during prolonged labor. Estrogen levels also increase, which stimulates uterine contraction, whereas progesterone levels fall off.

Signs of Approaching Parturition

As well as the obvious enlargement of the abdomen, the mammary glands enlarge and begin to secrete a milky material within a few days of parturition. There may be some edema (swelling) of the ventral abdominal wall about the same time as the mammary gland secretion begins, particularly in the first pregnancy. The vulva swells and usually discharges a thick mucus. Other signs include relaxation of the abdominal wall with sinking of the flanks, dropping of the belly, and sinking of the rump on both sides of the tail head.

As the time of parturition becomes imminent, the animal becomes restless, usually seeks seclusion, lies down and gets up frequently, attempts to urinate often, and then begins actual labor. The bitch and sow usually try to build a nest before starting labor.

Normal Presentation

The calf is normally presented front feet first with the head extended and the nose between the front feet (Fig. 27–6). The dor-

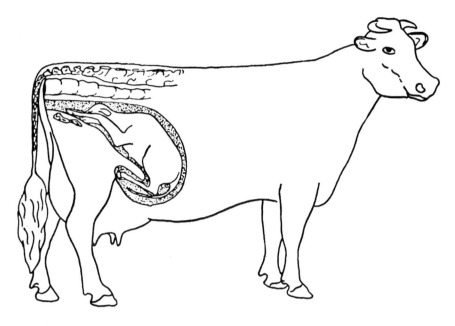

Fig. 27–6.   Position of the calf in the uterus after it has been oriented for normal delivery. (From *Physiology of Reproduction and Artificial Insemination of Cattle* by G. W. Salisbury and N. L. VanDemark. Copyright by W. H. Freeman and Company, 1961.)

sum of the calf is in contact with the sacrum of the dam. This position, called anterior presentation, takes advantage of the natural curvature of the birth canal of the dam and the curvature of the fetus. A posterior presentation with the hind feet first, hocks up, occurs frequently enough in cattle to be considered normal.

Contractions of the uterus force the *fetal placenta* (water bags) against the cervix of the uterus. This constant pressure causes the cervix to dilate gradually so the fetus can pass through into the pelvis of the dam. When the water bags break, the uterus contracts more strongly upon the fetus. About the same time, the abdominal muscles begin to contract forcefully to expel the fetus through the birth canal.

The contraction of abdominal muscles, called straining, is a reflex response to stimuli from the presence of parts of the fetus within the vagina and vulva of the dam. Straining is readily evoked by an operator inserting his hand and arm into the vulva and vagina of a cow when attempting to deliver a calf, unless the cow has received an appropriate local anesthetic. The neural stimulus also feeds back to the hypothalamus causing increased oxytocin secretion.

The uterus of the sheep and goat is similar to that of the cow, so nearly everything said about pregnancy in the cow applies to them except gestation period and the fact that multiple births are much more common than in cattle.

The legs of a colt are relatively longer than those of a calf, and the colt is carried to a larger extent in the body of the uterus, while a calf is carried almost entirely in one horn of the uterus. Presentation of the foal is essentially the same as that of a calf.

With pigs and dogs, the young are carried in both horns of the uterus and may be presented either anteriorly or posteriorly with equal facility.

Usually the placenta or afterbirth is delivered a short time following birth of the young, but it may accompany the fetus or, rarely, precede it. The placenta is considered to be retained pathologically if an abnormally long period of time elapses between birth of the young and delivery of the placenta.

Normally, the placenta of the cow and ewe should be delivered within 24 hours following parturition. Since the mare is susceptible to *metritis*, infection of the uterus, any retention of the placenta over two or three hours is a cause for concern. In the pig and dog, each placenta normally is still attached to the fetus and may completely surround it at birth. Immediate removal of the placenta from the nostrils of the newborn is essential for life and is usually done by the dam.

Manual removal of retained placenta from the cow is a common method of treatment. While this operation, commonly called "cleaning," is relatively simple for a skilled person, it may be dangerous to the cow and also to the operator if proper precautions are not observed. Cows infected with *Brucella abortus (Bang's disease)* often show a high incidence of retained placenta. Treatment of a retained placenta with *stilbestrol*, a synthetic female sex hormone, is sometimes used with varying degrees of success.

Retained placenta in species other than the cow may be more serious and often endangers the life of the animal. Early treatment of these cases requires not only removal of the placenta, but local treatment of the infected uterus and systemic treatment of the dam as well.

Dystocia—Difficult Birth

Normal parturition with no complications is by far the most common situation in domestic animals. However, there are occasions when the dam has difficulty giving birth to young and may need some assistance.

From the onset of actual labor, a cow should calve within a maximum of eight hours, or intervention likely will be necessary. The ewe should complete lambing within one to two hours. If a mare does not foal within one to three hours after starting labor, a veterinarian should be called. Pigs and dogs should average one offspring at least every hour, or else intervention may be necessary.

Improper presentation is a common cause of obstetric trouble. Other causes include disparity of size of dam and fetus (too large a calf or too small a birth canal), or some pathologic condition of dam or fetus.

Abnormal Presentations. Any deviation from the anterior presentation or posterior presentation as described is considered to be abnormal and usually requires correction before the fetus can be delivered. Figure 27–7 shows some of the many abnormal presentations that may be encountered.

Correction of any of these abnormal presentations requires returning the calf to an anterior or posterior presentation. In most instances this involves repelling the fetus into the uterus away from the pelvic inlet in order to have room for manipulation of the calf. An *epidural anesthetic* administered by a veterinarian will stop all straining by the cow and make the operation much easier on both the cow and the operator. A detailed description of abnormal presentations and their correction may be found in *Diseases of Cattle*, Atkinson et al., (1942) and in most standard textbooks of veterinary obstetrics.

Other Causes of Dystocia. Excessive size of the fetus in relation to the size of the birth canal of the dam presents a difficult problem. Even though the presentation may be normal, excessive traction in delivering the newborn will likely be damaging to both the fetus and the dam.

Treatment of Dystocia. Cesarean section (surgical removal of the calf) is the safest treatment for most types of dystocia, and is safe for both fetus and dam if the operation is performed by a skilled veterinarian before complications occur. The other alternative is *embryotomy* (cutting the fetus into pieces which are small enough to remove through the birth canal). This procedure may save the life of the dam.

Pathologic conditions of the fetus that cause difficulty in parturition include *hydrocephalus* (water on the brain), *ankylosed*

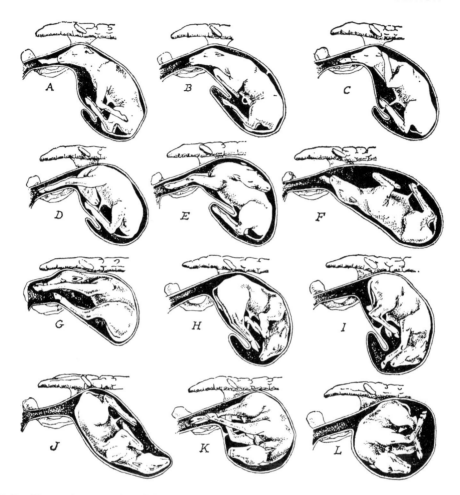

Fig. 27–7.   Abnormal presentation of the calf for delivery. (Redrawn from Diseases of Cattle, U.S.D.A. Special Report, 1942.) (From Physiology of Reproduction and Artificial Insemination of Cattle by G. W. Salisbury and N. L. VanDemark. Copyright by W. H. Freeman and Company 1961.) *A*, Anterior presentation, one foreleg retained; *B*, anterior presentation, forelegs bent at knee; *C*, anterior presentation, forelegs crossed over neck; *D*, anterior presentation, downward deviation of head; *E*, anterior presentation, upward deviation of head; *F*, anterior presentation, with back down; *G*, anterior presentation, with hind feet in pelvis; *H*, croup and thigh presentation; *I*, croup and hock presentation; *J*, posterior presentation, the fetus on its back; *K*, all feet presented; *L*, dorsolumbar presentation.

(fused) *joints*, shortened tendons, *Siamese twins*, and monstrosities such as calves with two heads or extra appendages.

Pathologic conditions in the dam that can interfere with parturition usually involve the birth canal. Such factors as fracture of the pelvis, tumors of the genitalia, and excess fat in the pelvis decrease the size of the birth canal, thereby interfering with passage of even a normal-sized fetus. In addition, torsion, or twisting, of the uterus, rupture of the uterus, or rupture of the *prepubic tendon*, which is the insertion of the *rectus abdominis* muscle, will seriously impair or prevent normal parturition. Again, the best treatment for the preceding conditions is cesarean section, with embryotomy a second choice.

Chapter **28**

Anatomy of the
Male Reproductive System

Embryologically, the reproductive system is closely related to the urinary system. Often both are considered together under the title "urogenital system." The *urethra* is used as a passage for both the urinary system and the male reproductive system.

The male reproductive system of farm mammals consists of two testes (or testicles) contained in the scrotum, accessory organs including ducts and glands, and the penis (Fig. 28–1). The testes produce *spermatozoa* (the male sex cells, also called *sperm*) and *testosterone* (the male sex hormone). The scrotum provides the favorable environment of a lower temperature for the production of spermatozoa. The remaining structures assist the spermatozoa to reach their ultimate goal, the *ovum* of the female, in a condition conducive to fertilization of the ovum. These structures include the epididymis and ductus deferens for each testis, accessory sex glands (seminal vesicles, prostate, and bulbo-urethral glands), and the urethra and the penis.

TESTIS

The *testes (testicles)* vary somewhat from species to species as far as shape, size, and location are concerned, but the essential structure is the same (Fig. 28–2). Each testis consists of a mass of *seminiferous tubules* (Fig. 28–3) surrounded by a heavy fibrous capsule called the *tunica albuginea*. A number of fibrous septa, or *trabeculae*, pass inward from the tunica albuginea to form a framework, or stroma, for support of the seminiferous tubules.

In all domestic animals except the horse, these trabeculae unite near the center of the

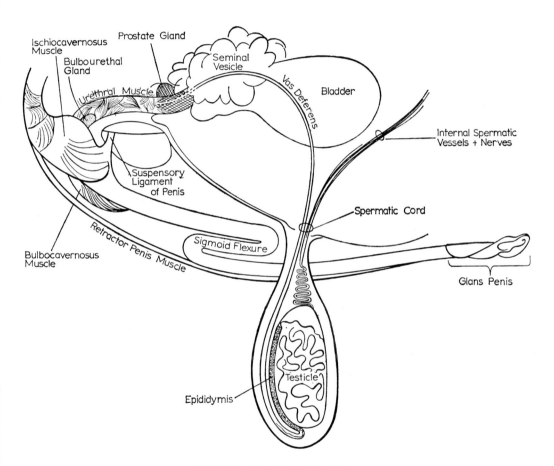

Fig. 28–1.   Genitalia of the bull.

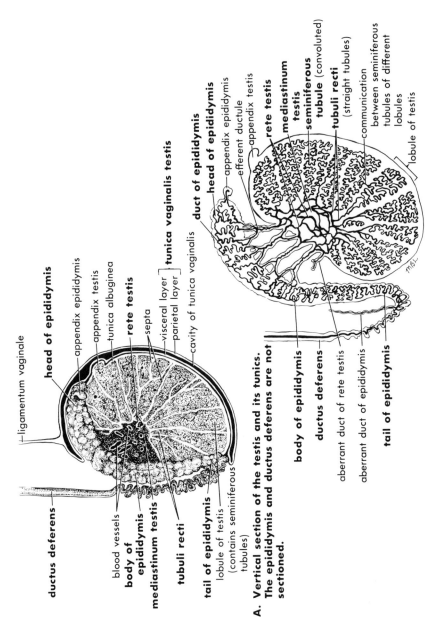

A. Vertical section of the testis and its tunics. The epididymis and ductus deferens are not sectioned.

ligamentum vaginale

head of epididymis

appendix epididymis

appendix testis

tunica albuginea

rete testis

septa

visceral layer
parietal layer] tunica vaginalis testis

cavity of tunica vaginalis

ductus deferens

blood vessels

body of epididymis

mediastinum testis

tubuli recti

tail of epididymis

lobule of testis (contains seminiferous tubules)

B. Diagram of a sectioned testis showing the seminiferous tubules and duct system. Epididymis has been separated from testis to show interconnecting ducts.

duct of epididymis

head of epididymis

appendix epididymis

efferent ductule

appendix testis

rete testis

mediastinum testis

seminiferous tubule (convoluted)

tubuli recti (straight tubules)

communication between seminiferous tubules of different lobules

lobule of testis

body of epididymis

ductus deferens

aberrant duct of rete testis

aberrant duct of epididymis

tail of epididymis

Fig. 28–2.   The testis, epididymis, and ductus deferens showing their relationships. (From Crouch, J. E.: Functional Human Anatomy. ed. 3. Philadelphia, Lea & Febiger, 1978.)

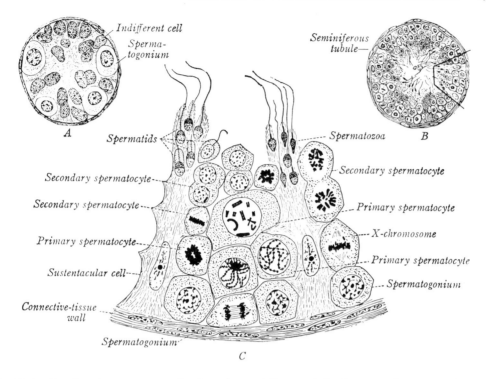

Fig. 28–3. Drawing of a transverse section through a seminiferous tubule of a mammal. (Arey, Developmental Anatomy, courtesy of W. B. Saunders Co.)

gland to form a fibrous cord, the *mediastinum testis*.

The *cells of Leydig*, which secrete the male hormone, testosterone, are located in the connective tissue between seminiferous tubules.

EPIDIDYMIS

The spermatozoa pass from the seminiferous tubules by way of the *vasa efferentia* to the head of the *epididymis*. The epididymis is a long, convoluted tube that connects the vasa efferentia of the testis with the vas deferens, or ductus deferens.

The *head of the epididymis* attaches to the same end of the testis that the blood vessels and nerves enter. The *body of the epididymis* parallels the long axis of the testis, and the *tail of the epididymis* continues as the *ductus deferens*, which doubles back along the body of the epididymis to the region of the head, where it enters the spermat-

ic cord. The epididymis serves as a place for spermatozoa to mature prior to the time they are expelled by ejaculation. Spermatozoa are immature when they leave the testicle and must undergo a period of maturation within the epididymis before they are capable of fertilizing ova.

DUCTUS DEFERENS

The *ductus deferens (vas deferens)* is a muscular tube which, at the time of ejaculation, propels the spermatozoa from the epididymis to the ejaculatory duct in the prostatic urethra.

The ductus deferens leaves the tail of the epididymis, passes through the *inguinal canal* as a part of the spermatic cord, and at the internal inguinal ring turns caudad, separating from the vascular and nervous parts of the cord. As the two ductus deferentia approach the urethra, they converge and continue caudad dorsal to the bladder, enclosed in a fold of peritoneum, the *urogenital fold (genital fold)*, which is comparable to the broad ligaments of the female. In fact, in some animals a homologue of the uterus, the *uterus masculinus*, is present in the genital fold between the two ductus deferentia. Homologous structures have the same embryologic origin.

SCROTUM

The *scrotum* is a cutaneous (skin) sac that conforms in size, shape, and location to the testes it contains. The scrotal skin is thin, pliable, and relatively hairless. A layer of fibroelastic tissue mixed with smooth muscle fibers, called the *tunica dartos*, is immediately deep to the skin, and in cold weather the muscle fibers of the dartos contract and help hold the testes against the abdominal wall. The tunica dartos passes on the median plane between the two testes to help form the scrotal septum, which divides the scrotum into two lateral compartments, one for each testicle.

Between the tunica dartos and the underlying deep fascia is a thin layer of areolar connective tissue, or superficial fascia.

There are three layers of deep fascia, which are difficult to separate by dissection. They are presumably derived from the aponeuroses of the three abdominal muscles, the *external abdominal oblique muscle*, the *internal abdominal oblique muscle*, and the *transversus abdominis muscle*.

The outer layer of peritoneum covering the testis, the *tunica vaginalis communis (parietalis)*, is deep to, and blends with, the deep fascia of the scrotum. Some authorities consider the tunica vaginalis communis to be a part of the scrotum. The *scrotal ligament* is derived from the *gubernaculum*. It is a band of connective tissue extending from the tail of the epididymis to the scrotum. Because the gubernaculum was always outside of the peritoneal cavity (retroperitoneal), both the tunica vaginalis communis and *tunica vaginalis propria (visceralis)* reflect around the scrotal ligament.

DESCENT OF THE TESTIS

In both the male and the female fetus, the gonads originate in the sublumbar region immediately caudal to the kidneys. In the female, the ovaries remain in the abdominal cavity fairly close to where they originate, but in the male, the testes travel a considerable distance from their point of origin to the scrotum, presumably under the influence of testosterone.

The descent of the testis normally is complete by birth or soon after (Fig. 28–4). It is guided by a fibrous cord, the gubernaculum, extending from the testis through the inguinal canal to the skin in the area that will become the scrotum. As the fetus enlarges, the gubernaculum either fails to lengthen or may actually shorten, thus in effect drawing the testis from the abdominal cavity into the scrotum. As the testis passes into the scrotum, it becomes enfolded by the vaginal process, a tube of peritoneum that previously passed from the abdominal cavity through the inguinal canal to the scrotum.

The superficial layer *(lamina parietalis)* of peritoneum lining the scrotum has been called the *tunica vaginalis communis*. It corresponds to parietal peritoneum of the abdominal cavity. The deeper layer *(lamina visceralis)* of peritoneum, called the *tunica vaginalis propria*, intimately covers the tunica albuginea of the testis and epididymis and covers the contents of the spermatic cord. The *mesorchium* is a delicate double layer of peritoneum connecting the visceral and parietal layers of tunica vaginalis, just as mesentery connects parietal and visceral layers of abdominal peritoneum. The double layer of peritoneum connecting to the ductus deferens is called the *mesoductus deferens*.

The testes of the bull and ram are located cranial to the *sigmoid (S-shaped) flexure* of the penis. The long axis of each testis is

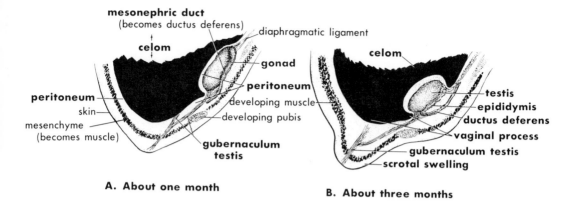

A. About one month

B. About three months

C. Seven to eight months

Fig. 28–4.   Sequence of events in the descent of the testis. The lower part of the celom and the vaginal process are indicated in black. (From Crouch, J. E.: Functional Human Anatomy. ed. 3. Philadelphia, Lea & Febiger, 1978.)

nearly vertical, so the scrotum is elongated dorsoventrally.

In the horse and dog, the long axis of each testis is nearly horizontal, and the testes are held fairly close to the abdominal wall near the external (superficial) inguinal ring.

The testes of the boar descend much farther than those of any other animal and come to rest caudal to the sigmoid flexure of the penis, just ventral to the anus. The long axis of each testis is nearly vertical, but the tail of the epididymis is dorsal rather than ventral, as in ruminants.

Spermatic Cord

As the testis descends from the region caudal to the kidney, it brings with it the same blood, nerve, and lymphatic supply present in the embryo. These structures, the *testicular vessels* and *nerves*, make up a large part of the *spermatic cord*, which connects the testis with the rest of the body (Fig. 28–5). The spermatic cord also includes the ductus deferens, which connects the tail of the epididymis with the prostatic urethra (the portion of the urethra surrounded by the

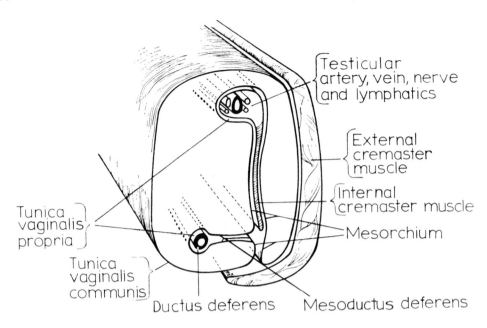

Fig. 28–5. The spermatic cord.

prostate gland). A few smooth muscle fibers scattered throughout the spermatic cord make up the *internal cremaster muscle*, which helps to hold the other structures of the cord together.

Inguinal Canal

The *inguinal canal* is a passage from the abdominal cavity to the exterior that extends from the internal inguinal ring to the external inguinal ring. In the stallion and usually in the bull, the *internal (deep) inguinal ring* is a space or potential space between the caudal border of the internal abdominal oblique muscle and the medial side (deep face) of the aponeurosis (flat tendon) of the external abdominal oblique muscle. The *external (superficial) inguinal ring* is merely a slit in the aponeurosis of the external abdominal oblique muscle.

The canal is bounded superficially by the caudal part of the aponeurosis of the external abdominal oblique muscle. In the horse, cow, sheep, and pig, the deep wall of the canal is formed mainly by the internal ab-

dominal oblique muscle; in the dog, the aponeurosis of the transversus abdominis muscle forms the deep wall.

Although the inguinal canal is potentially extensive, it normally is only large enough to permit passage of the spermatic cord and inguinal vessels and nerves. If the internal ring and canal are too relaxed, a loop of intestine may pass through the canal into the scrotum, producing an *inguinal hernia*. This is particularly likely to happen during the act of breeding.

Cryptorchid Testis

A testis that fails to descend is called a *cryptorchid testis*, and the animal with such a condition is called a *cryptorchid*. In most species, the testes descend into the scrotum by birth or shortly thereafter. An animal in which the testis descends into the inguinal canal but not into the scrotum is called a "*high flanker.*"

A cryptorchid with both testes retained in the abdominal cavity is likely to be sterile, since spermatogenesis does not occur normally unless the testis is cooler than body temperature, a condition provided by the scrotum. However, the relatively high temperature of the abdomen does not interfere with the production of testosterone, so the cryptorchid has all the actions and appearance of a normal male, except that no testes are evident and no normal spermatozoa are produced.

SECONDARY SEX CHARACTERISTICS

Male secondary sex characteristics depend on the presence of adequate amounts of testosterone in the body. Characteristics commonly associated with masculinity include massive head and shoulders in bulls, development of the crest in stallions, horns in some breeds of rams, and tusks in boars, as well as a general tendency for less subcutaneous fat, poorer marbling of muscle, and little or no mammary development in all species.

A male carcass may be identified by the presence of *cod fat* in the inguinal region, the *"pizzel eye"* (root of the penis) attached to the *aitch bone (symphysis pelvis)*, absence of mammary gland tissue in the inguinal region, and the fact that in a split carcass the aitch bone caudally touches muscle rather than fat, as in the female.

CASTRATION

Castration is a term usually applied to removal of the testes of the male, although technically it can apply to *spaying* or removal of the ovaries of the female as well.

Castration is practiced to prevent animals with inferior blood lines from reproducing. This is important in improving all breeds of animals. Early castration effectively improves the quality of individual animals used for food by inhibiting undesirable secondary sex characteristics.

Besides sanitation during and after castration, the most important factors for successful results are removal of as much spermatic cord and vaginal tunic as practical, and pro-

vision for adequate drainage from the incision. Postoperative care should include clean surroundings and exercise. Good clean pasture supplies both of these requirements.

The following terms are used for *castrates:* horses, *geldings;* cattle, *steers;* swine, *barrows;* sheep, *wethers;* chickens, *capons;* and men, *eunuchs. Stag*, or staggy, is a term used to describe animals that have acquired most secondary sex characteristics before being castrated. A *proud-cut* horse is one that is purported to have had the testes removed but not the epididymides. Needless to say, such a horse is sterile, but is alleged to develop stallion characteristics, probably much like a cryptorchid animal. Perhaps some of these animals actually are cryptorchids or were castrated after their stallion characteristics had developed.

Vasectomy refers to removal of a section of each of the ductus deferentia. This operation prevents passage of spermatozoa from the epididymides, but has no effect on the actions or appearance of the animal. It is sometimes used experimentally or for teaser animals used to identify females in heat.

Salpingectomy, which refers to removal of a section of the oviducts in the female, prevents passage of the ovum from the ovary to the uterus, but has no other effect on the animal.

Hysterectomy refers to removal of the uterus only, and *ovariohysterectomy* refers to removal of the ovaries and uterus.

ACCESSORY SEX GLANDS

The male accessory sex glands include the ampullae of the ductus deferentia; vesicular glands (seminal vesicles); prostate gland; and bulbourethral, or Cowper's glands. These glands produce the greater part of the ejaculate, or *semen*, which serves as a transport of sperm, as a favorable medium for nutrition, and as a buffer against excess acidity of the female genital tract.

There is considerable variation in shape and size of the various accessory sex glands in different species, but the relative location is similar in all animals

Ampullae

The *ampullae* are glandular enlargements of the terminal parts of the ductus deferentia. They are well developed in the stallion, bull, and ram; small in the dog; and absent in the boar. Glands of the ampullae empty into the ductus deferentia and contribute fluid to the semen.

Vesicular Glands (Seminal Vesicles)

The vesicular glands *(seminal vesicles)* are paired glands that empty in common with the ductus deferentia by way of the various ejaculatory ducts into the pelvic urethra just caudal to the neck of the bladder. The name "seminal vesicles" fits the stallion, while the name "vesicular glands" is more appropriate for most other animals. The seminal vesicles of the stallion are hollow, pear-shaped sacs; while those of the bull, ram, and boar are lobulated glands of considerable size. They are absent in the dog.

Prostate Gland

The *prostate gland* is an unpaired gland that more or less completely surrounds the pelvic urethra. The prostate gland of the dog and horse is a discrete structure shaped like a walnut. In other animals the prostate gland is more diffuse and extends a greater distance along the pelvic urethra under cover of the urethral muscle. The ducts open in two parallel rows, one on each side of the urethra. In older animals, the prostate may become enlarged and interfere with urination. It produces an alkaline secretion that helps give semen its characteristic odor.

Bullbourethral (Cowper's) Glands

The *bulbourethral (Cowper's) glands* are small paired glands located on either side of the pelvic urethra just cranial to the *ischial arch*, but caudal to the other accessory glands. Bulbourethral glands are found in all domestic animals except the dog, and they are large in the boar.

PENIS

The male organ of copulation, the *penis*, may be divided into three general areas: the glans, or free extremity; the main portion, or body; and the two crura, or roots, which attach to the ischial arch of the pelvis (Fig. 28–6).

The internal structure of the penis is cavernous tissue (erectile tissue) consisting of blood sinusoids separated by sheets of connective tissue called septa, which are derived from the tunica albuginea, a heavy fibrous capsule surrounding the penis.

The two *crura (roots)* of the *penis* originate on the caudal surface of the ischial arch, one on each side of the symphysis of the pelvis. They converge to form the *corpus penis (body of the penis)*. Ventral to the body is the urethra surrounded by the *corpus spongiosum penis (corpus cavernosum urethrae)*. The corpus spongiosum penis is a continuation of the erectile tissue of the *bulbus penis (urethral bulb)*, which is located between the roots of the penis. In most animals, the corpus spongiosum penis continues forward to become the erectile tissue of the glans penis.

The *glans penis* shows considerable variation from species to species. The horse and sheep both have a free portion of the urethra, the urethral process, which projects beyond the glans. The bull and ram have a helmet shaped glans called the *galea glandis*, and the external urethral opening of the bull opens into a twisted groove. The glans penis of the dog consists of two parts, a *pars longa glandis* and a *bulbus glandis*. Both parts surround a grooved bone, the *os penis*. The cranial extremity of the penis of the boar is twisted, but no glans is present.

Erection of the penis prior to copulation occurs when more blood enters the penis by

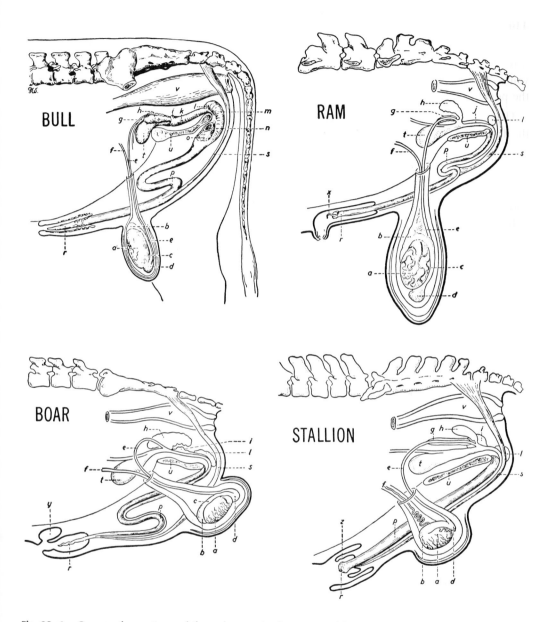

Fig. 28–6. Comparative anatomy of the male reproductive organs of farm mammals. *a*, Left testis; *b*, head of epididymis; *c*, body of epididymis; *d*, tail of epididymis; *e*, deferent duct; *f*, spermatic vessels and nerves; *g*, ampulla of deferent duct; *h*, vesicular gland; *i*, body of prostate; *j*, prostate disseminate (body is missing in the ram); *k*, pelvic part of the urogenital canal; *l*, Cowper's gland; *m*, bulbospongiosus muscle; *n*, left crus of the penis (cut); *o*, ischiocavernosus muscle (cut); *p*, penis; *r*, free part of the penis; *s*, retractor penis muscle; *t*, bladder; *u*, symphysis of pelvis; *v*, rectum; *x*, the urethral process (in ram); *y*, preputial pouch (in boar); *z*, fold of the internal prepuce (in stallion). (Bull, adapted from Blom & Christensen, 1947. Skand. Vet. tidskr. 37, 1. Ram, boar and stallion, adapted from Bielanski, 1962, Rozrod zwie rzat gospodarskich—Reproduction of Farm Animals, Warsaw, courtesy of P.W.R.I.L.)

way of the arterial supply than leaves by the veins. The increased blood volume enlarges the penis and makes it turgid.

The caudal part of the glans of the penis of the dog, the bulbus glandis, usually becomes engorged with blood after the penis enters the vagina of the female. This arrangement makes separation difficult until erection has subsided.

In the stallion, the arrangement of the penis is relatively simple, and there is a large amount of cavernous tissue in relation to connective tissue, so the penis becomes much larger in all dimensions upon erection. (See Chapter 29.)

Animals that have a *sigmoid,* or *S-shaped,* flexure of the penis, such as the bull, ram, and boar, have a higher proportion of connective tissue to erectile tissue. This results in a heavy capsule that distends little upon erection. The chief action of erection of the penis in these animals consists of lengthening the penis by straightening the sigmoid flexure, much as a garden hose tends to straighten when water pressure is increased.

Prepuce

The *prepuce* is an invaginated fold of skin surrounding the free extremity of the penis. The outer surface is fairly typical skin, while the inner membrane consists of a preputial layer lining the prepuce, and a penile layer covering the surface of the free extremity of the penis. The prepuce of the horse makes a double fold, so two concentric layers surround the penis when it is retracted. The prepuce of the hog has a diverticulum (pouch) dorsal to the preputial orifice. It accumulates urine, secretions, and dead cells, which contribute to the typical odor of a mature boar.

MUSCLES OF THE MALE GENITALIA

Figure 28–7 shows the circulation and muscles of the penis of the horse.

External Cremaster Muscle

The *external cremaster muscle* is formed from the caudal fibers of the internal abdominal oblique muscle. It passes through the inguinal canal with the vaginal process and attaches to the lamina parietalis of the tunica vaginalis. In most animals, the external cremaster muscle pulls the testis up against the external inguinal ring, particularly in cold weather. The testes of some animals are drawn into the abdominal cavity by the external cremaster muscle, except during the breeding season.

Internal Cremaster Muscle

The *internal cremaster muscle* consists of fibers of smooth muscle scattered among the contents of the spermatic cord.

Urethral Muscle

The *urethral muscle* is the pelvic continuation of the smooth muscle wall of the bladder. It surrounds the pelvic portion of the urethra, where it transports urine or seminal fluid caudally by peristaltic action. The urethral muscle appears striated in the bull and ram.

Bulbospongiosus Muscle

The extrapelvic continuation of the urethral muscle is a striated muscle called the *bulbospongiosus (bulbocavernosus) muscle.* The muscle fibers run transversely across the superficial surface of the corpus cavernosum urethrae, attaching to the tunica albuginea of the penis on each side. The bulbospongiosus muscle of the horse extends from the urethral bulb between the roots of the penis along the entire urethra to the glans penis. In other animals it covers the urethral bulb and extends only a short distance along the penile urethra. The bulbospongiosus muscle continues the action of

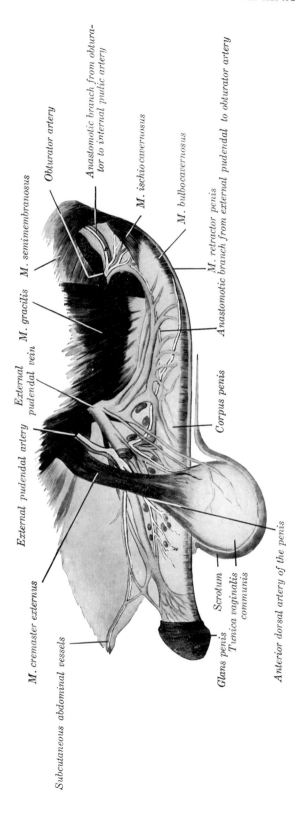

Obturator artery

Anastomotic branch from obturator to internal pudic artery

M. semimembranosus

M. ischiocavernosus

M. bulbocavernosus

M. retractor penis

Anastomotic branch from external pudendal to obturator artery

M. gracilis

External pudendal vein

Corpus penis

External pudendal artery

M. cremaster externus

Subcutaneous abdominal vessels

Glans penis

Scrotum

Tunica vaginalis communis

Anterior dorsal artery of the penis

Fig. 28–7. Penis of horse; lateral view, showing circulation and muscles. The superficial inguinal nodes are shown in the meshes of the plexus dorsalis penis. (Sisson and Grossman, The Anatomy of the Domestic Animals, courtesy of W. B. Saunders Co.)

the urethral muscle in emptying the urethra by peristaltic contractions.

Ischiocavernosus Muscles

The *ischiocavernosus muscles* are paired striated muscles that cover the superficial aspect of the respective roots of the penis. The two muscles converge from their origins on the lateral sides of the ischial arch toward the body of the penis. When these muscles contract, they pull the penis dorsocraniad against the bony pelvis, aiding erection by shutting off much of the venous drainage from the penis.

Retractor Penis Muscles

The retractor penis muscles are paired smooth muscles derived from the suspensory ligaments of the anus. The two muscles continue ventrad, one on each side of the anus, to converge caudal to the body of the penis. The two muscles then travel together ventral to the urethra as far as the glans penis, where they insert on the tunica albuginea. Following erection, the retractor penis muscles pull the flaccid penis back into the prepuce.

BLOOD AND NERVE SUPPLY OF THE MALE GENITALIA

The testis derives its blood supply from the *testicular artery,* which branches directly from the aorta a short distance behind the renal artery of the same side. This testicular artery lengthens as the testis descends into the scrotum. The *testicular vein* parallels the course of the artery, except that in the vicinity of the testis it is more tortuous and convoluted. This mass of veins just above the testis is called the *pampiniform plexus;* it is a remnant of the renal portal circulation found in the kidney of lower animals such as amphibians and reptiles.

The nerve supply to the testis is chiefly autonomic, by way of the *renal* and *caudal mesenteric plexuses.* The nerve fibers accompany the *testicular* (internal spermatic) artery.

The *internal pudendal artery* supplies most of the penis, bladder, urethra, and accessory sex glands in the bull, ram, boar, and dog. The terminal branches of each internal pudendal artery usually include an *artery to the urethral bulb,* a *deep artery of the penis* to the root of the penis, and a *dorsal artery of the penis* that runs along the dorsum of the penis with the dorsal veins and dorsal nerves of the penis. The blood supply to the penis of the horse is more extensive, with the deep artery and the caudal part of the dorsal artery supplied by the *obturator artery,* which passes through the *obturator foramen* of the pelvis. The cranial part of the dorsal artery of the penis comes from the *external pudendal artery* after it passes through the inguinal canal.

The *dorsal nerve of the penis* is a continuation of the *pudendal nerve,* which is derived from ventral branches of sacral nerves. It crosses the ischial arch and passes along the dorsum of the penis to ramify in the glans penis. Sensory fibers from the glans provide an afferent side of reflexes for erection and ejaculation. The reflex centers for erection and ejaculation are located in the lumbar portion of the spinal cord.

Chapter 29

Physiology of Male Reproduction

ERECTION

Erection of the penis is essentially an increase in the turgidity of the organ caused by a greater inflow than outflow of blood, with resultant increase in pressure within the penis. Both vasodilation of the arteries (caused by stimulation of the *nervi erigentes* from the pelvic plexus) and a decrease in the venous drainage from the penis are factors in producing erection. The decrease in venous drainage is caused at least in part by compressing the *dorsal veins of the penis* between the ischial arch and the body of the penis when the *ischiocavernosus muscles* contract.

When the penis of the horse or dog erects, an increase in diameter as well as in length occurs because these species have a relatively large amount of erectile tissue, or cavernous tissue, in comparison with the quantity of tunica albuginea and other connective tissue (Fig. 29–1).

The *penis* of ruminants and swine erects chiefly by straightening of the sigmoid flexures. Although the turgidity increases, the length and diameter of the penis remain nearly the same as in the relaxed condition, because there is relatively little erectile tissue in comparison to the amount of connective tissue (Fig. 29–1).

The *glans penis* of the horse erects later than the body because the glans receives much of its blood supply from veins of the prepuce. This arrangement permits entrance into the *vagina* of the mare before complete erection of the glans occurs, which is particularly useful in small or virgin mares.

A somewhat similar situation is present in the dog, with the *bulbus glandis* portion of the penis erecting after entrance is made into the vagina of the bitch. This engorgement of the bulb, plus the clamping of sphincter muscles of the vulva and vagina of the bitch, prevents separation of the dogs during the "tie" until the penis of the male becomes flaccid following ejaculation.

EJACULATION

Ejaculation is a reflex emptying of the epididymis, urethra, and accessory sex

443

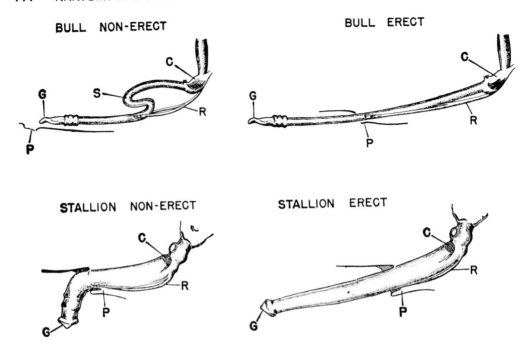

Fig. 29–1. Penis of bull and stallion in nonerect and erect states. C, ischiocavernosus muscle; G, glans; P, prepuce; R, retractor penis muscle; and S, sigmoid flexure. (From Hafez, in Reproduction in Farm Animals, Lea & Febiger.)

glands of the male. The reflex most commonly is caused by stimulation of the glans penis, either during natural service, or by an artificial vagina used for collecting semen for examination or artificial insemination. Ejaculation can also be produced by manual massage of the accessory sex glands through the rectum or by the use of an electric ejaculator. Figure 29–2 illustrates the nervous pathways involved in erection and ejaculation in man and presumably in other animals.

HORMONES OF MALE REPRODUCTION

The endocrine function of the testes consists mainly of production of *testosterone*, the male sex hormone, by the *interstitial cells* (also called the *cells of Leydig*). Hormones, such as testosterone, with masculinizing effects are known as *androgens*. The testes are the chief source of androgens, but small amounts are also produced by the *adrenal cortex*, the *female ovaries*, and the

placenta. Some of the actions of testosterone were known for centuries before the word hormone was coined and applied to products of internal secretion, because the practice of castration of both male animals and man goes back into early history.

Lack of *libido* (sex drive) and inability to produce offspring are two of the most obvious effects of castration and the resultant lack of testosterone. However, animals castrated after attaining sexual maturity may continue to mate for some time if they had sexual experience before castration. If an animal is castrated before puberty, many of the masculine secondary sex characteristics fail to develop, and the castrate animal tends to resemble the female of the species. In addition, the accessory sex glands fail to develop normally if castration occurs early in life, and they regress and become nonfunctional if castration occurs after sexual maturity (Fig. 29–3). Lack of development of accessory sex glands, the penis, and the urethra may be a contributing factor in

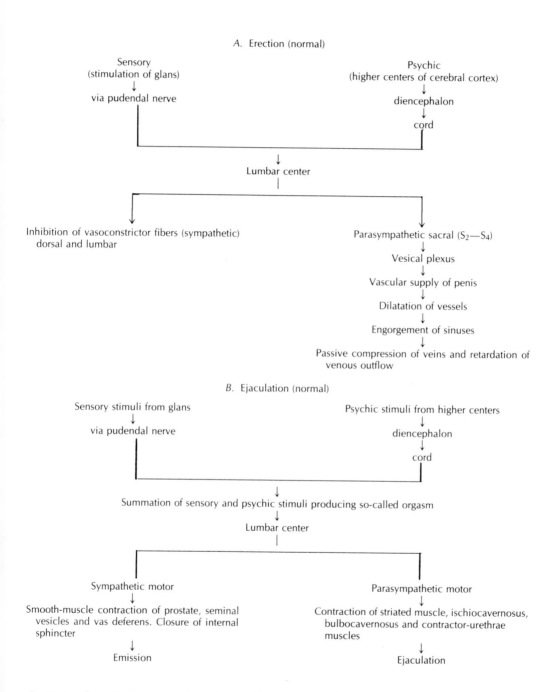

Fig. 29–2. The probable neural pathways involved in *A*, erection, and *B*, ejaculation. (Whitelaw and Smitherick, courtesy of New Engl. J. Med.)

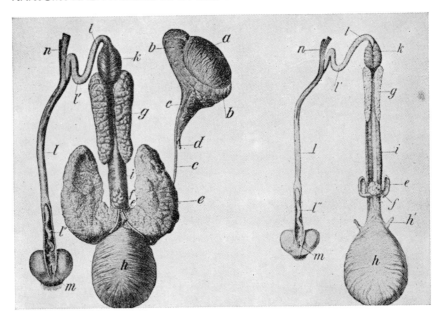

Fig. 29–3.   Genital organs of a normal and a castrated boar. (From Handbuch der vergleichenden Anatomie der Haustiere by permission of the Springer Verlag, Heidelberg.)

a — testis	g — bulbourethral gland	l' — sigmoid flexure
b — epididymis	h — bladder	l" — twisted portion of penis
c — ductus deferens	h' — ureter	m — orifice of preputial pouch
d — spermatic cord	i — urethral muscle	n — retractor penis muscle
e — seminal vesicle	k — cavernous muscle	
f — prostate gland	l — penis	

obstructions caused by urinary calculi in feedlot steers and wethers.

The actions of testosterone have been determined largely by using it as replacement treatment in experimental castrated animals. Testosterone promotes the development and function of accessory sex glands, causes development of secondary sex characteristics, and controls secretion of *LH* (*luteinizing hormone, ICSH* or *interstitial cell stimulating hormone*) in the male. Testosterone promotes protein anabolism, resulting in increased body size as compared to the female. The skeleton also responds to testosterone, with the bones becoming larger and thicker.

Spermatogenesis is initiated by *FSH* (*follicle-stimulating hormone*) from the *anterior pituitary gland*, but testosterone is necessary for completing the process. The pituitary gonadotrophins directly control germ-cell mitosis and meiosis and indirectly control maturation of *spermatids (spermiogenesis)*. Inasmuch as interstitial cells are stimulated to produce testosterone by LH *(interstitial-cell-stimulating hormone,* or *ICSH)*, the testosterone acts in a feedback mechanism to inhibit further production of LH. FSH is necessary for final maturation of spermatids. LH controls the secretion of testosterone; and prolactin enhances LH in maintaining testosterone production.

The testis produces an appreciable amount of estrogen (female sex hormone), presumably from the *Sertoli's cells* in the *seminiferous tubules*. The function of estrogen in the male is obscure, but it may act to inhibit FSH from the anterior pituitary. High levels of estrogen are found in the urine of stallions.

FACTORS AFFECTING TESTICULAR FUNCTION

FSH and LH primarily control testicular function. These in turn are regulated by *releasing factors* in the hypothalamus of the brain that act on the adenohypophysis (anterior pituitary), regulating the release of FSH and LH directly, or indirectly by feedback mechanisms from blood levels of the hormones.

The amount of daylight also has a strong effect on testicular function and breeding times through its effects on the pituitary gland. The farm animals have been classified (in Dukes Physiology of Domestic Animals, 1977) into three groups based on light periods: (1) those in which the pituitary gland is activated by periods of short or decreasing daylight, as in the sheep and goats, (2) those in which the pituitary is activated by long or increasing light periods, as in the horse and donkey, and (3) those in which photoperiod sensitivity is difficult to pattern, as in cattle and pigs.

Although the ram and male goat can reproduce all year, the sperm count and spermatogenic activity are maximal in the *fall* (normal breeding season), and then gradually decrease to their lowest levels in the summer, as do also the quality of the semen (viability and motility) and the amount of fructose in the seminal plasma. These normal seasonal changes can be altered by artificially controlling the light periods that the animals are exposed to.

While the bull is less affected by photoperiod changes than the ram and goat, it appears that semen quality is lowest in summer and highest in winter or spring. Semen fructose concentration is highest in March and September. Fertility from artificial insemination usually is low in summer and highest in the fall.

Semen volume in the stallion appreciably increases in April of the breeding season.

High environmental temperatures, as in the summer, seem to decrease sheep, cattle, and swine fertility; sperm production is decreased in these males, probably due to the direct effect of heat on the testes.

Nutritional deficiencies may delay puberty and inhibit testicular function in the young male, but have much less effect on testicular function in the adult.

SEX DETERMINATION

Sex of mammals normally is determined by the genetic makeup of the individual embryo, with the dam contributing an *X chromosome* and the sire contributing either an *X* or *Y chromosome*. The embryo with XX chromosomes will become a female, and the embryo with XY chromosomes will become a male.

Although this concept of sex determination is basically true, the genetic mechanism is actually more complex. A genetic and hormonal balance normally exists between the sexes, but maleness and femaleness are a matter of degree, with many gradations being possible between the two extremes. An interesting finding in *somatic cells* is the presence of a small clump of chromatin material, called a *Barr body*, adherent to the inner surface of the nuclear membrane. This sex chromatin is found in 60 to 80% of the somatic nuclei of females, and not over 10% of the somatic nuclei of males. The presence or absence of the sex chromatin is accepted as a presumptive test for genetic sex of the individual.

The understanding of *hermaphrodites*, males with female characteristics and females with male characteristics, was aided considerably by the study of *freemartins* in cattle. A freemartin is a female calf that develops in the same uterus with a normal male twin, and with a common blood supply for both twins. (If the placentas and blood supply are separate, a normal female calf will develop.) The freemartin usually has female external genitalia, but may have any degree of masculinization of the internal genitalia. The amount of masculinity appears to be correlated with the amount of vascular connection between the twins, and presumably with the stage of development at which the connection was established.

The conclusion that the abnormal development of the female twin is due to a hormone from the testes of the male calf that is carried to the female calf by way of the common circulation has been well accepted, although attempts have been made to incriminate an antigen-antibody reaction. To test a heifer calf born with a bull twin, a blunt instrument such as a small test tube may be inserted into the vagina of the suspected calf. If the tube can be inserted several inches without difficulty, the heifer probably is normal, but if the passage is blocked within an inch or so of the opening, the heifer is likely to be a freemartin, and she cannot be used for breeding.

The term freemartin is applied exclusively to cattle, but similar intersex females have been reported in pigs and have been suspected in sheep, with apparently the same mechanism of formation as in cattle.

Regardless of the genetic sex of an embryo, it is possible to produce a functioning animal of the opposite sex by the use of the right amounts of the right hormones administered to the embryo in the indifferent stage and continued for the proper length of time. Every vertebrate embryo goes through an indifferent stage in which all embryonic structures needed for the development of either sex are present as definite structures (Fig. 29–4). Both *mullerian* and *wolffian* ducts are present in the embryo. With normal male hormonal stimulation, the wolffian ducts become tubular portions of the male reproductive system, and the müllerian ducts regress. Under normal female hormonal stimulation, the müllerian ducts become tubular portions of the female reproductive system, and the wolffian ducts regress. In the case of the freemartin, the testes of the male twin develop before the ovaries of the female twin, and the male hormone adversely affects the development of the female genitalia.

SPERMATOGENESIS

The germinal epithelium containing primary male sex cells makes up the periphery of the seminiferous tubules. These primary sex cells are constantly dividing, and as new cells form they migrate toward the lumen (interior) of the tubules, develop tails, and become *spermatozoa*.

Spermatogenesis is the process by which primary sex cells in the testis produce spermatozoa (Figs. 3–11 and 28–3).

During spermatogenesis, the number of chromosomes is reduced to one-half the number normally found in the somatic (body) cells of each species. *Chromosomes* are the structures in the nucleus of each cell that are basically composed of *genes*, the hereditary determiners, which are transmitted from one generation to the next. They are the units responsible for inheritable characteristics of animals and man. The manner in which each of these characteristics is inherited depends on the location of its gene on a chromosome, and the relation of that gene to other genes of the same chromosome.

Spermatogenesis involves a series of steps in the formation of spermatozoa:

1. *Spermatogonia*, generalized cells at the periphery of seminiferous tubules, increase in number by *mitosis*, a type of cell division in which the daughter cells are nearly identical with the parent cell.

2. *Primary spermatocytes*, produced by spermatogonia, migrate toward the center of the tubule and undergo *meiotic division*, in which the chromosomes unite in pairs and then one chromosome from each pair goes to each of the two secondary spermatocytes. Thus, the chromosome number is halved in the secondary spermatocytes.

3. The two *secondary spermatocytes*

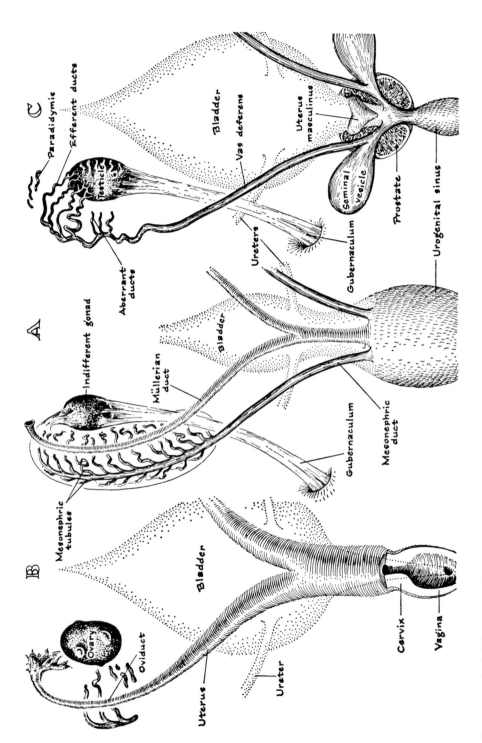

Fig. 29–4.   The indifferent reproductive system (A), and its modification into the female (B) and male (C) reproductive systems. Note that in A, the duct systems of both sexes are present. In phenotypic males, Müller's duct disappears (except for the uterus masculinus); in females, the mesonephric duct disappears (except for oviductal appendages). (Modified and redrawn from Blom and Christensen, 1947, Skandinavisk Veterinaztidskrift, in A. V. Nalbandov, Reproductive Physiology, courtesy of W. H. Freeman and Co., copyright 1964.)

formed from each primary spermatocyte divide by mitosis to form four *spermatids*.

4. Each spermatid undergoes a series of nuclear and cytoplasmic changes *(spermiogenesis)* from a nonmotile cell to a potentially motile cell (cell capable of movement) by developing a flagellum (tail) to form a spermatozoon.

5. *Spermatozoa* are the germ cells which, after maturing while passing through the epididymis, are capable of fertilizing an ovum following *capacitation* in the female. They become actively motile when exposed to the material secreted by the accessory glands (vesicular glands, bulbourethral glands, and prostate gland). However, many of them degenerate and are resorbed by the epithelial cells of the epididymis and ductus deferens, and many are excreted in the urine.

Of the four sperm cells developed from each primary spermatocyte, two cells contain the Y chromosome to produce male offspring (XY), and two contain the X chromosome to produce female offspring (XX) when united with the ovum, which contains the X chromosome.

The *acrosome system* (acrosome and head cap) of the spermatozoon is derived from an acrosomic vesicle formed within the Golgi complex of the spermatid. The vesicle becomes flattened and forms the head cap. Further changes form the acrosome.

Sertoli's cells, also called *sustentacular cells*, or *nurse cells*, are found scattered among the sex cells within the seminiferous tubules. The Sertoli's cells apparently supply nutrition to the maturing spermatids and possibly transport androgens to the germinal cells. In cases of Sertoli's cell tumors, the affected animal often develops feminine characteristics, such as enlarged mammary glands and a feminine pattern of fat distribution.

Daily Production of Spermatozoa

Daily production of spermatozoa is large in normal male animals. The number has

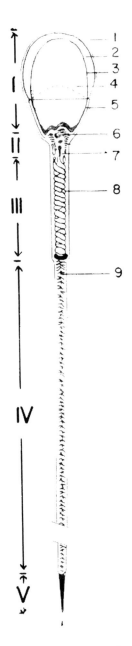

Fig. 29–5. **Diagrammatic representation of a bovine spermatozoon. The parts are labeled with terms largely according to those suggested by Fawcett. I, head; II, neck; III, middle piece; IV, principal piece; V, end piece; 1, cytoplasmic membrane; 2, acrosome; 3, nuclear membrane; 4, nucleus; 5, postnuclear cap; 6, proximal centriole; 7, axial filament; 8, mitochondrial helix; and 9, fibrous sheath. (Wu, S. H., and Newstead, J. D.: J. An. Sci. 25:1186, 1966.)**

been calculated as 4.4×10^9 in the ram and 2.0×10^9 in the bull. Eight ejaculations of a bull within an hour reduced the volume of semen from 4.2 ml at the first collection to 2.9 ml at the eighth collection, and the number of sperm was correspondingly reduced from 1664 million to 98 million/ml.

SPERMATOZOA

Each spermatozoon, or sperm cell, consists of a head, midpiece, and tail (Fig. 29–5). A nucleus extending about one third the length of the *head* contains the genetic material needed in fertilization of the ovum (Fig. 29–6). A sperm nucleus contains half as much *DNA (deoxyribonucleic acid)* as the diploid nucleus of a corresponding somatic cell; of course, DNA is responsible for transmission of heritable characteristics.

The actual amount of DNA in the nucleus of one bull spermatozoon has been calculated to be 3.3×10^{-9} mg. Sperm from infertile animals tend to have less DNA than normal. *RNA (ribonucleic acid)* is also present in the nucleus of the spermatozoon, but in small quantities (about 0.1×10^{-9} mg in one bull spermatozoon).

The *midpiece* has been described as the

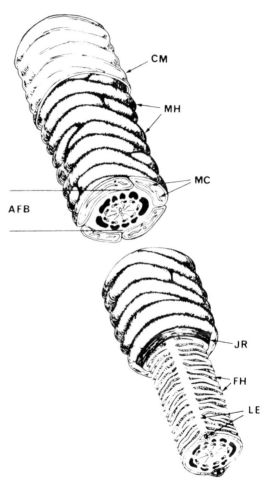

Fig. 29–7. Graphic illustration summarizing ultrastructural features of the middle piece and anterior portion of the principal piece. The cell membrane has been partially removed and the flagellum cut to show internal structure. Cell membrane, (CM); mitochondrial helix, (MH); mitochondrial cristae, (MC); Jensen's ring, (JR); fibrous helix, (FH); longitudinal element, (LE); axial fiber bundle, (AFB), consisting of the nine outer coarse fibers, the nine inner fibers or doublets, and the central pair of fibers. (Saacke, R. G., and Almquist, J. O.: Am. J. Anat. *115*:165, 1964.)

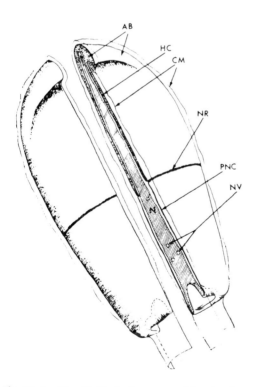

Fig. 29–6. Graphic illustration summarizing the ultrastructural features of the bovine sperm head. Apical body, (AB); head cap, (HC); cell membrane, (CM); nuclear ring, (NR); nucleus, (N); post-nuclear cap, (PNC); nuclear vacuoles, (NV). (Saacke, R. G., and Almquist, J. O.: Am. J. Anat. *115*:144, 1964.)

power plant of the sperm, since the *mitochondria* are concentrated in this area (Fig. 29–7). They line up end-to-end in strands that spiral to form a twisted helix. Mitochondria contain the enzyme systems that carry out the tricarboxylic acid cycle (Krebs cycle), and the electron transport and oxidative phosphorylation, producing the ATP energy for sperm mobility.

The sperm *tail* resembles a flagellum. Two *centrioles* are located in the midpiece. From here fibrils similar to those of cilia extend into the tail. There are two central fibrils surrounded by a ring of nine peripheral pairs of fibrils (Figs. 29–7, 29–8). These fibrils are contractile and produce movement of the sperm tail.

When examined with the electron microscope, the cell membrane of a *spermatozoon* looks identical to the cell membrane of a spermatid.

Although some spermatozoa experimentally removed directly from the testes may have the ability to fertilize ova, their capacity for fertilization normally requires maturation. This occurs as the spermatozoa pass through the epididymis. There is a decrease in water content and an increase in specific gravity, and there are some changes in ionic concentrations in the spermatozoa.

Movement of Spermatozoa

The movement of spermatozoa through the male reproductive tract is mostly passive, because motility of spermatozoa usually becomes apparent only after mixing with the accessory sex gland secretions at the time of ejaculation. Currents of fluid within the seminiferous tubules have been suggested as a means of moving spermatozoa from the tubules to the efferent ducts and then to the epididymis. Secretions of Sertoli's cells and contractions of smooth muscle may also aid movement of spermatozoa. Peristaltic movements of the epididymis may be the major factor in movement of spermatozoa within and through the epididymis. A spermatozoon can move through the epididymis in about 14 to 20 days in the ram, 8 to 11 days in the bull, and 10 days in the boar. Most spermatozoa are stored in the tail of the epididymis, where they may survive for an unknown length of time, up to a matter of weeks or months in the immotile state. Unejaculated spermatozoa are eventually phagocytized in the epididymis, as also occurs in vasectomized animals.

Under normal conditions, survival time of activated spermatozoa in the female repro-

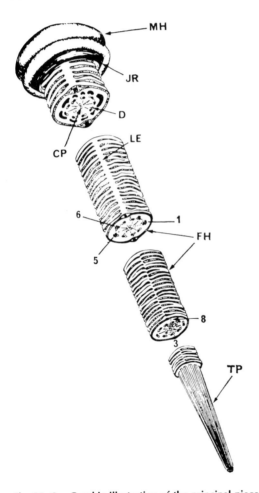

Fig. 29–8. Graphic illustration of the principal piece and terminal piece. The cell membrane has been removed and the principal piece cut at various locations to show internal structure. Mitachondrial helix, (MH); Jensen's ring, (JR); central pair of fibers, (CP); doublet, (D); longitudinal element, (LE); fibrous helix, (FH); terminal piece, (TP). (Saacke, R. G., and Almquist, J. O.: Am. J. Anat. *115*:169, 1964.)

ductive tract is only a matter of hours. Length of fertility in the female tract is given as: sheep, 30 to 48 hours; cow, 28 to 50 hours; and horse, 144 hours. Although motility usually is equated with fertility (the ability to fertilize an ovum), motility may last somewhat longer than fertility.

Even though spermatozoa are motile following ejaculation into the female genital tract, the major factor in the movement of spermatozoa to the *uterine tubes* apparently is muscular activity of the tubular genitalia following insemination. Semen appears to be deposited in the uterus of the sow and mare during normal service, but in the vagina in the cow, ewe, and bitch. *Oxytocin* assists transport of spermatozoa, and it is released in the cow both during natural mating and during artificial insemination. Oxytocin produces uterine contractions.

Based on the calculated speed of bull spermatozoa swimming under their own power (about 100μ/sec), 1½ hours would be required for a spermatozoon to swim directly to the uterine tubes. Actually, the elapsed time in a natural mating is about 2½ minutes for spermatozoa to reach the uterine tubes. In both artificial insemination and natural mating, the time ranges from 2 to 4 minutes. This extremely short time suggests strongly that spermatozoa are transported by the female genitalia to the uterine tubes rather than traveling only under their own power. There is evidence that even within the uterine tubes, sperm transport is largely a matter of tubal contractions. The fact that cilia of the uterine tubes beat mainly in a direction toward the uterus may serve to orient the spermatozoa because they tend to swim against the current. This ciliary action

is a factor in moving the fertilized ovum into the uterus.

Acrosin and *hyaluronidase*, enzymes present in mammalian spermatozoa, have the ability to disperse the cells surrounding the ovum. This is important in fertilization during penetration of the ovum by the sperm cell. One ejaculate of a bull can be divided into as many as 500 portions, and if properly handled, each portion can result in conception. In fact, over 30,000 cows can be bred each year with the semen collected from one good bull. The semen can also be frozen and stored for several years. Relatively few viable spermatozoa reach the uterine tubes following mating. The large number produced and ejaculated apparently ensures that some viable spermatozoa reach the ovum.

ACCESSORY SEX GLANDS

The *accessory sex glands* function only in the production of seminal fluid, which is not absolutely essential for fertilization if the pH of the female genital tract is not too acidic. In experimental situations, spermatozoa removed from the testis and from the epididymis, when mixed with artificial media, can produce conception.

Functional activity of the accessory sex glands depends on *testicular androgens*. Androgens from the adrenal cortex do not appear able to maintain function of accessory sex glands in castrated males.

Smooth muscle fibers in the accessory glands empty them at the time of ejaculation in response to stimuli carried by way of autonomic nerves, including the parasympathetic *nervi erigentes* and the sympathetic *hypogastric nerve*.

Chapter 30

Anatomy of the Mammary Glands

The mammary glands (mammae) are modified sudoriferous (sweat) glands. They develop along the so-called milk line of the embryo, which is a line on each side of the abdominal wall parallel to the midline (Fig.

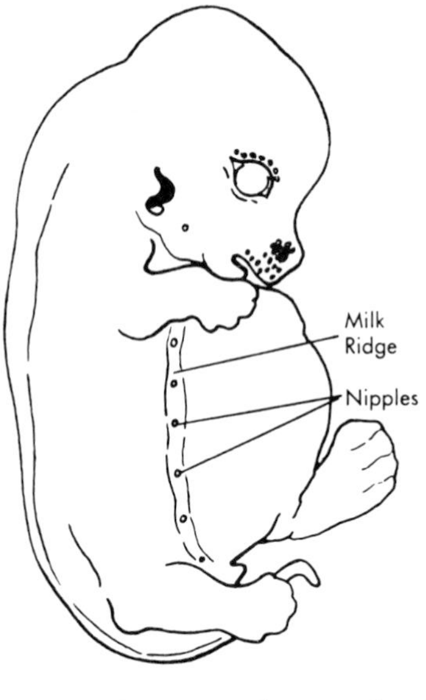

Fig. 30–1. Drawing (× 515) of 20-mm. pig embryo, showing milk ridge (milk line). (After Minot.)

30–1). In the bitch and the sow, the mammary glands are found over the entire length of the milk line. However, in most domestic animals, only the inguinal mammary glands develop. Of these, the most caudal group, either a pair or four mammary glands, develop. In the anthropoids and the elephant, the pectoral mammary glands are the only ones that develop.

MAMMARY GLANDS OF THE COW

The *mammary glands* or *udder of the cow* consist of four quarters. The skin of the udder is covered with fine hair; however, the teat is completely hairless. As far as the gland tissue is concerned, each quarter is a separate entity. The right half and the left half each consists of a cranial (front) quarter and a caudal (hind) quarter, each of which is more or less an entity. Each half is almost completely independent from the other half of the udder as far as blood supply, nerve supply, and suspensory apparatus is concerned.

Ventrally the separation of halves of the

udder is marked by a longitudinal furrow, the intermammary groove. Occasionally a transverse furrow is located ventrally between the two quarters of each half. One half of the udder can be removed surgically without damaging the other half. The two quarters of the half are separate as far as the gland tissue and duct system are concerned. They more or less resemble two trees close together, in which the branches intermingle but each retains its own identity. Thus all the milk from one teat is produced by the glandular tissue of that respective quarter. However, the blood supply, nerve supply, venous drainage, and lymphatic drainage are common to both quarters (Fig. 30–2).

The parenchyma (epithelial tissue) of the mammary gland to some extent resembles the lung tissue, or in other words, a bunch of grapes, with the alveoli representing the grapes and the various orders of ducts representing the stems of the grapes. The alveoli are the chief structures for actual milk production.

The various orders of ducts converge to form larger ducts, which eventually empty into a large basin, the *lactiferous sinus*. The lactiferous sinus may be divided into a large cavity within the quarter proper, the *gland cistern (pars glandularis)* and a smaller cavity within the teat called the *teat cistern (pars papillaris)*. The term lactiferous sinus is also sometimes used as a synonym for teat cistern and also for gland cistern.

Within the quarter, the gland cistern is the cavity located above the base of the teat and is continuous with the teat cistern. The demarcation between gland cistern and teat

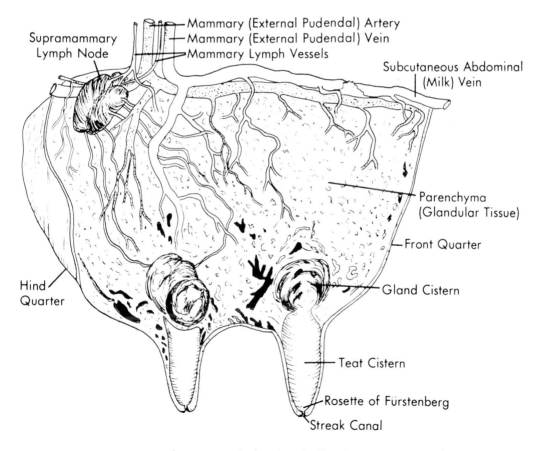

Fig. 30–2.   Sagittal section of udder of cow.

cistern frequently is marked by a circular ridge that contains a vein and some smooth muscle fibers.

The wall of the empty teat cistern contains numerous overlapping longitudinal and circular folds that are obliterated through expansion of the wall when the teat is full of milk. There may also be diverticula (pockets) in the wall of the teat cistern.

The teat cistern is continuous with the exterior of the teat through a narrow opening in the end of the teat, the *streak canal*, which opens at the *ostium papillae*. The streak canal is about 8.5 mm long, and the lumen normally is closed by epithelial folds that project inward from the wall of the streak canal, leaving only a star-shaped potential opening. At the junction of the teat cistern and streak canal, the lining of the teat is arranged in a group of radial folds called the *rosette of Fürstenberg*. There are usually about eight primary folds and several secondary folds, all of which are effaced through expansion of the wall during milking by pressure from milk in the teat cistern.

The *streak canal* at the end of the teat is surrounded by a sphincter composed of circular smooth muscle fibers. In "hard milkers," this sphincter is too tight. In cows that tend to leak milk, the sphincter is not tight enough. A tight sphincter can be corrected surgically, but *mastitis* is always a possible sequel to operations on the udder or teat.

Suspensory Apparatus

The suspensory apparatus of the udder consists of the *medial suspensory ligament* and the *lateral suspensory ligament* of the udder (Fig. 30–3). The medial suspensory ligament contains a considerable amount of yellow elastic tissue because it is derived from the *abdominal tunic*, which is an elastic modification of the fascia (connective tissue) covering the superficial surface of the *external abdominal oblique* muscle. This medial suspensory ligament passes down between the two halves of the udder. One layer of the ligament intimately covers the medial side of each half of the udder. The two layers of the ligament can be readily separated, since they are joined only by a small amount of loose areolar connective tissue. Practically no vessels or nerves pass through the medial ligament from one half of the udder to the other.

Each ligament covers the medial side of the respective half of the udder; it passes around the front quarter to about the middle of the cranial side of the quarter, and it pas-

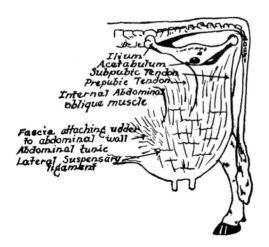
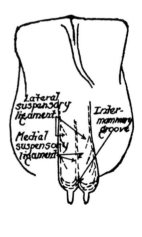

Fig. 30–3.   Suspensory apparatus of the udder. (From Espe in Turner, The Comparative Anatomy of the Mammary Glands, courtesy of Columbia, Missouri, University Cooperative Bookstore.)

ses back around the hind quarter to about the middle of the caudal side of the hind quarter. The medial suspensory ligament is continued laterad by the cranial and caudal portions of the lateral suspensory ligament.

The *lateral suspensory ligament* is largely composed of white fibrous tissue, making it much less elastic than the medial suspensory ligament.

The lateral suspensory ligament is derived in a large measure from the *subpelvic tendon*. The subpelvic tendon is a medial vertical sheet of connective tissue that attaches to the *symphysis pelvis* and the *prepubic tendon* (the tendon of insertion of the *rectus abdominis muscle*) and in part gives origin to the medial muscles of the thigh, including the *gracilis* and the *adductor* muscles. From the subpelvic tendon the lateral suspensory ligament passes outward, downward, and forward around the lateral side of each half of the mammary gland, to meet the medial suspensory ligament at the front and back of each half.

Connective tissue laminae branch off from both the lateral suspensory ligament and the medial suspensory ligament, to enter the mammary gland. These laminae subdivide the gland into large compartments, the lobes, and these lobes into smaller compartments, the lobules, to form the stroma (framework) of the mammary gland. Both the medial suspensory ligament and the lateral suspensory ligament cover their respective portions of the surface of the udder, but they stop at the base of the teat. An additional lamina from the lateral suspensory ligament sometimes is described as joining the connective tissue on the medial surface of the thigh. Some fibers may also be derived from the aponeurosis of the external abdominal oblique muscle to aid in forming the lateral suspensory ligament of the udder.

Blood Supply

The blood supply to the udder is largely by way of the *external pudendal artery* (Fig. 30–4), which is a branch of the *pudendo-epigastric trunk*. The external pudendal artery passes downward through the inguinal canal in a more or less tortuous manner, and divides into several branches that supply the front and hind quarters on the same side as the artery. A small artery that may be single or paired (as determined simply by chance) is the *perineal artery*, which continues from the *internal pudendal artery* and passes

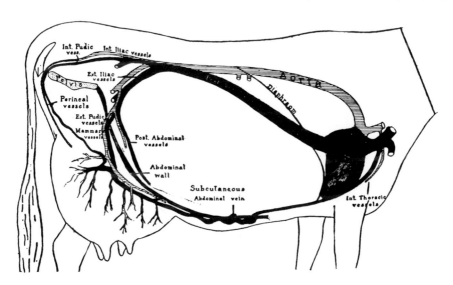

Fig. 30–4. Diagram of circulation of udder of the cow. (Sisson and Grossman, The Anatomy of Domestic Animals, courtesy of W. B. Saunders Co.)

downward from the vulva just deep to the skin on the median line. The perineal artery usually supplies a small amount of blood to the caudal part of both halves of the udder.

The venous drainage from the udder is largely by way of a venous circle at the base of the udder, where it attaches to the abdominal wall. This venous circle is formed from the main veins that drain the udder. The *external pudendal vein* of each side receives blood from both the cranial and caudal quarters of the same side. Cranially, each external pudendal vein is continuous with the *subcutaneous abdominal (milk) vein* and caudally with the *perineal vein*. An anastomosis between the two *caudal superficial epigastric (subcutaneous abdominal) veins* just at or in front of the udder completes the venous circle. Each subcutaneous abdominal vein is a large tortuous vein in high-producing dairy cows. It passes forward in a sagittal plane lateral to the midline on the ventral abdominal wall.

The subcutaneous abdominal vein passes through a foramen in the rectus abdominis muscle (the *milk well*) and joins the *internal thoracic vein*. Some authorities include the perineal vein as one of the veins draining the udder. Other authorities believe it carries blood toward the udder. The perineal vein may be single or paired (according to chance), and is a satellite of the perineal artery. It joins the internal pudendal vein.

Innervation

According to St. Clair (1942), sensory and sympathetic nerves reach the udder by way of the *inguinal nerves* (from *2, 3, 4, lumbar nerves*), ventral branches of the first two *lumbar nerves* (portions not in the inguinal nerves), and the *perineal nerve* (from *2, 3, 4 sacral nerves* by way of the *pudendal nerve*). There apparently are no secretory nerves in the udder, and the nerves to vessels (vasomotor nerves) do not follow the arteries to the udder but go by way of the spinal nerves. As will be described in the next chapter, secretion of milk is largely under hormonal control.

Lymph Vessels

The lymph vessels draining the udder show up rather well superficially just under the skin, particularly in high-producing cattle. They drain from the entire udder, including the teat, to the *superficial inguinal (mammary or supramammary) lymph nodes* located near the external inguinal ring above the caudal part of the base of the udder.

MICROANATOMY OF THE MAMMARY GLAND

The mammary gland is classified as a compound tubulo-alveolar gland. It consists of a stroma (connective tissue framework), parenchyma (epithelial portion), ducts, vessels, and nerves.

The surface of the teat is covered with stratified squamous epithelium, which is continuous into the streak canal as the same type of epithelium.

Surrounding the streak canal are a large number of smooth muscle fibers. Most of these fibers are arranged in a circular (annular) fashion around the streak canal to form a sphincter. Some muscle fibers close to the lining of the streak canal are arranged longitudinally parallel to the lumen of the streak canal.

At the junction of the streak canal and the teat cistern, the location of the *rosette of Fürstenberg*, the epithelial lining changes abruptly to a stratified columnar epithelium that is usually two cells thick. This stratified columnar epithelium lines both the teat cistern and gland cistern. The lining of the larger lactiferous ducts is the same as the lining of the gland cistern. As the ducts branch and become smaller, the epithelial lining changes first to simple columnar and then to secretory epithelium in the alveoli. The height of the alveolar epithelium varies considerably with the activity of that particular portion of the gland.

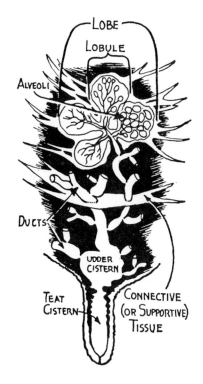

Fig. 30–5.   Connection of the ducts with the lobule-alveolar system (Hendren). (Turner, The Mammary Gland I. The Anatomy of the Udder of Cattle and Domestic Animals, courtesy of Lucas Bros.)

The mammary gland differs from most other exocrine glands in that the secretory portion is not limited to the terminations of the smallest ducts, but milk-secreting structures empty directly into the larger ducts and also directly into the gland cistern and the teat cistern (Fig. 30–5).

Turner classifies the ducts in increasing size as *intralobular, interlobular, intralobar,* and *interlobar.* A group of alveoli surrounded by a connective tissue septum form a more or less distinct unit called a lobule (Fig. 30–5). The alveoli making up the lobule empty into small ducts within the lobule, the intralobular ducts (Fig. 30–6). These intralobular ducts drain into a central collecting space, from which the interlobular ducts emerge. A group of lobules within a connective tissue compartment forms a lobe. Within the lobe the interlobular ducts unite to form a single intralobar duct, which is called an interlobar duct as soon as it emerges from the lobe. The interlobar duct may enter the gland cistern directly or it may join one or more other interlobar ducts before entering the gland cistern. Many of the ducts have numerous dilatations that act, in addition to the lactiferous sinus, as collecting spaces for milk.

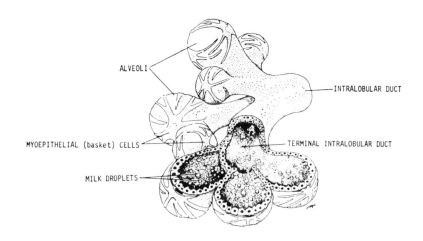

Fig. 30–6.   Active milk-producing alveoli. (Bradley, J. V., Elementary Microstudies of Human Tissue, 1972. Courtesy of Charles C Thomas, Publisher, Springfield, Illinois.)

The alveoli and ducts are surrounded by contractile *myoepithelial cells*, which are also called *basket cells*. These cells resemble smooth muscle fibers and are in contact with the epithelium of the mammary gland parenchyma, forming a basket-like covering of the alveoli and ducts. These cells contract when the milk "let-down" occurs.

In addition to the epithelial parenchyma and the myoepithelial cells, the mammary gland is made up of a stroma of white fibrous connective tissue and yellow elastic connective tissue. Blood vessels, lymph vessels, and nerves ramify throughout the stroma in relation to the epithelial structures. Networks of capillaries surround the ducts and alveoli. The veins are valveless and form a rich network throughout the gland and within the wall of the teat. The vascular layer of the teat is called a corpus cavernosum because of its resemblance to the erectile tissue of the penis in the male. Lymphatic plexuses are found throughout the udder just deep to the skin and scattered throughout the parenchyma of the gland. Nerves appear to be largely sensory and vasomotor.

MAMMARY GLANDS OF DOGS AND SWINE

The normal number of teats in the domestic hog is seven pairs or 14 teats, with the first pair just behind the junction of the sternum and ribs and the last pair in the inguinal region. The number may range from four pairs to nine pairs, and supernumerary teats are sometimes found between normal teats. Sows average 2.5 more teats than the number of pigs in their average litter. When litter size is 11 or more, sows with more teats produce slightly higher litter weights than sows with fewer teats.

Inverted teats (concave nipples) and mastitis are two of the most common conditions adversely affecting the mammary glands of sows.

The bitch usually has five pairs of teats (or mammary glands). The cranial two pair are called cranial thoracic and caudal thoracic, the middle two pair are cranial abdominal and caudal abdominal, and the caudal pair are called inguinal.

Blood supply to the caudal mammary glands is similar in the bitch and sow. The caudal mammary glands receive blood from the *caudal superficial epigastric arteries* and to some extent from the *caudal deep epigastric arteries*. The cranial pairs of mammary glands in the bitch receive blood from the *cranial superficial epigastric arteries* and the *cranial deep epigastric arteries*. The cranial mammary glands of the sow receive blood from the branches of the cranial deep epigastric arteries. Cranial and caudal epigastric arteries anastomose dorsal to the abdominal mammary glands.

The lymphatic vessels from all but the cranial one or two glands drain to the *superficial inguinal lymph nodes*. The lymphatic vessels from the cranial few glands may drain to the *cranial mediastinal lymph nodes*, the *caudal superficial cervical lymph nodes*, or both.

The teat of the sow contains two streak canals and two teat cisterns, one cranial to the other. Each teat cistern is continuous with a gland cistern. No hair is present on the teat, but hair is found at the base of the teat and on the gland.

Seedy cut bacon is due to pigmentation of mammary tissue, giving the appearance of small seeds in the bacon. Black seedy cut is due to invagination of pigmented epithelium at the time of mammary gland formation. It occurs only in dark-colored glands. Red seedy cut may occur in any color sow or gilt past puberty, as it is due to inflammation of mammary glands associated with the estrous cycle.

MAMMARY GLANDS OF SHEEP AND GOATS

The udders of the sheep and the goat differ from that of the cow in that each half of the udder has only one teat, one streak canal, one teat cistern, and one gland cistern. One half of the sheep and goat udder resembles one quarter of the cow udder. The teat is sparsely covered with fine hair. Each half of the udder of the sheep is located medially and cranially to the inguinal pocket (pouch) of the same side. Supernumerary teats in the ewe do not appear to have separate gland tissue, as is frequently found in the cow. Although attempts have been made to increase the number of teats in sheep by selective breeding, the additional teats have little effect on milk production.

The sphincter muscle around the streak canal is poorly developed, so closure is effected by elastic tissue in the end of the teat.

MAMMARY GLANDS OF THE HORSE

The mammary glands of the horse consist of one teat on each side attached to one-half of the udder. Each teat has two streak canals and two teat cisterns, each of which is continuous with a separate gland cistern and its system of ducts and alveoli. Turner (1939) reported that different colored dyes injected into the two glands never intermingle, which proves that there is no communication between ducts or cisterns within the same half of the udder.

The udder and teats of the mare are covered with thin fine hair, as well as with numerous sebaceous (oil) glands and sudoriferous (sweat) glands.

The streak canal, lined with darkly pigmented epithelium, is between 5 and 10 mm long. The junction of streak canal and teat cistern is marked by a distinctive rosette. In relation to the streak canal, the longitudinal smooth muscle fibers are better developed than in the cow, but the circular fibers are more poorly developed.

There is a difference of opinion regarding the presence or absence of rudimentary teats in the stallion and gelding. They have been described in the skin forming the cranial part of the prepuce, but their presence here has also been denied. Apparently no adequate embryologic study of this subject has been reported.

Ruminants have 1 duct per teat; the sow, 2 to 3 ducts per teat; the mare, 2 to 4 ducts per teat; the cat, 4 to 7 ducts per teat; the bitch, 8 to 20 ducts per teat; and the woman, 15 to 24 ducts per teat.

Chapter *31*

Physiology of Lactation

CONTROL OF MAMMARY GLAND DEVELOPMENT

Extensive development of the mammary gland is usually associated with puberty, the beginning of sexual maturity (Fig. 31–1). Ovarian hormones are largely responsible for mammary growth. *Estrogen* is particularly concerned with development of the ductile system at each estrus period and all through pregnancy. *Progesterone* acting with estrogen is required for full alveolar growth.

Experiments have shown that modification of this pattern exists in some animals. In domestic ruminants and the guinea pig, estrogen alone will produce growth of ducts and alveoli, but the alveoli may be cystic, immature, or papillomatous (tumor-like) unless progesterone is also administered. The proper combination and amount of estrogen and progesterone in spayed female ruminants will produce mammary development and even milk production nearly equal to that produced by a normal pregnancy. In the spayed and unspayed bitch, physiologic

levels of estrogen cause little if any duct or alveolar development. In some species the placenta is a source of estrogen and progesterone.

The anterior lobe of the *pituitary gland* is important in controlling the development of the mammary gland. There is no question about anterior pituitary control of the ovarian hormones, estrogen and progesterone, and their effect on the gland. In addition, the anterior pituitary influences the mammary gland directly with prolactin and STH (somatotropin) and indirectly by its control of the hormones of the thyroid gland and the adrenal cortex. *Prolactin, ACTH (adrenocorticotrophic hormone), somatotropin (growth hormone),* and *TSH (thyroid stimulating hormone)* all influence mammary functions either directly or indirectly through their respective target organs, along with the indirect involvement of FSH and LH. Hence, all of the hormones from the adenohypophysis, in addition to ovarian steroids, are involved in the production of a fully developed mammary gland (Fig. 31–2.). On the other hand, administered

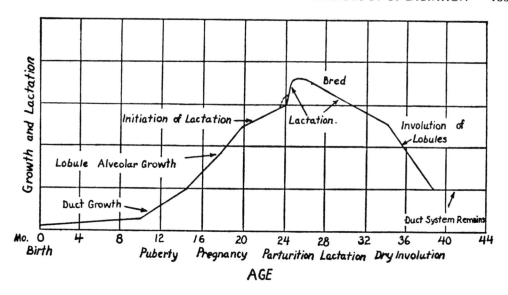

Fig. 31–1. Graph of growth, lactation, and involution of the mammary gland of the cow. (Turner, The Comparative Anatomy of the Mammary Glands, courtesy of Columbia, Missouri, University Cooperative Book Store.)

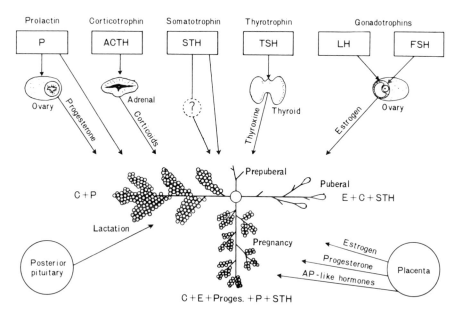

Fig. 31–2. A simplified diagram showing the action of hormones on mammary growth and lactation. In the diagram of the gland: upper—rudimentary gland; right—prepuberal to puberal gland; lower—prolactational gland of pregnancy; left—lactating gland. (Lyons, Li, and Johnson: Rec. Prog. Horm. Res., 14, 1958.)

thyroxine and *cortisone* appear to inhibit mammary gland development, whereas normal physiologic secretions of thyroxine and corticosteroids enhance development because they promote normal growth of the whole animal.

The unproven possibility exists that nervous stimuli and even psychic stimuli may indirectly influence mammary gland development by way of the *hypothalamus* and *hypothalamico-pituitary tracts*.

LACTOGENESIS (MILK SECRETION)

The concentrations of estrogen and progesterone, maintained primarily by the ovaries and placenta during pregnancy, stimulate development of the mammary gland, particularly toward the end of pregnancy, while at the same time inhibiting *lactogenesis*. When these concentrations change at parturition (or following ovariectomy or removal of the pregnant uterus, which results in involution of the corpus luteum), lactogenesis occurs. Lactation can be initiated experimentally with such diverse products as prolactin, estrogen, cortisone, and even the tranquilizers, chlorpromazine and reserpine.

At parturition, the circulating titers of ovarian and placental steroids fall. Progesterone abruptly falls off, as does the high level of placental estrogen. This promotes the release of prolactin from the adenohypophysis by acting on the hypothalamus to release its inhibiting effect on prolactin. Prolactin, growth hormone (STH), and the adrenal corticoids are the essential hormones for initiation of lactation.

GALACTOPOIESIS (MAINTENANCE OF LACTATION)

The pituitary gland is as essential for maintenance of lactation as it is for the initiation of milk secretion, and the hormonal mechanisms involved are similar. The continued production of prolactin is essential throughout the lactation period, as are also STH (growth hormone), ACTH (adrenocorticotropic hormone), and TSH (thyroid-stimulating hormone). Regular application of the suckling stimulus maintains prolactin secretion at a high level, along with the other galactopoietic hormones from the hypophysis, all of which are involved in the maintenance of lactation.

Milk production can be decreased or in some cases stopped by removal of one or more of the following glands: pituitary gland, adrenal glands, ovaries, and thyroid gland. Even though the pituitary gland is necessary for lactation, injections of ACTH in cows appear to cause temporary decrease in milk production. On the other hand, injection of STH will increase milk production in dairy cattle.

Thyroidectomy reduces milk production, but thyroxine will bring production back to normal in thyroidectomized animals and will even increase milk production in normal animals.

Iodocasein, which also has thyroid activity, has been used for artificially stimulating increased milk production. However, it has a number of disadvantages, including an excess of iodine, a need for biologic standardization, and a flavor that is unacceptable to some cows. *L-Thyroxine* contains less iodine, can be assayed chemically, and increases milk production when given orally to ruminants.

Injection of estradiol-testosterone will greatly decrease lactation in cattle, goats, and sheep. Also, feeding a high-calorie diet to cows during their life before their first calf will generally reduce their milk yield. The early high-calorie diet, in addition, decreases the animal's productive life and causes a high level of fat to be deposited in the udder, with less formation of secretory tissue, along with decreased milk production. Conversely, if the animal is underfed in its early life, then its sexual maturation will be delayed and so will the age for first calving. However, if the cow is fed well following the first calf, milk production will rise to nearly that of those that were properly well-fed before first calving. The same applies to milk volume of ewes and sows.

MILK EJECTION (MILK LET-DOWN)

Milking or *nursing* alone can empty only the cisterns and largest ducts of the udder. In fact, the resulting negative pressure will cause the ducts to collapse and prevent emptying of the alveoli and smaller ducts. Thus, the dam must take an active although unconscious part in the milking process to force the milk from the alveoli into the cisterns. This is accomplished by active contraction of the *myoepithelial cells* surrounding the alveoli and smaller ducts to produce *milk ejection (milk let-down)*. These myoepithelial cells contract when stimulated by *oxytocin*, a hormone found in the posterior lobe of the pituitary (Fig. 31–3).

Milk let-down is a *systemic reflex* in which the afferent side consists of sensory nerves from the mammary glands, particularly the nipples or teats. These nerves carry impulses that reach the hypothalamus and initiate the release of posterior pituitary hormones by way of the hypothalamico-pituitary tract. *Suckling* the teats by the young is the usual stimulus for the milk let-down reflex. The response is relatively slow compared with the usual neural reflex because of the time necessary for the hormone to travel from the posterior pituitary to the mammary gland by way of the blood stream. Whether milk is withdrawn from the teat or not, the milk ejection reflex produces a measurable increase in milk pressure within the cisterns of the udder (Fig. 31–4).

The fact that the *ejection reflex* is systemic in nature has been illustrated by experiments in which the abdominal mammary glands of rats were denervated to destroy the afferent side of the reflex. The young rats died if they were permitted to nurse only the abdominal mammary glands. However, if the thoracic glands were suckled, milk let-down occurred in all mammary glands, and the abdominal glands gave adequate amounts of milk for the young to survive.

If one half of an isolated udder (one surgically removed from a cow) is perfused with blood from a cow shortly after she receives a milking stimulus and the other half is perfused with blood from an unstimulated cow, the half receiving the blood from the stimulated cow will produce much more milk than the half receiving blood from an unstimulated cow.

It has been known for many years that injecting an extract of the posterior pituitary will simulate the suckling reflex and cause milk let-down. Oxytocin is the main factor responsible for this action. Immediately after completion of milking, an injection of posterior pituitary extract or oxytocin will release additional milk from the alveoli and small ducts that is richer in fat than the original milk. If the teats of a lactating cow are canulated (teat tubes inserted), an injection of oxytocin will cause milk to gush out in streams.

Ether anesthesia inhibits the suckling reflex in the bitch, but an injection of posterior

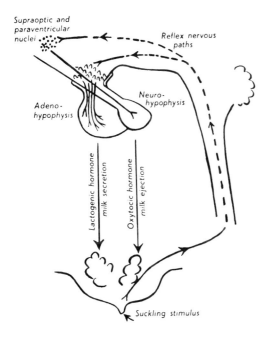

Fig. 31–3. Diagram illustrating probable neurohormonal reflexes involved in milk secretion and milk ejection. (Harris, Neural Control of the Pituitary Gland, Courtesy of Edward Arnold Publishers.)

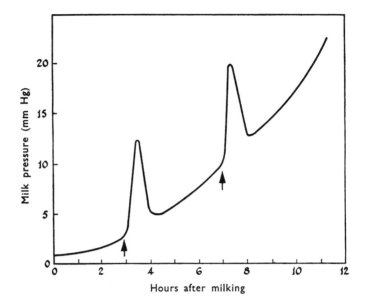

Fig. 31–4.   Milk pressure curve between one milking and the next (cow). Each arrow indicates the time the milking stimulus was applied but milk not withdrawn. (From Tgetgel, in Folley, The Physiology and Biochemistry of Lactation, courtesy of Oliver and Boyd.)

pituitary extract will cause milk let-down in the anesthetized bitch. (See Fig. 31–5.)

If oxytocin is given daily, *neurohypophysectomized* dams (with posterior pituitary removed) are able to produce normal litters. Electrical stimulation of the hypothalamus and of the *supraopticohypophysial tract* causes milk ejection, unless lesions are present in the tract. In animals with lesions in the tract between the hypothalamus and the posterior pituitary gland (supraopticohypophysial tract), suckling will not cause milk ejection.

The suckling stimulus primarily releases oxytocin from the posterior lobe of the pituitary gland (the neurohypophysis); however, some ADH (antidiuretic hormone, vasopressin) is also released and contributes to

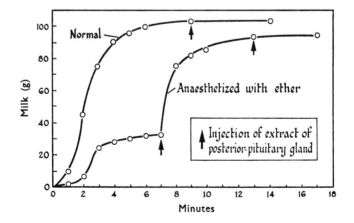

Fig. 31–5.   Milk flow curves for a bitch nursing puppies. (From Gains, 1915, in Folley, The Physiology and Biochemistry of Lactation, courtesy of Oliver and Boyd.)

the effect on milk ejection as well as on the conservation of body water for milk formation. The suckling reflex also affects the anterior lobe of the pituitary, influencing the release of prolactin and the other hormones involved with galactopoiesis.

The milk ejection reflex can be conditioned to stimuli associated with milking routine, such as feeding, barn noises, sight of the calf, and washing the udder. It can also be inhibited by emotionally disturbing stimuli such as dogs barking, other loud noises, excess muscular activity, and pain. That the *sympathetic nervous system* is responsible for this inhibition is demonstrated by the fact that *epinephrine* blocks the normal milk ejection reflex as well as experimental ejection caused by electrical stimulation of the hypothalamus. The site of action of epinephrine in this instance may be on the circulatory system arterioles in the mammary gland, although some authorities believe that emotional stress directly interferes with the release of oxytocin from the posterior pituitary.

If failure to get an adequate stimulus for milk let-down, possibly due to inadequate preparation before milking, becomes habitual, the lactation period may be shortened because of excessive retention of milk in the udder.

Essentially all the milk obtained at any one milking is present in the mammary gland at the beginning of milking or nursing. Washing the udder stimulates the milk let-down in about one minute. This builds up pressure in the gland which then slowly declines even if no milk is removed. The let-down effect ends in about 15 minutes, which is attributed to either inactivation or dissipation of the oxytocin.

It was formerly believed that dairy cattle would yield the greatest milk volume if they were milked on a regular schedule every 8 or 12 hours. However, the decrease in yield is almost negligible when milking is done at odd intervals. Furthermore, odd or unequal intervals seem to have no bad effects on the health of the udder or on the development of

ketosis. The same has been found to be true with ewes.

On the other hand, it has been found that supplemental *lighting* stimulates both lactation and growth in cattle. This was reported by Peters et al., (1978). They found that 16 hours of light each day (114–207 lux) increased weight gains and milk yield between 10 and 15% in Holstein cattle, in comparison with cattle exposed to normal photoperiods of 9 to 12 hours. The gains were accomplished without any increase in feed consumption. It was noted that the light increased the concentration of prolactin in the blood. Also, lambs grew at least 21% faster on 16-hour light periods than they did on 8-hour light periods. This suggests that light affects the pituitary-gonadal function also, because the concentrations of LH (luteinizing hormone) also varied with light exposure. Light has a stimulatory effect on development and function of the gonads—apparently mediated through the pineal gland, whose secretory activity is controlled by light.

COLOSTRUM

Colostrum, the first milk produced upon delivery of the newborn, is important to the offspring. Besides containing lymphocytes and monocytes that protect against exposure to infection, it contains a greatly increased amount of protein, especially albumins and globulins (the whey proteins), plus high levels of vitamins A, E, carotene, and riboflavin. However, lactose, vitamin D, and iron are all low compared to normal milk. If inflammation of the udder is present in the dam at the time of parturition, the colostrum will also contain polymorphonuclear leukocytes, especially neutrophils for combating the infection, as well as macrophages of the reticuloendothelial system.

Because colostrum contains antibodies against diseases to which the dam has been exposed, it is extremely important for the newborn animals to drink the colostrum. In this way, the young animals obtain passive immunity until they can develop their own antibodies.

Colostrum contains a high titer of immunoglobulins of the gamma-globulin fraction of the blood, which the neonate does not yet have. Cattle, sheep, goats, pigs, horses, and dogs, as newborns, are all dependent on colostrum for these antibodies. Whole milk or a whole milk replacer is also required until the young can eat enough dry feed to get the necessary nutrition. However, if the diet is restricted to just milk for too long a time, low magnesium levels in the blood can result, a condition called *hypomagnesemia*. Another special type of colostral secretion is the so-called *witch's milk* that newborn animals of both sexes sometimes secrete, presumably due to hormones from the dam stimulating mammary activity in the fetus just before birth.

NORMAL LACTATION

Normal lactation results from a combination of action of anterior pituitary hormones on the glandular cells of the mammary gland and action of the posterior pituitary hormones on the myoepithelial cells surrounding the alveoli and ducts (Fig. 31–6). A secretory cycle within the alveolus has been described that includes a resting phase, a secretory phase, and an excretory phase. The secretory cycle is *merocrine* at first and then at least partially *holocrine* in nature.

An alveolar cell in the resting phase appears empty; the nucleus is dark, the chromatin material is dispersed, and relatively few inclusions are present. During the *secretory phase*, the nucleus is displaced toward the tip of the cell and becomes more vesicular. Fat and protein materials accumulate in the tip of the cell, which is tall by this time.

The nature of the *excretory phase* is still subject to some controversy. The main question is whether the inclusions, particularly fats and proteins, can and do pass from the cells to the lumen of the alveolus without breaking the cell membrane. This type of excretion is called merocrine; however, if and when the cell membrane is broken and a

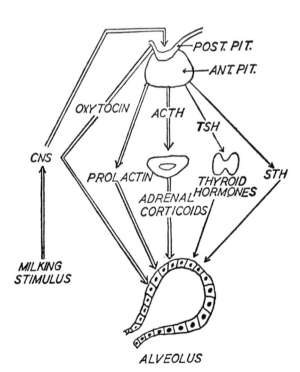

Fig. 31–6. Nervous and hormonal factors believed to maintain lactation after parturition. The milking stimulus is believed to induce the release primarily of oxytocin, prolactin, ACTH, and adrenal corticoids. Other hormones favorable to lactation may also be released by the milking stimulus. STH (somatotrophic or growth hormone) and thyroid hormones exert an important influence on the rate of milk production in some species. CNS refers to central nervous system. (Cole and Cups, Reproduction in Domestic Animals, courtesy of Academic Press.)

part of the cell is also discharged into the lumen (decapitation), this type of excretion is called holocrine.

Turner (1952) suggests that during the interval between milkings when the intra-alveolar pressure is high, the secretory products may pass from the cell into the lumen through the intact membrane, because the milk produced during this period is relatively dilute. Toward the end of milking, however, when the intramammary pressure is lower and the myoepithelial cells are actively contracting, the alveolar cells may rupture, and decapitation of the cells occurs. This could account for the higher fat and protein content of the last part of the milk extracted during a normal milking. Following a normal milking, an injection of oxytocin releases additional milk that is rich in fat and protein.

Studies of the mammary gland made with the electron microscope do not support the theory of excretion of cell contents by decapitation. These studies suggest that both fat and protein can be extruded from the cell by emiocytosis without rupturing much of the cell membrane. The exact mode of release of these products is still in doubt.

HORMONAL CONTROL OF LIPOGENESIS

In the nonruminant, *insulin* indirectly promotes the formation of milk fat from carbohydrates by speeding up their entry into the cells where lipogenesis takes place. Insulin also stimulates proliferation of more epithelial cells in the mammary gland (hyperplasia). *Cortisone, corticosterone,* and *deoxycorticosterone* tend to inhibit the stimulating effect of insulin and may inhibit lipogenesis itself.

Neither insulin nor cortisone appears to have much effect on lipogenesis in the ruminant mammary gland. The action of insulin is related to the cellular uptake and breakdown of glucose rather than the synthesis of fat, a situation that would account for the difference in species action, since nonruminants utilize glucose by way of glycolysis in lipogenesis and ruminants do not.

LACTOSE (MILK SUGAR)

Lactose, a disaccharide (glucose 4-β-galactoside), normally is found only in the mammary gland or in the milk, unless some lactose is absorbed into the blood stream during or after milking is discontinued.

Lactose is the principal carbohydrate of milk, and it is synthesized in the mammary gland. Lactose is composed of glucose and galactose. Blood glucose is the primary substance used by the mammary gland to form lactose, and so it is understandable that there is much less glucose in the venous blood leaving the udder than in the arterial blood entering it. Propionic acid is also readily used in the synthesis of lactose, by way of gluconeogenesis first.

Galactose synthesis can take place in other tissues of the animal's body besides the mammary gland, and galactose is also a component of galactolipids, galactoproteins, and cerebrosides. Therefore, the galactose component of lactose may also be obtained from the blood as well as being synthesized from glucose substrate in the udder.

Anything that lowers or decreases the concentration of glucose in the blood tends to decrease the lactose content of milk. Conversely, a condition of *hyperglycemia* (increased levels of glucose in the blood) will increase the lactose content of milk.

MILK PROTEIN SYNTHESIS

The following proteins are found in relatively large quantities in cow's milk, including four different forms of casein; αs-casein, β-casein, γ-casein, κ-casein, α-lactalbumin, β-lactoglobulin, blood plasma albumin, immunoglobulins, and a proteose-peptone fraction. The major milk proteins are the caseins, and αs-casein is the most prevalent. Amino acids are the precursors for direct

Table 31–1. Species Differences in Milk Composition (By Percentages)

Species	Fat	Protein	Lactose
Cattle			
Ayrshire	4.1	3.6	4.7
Brown Swiss	4.0	3.6	5.0
Guernsey	5.0	3.8	4.9
Holstein	3.5	3.1	4.9
Jersey	5.5	3.9	4.9
Shorthorn	3.6	3.3	4.5
Goat	3.5	3.1	4.6
Horse	1.6	2.4	6.1
Human	4.3	1.4	6.9
Mule	1.8	2.0	5.5
Sheep	10.4	6.8	3.7
Swine	7.9	5.9	4.9

Reprinted from Swenson, M.J. (ed.): Dukes' Physiology of Domestic Animals. Copyright © 1970, 1977, by Cornell University. Used by permission of the publisher, Cornell University Press.

synthesis of the caseins (except γ-casein), the α-lactalbumin, and the β-lactoglobulins in the cells of the mammary gland. The other proteins are primarily synthesized in tissues other than the udder cells.

Also found in milk are the nonprotein nitrogen (NPN) compounds: urea, uric acid, creatine, creatinine, ammonia, and (notably in cow's milk) orotic acid. These are derived from the blood circulation and as normal waste products from cellular metabolism in the mammary gland.

The composition of milk differs from one species to another, and even between different breeds within the same species. This is evidenced in Table 31–1, which shows the differences in fat, proteins, and lactose concentrations.

SYNTHESIS OF MILK FATS (LIPOGENESIS)

In the first weeks that follow calving, the percentage of fat in the cow's milk is high. Then it progressively decreases over the next three to four months, followed by a progressive increase again. The fat percent-

age at parturition is usually higher in well-fed healthy cows and sows than in underfed, thin animals. However, the amount of fat in a cow's diet has little effect on the fat content of the milk.

The *milk fats (glycerides)* of the herbivorous farm animals, particularly ruminants, contain large numbers of short-chain fatty acids, ranging from 4 to 14 carbon atoms in length. These short-chain fatty acids are not generally found in *depot (storage) fats* in the adipose tissue of animals. Milk fat can be formed either by breaking down long-chain fatty acids found in the circulating blood, or by synthesis from precursor substances. The fatty acids, butyric to palmitic, are mostly synthesized in the mammary gland, starting with either acetic acid or β-hydroxybutyric acid. Then, by the addition of two-carbon fragments from acetyl-CoA, fatty acids with longer and longer chains are formed. However, all of the C–18 acids come from sources other than synthesis in the mammary gland.

Most of the lipids in milk are in the form of triglycerides. Nonruminant mammary glands utilize *glucose* for both energy and as the source of carbon for lipogenesis, whereas ruminants depend more extensively on *acetate* (a salt of acetic acid) for fatty acid synthesis. The triglycerides are composed of three fatty acids and glycerol. The glycerol is derived mostly from glucose catabolism in the process of glycolysis. The acetate in the ruminants, along with other volatile fatty acids, are the products of polysaccharide metabolism in the rumen, carried on by microorganisms that inhabit the rumen. These volatile fatty acids are then absorbed into the blood stream of the ruminant and thereby become available for synthesis of milk fat in the mammary gland.

The differences in substrate (precursors) used in ruminants and nonruminants for fat production have been determined by experiments using udder slices, udder homogenates, and glucose labeled with radioactive carbon.

CESSATION OF LACTATION

As lactation progresses, there is a tendency for a gradual decrease in number of active alveoli, involution (decrease in size) of epithelial tissue, loss of secretory activity, and an increase of connective tissue stroma.

The normal decrease in lactation is due to hormonal changes that result from changes in neurohumoral stimuli associated with suckling. Addition of anterior pituitary hormones or thyroid hormones will lengthen the lactation period.

When milking is stopped abruptly, a number of changes in the udder occur. At the end of 24 hours, the alveoli become dis-tended to a maximum, and the capillaries are full of blood. Between 36 and 48 hours, there is a decrease in the number of patent (open) capillaries, and the alveoli do not respond to intravenous oxytocin.

Premature *weaning* causes earlier involution of the alveoli, retention of secretory products, and infiltration with lymphocytes. Some alveoli may distend and rupture and others become smaller as the contents are resorbed and the lumens become obliterated. When involution is complete, the lobules consist mainly of ducts within a vascular loose connective tissue. However, the gland never regresses to the condition it was in before the first pregnancy.

Chapter *32*

Endocrinology

The glands of internal secretion, or the endocrines, comprise a system of ductless glands that influences various vital functions of the animal from before birth until death. The events leading up to and controlling conception, gestation, and parturition are endocrine influenced, as are digestion, metabolism, growth, puberty, aging, and many other physiologic functions. *Homeokinesis (homeostasis)* is largely under the control of the secretions of these endocrine organs, the hormones. These endocrine products are secreted without benefit of a duct, directly into the vascular system, where they circulate and can profoundly influence various fundamental mechanisms. They may be considered biocatalysts in function, and the sharp distinction sometimes made between hormones and enzymes largely disappears when their mechanisms of action are studied at the cellular level.

Glands usually considered to be endocrines include the pituitary, thyroid, parathyroid, pancreas, adrenal, the gonads (ovaries and testes), and the placenta. The pineal gland and thymus are sometimes also included.

The subject of *endocrinology* is becoming more difficult to define in a meaningful way. The concept has been accepted for many years that an endocrine gland produces a chemical substance *(hormone)* that is carried by the circulation to a target organ at some distance from the original endocrine gland.

As an example of the difficulty of classification under this definition, the adrenal medulla produces epinephrine and norepinephrine, which are carried by the blood to distant target organs. Sympathetic nerves, however, also produce norepinephrine, which acts in the immediate vicinity of the nerve ending. It is difficult to classify one substance as a hormone and not the other, because they have so many similarities, and yet one fits the classic definition and the other does not. On the other hand, if the definition is broadened to include all chemically integrative products, many substances that are not usually considered to be hormones would fit the definition, such as carbon dioxide. No doubt concepts of endocrine function will change as studies move even farther from a strictly clinical approach, which considers the entire animal, to cellular and subcellular studies.

Hormones can be classified according to their chemical structure or nature of action. Chemically they are divided into two groups: the proteins, or *polypeptides,* and their derivatives and *steroids.* The major steroid-producing organs are the gonads, the adrenal cortex, and certain fetal membranes. Protein derivative hormones originate in either the adrenal medulla, thyroid, pituitary, parathyroid, pancreas, fetal membranes, or the endometrium. All are capable of elaborating polypeptides. An exception is the protein hormone *relaxin,* which is mostly secreted by the ovary.

Hormones must have an exact structural arrangement to exert their actions (Fig. 32–1). Even small changes in structure or chemical composition result in vastly different hormonal activity or possibly no activity at all, if the active sites on the molecule are changed or modified. However, some hormones are apparently still as active when some parts of the molecule are changed or removed, indicating that the criterion for function is having the active sites intact.

Some hormones affect all body tissues, but others act on one organ or gland in particular. In this latter case, the organ primarily affected is known as the *target organ,* and the hormone exerting this rather specialized influence is referred to as a *tropic* or *trophic* hormone. The major sites of trophic-hormone production are the anterior pituitary gland and certain fetal membranes, whereas the chief target organs of the body

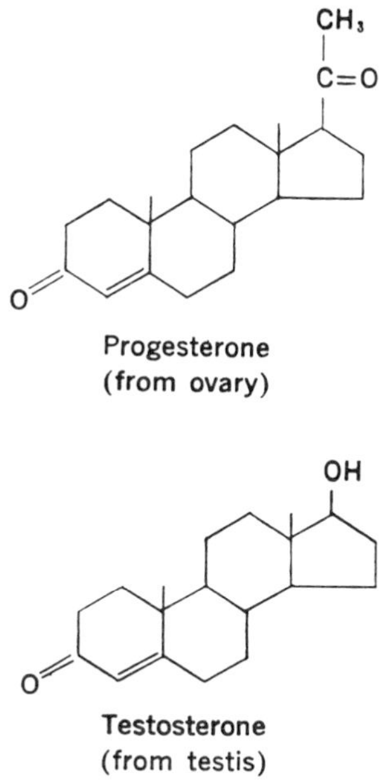

Fig. 32–1. Some naturally occurring steroid hormones.

are the gonads, the thyroid, and the adrenal cortices. Why one type of cell responds to a specific hormone and some other cell type does not is unknown, but the reason probably is related to activity of specific enzyme systems and may be associated with the binding of some hormones to certain proteins.

MECHANISM OF ACTION

The mechanisms of action of hormones on target organ cells, based on extensive research, is postulated to involve two processes. One is by *direct intracellular stimulation* of cellular nuclear transcription from chromosomes; the other is the *second-messenger* concept.

In the *direct* mechanism, the hormone being carried in the blood will, at the cellular sites, leave the blood and cross the cell's plasma membrane. Once inside the cell, it is believed to link up with a cytoplasmic protein receptor. Then this hormone-receptor complex enters the nucleus and acts on the chromosomal genes to activate or depress the process of transcription. This results in the synthesis of messenger RNA, which leaves the nucleus and stimulates protein and enzyme synthesis in the cytoplasm through ribosomal interaction.

The *second-messenger* concept begins with the hormone in the blood as the first messenger (Fig. 32–2). At the plasma membrane of the target cells, the hormone binds with a specific membrane-receptor protein. It is postulated that this activates the membrane enzyme *adenyl cyclase*, which increases the formation of cyclic 3', 5'–AMP from ATP in the cell cytoplasm. This cyclic AMP (cAMP) is believed to be the *second messenger*. It, in turn, changes the concentration of cellular Ca^{++}, which affects enzyme activation, protein kinase phosphorylation, and the rate of protein synthesis and hormone secretion. The hormones ACTH, LH, ADH, parathormone, glucagon, and the catecholamines seem to act by this mechanism.

Historically, proof of the presence of an endocrine hormone has consisted of experimental removal of the gland believed to produce the hormone in question. If this operation is always followed by the same symptoms, and if these symptoms can be relieved by appropriate extracts of the gland, it is presumed that the existence of a hormone produced by the gland has been proven. Although this technique produces spectacular results that can be repeated readily, it leaves many questions unanswered about the mode of hormone action and about hormone relationships. Hormones and their actions are also studied by treatment with known hormones in diseases of endocrine glands, and by the use of radioactive isotopes as tracers in hormone studies.

The actions of endocrine gland hormones are slower and more sustained than actions of the nervous system, although autonomic nerves tend to act over a longer period of time than other peripheral nerves. Some reflexes involve nerves on the afferent limb and hormones on the efferent side of the reflex arc. Hence, in these cases, the endocrine system can be said to be an effector arm of the nervous system.

Various "neuroendocrine" reflexes, such as induced ovulation following coitus in the rabbit, the suckling stimulus for milk let-

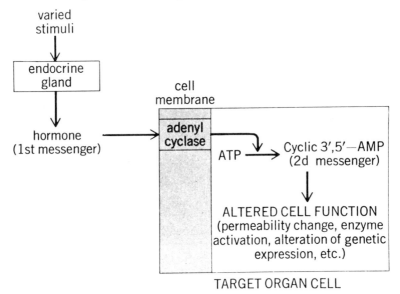

Fig. 32–2.   Second-messenger or cyclic AMP mechanism of hormone action. (From Vander, A. J., et al.: Human Physiology. ed. 2. New York, McGraw-Hill, 1975.)

down, and the effect of light on seasonally breeding species, are examples of the combination of nerve action and hormone action.

Tables and diagrams designed to illustrate hormone activity are likely to oversimplify the many factors involved in the action of a given hormone. The amount of the hormone circulating, the interrelationship with other hormones, and the receptivity of target tissues all influence hormone activity. Some hormones increase the activity of other hormones; this is called *potentiation* or *synergistic action*. The opposite effect also occurs, in which one hormone inhibits the action of another, in which case they are said to have *antagonistic action*.

One other basic consideration is the interaction between different endocrine glands, which is best seen in the interplay between a trophic hormone and its target gland. *Trophic hormones* are generally stimulating in nature, causing the target organ to elaborate and release increased amounts of its own hormone. This target-gland hormone, as well as acting on the body cells in general, also acts back on the site of trophic hormone production to inhibit further production of the trophin—thus a delicate balance can be maintained. Increased trophin production causes increased release of some other hormone, which reciprocally inhibits further trophin production. Conversely, decreased circulating level of some hormone may release the gland producing the trophic hormone from its inhibition. Then the trophic hormone is produced,which in turn, elevates the blood level of the hormone that initially was low by stimulating its parent gland. (This mechanism is called "feedback regulation.")

With these fundamental concepts in mind, we may proceed to a discussion of the various endocrine organs.

PITUITARY GLAND

The *pituitary gland (hypophysis cerebri)* is located at the base of the brain in the *sella turcica (Turkish saddle)*, a depression in the sphenoid bone on the floor of the cranial cavity (see Fig. 32–3). The pituitary gland consists of an anterior lobe, an intermediate lobe, and a posterior lobe. The anterior lobe and intermediate lobe are formed from *Rathke's pocket* or *pouch,* a structure derived from the mucous membrane of the embryonic pharynx. This accounts for the epithelial structure of these lobes. The posterior lobe *(pars nervosa* or *neurohypophysis)* originates from the embryonic brain, and in the adult is still connected to the brain by means of the *pituitary stalk.* The *infundibulum* of the stalk attaches to the *tuber cinereum,* a cone-shaped projection from the brain located at the base of the brain between the *optic chiasm* (crossing of the optic nerves) and the *mammillary body.*

The *anterior lobe* of the pituitary *(adenohypophysis)* has a projection called the *pars tuberalis,* which extends a variable distance along the front of the pituitary stalk toward the brain. Microscopically, the anterior lobe consists of cords of epithelial cells and connective tissue, separated by blood sinusoids. Six types of cells have been identified in the anterior lobe. The cells toward the center of the cords (called *chromo-*

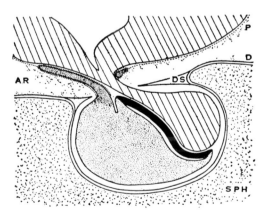

Fig. 32–3. Diagrammatic sagittal section of pituitary, illustrating relation to meninges. Brain floor and pars nervosa are lined; pars distalis, lightly stippled; pars tuberalis, closely stippled; pars intermedia, solid black. *AR,* Arachnoid spaces; *D,* dura; *DS,* diaphragma sellae; *P,* pia mater; *SPH,* sphenoid bone. (Atwell, Am. J. Anat.)

phobes) show little affinity for stains because they contain few granules. The cells near the periphery of the cords (called *chromophils*) stain readily because they have more granules. Cells that contain acidophilic cytoplasmic granules are called *acidophils* (or *alpha cells*), and cells that contain basophilic cytoplasmic granules are called *basophils* (or *beta cells*). The cells with few granules, which comprise about half of all the cells, are believed to be responsible for secreting ACTH; the acidophils appear to secrete growth hormone and prolactin; the basophils may secrete FSH, LH, and TSH.

The pars tuberalis differs microscopically from the rest of the anterior lobe, as does the intermediate lobe. The pars tuberalis is not known to have any definite endocrine function. The intermediate lobe (pars intermedia), however, is present in the majority of vertebrates, and it produces *melanocyte-* or *melanophore-stimulating hormone* (MSH), which controls skin pigmentation. It is obscure as a lobe in a few mammals, including the adult human.

The posterior lobe of the pituitary gland consists largely of special neuroglial cells (called *pituicytes*) and nerve fibers derived from nerve cells in *hypothalamic nuclei*, particularly the *supraoptic* and *paraventricular nuclei*. For many years it was believed that the pituicytes produced the posterior lobe hormones, but it has now been established that the hormones are produced by the secretory nerve cells in the hypo-

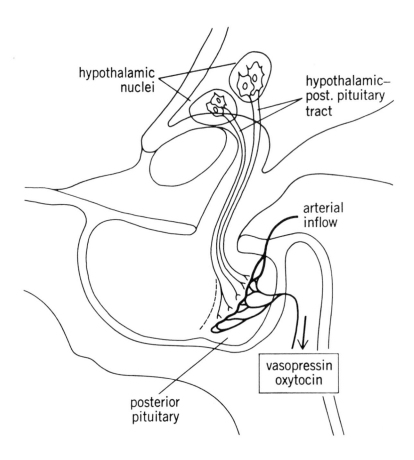

Fig. 32–4. Relationship between the hypothalamus and posterior pituitary. (From Vander, A. J., et al.: Human Physiology. ed. 2. New York, McGraw-Hill, 1975.)

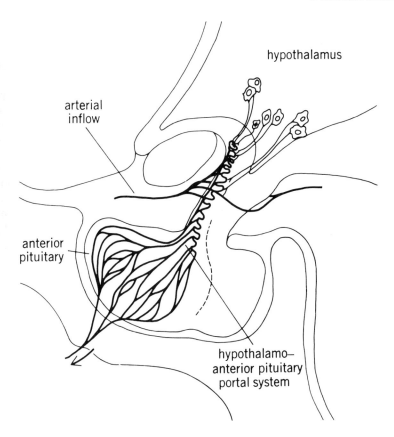

Fig. 32–5. Schematized summary of hypothalamus-anterior pituitary vascular connections. The hypothalamic neurons, which secrete releasing factors, end on the capillary loops, which are the beginning of the portal system, carrying blood from the hypothalamus to the anterior pituitary. (From Vander, A. J., et al.: Human Physiology. ed. 2. New York, McGraw-Hill, 1975.)

thalamic nuclei, and then pass down the nerve fibers to the posterior lobe (Figs. 32–4, 32–5).

The few nerves that enter the anterior lobe of the pituitary gland probably control vessel size rather than directly causing glandular secretion. Actual control of secretion is by way of veins that carry blood from the pituitary stalk and the median eminence of the brain to the anterior lobe of the pituitary gland. These veins break up into capillaries in the substance of the anterior lobe, forming the *hypothalamic-hypophysial portal system*. This route of control from the hypothalamus is well accepted, but some details about the mechanism of anterior pituitary control are yet to be worked out. All parts of the pituitary gland receive arterial blood from adjacent arteries (the *circle of Willis* in most animals).

Anterior Lobe Hormones

Hormones definitely known to be produced by the *anterior lobe* of the pituitary gland include: STH (somatotropic hormone, somatotropin, or growth hormone), ACTH (adrenocorticotropin, adrenocorticotropic hormone, or corticotropin), TSH (thyrotropin or thyroid stimulating hormone), FSH (follicle-stimulating hormone), LH (luteinizing hormone or interstitial-cell-stimulating hormone or ICSH), and LTH (luteotropic hormone, luteotropin, lactogenic hormone, or prolactin). These hormones are all *polypeptides*, and TSH, FSH, and LH also contain carbohydrate, making them *muco-proteins*.

Most attempts to correlate cell types within the pituitary gland with specific hormones are related to the changes in histochemical appearance of the cells in various physiologic and pathologic states.

Somatotropic Hormone. STH (somatotropic hormone, *somatotropin*, or *growth hormone, GH*) stimulates the growth of all body cells that can grow, and it is particularly effective on bone and muscle tissue. The action of STH (GH) is most noticeable when either an excess or deficiency of the hormone exists. An excess of STH in the immature animal results in over-all excess growth, including longer limbs, which produces a giant individual. In the mature animal, after the epiphyses of long bones have closed, the extremities enlarge in diameter but not in length, and other areas and tissues enlarge under the influence of excess STH, producing a condition called *acromegaly*.

Deficiency of STH is seen typically in hypophysectomized (pituitary gland removed) young animals. These animals are dwarfs and, of course, lack not only STH but all other pituitary hormones as well. A lack of STH in the adult usually is associated with undersecretion of all anterior-lobe hormones, a condition called *panhypopituitarism*, or *Simmonds' disease*.

STH has an important effect in encouraging protein synthesis and protein retention by the body: it prevents excessive breakdown of body protein. This is known as the *protein anabolic effect* and is due to the hormone increasing the transport of amino acids across cell membranes, and increasing the incorporation of amino acids into proteins. STH increases the severity of *diabetes mellitus* and causes a decrease in body fat.

Somatotropin (STH) also has other actions on the cells of the body. It increases the breakdown of glycogen (glycogenolysis). It increases gluconeogenesis (synthesis of glucose) from nonamino acid precursors, such as pyruvate, lactate, and glycerol. This is mediated through the enzymes fructose-1, 6-diphosphatase and glucose-6-phosphate. On the other hand, STH decreases gluconeogenesis from amino acids by decreasing the activity of the enzyme transaminase. STH increases the breakdown of fat (lipolysis) by increasing the activity of hormone-sensitive lipase.

Secretion or release of somatotropin (STH) from the adenohypophysis is affected by many things. The release of somatotropin increases with fasting, exercise, and sleep. Stress increases STH release, along with increased secretion of ACTH and glucocorticoids. It increases as ADH release increases, if the animal becomes hypoglycemic (low blood glucose level), and if the animal has a chronic protein deficiency. This is an excellent example of how hormones affect, and are affected by, multiple conditions or states of the body in maintaining the homeokinetic balance of all organs and tissues.

The ultimate effect of somatotropin in all instances then, as just cited, is to increase the blood sugar level without using up protein to do so. It also affects a certain class of proteins (called *somatomedins*) secreted by the liver, which stimulate the growth of the long bones in the pre-adult animal, and thereby stimulate an increase in body size. The effects of the hormone are most readily seen in increased mass of bone, muscle, kidney, and liver.

Somatotropin worsens diabetes mellitus because it acts as an antagonist to insulin in muscle and adipose tissue; since it increases lipolysis, it increases ketone bodies in the blood. Excessive growth hormone can damage the insulin-secreting cells of the pancreatic islets and thereby worsen the ketogenic condition.

STH apparently is not important to the growth and development of the thyroid gland, the gonads, the adrenal glands, or the central nervous system.

Adrenocorticotropic Hormone. As the name implies, *ACTH (adrenocorticotropic hormone* or *corticotropin)* has its greatest effect in stimulating the adrenal cortex (but not the adrenal medulla). The zona fasciculata and zona reticularis, which produce the glucocorticoids, appear to be much more sensitive to ACTH than the zona glomerulosa, which produces mineralocorticoids. The primary effects of ACTH are hypertrophy and hyperplasia of adrenal cortical tissue, increased production of adrenal cortical steroid hormones, and a decrease of lipids, cholesterol, and *ascorbic acid (vitamin C)* in the adrenal cortical cells. ACTH activity of a substance can be roughly measured by determining the amount of ascorbic acid depleted from the adrenal cortex in appropriate experimental animals; however this is not an accurate or reliable test because many other hormones and substances also reduce or deplete adrenal ascorbic acid. (The actions of the hormones of the adrenal cortex are discussed with the adrenal gland on p. 483.) The interrelationship between the pituitary gland and the adrenal cortex is important in maintaining homeostasis (or homeokinesis) of the animal body. Direct action of ACTH, other than its action on the adrenal cortex, is difficult to determine, but it appears to resemble that of STH in many respects. While ACTH indirectly affects other tissues, its primary action is on the adrenal cortex.

The scarcity of nerve endings in the anterior lobe of the pituitary gland reinforces the conclusion that control of the anterior lobe is by way of substances carried to the gland by the blood supply, especially by the hypophysial portal system. The usual feedback mechanism is that a decrease in circulating adrenal cortical hormones calls forth an increase in ACTH, whereas an increase in circulating adrenal cortical hormones inhibits release of ACTH. This relationship appears to function as a simple circulatory feedback mechanism in relatively quiet situations. In conditions of stress, however, the release of ACTH is too rapid to be explained as a simple feedback phenomenon. Instead, afferent nerve impulses to the hypothalamus, particularly from the cerebral cortex, with the subsequent release of controlling substances by way of the hypophysial portal circulation, are responsible for pituitary control.

CRH, corticotropin-releasing hormone, is the substance responsible for ACTH release from the anterior lobe of the pituitary gland. Specifically, CRH extract has been obtained from the portal blood, and it is the alpha form that appears to be the releasing factor of ACTH. It is a polypeptide closely resembling alpha-MSH. It is synthesized by the neurosecretory cells of the hypothalamus, and is released in response to stress, activated by a neuroendocrine reflex. Epinephrine, norepinephrine, histamine, and the posterior lobe hormones (vasopressin and oxytocin) have all been suggested as playing a role either directly or indirectly in the control of ACTH release, but it now appears that alpha-CRH is the controlling factor.

TSH (thyroid-stimulating hormone or *thyrotropin)* has its primary action on the thyroid gland proper. Thyroid epithelial cells undergo hypertrophy and hyperplasia and increased production and release of thyroid hormone under the influence of TSH. Effects of increased or decreased TSH in the body are manifested only by the changes seen with the concurrent increase or decrease in production of thyroid hormone. As with the control of ACTH, the feedback mechanism from the target organ seems to be the main method of control of TSH secretion, acting either directly on appropriate cells in the adenohypophysis, or on the neurosecretory cells in the hypothalamus to release TRF *(thyroid releasing factor)*, which in turn releases TSH by way of the hypophysial portal system.

Pituitary gonadotropins (gonad-stimulating hormones) include FSH (follicle-stimulating hormone), LH (luteinizing hormone), and LTH (luteotropic hormone, luteotropin, or prolactin).

FSH (follicle-stimulating hormone), as the name suggests, causes follicles in the ovary to develop and enlarge, with the resultant elaboration of *estrogen* from the follicle as LH secretion increases. As the level of circulating estrogen increases, production of FSH is inhibited, as in other feedback mechanisms. As FSH production decreases, LH production increases, with the result that the follicle matures and ovulates. FSH also stimulates gametogenesis in the seminiferous tubules of the *testis* of the male through development of the secondary spermatocytes. However, testosterone is required to complete the process of spermatozoa development, along with pituitary secretion of interstitial cell stimulating hormone (ICSH or LH) acting with the testosterone (Fig. 32–6).

LH (luteinizing hormone) production increases as FSH decreases. This increase in LH is correlated with increased estrogen

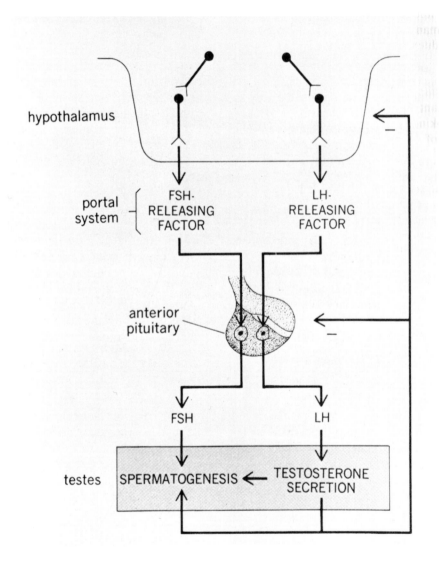

Fig. 32–6. Summary of hormonal control of testicular function. The negative signs indicate that testosterone inhibits LH secretion in both the hypothalamus and the anterior pituitary. Testosterone reaches the seminiferous tubules to stimulate spermatogenesis by local diffusion and by release into the blood and recirculation to the testes. See text for a discussion of FSH control. (From Vander, A. J., et al.: Human Physiology. New York, McGraw-Hill, 1975.)

secretion, maturation of the *ovum, ovulation,* and *formation* of the *corpus luteum*. The corpus luteum produces the hormone *progesterone*, which not only inhibits the production of more LH, but also prevents more follicle growth and ovulation, thus preventing estrus during the life of the corpus luteum. In animals that ovulate only following coitus, the secretion of LH is stimulated by way of the neuroendocrine reflex of the *hypothalamus*. Because of the action of LH in stimulating the interstitial cells *(cells of Leydig)* in the testis, LH is also called *ICSH (interstitial-cell-stimulating hormone)*. The interstitial cells of the testis produce *testosterone*, the male sex hormone.

LTH (prolactin, lactogenic hormone, luteotropic hormone, or *luteotropin)* is associated with the initiation and maintenance of milk secretion in all mammals. The release of LTH in the mammal is reflexly stimulated by suckling (nursing). In the rat, mouse, and sheep, LTH has been shown to help maintain the corpus luteum of pregnancy. This luteotropic action has not been proven in other large mammals. Prolactin has no known function in the male animal.

Intermediate Lobe Hormone

The intermediate lobe of the pituitary gland produces *MSH (melanocyte-stimulating hormone,* or *intermedin)*. This hormone is associated with the control of pigment cells (melanocytes) in lower forms of animals, including fish, amphibians, and reptiles. The administration of MSH causes darkening of the skin in these animals, and also in man. The melanocytes are located in the skin, and they contain melanin, a black pigment. Stimulation by MSH apparently increases synthesis of melanin and disperses this pigment throughout the cytoplasm and also out of the cells into the surrounding tissues. Darkening of human skin during pregnancy and in *Addison's disease* (adrenal deficiency) may be caused by MSH or possibly by ACTH, because the first third of the amino acid chain that makes up ACTH is identical to the polypeptide MSH. Knowledge is incomplete as to the activity of MSH in most mammals, and much work is needed before its function can be totally understood.

Posterior Lobe Hormones

The actual source of posterior pituitary gland hormones is from the nerve cells in the supraoptic and paraventricular nuclei of the hypothalamus. From here the hormones are carried to the posterior lobe by way of the axoplasm in the nerve fibers that pass from the hypothalamus to the posterior lobe of the pituitary (pars nervosa), where they are stored until released. The posterior lobe hormones are ADH (antidiuretic hormone, also termed vasopressin) and oxytocin.

ADH (antidiuretic hormone) has an important function in the control of water loss from the kidney by facilitating reabsorption of water from the distal portions of the nephron. Lack of ADH produces a disease called *diabetes insipidus*, which is characterized by excess loss of fluid, coupled with retention of sodium. In the normal animal, release of ADH is stimulated by increased osmotic pressure (hypertonicity) of the blood reaching the osmoreceptors of the hypothalamus. Conditions requiring conservation of water that stimulate release of ADH include dehydration and hemoconcentration. Conversely low osmotic pressure of the blood, as caused by drinking hypotonic fluids, inhibits the release of ADH and permits diuresis to occur. This loss of fluid in turn restores normal osmotic pressure of the blood. As its synonym *"vasopressin"* implies, ADH can also help to elevate the general blood pressure, but this action has not been proven to be of significant physiologic importance, except perhaps during hemorrhage.

Oxytocin, the other posterior pituitary hormone, acts on the *myometrium* (uterine muscle) and on myoepithelial cells in the mammary gland. During parturition, oxytocin causes contraction of the uterus and, in this manner, aids expulsion of the fetus. Following coitus, oxytocin is believed to stimulate uterine contraction in a manner that aids the transport of sperm to the uterine tubes.

Nursing causes reflex release of oxytocin, which stimulates the myoepithelial cells surrounding alveoli of the mammary gland to contract. This process, called *milk let-down*, forces milk out of the alveoli into the ducts of the mammary gland. Oxytocin may also be involved in the release of prolactin.

ADRENAL GLANDS

The *adrenal glands* (also called *suprarenal glands* from their position in man) are located close to the kidneys. Shape, size, and exact location vary from one species to another. Each adrenal gland consists of an outer (peripheral) zone (the cortex) and an inner zone (the medulla), with the entire gland surrounded by a connective-tissue capsule. The parenchymal cells of both the cortex and medulla are arranged in clumps that are related to blood vessels.

Histology of the Adrenal Glands

Microscopically, the cortex is arbitrarily divided into three layers named, from superficial to deep, the zona glomerulosa, zona fasciculata, and zona reticularis (Fig. 32–7). The *zona glomerulosa*, just deep to the capsule, contains slightly basophilic columnar cells that contain lipoid droplets. Cells of the *zona fasciculata*, the thickest layer, are irregular in shape and are arranged in relatively straight cords that run at right angles to the surface, interspersed with straight capillaries. The cytoplasm of these cells is slightly acidophilic and contains more lipoid inclusions than the superficial layers of cells (zona glomerulosa). The thin *zona reticularis* contains irregularly shaped cells arranged in cords that run in various directions, separated by irregular sinusoids. There has been little success in relating microscopic appearance of these cells to differences in the many hormones produced by the adrenal cortex.

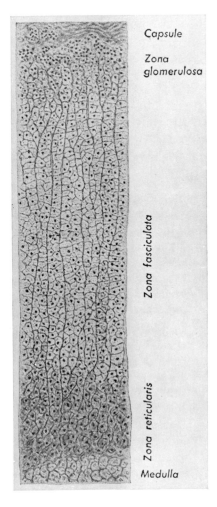

Fig. 32–7. Section through the adrenal gland. (Copenhaver, Bailey's Textbook of Histology, courtesy Williams & Wilkins Co.)

ferences in the many hormones produced by the adrenal cortex.

The adrenal medulla is derived from the same type of embryonic cells that sympathetic ganglia cells are derived from. The cells range from ovoid to columnar, and in properly prepared sections, they appear to be oriented toward veins or capillaries. Sympathetic preganglionic nerve fibers enter the adrenal medulla and stimulate the cells to release *epinephrine* (also called *adrenalin*) and *norepinephrine*.

The blood supply to the adrenal gland is variable, but in general, small arteries enter the capsule. These arteries are derived from the aorta directly or from branches of the aorta, including the *renal arteries, intercostal arteries*, and *lumbar arteries*. Some branches of the adrenal arteries supply the capsule, some supply the cortex, and some supply the medulla directly. The *medullary vein* drains both the cortex and medulla.

Hormones of the Adrenal Cortex

Many steroid compounds have been found in the adrenal cortex. These include adrenal cortical hormones with glycogenic activity *(glucocorticoids)*, adrenal cortical hormones with electrolytic activity *(mineralocorticoids)*, and sex androgenic hormones *(androgens)*. Other steroids of unknown function, which may be used in synthesizing hormones or may be metabolic end-products of hormones, or both, are also found in the adrenal cortex. Chemical naming of steroid hormones is rather complicated, but they all bear some resemblance to *cholesterol*, with various functional groups added, removed, or substituted at specific locations on the structural formula. Figure 32–8 shows the letter designation of rings

and the numbering scheme of carbon atoms in a typical steroid (cholesterol).

The presence or absence of oxygen or the hydroxyl group (OH) at the 11-carbon position is an important factor in the biologic activity of adrenal cortical hormones (corticoids). Corticoids without oxygen at the 11-carbon position are much more active in the control of electrolytes and water than in carbohydrate and protein metabolism. These mineralocorticoids include *DOC (11-deoxycorticosterone)* and *17α-hydroxy-11-deoxycorticosterone*. Although *aldosterone* has oxygen at the 11-carbon position, it is the most effective adrenocortical steroid in electrolyte control.

Steroids with either a hydroxyl (OH) or ketone (C = O) group at the 11 position tend to be effective in the metabolism of carbohydrate and protein, but have little effect on water or on electrolytes. Active steroids in this group include *11-dehydrocorticosterone, corticosterone, cortisone*, and *cortisol*.

In addition to the preceding natural steroids, modifications of some of them have been artificially prepared in the laboratory. Some of these artificial steroids are much

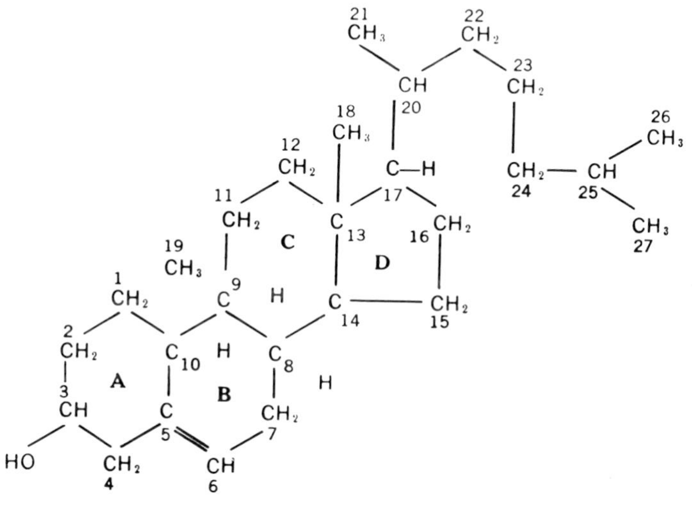

Cholesterol

Fig. 32–8. The structure of cholesterol to show the conventional system of numbering the carbon atoms and designating the rings.

more potent than the parent compound. For example, the addition of *fluorine* greatly increases the biologic activity of some steroids.

Adrenalectomy (removal of the adrenal glands) of experimental animals gives a good concept of the functions of the adrenal cortical hormones by showing what occurs when they are absent. If no adrenal cortical tissue is left and no treatment is given, adrenalectomized animals usually will not live more than two weeks. Young animals stop growing, and there is a reduction in blood sugar, blood pressure, and body temperature. The kidneys cannot function properly, and the animal lacks resistance to stresses of all kinds, including extreme temperatures, lack of food, too much exercise, infections, and injuries. The thymus and lymph nodes may become enlarged, *gluconeogenesis* is inhibited, sodium bicarbonate and chloride are lost, and potassium is retained. These disturbances, also seen in Addison's disease, can be corrected by the administration of adrenal cortical hormones. The addition of salt to the diet without hormone therapy corrects some of the symptoms of adrenalectomy, but the renal tubules still are unable to reabsorb sodium, chloride, and water from the glomerular filtrate and cannot excrete potassium into the filtrate if cortical insufficiency is present, especially aldosterone.

Aldosterone, the most effective mineralocorticoid, and deoxycorticosterone to some extent are more useful for aiding sodium retention and potassium excretion than are the 11-oxygenated steroids. Impairment of carbohydrate metabolism in adrenalectomized animals includes low blood sugar, decreased glucose absorption, depletion of liver glycogen, and failure of gluconeogenesis. At the same time, glucose oxidation is increased and conversion of carbohydrate to fat is also increased.

The 11-oxygenated corticoids have a slight action on electrolytes and on enhancing water diuresis, but they are particularly effective in correcting carbohydrate metabolic upsets due to adrenalectomy.

They also decrease the number of *eosinophils* and *lymphocytes* in circulating blood. The effects of various stresses are reduced, inflammation is decreased, and the time of wound healing is increased under the influence of oxygenated corticoids.

ACTH is the chief factor in adrenal corticoid production, and the pituitary ordinarily responds to lowered levels of circulating adrenal cortical hormones with an increase in ACTH. Additional ACTH given to both the hypophysectomized animal and the normal animal causes an increase in cortical steroids, particularly 11-oxycorticosteroids, in the venous blood from the adrenal gland. ACTH has less influence on the production of aldosterone than do the other factors of sodium-potassium ratio in the blood and the *renin-angiotensin system*.

The pathologic conditions seen with lack of adrenal cortical secretion have been described on this page. Excess secretion by the adrenal cortex may occur in cases of adrenal tumors or in response to more ACTH than normal. In both instances, the resulting signs and symptoms are partly due to increased amounts of androgens (male sex hormones) produced by the adrenal cortex, with the consequent masculinization of the animal regardless of sex, except in the *adult* male. The adrenal gland not only hypersecretes weak androgens under the influence of excess ACTH, causing cortical hyperplasia of the adrenals, but also hypersecretes cortisol, which increases blood glucose and protein degradation in the body tissues.

Hormones of the Adrenal Medulla

The adrenal medulla produces two hormones, *epinephrine* and *norepinephrine* (Fig. 32–9). Epinephrine contains a methyl (CH_3) group not found in norepinephrine. Higher proportions of norepinephrine in the adrenal medulla are found in aggressive animals, such as members of the cat family, than in the quieter animals, including the rabbit and guinea pig. In man, the adult ad-

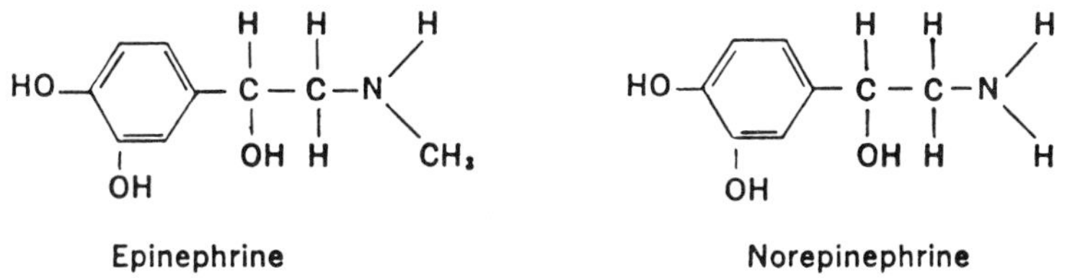

Fig. 32–9. Two hormones of the adrenal medulla.

renals secrete about four times as much epinephrine as norepinephrine. In the pig, 50% of the medullary secretion is norepinephrine, whereas it is 40% in the adult cat, 30% in the cow, 20% in the horse, and 35% in sheep.

Synthesis of the catecholamines begins with the conversion of the amino acid *tyrosine* to dihydroxyphenylalanine (DOPA), which is then converted to dopamine by a decarboxylase enzyme. The β-hydroxylation of dopamine forms norepinephrine, and subsequent methylation forms epinephrine. Acetylcholine, released by the preganglionic sympathetic fibers that enter the adrenal medulla, provides the normal stimulus for release of medullary hormones. The exact mechanism of differential release of the two hormones is not completely known, although histochemical studies have attempted to correlate a different cell type in the adrenal medulla with each of the hormones. It may be that each cell type has its own independent nerve supply to account for differences in secretory activity of the adrenal medulla under different conditions or different stimuli. In man, aggressive activity seems to be associated with increased norepinephrine, but passive emotional tension is associated more with increased epinephrine.

Postganglionic sympathetic nerve endings also elaborate norepinephrine, which is the transmitter substance from sympathetic nerves to visceral structures. It helps to maintain the tone of the vascular system (smooth muscle in vessel walls), even in the absence of the adrenal medulla, and is an important factor in the maintenance of blood pressure. Adjustment to stress situations (the fight or flight mechanism) is more dependent on epinephrine than on norepinephrine, particularly in relation to metabolism.

Epinephrine counteracts the depressing action of insulin on blood sugar level by initiating the enzymatic breakdown of glycogen, from both the liver and the muscles, thus raising the glucose level in the blood. It also causes the anterior lobe of the pituitary to secrete ACTH, which in turn stimulates the production of adrenal cortical hormones that promote the synthesis of carbohydrate from protein (gluconeogenesis). The muscle glycogen is degraded to lactic acid, from which the liver synthesizes glucose. Utilization of glucose by the tissues is also depressed.

Increased thyroid secretion increases the sensitivity of the body to epinephrine, and decreased thyroid secretion makes the body less sensitive to epinephrine. This latter effect may be due to depressed general body metabolism of cells, slower distribution of the epinephrine, and subsequently longer exposure to *monoamine oxidase*, the enzyme that inactivates epinephrine.

Under laboratory conditions, where stress can be held to a minimum, animals survive well without the adrenal medulla as long as the sympathetic nervous system remains intact. However, animals exposed to stresses of ordinary living cannot adapt to the environment if deprived of both adrenal medullae. For a detailed description of the effects of epinephrine and norephinephrine on the body, refer to Chapter 6, page 95, physiology of the autonomic nervous system.

THYROID GLAND

The thyroid gland consists of two lobes located near the thyroid cartilage of the larynx. One lobe is found on each side of the trachea, and an isthmus may or may not connect the two lobes, depending on the species. A connective-tissue capsule covers the gland and sends septa into the substance of the thyroid, which give support and conduct vessels to the epithelial cells. Microscopically, the thyroid gland consists of follicles filled with material called *colloid*, the majority of which consists of a protein-iodine complex called *thyroglobulin*. The height of the epithelial cells forming the follicular walls varies from low cuboidal to high columnar, depending on the secretory activity of the thyroid gland. (See Fig. 32–10.)

Hormones of the Thyroid Gland

Thyroid hormone influences cellular processes throughout the body, rather than having one specific target organ, as is the case with most hormones. Thyroid hormone and its immediate precursors require iodine as an essential part of the molecule in order to be biologically active. The thyroid gland traps iodide in the colloid and oxidizes it to iodine. The iodine is then incorporated into the amino acid, tyrosine, to form *monoiodotyrosine* (MIT) and *diiodotyrosine* (DIT). Subsequent coupling of these iodotyrosines form the *iodothyronines* T_3 and T_4 (Fig. 32–11). Specifically, T_3 is *triiodothyronine*, and T_4 is *tetraiodothyronine* or *thyroxine*. These two (T_3 and T_4) are secreted into the blood circulation, whereas the two iodotyrosines are deiodinated in the thyroid gland, so that the iodine can be reclaimed to be used in synthesizing the active iodinated thyronines. T_3 and T_4 may be conjugated, deiodinated, or deaminated in other tissues of the body, particularly the liver. Thyroxine (T_4) is most prevalent in all farm animals; there is about three times as much T_4 as there is T_3 in the thyroid.

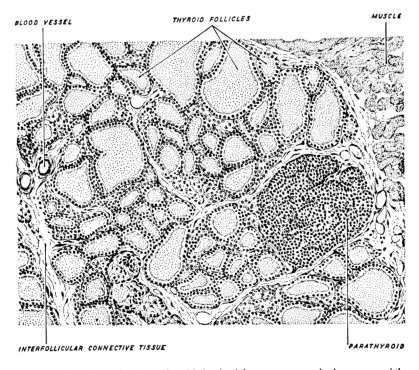

BLOOD VESSEL THYROID FOLLICLES MUSCLE

INTERFOLLICULAR CONNECTIVE TISSUE PARATHYROID

Fig. 32–10. A section of the thyroid and parathyroid glands of the rat as seen under low power of the microscope. (Turner, General Endocrinology, courtesy of W. B. Saunders Company.)

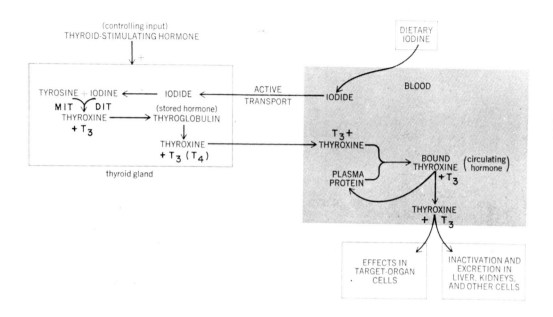

Fig. 32–11.   Summary of thyroxine pathways. Besides iodine, the diet must also supply the amino acids that are used for the synthesis of tyrosine, colloid globulin, and plasma protein. Thyroid-stimulating hormone is produced by the anterior pituitary. Iodine is converted to iodide in the process of absorption by the gastointestinal tract. (Modified from Vander, A. J., et al.: Human Physiology. ed. 2. New York, McGraw-Hill, 1975.)

Much of the T_3 and T_4 is carried in the blood by binding with other substances, principally an alpha-globulin called *thyroid-binding globulin* (TBG). In horses, a small amount is carried in the blood with *thyroid-binding prealbumin* (TBPA), and in some animals the carrier is albumin itself.

All the iodine that is bound to blood proteins is called *protein-bound iodine* (PBI), and this is the basis for an assay called the *competitive protein binding assay* (CPB), which determines the amounts of bound and free hormone in the blood. T_4 has a much greater affinity for the blood binding proteins than T_3. In the free form (unbound), T_3 is much more active biologically as a hormone. It is postulated that T_4 may, therefore, be only a prohormone or a blood source of more T_3, whereas T_3 is the active hormone. However, they may both be active, but T_4 has a slower onset of action than T_3. Both are also found bound to red blood cells. The major store of T_3 and T_4, outside

of the thyroid gland and the blood, is in skeletal muscle, probably simply because of the large mass of body muscle. Nevertheless, T_3 and T_4 have been found in all tissues and cells of the body, corresponding to their ubiquitous effects.

Once in the cells, T_3 and T_4 facilitate cellular metabolism, whereupon they are converted to disposable metabolites (Fig. 32–11). This occurs mostly by deiodination, as occurs in skeletal muscle and liver, but also by deamination and by glucuronide or sulfate conjugation, as also occurs in the liver. The ester products are then mostly excreted in the bile into the intestine, where they are degraded, and much of the iodine is reabsorbed into the blood circulation. This latter phase is called the *enterohepatic cycle*.

At the cellular level, thyroid hormone (TH) increases absorption of glucose and its utilization. It also increases glycogenolysis. A deficiency of the hormone shows up in the blood as an increase in cholesterol levels, probably because of reduced elimination in the bile, because in fact TH actually increases cholesterol synthesis. So, synthesis of cholesterol is decreased by TH deficiency, but blood levels of cholesterol rise. In addition, TH increases the synthesis of proteins in all cells, along with greater activity of nuclear and ribosomal RNA.

The calorigenic (heat-producing) activity of the thyroid hormone accounts for about one-half of the basal metabolic rate of the normal animal, since the hormone increases the rate of oxygen consumption in all cellular metabolism and stimulates cytoplasmic protein synthesis. Exposure to long-term cold causes increased release of thyroid hormone and consequent increase in metabolism for internal heat production. This response in some mammals is too rapid to be a usual feedback mechanism, so a nervous reflex stimulated by cold is involved, at least initially. Prolonged exposure to cold is followed by hyperplasia of the thyroid gland.

Emotional and physical stresses acutely tend to inhibit secretion by the thyroid gland. This is also so rapid that a nervous reflex probably is involved, since the sympathetic nervous system has been stimulated. Thyroxine also potentiates the effects of norepinephrine. Thyroid hormone is necessary for normal growth and tissue differentiation.

Lack of thyroid hormone *(hypothyroidism)* in the young animal causes a dwarf condition called *cretinism*. Deficiency of thyroid hormone affects most, if not all, systems of the body, and interferes with metabolism of carbohydrates, fats, proteins, and electrolytes. Deficiency can result in delayed puberty, irregular estrus, and decreased fertility in the female. In the male it decreases spermatogenesis, testicular growth, and semen quality. Hypothyroidism in the adult results in lowered metabolism, lethargy, loss of hair, and a tendency to gain weight; it also may produce *myxedema*, a condition characterized by retention of sodium and chloride and water (edematous appearance) with a reduced blood volume. Myxedema has been observed in calves and pigs born to mothers who were deficient in iodine. A thyroid deficiency in a growing lamb will greatly decrease the quality of its fleece as an adult. Reproductive failure is a major sign of hypothyroidism, often manifested by abortion or birth of weak young.

Hyperthyroidism (excess thyroid hormone) is associated with increased metabolic rate, loss of weight with a normal or increased appetite, irritability, and nervousness. In man, *exophthalmos* (protrusion of the eyeball) may be seen in hyperthyroidism.

Control of thyroid hormone secretion depends largely on TSH (thyroid-stimulating hormone) from the anterior lobe of the pituitary gland. It functions by means of the typical feedback mechanism, in which a low level of circulating thyroid hormone stimulates the release of TSH, and a high level of circulating thyroid hormone inhibits the release of TSH, thereby indirectly increasing or decreasing thyroid hormone synthesis and secretion by the thyroid gland. The TSH is released either by direct feedback or by feedback to the hypothalamic nuclei, which secrete TRH. In some situations, changes in the level of thyroid hormone secretion are too quick to be explained by the circulating feedback response, and must be mediated through the nervous system by way of the hypothalamus and the pituitary.

The normal thyroid gland is able to concentrate iodide to levels that are 25 to 50 times that in the circulating blood. Most iodine in the blood is in the form of iodides, but in the thyroid gland it is either in the form of iodine or it is oxidized. The oxidized form then combines with the amino acid tyrosine in the synthesis of T_3 and T_4. (See Fig. 32–12.)

An insufficient amount of circulating thyroid hormone, from any cause, leads to an increased output of TSH from the anterior pituitary. If the thyroid gland cannot respond by increasing elaboration of thyroid hormone, it hypertrophies (increases in

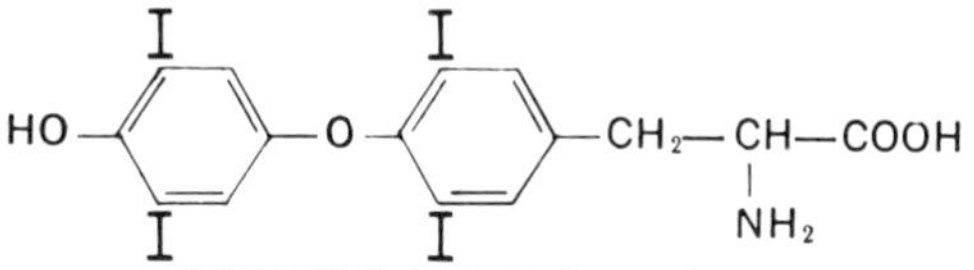

3,5,3',5'-Tetraiodothyronine
(Thyroxine)

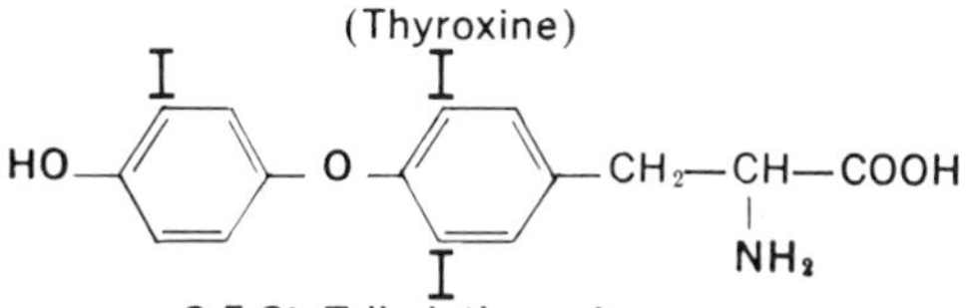

3,5,3',-Triiodothyronine

Fig. 32–12. Iodinated amino acids of the thyroid gland.

size). An appreciable enlargement of the thyroid gland is termed *goiter*. A deficiency of iodine in the diet over an extended period of time has been a common cause of goiter. The use of iodized salt by man has essentially eliminated this type of goiter in the United States.

In addition to iodine deficiency, certain drugs and vegetables, such as cabbage, soybeans, peas, peanuts, and lentils, contain compounds called *goitrogens* or antithyroid compounds, which also produce goiters by blocking formation of the thyroid hormone. This may be done by preventing iodination of tyrosine, the amino acid component of the thyroid hormone. *Sulfonamides* and related drugs act as goitrogens if administered over long periods of time. The thiocarbamids are potent goitrogens. Goiter, therefore, can be associated with either hyperthyroidism or with hypothyroidism.

PARATHYROID GLANDS

The *parathyroid glands* are small nodules located within or near the thyroid gland. Commonly there are two parathyroid glands on each side, but the exact number and location vary with the species. Accessory parathyroid glands may be found at a considerable distance from the usual glands. These accessory glands may cause inconstant results in experiments involving removal of the parathyroid glands.

Parenchyma of the parathyroid glands consists of clumps and cords of epithelial cells interspersed with capillaries. Two types of cells are described, chief cells and oxyphil cells. *Chief cells* are small cells with dark-staining nuclei and either granular or clear cytoplasm. The closeness of the nuclei to each other gives the tissue a dark appearance. *Oxyphil cells* are not present in some animals and are not found in man until the fourth to seventh years of age. The cytoplasm of oxyphil cells is acid-staining. Relationship between cell appearance and secretory activity has not been well established, but the chief cells secrete most of the parathyroid hormone.

The parathyroid glands were difficult to differentiate from the thyroid gland because of their close anatomic relationship, and the function of the parathyroid was believed to be a function of the thyroid gland. The parathyroids are now known to be separate entities from the thyroids, and active parathyroid hormone has been prepared in pure form.

Parathyroid Gland Hormone

Removal of the parathyroids is particularly damaging to carnivorous animals, because their diet is relatively high in phosphorus and low in calcium, and *PTH (parathyroid hormone)* is the major factor controlling the level of blood calcium. Parathyroidectomy results in low ionic calcium in the blood and urine, with concurrent increase in phosphorus in the blood but reduced phosphorus in the urine. Blood calcium drops from a normal of about 10 mg/100 ml to as low as 5 mg/100 ml. Low ionic calcium blood levels affect the neuromuscular system leading, in increasing severity, from twitchings to tremors and spasms of the muscles and finally to convulsions. *Tetany* (sustained muscular contraction) from parathyroidectomy leads to increased body temperature, rapid breathing, and alkalosis of the blood. The alkaline condition of the blood in turn further inhibits ionization of calcium, thus leading to more convulsions and finally death. Forced exercises or increased body temperature makes the condition even more acute.

An excess of PTH causes an increased mobilization of calcium that may reach as high as 20 mg/100 ml of serum. There is also increased excretion of calcium and phosphorus in the urine, with accompanying diuresis (increased urinary output). Continued withdrawal of calcium from the skeleton causes it to become softened and weak and subject to deformities, resulting in a condition called *osteitis fibrosa*, or *von Recklinghausen's disease*. The high blood serum calcium predisposes to the formation of calcium deposits in various soft tissues of the body, including the kidneys, lungs, heart, stomach, intestines, and blood vessels. *Hypercalcemia* decreases excitability of nerves and increases the coagulation tendency of the blood.

The main functions of PTH are mobilizing calcium from the skeleton, promoting absorption of calcium and phosphorus from the digestive tract, and causing the kidneys to excrete phosphorus while retaining Ca^{++} by reabsorption.

Regarding the mechanism of action of PTH, it promotes bone resorption by acting on the osteocytes, inciting them to engulf and destroy matrix structure so that the trapped calcium in the matrix can be released into the blood. At the same time it acts on the osteoclasts on the bone surface to increase their resorptive activity.

Current evidence points to the hypothesis that parathormone produces its calcium-mobilizing effect by (1) increasing the uptake of calcium into the bone cells, and (2) activating the enzyme *adenyl cyclase* in the cell's membrane to produce cyclic-AMP from ATP, which in turn interrupts the active transport of calcium from the cell cytoplasm into the cell organelles, and so calcium accumulates in the cytoplasm. This causes the cell to begin resorbing the surrounding matrix of bone tissue. Parathormone may also release bone citrate to lower the pH of the bone and thereby increase calcium solubility. The hormone PTH therefore becomes the "first messenger" and cyclic-AMP may be the "second messenger" in the process of calcium mobilization from bone.

Thyrocalcitonin (also called *calcitonin*) contributes to the regulation of extracellular calcium and phosphate levels. It is a single-chain polypeptide of 32 amino acids, and it has been isolated in pure form and synthesized completely in the laboratory. It is produced and released from the parafollicular "C" cells of the *thyroid* gland when the calcium concentration of the extracellular fluid bathing these thyroid cells is increased. It was named thyrocalcitonin because of its source and because it helps to regulate the "tone" or concentration of calcium in the blood. Once released into the blood, its effect is opposite to that of parathormone: it inhibits the resorption of bone and decreases the release of calcium from bone to the blood.

Calcitonin secretion increases in direct proportion to the rise in blood calcium content, and therefore keeps the blood calcium level from rising dangerously high. It does *not* act by inactivating cyclic-AMP, nor by preventing parathormone from producing cyclic-AMP. Instead, it seems to stimulate the active pumping of ionic calcium *out* of the bone cells into the extracellular spaces. This pumping of the calcium out of the cell cytoplasm nullifies the action of parathormone and so cancels the parathormone message for mobilizing calcium from the bone, and thereby decreases the resorptive activity of the osteocytes and osteoclasts.

The physiologic control system that keeps the blood's calcium supply at a stable level thus consists of two feedback loops: parathormone operating to sustain the supply, and calcitonin operating to prevent calcium from rising above the desired level in the blood. Therefore, hypercalcemia releases calcitonin while inhibiting parathormone secretion, and hypocalcemia has the opposite effect.

Normal control of secretion by the parathyroids depends on the level of circulating plasma calcium and is independent of the pituitary gland. A high level of plasma calcium inhibits PTH production, and a low level of plasma calcium stimulates release of PTH.

PANCREAS

The *islets of Langerhans* are clumps of pale-staining cells (hematoxylin and eosin stain) scattered among the alveoli and ducts of the *pancreas*. Cells of the islets, the endocrine portion of the pancreas, are arranged in irregular cords separated by capillaries. Special stains are used to demonstrate the types of epithelial cells found in the islets of Langerhans. These are the α or *alpha cells*, β or *beta cells*, *C cells* and *D cells*. The beta cells are the most common and produce the hormone *insulin*, which is necessary to prevent *diabetes mellitus*. Alpha cells produce the hormone, *glucagon*, which is antagonistic to insulin. The C and D cells look much the same, and their significance is unknown. However, since they contain no secretory granules, they may be either the precursors or the aged forms of α and β cells, they may be separate entities, or they may be α and β cells that have discharged their secretory granules.

Hormones of the Pancreas

Removal of the pancreas or loss of the secretory capability of the β cells simulates *diabetes mellitus*, a disease caused by lack of insulin or inability to utilize insulin. The most obvious effect of insulin shortage is a sharp rise in the blood sugar level (hyperglycemia) that soon passes the renal threshold (about 160 to 180 mg/100 ml), and glucose spills over into the urine (glycosuria). There is a concomitant loss of water and electrolytes, causing dehydration, and the oncotic (osmotic) pressure of the blood increases (hypertonicity) while the volume decreases.

Without insulin, there is a much reduced ability to metabolize glucose to energy, carbon dioxide, and water or to synthesize fat from glucose. Insulin has its primary effect in getting glucose across cell membranes into the cell where it can be metabolized. Without insulin, normal glucose metabolism is virtually eliminated and the cell must depend on gluconeogenesis from the degradation of fats and proteins for energy. Glycogen stores of the liver and muscles are low because of glycogenolysis, and resynthesis is slow if it occurs at all in the absence of insulin.

Since the large amount of glucose in the blood cannot be utilized effectively by the tissues, both fat and protein serve as energy sources in the diabetic animal, resulting in wasting away of body tissues. The blood contains greater amounts of fat and products of incomplete metabolism of fats and proteins, particularly ketone bodies including aceto-acetic acid, acetone, and β-hydroxybutyric acid. The presence of ketones in the blood is called *ketonemia*, which causes acidosis in the animal. When ketones spill over into the urine, *ketonuria* exists. The diabetic animal also exhibits polydipsia (thirst), polyphagia (great hunger), and hypercholesterolemia.

In the pancreatectomized animal, nearly all of the diabetic tendency can be corrected by the administration of insulin, and the animal can be kept alive in relatively good health if the diet is suitable. Normally the brain, kidneys, intestines, and erythrocytes depend very little on insulin anyway.

Insulin corrects the hyperglycemia and glycosuria and increases the utilization of glucose by the tissues. It also aids the conversion of glucose to fat, stimulates protein synthesis, reduces ketone formation, and increases the storage of glycogen by the liver and muscles.

A complex relationship exists between insulin, the thyroid, the adrenal cortex, and the anterior pituitary. Hyperthyroidism may increase the severity of diabetes, but removal of the adrenal glands relieves many of the symptoms of diabetes. The anterior pituitary may have a direct or indirect effect in increasing the severity of diabetes. If both the pancreas and pituitary gland are removed, the animal (called a *Houssay animal*) is more resistant to disease and will survive longer than one with only the pancreas removed. However, the Houssay animal has difficulty controlling blood sugar level. A diabetic state may result from any interference with the action of insulin, as well as from its complete absence.

The control of insulin synthesis and secretion depends almost entirely on blood sugar level. An increased amount of blood sugar stimulates the release of insulin. The insulin in turn decreases the blood sugar, and the resulting low level of blood sugar inhibits further insulin secretion. Amino acids also stimulate insulin secretion. In sheep, butyrate and proprionate stimulate insulin secretion, since these short chain fatty acids are important energy sources to sheep. The stomach hormone *gastrin* also stimulates insulin release. The CNS may also be involved.

Glucagon is a substance that has been isolated from the pancreas and is produced by the alpha cells of the islets of Langerhans. Glucagon elevates the blood sugar level by stimulating *glycogenolysis* (formation of glucose from glycogen) in the liver. The relation of the action of glucagon to that of insulin is antagonistic, so far as both hormones essentially have opposite effects, but both hormones must be considered integral components of the blood sugar regulating mechanism. Regarding the mechanism of action of glucagon, it accelerates the generation of 3′,5′-cyclic AMP in the liver, which facilitates the activation of phosphorylase, the enzyme that catalyzes the first step in the breakdown of liver glycogen to form blood glucose.

Glucagon is classified as a ``counterinsulin substance.'' Other substances in this category are cortisol from the adrenal cortex, epinephrine from the adrenal medulla, and somatotropic hormone, STH (also called

growth hormone, GH), from the adenohypophysis. Somatomedin, on the other hand, acts much like insulin. Glucagon has been isolated from the pancreas of swine and cattle; it is a small polypeptide of 29 amino acids.

The insulin molecule is nearly twice the molecular weight (MW) of glucagon. It consists of an A chain and a B chain connected by disulfide (S–S) bridges. Insulins from the horse, pig, dog, sheep, and ox differ only in positions 8, 9, and 10 of the A chain of amino acids.

PINEAL BODY

The *pineal body (epiphysis cerebri)* is sometimes included as an endocrine gland. The pineal body is located above the thalamus and is attached to the roof of the third ventricle. Parenchymal cells, neuroglial cells, and nerve fibers are found in the substance of the pineal body. It contains a high content of serotonin and an enzyme that converts this to *melatonin*. The enzyme, hydroxyindole-O-methyl transferase, has not been found in any tissue other than the pineal body. There is a daily increase in melatonin synthesis and release that depends on the amount of daylight; the highest blood concentrations occur during darkness. Melatonin is N-acetyl-5-methoxytryptamine.

The fact that the pineal body functions with a circadian rhythm, and hence does not release its products constantly, points to the consideration that photoperiods have an influence on animals via this body, especially in view of the belief that the pineal body is a remnant of a median eye of some extinct amphibians and reptiles. There is some evidence that the pineal body tends to inhibit development of the gonads, but in the final view, its true function is still unknown.

THYMUS GLAND

The *thymus gland* is the true sweetbread, although the pancreas is sometimes classed as a sweetbread. The thymus is a lymphoid organ found on both sides of the trachea within the cranial mediastinal space and along the neck for a variable distance, depending on the age and species of animal. Normally the gland begins to disappear shortly after puberty, but castration or adrenalectomy may postpone or slow involution of the gland.

During its early development, the thymus resembles an endocrine gland, because of the arrangement of parenchymal cells in cords. However, production of a hormone has not been proven. As development progresses, the parenchymal cells are crowded by cells that appear to be identical to small lymphocytes; these are called *thymocytes*. Odd groups of degenerating cells called *thymic corpuscles (Hassal's corpuscles)* are scattered throughout the substance of the thymus.

Current evidence suggests that the thymus is the source of a blood-borne factor that induces the differentiation of lymphoid precursor or stem cells, making them capable of taking part in immune reactions. The thymus is essential for the normal development and maintenance of immunologic competence. Protein substances that have been isolated from the thymus in the years since 1965 and proposed as thymic hormones are: homeostatic thymic hormone (HTH), thymic humoral factor (THF), thymosin, and lymphocyte-stimulating hormone (LSH). HTH and LSH are said to increase the ratio of lymphocytes to polymorphonuclear (PMN) leukocytes. Thymosin and THF are said to stimulate cell-mediated immunity. A thymic steroid substance, called *thymosterin*, isolated in 1973, inhibits both lymphocytopoiesis and tumor growth. See Chapter 15 for a discussion of immunity.

HORMONES OF THE SEX GLANDS

The hormones classified as *sex hormones* are grouped in categories as *androgens, estrogens, progestins,* and *relaxin.* The first three are steroids. The major androgen (male hormone) is testosterone. Metabolic degradation products of testosterone are androsterone, epiandrosterone, and etiocholanolone. These are 17-ketosteroids, which are excreted in the urine and can be measured as such.

The major estrogen produced from the ovaries of the cow, pig, mare, and bitch is estradiol-17β. The primary estrogen produced by the placenta of the sheep and goat is estradiol-17α, whereas in the sow placenta, estrone is the primary product. The most prevalent metabolic breakdown products of estrogen excreted in the urine are estradiol-17α and estrone, depending on the species.

The major progestin is progesterone, although two others have been isolated that also have important progestin activity. In the mare, pregnanediol is the primary metabolite of progesterone. The liver accounts for most of the catabolism or degradation of the sex hormone steroids into excretable end-products.

Relaxin is a polypeptide. It induces relaxation of the sacroiliac joints in the cow and sheep, which widens the birth canal at parturition. Relaxin also causes dilation of the cervix.

Testosterone is primarily synthesized by the interstitial cells of the testes, under the influence of hypophysial interstitial cell stimulating hormone (ICSH) release. Progestins and estrogens are secreted by the ovaries and, in pregnancy, the placenta becomes an important source of these hormones. Relaxin is secreted by the ovaries and/or the placenta, depending on the species of animal.

PROSTAGLANDINS

Prostaglandins are humoral compounds that have been isolated from many tissues of the animal body, including the skin, intestine, kidney, brain, lungs, reproductive organs, menstrual fluid, and amniotic fluid. They exert their effects either within the organ in which they are synthesized, or on an organ that is reached by the venous blood from the originating organ. Prostaglandins are quickly and totally deactivated in the lung and the liver.

There are four basic types of natural prostaglandins. All are unsaturated fatty acids having a 20-carbon atom structure and consisting of a five-carbon ring with two aliphatic side chains, one of which has a carboxyl group. The four classes, A, B, E, and F, are named according to the differences in their five-carbon ring. Members of each group are further designated by a system of subscript numbers indicating the number of double bonds (degree of unsaturation) in the aliphatic side chains. Also, subscript Greek letters are used to indicate stereoisomeric forms, e.g., $PGF_{1\alpha}$. All of them are derived in the animal body from unsaturated fatty acids of the diet.

The greatest amount of research on prostaglandins has been associated with reproduction. From this it appears that prostaglandin $F_{2\alpha}$ ($PGF_{2\alpha}$) is the natural luteolytic substance which, in the absence of pregnancy, ends one estrous cycle in the female animal and allows the next one to begin. It will also terminate early pregnancy. Therefore, it has become an effective drug for synchronizing estrus in farm animals.

Essentially, PGF_2 is a blood vessel constrictor, whereas both PGE_1 and PGE_2 are blood vessel dilators. It has been postulated that PGA_2 and PGE_2 cause vasodilation in the kidney cortex, in turn causing diuresis.

Because of their presence in all tissues examined, it is further postulated that prostaglandins are involved in relaxing the muscles of the bronchial system, inhibiting the release of sympathetic neurotransmitter substances, inhibiting gastric secretions, and increasing the inflammation response in tissues.

The prostaglandins were so named because it was originally believed that they were synthesized by and secreted from the prostate gland. Now, of course, it is recognized that they are produced in many organs and tissues, and they have been synthesized on a relatively large scale by pharmaceutical firms. The best exogenous source is the Caribbean sea coral (sea-whip).

Within the animal, biosynthesis of prostaglandins apparently occurs in cell membranes as a result of stimuli that activate the phospholipase enzyme to cause phospholipids to release prostaglandin precursors, especially *arachidonic* acid, which are then somehow converted to the specific prostaglandins of the tissue. The effects of prostaglandins may be mediated by either stimulating or inhibiting adenyl cyclase to produce cyclic AMP in the target cells, depending on which cells are acted upon. It is possible that prostaglandins may also affect the synthesis and action of the major hormones of the body through the adenyl cyclase-cAMP "second messenger" mechanism.

Some other effects of prostaglandins are: (1) decreasing blood pressure and increasing heart rate (by PGE_1), (2) inducing labor and menstruation in women, (3) increasing renal blood flow, (4) decreasing volume and acidity of fluid in the stomach, and (5) regulating platelet aggregation to prevent blood clotting [prostacyclin (PGI_2), made by endothelial cells, prevents aggregation; thromboxane (TXA_2), made by the platelets, causes aggregation]. Aspirin inhibits prostaglandin biosynthesis and thereby decreases the inflammatory response.

The ovaries are described in Chapter 25, and the testes in Chapter 28.

OTHER HORMONES OR HORMONE-LIKE SUBSTANCES

There are several substances synthesized and secreted by cells of the gastrointestinal tract and the kidney that have hormone-like action, even though they do not exactly fit the classic definition of a hormone.

The so-called gastrointestinal hormones include gastrin, secretin, and pancreozymin (cholecystokinin).

Gastrin is a heptadecapeptide that is released into the blood from secretory cells in the antrum of the stomach. It causes the parietal cells to secrete HCl and intrinsic factor (IF), and the chief cells to secrete pepsinogen. Histamine has the same effect but is less potent. Gastrin also acts on the liver to increase the volume of bile secreted.

Secretin was the first substance called a hormone. It is a small protein synthesized in cells of the duodenal mucosa as inactive prosecretin, which is released into the blood when an acid chyme enters the duodenum from the stomach. It acts on the pancreas to stimulate a copious watery secretion containing a high $NaHCO_3$ concentration from the exocrine gland cells of the pancreas. It also stimulates bicarbonate synthesis in the pancreatic duct cells. The most potent stimulus for the release of secretin is acid in the duodenum. Secretin also acts on the liver to increase the volume of bile secretion.

Pancreozymin (cholecystokinin) is the other "hormone" secreted into the blood by cells of the duodenal mucosa and acts back on the pancreas. It is released in response to peptide fragments, amino acids, and free fatty acids (FFA) in the duodenum. Pancreozymin causes pancreatic secretion of enzymes from the acinar cells.

Both secretin and pancreozymin also act on the stomach to inhibit or slow gastric motility and secretion, thereby slowing the passage of chyme into the duodenum, while simultaneously causing pancreatic bicarbonate and enzyme secretions, which buffer the duodenal acid and digest the chyme.

Cholecystokinin had long been believed to be another "hormone" secreted by cells of the duodenal mucosa in response to the presence of free fatty acids in the chyme entering the duodenum. It was noted to cause contraction of the gallbladder for release of bile. However, it is now known that cholecystokinin and pancreozymin are one and the same hormone. Pancreozymin also causes gallbladder contraction. Contraction occurs by this hormonal influence without nerve innervation, as demonstrated following gallbladder denervation or when the gallbladder has been transplanted to another site in the body.

The kidney produces a hormone-like substance, *renin*, which is secreted from cells of the juxtaglomerular apparatus whenever the mean arterial pressure or blood flow volume through the kidneys is reduced, or whenever the sodium concentration of the extracellular fluid is reduced. Once secreted into the blood, the renin activates plasma angiotensinogen to form angiotensin, which acts on the adrenal zona glomerulosa to cause secretion of aldosterone. The aldosterone acts on the kidney tubules to conserve sodium, which osmotically assists in increasing extracellular fluid volume. The angiotensin also causes some general systemic arteriole constriction to increase arterial pressure.

The kidney also secretes an enzyme called *renal erythropoietic factor (REF)*, which acts on a precursor globin in the blood to form the hormone *erythropoietin*, known also as *hemopoietin* and *erythropoietic stimulating factor*. Erythropoietin is a glycoprotein that is formed whenever tissue hypoxia occurs. Some REF is also produced by the liver. This hormonal response to hypoxia exerts its effect primarily on the stem cells of the bone marrow to increase the formation of more red blood cells, so that more oxygen can be carried to the tissues. It is a feedback mechanism that decreases or shuts off secretion of REF when the O_2 demands of the tissues are satisfied. By its feedback control, erythropoietin is another important factor in maintaining total body function in homeokinetic balance—the ultimate purpose of the endocrine and nervous systems functioning together.

Table 32–1. Endocrine Glands

Gland(s)	Hormone(s)	Principal Actions
Thyroid	Thyroid hormone (TH) Calcitonin (thyrocalcitonin)	Accelerates metabolic rate Regulates calcium metabolism
Parathyroid	Parathormone (PTH)	Regulates metabolism of calcium and phosphorus
Adrenal		
Cortex	Glucocorticoids	Stimulate conversion of proteins to carbohydrates for energy (gluconeogenesis)
	Mineralocorticoids	Regulate Na-K metabolism Control electrolytes and water
Medulla	Epinephrine and Norepinephrine	Augment sympathetic nervous system, preparation for emergency, mobilization of energy
Pituitary (Hypophysis)		
Anterior lobe	Somatotropin (STH, or GH)	Stimulates growth
	Thyrotropin (TSH)	Stimulates thyroid gland
	Adrenocorticotropin (ACTH)	Stimulates adrenal cortex
	Gonadotropins:	
	Follicle-stimulating (FSH)	Stimulates ovarian follicle development in female and spermatogenesis in male
	Luteinizing (LH or ICSH)	Stimulates ovulation and luteinization in female, and interstitial cell secretion in male
	Luteotropin (LTH, lactogenic, prolactin)	Maintains corpora lutea and stimulates lactation
Intermediate lobe	Intermedin (MSH)	Regulates pigment cells
Posterior lobe	Oxytocin	Stimulates uterine contraction and causes milk let-down
	Antidiuretic hormone (ADH or vasopressin)	Inhibits diuresis and stimulates contraction of smooth muscle of arterioles; conserves water
Islets of Langerhans of Pancreas	Insulin Glucagon	Regulates carbohydrate metabolism Increases blood sugar: counter-insulin
Ovaries		
Follicles	Estrogen	Regulates female secondary sexual characters and sexual behavior
	Relaxin	Dilation of birth canal
Corpus luteum	Progesterone	Maintains pregnancy and prepares mammary glands for lactation
Testes	Androgen (testosterone)	Regulates male secondary sexual characters and sexual behavior
Placenta	Estrogen	Maintains normal pregnancy
	Progesterone	Maintains normal pregnancy
	Gonadotropin (chorionic)	Maintains normal pregnancy
	Relaxin	Dilation of birth canal
Duodenal mucosa	Secretin	Stimulates flow of pancreatic $NaHCO_3$ solution
	Pancreozymin (cholecystokinin)	Increases enzymes in pancreatic secretion and stimulates contraction of gallbladder
Stomach mucosa	Gastrin	Stimulates secretion of HCl, pepsinogen, and IF

(Modified from Finerty and Cowdry, *A Textbook of Histology,* 5th ed., Lea & Febiger.)

Appendix I. Abbreviations

A .... Vitamin A (retinol)
Å .... Ångstrom unit, 10^{-7} mm
A-band .... The anisotropic part of a sarcomere
A-cells .... Alpha cells of pancreas—produce glucagon
A-disc .... The anisotropic part of a sarcomere
Acetyl .... Combining form of acetic acid
Acetyl-coA .... Acetyl coenzyme A, active acetate
ACh .... Acetylcholine (a neurotransmitter)
AChE .... Acetylcholinesterase
ACTH .... Adrenocorticotropic hormone
ADH .... Antidiuretic hormone
ADP .... Adenosine diphosphate
AHF .... Factor VIII (antihemophilic factor)
AMP .... Adenosine monophosphate
ANS .... Autonomic nervous system
ATP .... Adenosine triphosphate
ATPase .... Adenosine triphosphatase
AV or A-V .... Atrioventricular
B_1 .... Vitamin B_1 (thiamine)
B_2 .... Vitamin B_2 (riboflavin)
B_6 .... Vitamin B_6 (pyridoxine)
B_{12} .... Vitamin B_{12} (cyanocobalamin)
B-cells .... Beta cells of pancreas—produce insulin; beta cells of pituitary
                believed to produce gonadotropins
bel .... A unit of sound intensity
B lymphocytes ..... Bursa-equivalent lymphocytes
BVD .... Bovine viral diarrhea
C .... Vitamin C (ascorbic acid)
Ca .... Calcium
Ca^{++} .... Calcium ion
cAMP .... Cyclic adenosine monophosphate (second messenger in hormone
                action)
CHO .... Carbohydrate
Cl .... Chlorine
Cl^- .... Chloride ion

CNS .... Central nervous system
CO .... Carbon monoxide
CO_2 .... Carbon dioxide
CP .... Creatine phosphate
CRH .... Cortiocotropin releasing hormone
CSF .... Cerebrospinal fluid
D .... Vitamin D (antirichitic vitamin)
db .... Decibel—a unit for measuring sound intensity
D cells .... Delta cells of pancreas—source of somatostatin (may be gastrin-like hormone); delta cells of anterior pituitary have basophilic granules
DHA .... Dehydroepiandrosterone
DNA .... Deoxyribonucleic acid
DNP .... Deoxyribonucleic protein (nucleoprotein)
DOC .... Deoxycholate
E .... Vitamin E (tocopherol)
EBA .... Epizootic bovine abortion
ECF .... Extracellular fluid
EDTA .... Ethylene diaminetetraacetic acid
EMG .... Electromyogram
EPP .... End-plate potential
EPSP .... Excitatory postsynaptic potential
ER .... Endoplasmic reticulum
ERV .... Expiratory reserve volume
Factor I .... Fibrinogen
Factor II .... Prothrombin
Factor III .... Tissue thromboplastin
Factor IV .... Calcium
Factor V .... Proaccelerin
Factor VIII ...... Antihemophilic factor (AHF, proconvertin)
Factor IX .... Plasma thromboplastin component (PTC, Christmas factor)
Factor X .... Stuart-Prower factor
Factor XI .... Plasma thromboplastin antecedent (PTA)
Factor XII ...... Hageman factor
Factor XIII ..... Fibrin stabilizing factor
Fe .... Iron
FP .... Filtration pressure
FFA .... Free fatty acids
FRC .... Functional residual capacity
FRH .... Follicle-stimulating-hormone releasing hormone
FSH .... Follicle-stimulating hormone
FSHRH .... Follicle-stimulating-hormone releasing hormone (GnRH)
GABA .... Gamma-aminobutyric acid
GI or G-I .... Gastrointestinal
GFR .... Glomerular filtration rate
GH .... Growth hormone
GHRF .... Growth-hormone releasing factor
g .... Gram
GIF .... Growth-hormone inhibiting factor (somatostatin)
GnRH .... Gonadotropin-releasing hormone (LHRH and FSHRH)

H .... Hydrogen
H&E .... Hematoxylin and eosin stain
Hb .... Hemoglobin
HbO$_2$ .... Oxyhemoglobin
HCG .... Human chorionic gonadotropin
HCl .... Hydrochloric acid
HCO$_3^-$ .... Bicarbonate ion
H$_2$CO$_3$ .... Carbonic acid
HMM .... Heavy meromyosin
HPO$_4^=$ .... Monobasic phosphate ion
H-zone .... Central light zone of A-disc in a sarcomere
H$_2$O .... Water
H$_2$O$_2$ .... Hydrogen peroxide
I .... Iodine
I-band .... The isotropic part of a sarcomere
IBR .... Infectious bovine rhinotracheitis
IC .... Inspiratory capacity
ICSH .... Interstitial-cell stimulating hormone (LH)
IF .... Intrinsic factor
IM .... Intramuscular
IPSP .... Inhibitory postsynaptic potential
IRV .... Inspiratory reserve volume
IU .... International unit
IV .... Intravenous
K .... Potassium; vitamin K (antihemorrhagic vitamin)
L .... Lethal
LH .... Luteinizing hormone
LHRF .... Luteinizing-hormone releasing factor
LHRH .... Luteinizing-hormone releasing hormone (LHRF, LRF, LRH, GnRH)
LMM .... Light meromyosin
LRF .... Luteinizing-hormone releasing factor (LHRF, GnRH)
LSH .... Lutein-stimulating hormone
LRH .... Luteinizing-hormone releasing hormone (LRF, GnRH)
MAO .... Monoamine oxidase
M .... Muscle; molecular weight; molar concentration
mEq .... Milliequivalent
Ma .... Milliampere
MD .... Mucosal disease
mg .... Milligram (1/1000 of a gram)
Micron (μ) .... Micrometer (1/1,000,000 meter)
ml .... Milliliter (1/1000 of a liter)
MLD .... Minimal lethal dose
M-line .... Fine filaments in middle of A-disc (A-band)
mm .... Millimole; millimeter (1/1000 of a meter); muscles
mμ .... Millimicron (1/1000 of a micron; nanometer, 10^{-9} meter)
MOsm or mOsm ... Milliosmole
MP .... Melting point
MPD .... Maximal permissible dose

mRNA .... Messenger ribonucleic acid
MR .... Milliroentgen
msec .... Millisecond (1/1000 second)
MSH .... Melanocyte-stimulating hormone
MV .... Megavolt (1,000,000 volts)
mv .... Millivolt (1/1000 volt)
MW .... Molecular weight
N .... Normal; nitrogen
Na .... Sodium
NaCl .... Sodium chloride—table salt
NAD .... Oxidized nicotinamide adenine dinucleotide
NADH .... Reduced nicotinamide adenine dinucleotide
$NaHCO_3$ .... Sodium bicarbonate
NaOH .... Sodium hydroxide
Na^+, K^+, ATPase .. Sodium- and potassium-activated adenosine triphosphatase
NE .... Norepinephrine
ng .... Nanogram (1 billionth of a gram; 10^{-9} gram)
NGF .... Nerve growth factor
NH_2^- .... Amino group
NH_3 .... Ammonia
NH_4^+ .... Ammonium ion
NH_4Cl .... Ammonium chloride
NH_4OH .... Ammonium hydroxide
Ni .... Nickel
NMJ .... Neuromuscular junction
NPN .... Nonprotein nitrogen
O_2 .... Oxygen
OAAD .... Ovarian ascorbic acid depletion
OH^- .... Hydroxyl ion
P .... Phosphorus
PABA .... Para-aminobenzoic acid
P_{CO_2} .... Partial pressure of carbon dioxide
PF3 .... Platelet factor 3 (platelet phospholipid)
PG .... Prostaglandin
PGF_2 .... Prostaglandin F_2
PGE_2 .... Prostaglandin E_2
pH .... A measure of acidity or alkalinity
PIH .... Prolactin inhibiting hormone
PJM .... Postjunctional membrane
PMSG .... Pregnant mare serum gonadotropin
PNS .... Peripheral nervous system
P_{O_2} .... Partial pressure of oxygen
PO_4^{--} .... Phosphate ion
PRF .... Prolactin releasing factor
PIF .... Prolactin inhibiting factor
PSS .... Physiologic saline solution
PTA .... Plasma thromboplastin antecedent, phosphotungstic acid
PTC .... Plasma thromboplastin component (Christmas factor)
PTH .... Parathormone

RBC .... Red blood cell (erythrocyte)
RER or rer .... Rough endoplasmic reticulum
RES .... Reticuloendothelial system
RNA .... Ribonucleic acid
RNP .... Ribonucleic protein
RPN .... Reverse Polish notation
RV .... Residual volume
S .... Sulfur
SER .... Smooth endoplasmic reticulum
SR .... Sarcoplasmic reticulum
STH .... Somatotropin (growth hormone)
T_3 .... Triiodothyronine
T_4 .... Thyroxine (tetraiodothyronine)
TLC .... Total lung capacity
T-lymphocyte ..... Thymus-derived lymphocyte
T-tubules .... Transverse tubules
TRH .... Thyrotropin releasing hormone
TSH .... Thyrotropic stimulating hormone
TV .... Tidal volume
ULF .... Uterine luteolytic factor
VC .... Vital capacity
WBC .... White blood cell (leucocyte)
X-rays .... Rays with wavelengths between 0.05 and 100 Å; roentgen rays
Z-line .... Boundary of a sarcomere

Appendix II.   Table of the Organs

TONGUE

	Horse	Cow	Sheep	Pig	Dog	Cat
Apex	Spatula shaped	Pointed	Slightly pointed	Thin and pointed	Wide, and round, and thin	Wide, round, and thin
Shape	Long and relatively even width	Root and body wider than horse	Narrower in middle of body; root and apex same width	Long and narrow	Narrow root and body with wider apex	Short and wide body and root
Color	Pinkish	Variable pigmentation	Variable pigmentation	Pinkish	Bright red	Pink
Papillae	2 or 3 vallate on dorsum caudally. Foliate near anterior pillars of soft palate	8 to 17 vallate in caudo-lateral region. No foliate. Large papillae on prominence, which increase in size toward root. Long horny papillae on apex, pointing caudally	14 to 16 vallate in caudo-lateral region. No foliate. Papillae on prominence more conical and relatively larger than cow	2 or 3 vallate as in horse. Large conical papillae on root with free end directed caudally. Foliate	4 vallate (2 each side) near median sulcus. 2 foliate laterally near root	Horny papillae on apex pointing caudally. 2 foliated, each 1 to 2 cm long
Specific characters	Relatively smooth, but thick and dense on the dorsum	Prominence on caudal part of dorsum with well-defined transverse depression in front of this elevation	As cow but not as well marked	2 frenula	Definite median sulcus	No median sulcus

Reprinted from *The Anatomy of the Sheep*, 2nd edition, 1964, by N. D. S. May and by permission of the University of Queensland Press, St. Lucia, Queensland Australia.

STOMACH

	Horse	Cow	Sheep	Pig	Dog	Cat
Capacity	1.5 to 3 gal (7 to 14 liters)	3 to 17 gal (13 to 77 liters), Blamire. 20 to 48 gal (90 to 218 liters), Sisson	2.5 gal (11.3 liters)	1.25 to 1.5 gal (5.5 to 7 liters)	5 pints to 1.75 gal (3 to 8 liters)	0.5 pints (0.3 liters)
Shape	J-shaped. Left extremity enlarged	Complex, with four parts, in order of capacity: rumen, 80% omasum, 7 to 8% abomasum, 7 to 8% reticulum, 5%	Complex, as cow. Capacity: rumen, 78% abomasum, 12.5% reticulum, 6.5% omasum, 3.0%	Somewhat J-shaped, with diverticulum ventriculi to left of the esophageal opening	Irregularly piriform, and V-shaped. Shape varies with fullness. Stomach is sharply curved when empty, with the contraction mainly affecting the fundus; when full, has three distinct regions. Fundus fills rapidly and ingesta moves through cavity relatively fast	Irregularly piriform and a more uneven V-shape. Fundus longer than pyloric region
Position	Mainly to left of median plane in the epigastrium and dorsal to the coils of the large colon. On the external surface of the body, the outline extends from the 9th to the 14th rib in an oblique manner	Occupies most of the left half of the abdominal cavity, extending over the median plane ventrally	As cow, but right face of ventral sac of rumen often against right abdominal wall	Mainly to left of median plane with long axis in a transverse direction. Reaches floor of abdominal cavity between xiphoid cartilage and umbilicus	Position variable with fullness. When empty, stomach is separated from abdominal floor by liver and intestines. When full, it migrates caudally and reaches floor near umbilicus	Like dog, but movements are not as great

STOMACH (Continued)

	Horse	Cow	Sheep	Pig	Dog	Cat
External characters	Large area of external surface devoid of serous covering. Relatively small stomach situated dorsally	Dorsal posterior blind sac extends more caudally than ventral sac	Left longitudinal groove extends dorsally and does not join posterior transverse groove. Right longitudinal groove in two parts. Dorsal part occupied by vessels; ventral part corresponds to internal longitudinal pillar. Ventral posterior blind sac extends more caudally than the dorsal sac	Blind diverticulum ventriculi directed caudally. Relatively large stomach	Extensive fundus. Stomach has relatively sharp inflection	Inflection more pronounced than dog. Constriction between fundus and pylorus less marked
Internal characters	Marked division by margo plicatus into white nonglandular esophageal part and darker and softer glandular part. The glandular part is formed of: (1) cardiac area, (2) fundus, and (3) pyloric region	Rumen papillated but papillae absent on dorsal wall and on edges of pillars. More numerous in posterior blind sacs Reticulum—half-inch high folds of mucous membrane enclose 4- to 6-sided spaces or "cells" Omasum—12 or more large leaves with many shorter laminae between Abomasum—soft, glandular mucous membrane forming spiral folds in the fundus gland region; smooth in pyloric region	Rumen completely papillated. Smaller on ridges. Reticulum—cells have serrated edges Omasum—40 leaves Abomasum—as cow Reticular groove—10 to 12.5 cm	Four regions: Esophageal—small folds Cardiac—pale gray Fundus—thick and red brown Pyloric—thinner and paler than fundus	Fundus—thick and red brown Pyloric—thinner and lighter Folds relatively even in height and extending almost length of organ	As dog, but folds begin midway along fundus and are more marked in the pyloric region

SMALL INTESTINES

	Horse	Cow	Sheep	Pig	Dog	Cat
Size	60 to 100 ft (19.0 to 30.0 m) long, 3 to 4 inch (7 to 10 cm) diameter	90 to 150 ft (27 to 49 m) long, 2 inch (5 cm) diameter	60 to 110 ft (18 to 35 m) long, 1 inch (2.5 cm) diameter	50 to 65 ft (15 to 21 m) long, 1.5 inch (4 cm) diameter	6 to 16 ft (2 to 4.8 m) long, 1 inch (2.5 cm) diameter	3 to 4 ft (0.9 to 1.2 m) long, 1 inch (2.5 cm) diameter
Duodenum	3 to 5 ft (1 to 1.5 m) long	3 to 4 ft (1 to 1.2 m) long	2 to 3 ft (0.6 to 0.9 m) long	2 to 3 ft (0.6 to 0.9 m) long	About 1 to 2 ft (0.2 to 0.6 m) long	About 4 in (0.12 m) long
Position	Chiefly in dorsal part of left half of abdominal cavity with duodenum mainly in right costal region. Coils reach the abdominal floor and pelvic cavity	In the right half of abdominal cavity with a few coils caudal and ventral to the rumen. Ventral to large intestine. Duodenum is often highest part of alimentary tube in right flank	As cow	Mesenteric part above colon and to right of cecum. Against dorsal right flank and caudal abdominal floor. Duodenum in similar position to the cow	When stomach empty, intestines lie ventrally and caudally but are forced more caudally when stomach full	Similar to dog but proportionately longer with less movement
Omentum	Greater omentum is not visible ventrally but lies between stomach and large colon. Lace-like	Greater omentum covers intestinal mass ventrally. Stonger in texture than horse, with fatty deposit. Lymph nodes in mesentery lie between small and large intestines	Greater omentum as cow but fat firmer and whiter. Small and large intestines lie adjacent, with lymph nodes in the mesentery on the attached side of the large intestine	Covered by fatty greater omentum, as in cow	Lace-like omentum, but not as thin as horse	As dog

LARGE INTESTINES

	Horse	Cow	Sheep	Pig	Dog	Cat
Size	(1) Large colon: 10 to 12 ft (3 to 3.5 m) long; 10 inch (25 cm) diameter, (average) (2) Small colon: 10 to 12 ft (3 to 3.5 m) long, 3 inch (7.5 cm) diameter	35 ft (10.5 m) long; 3 inch (7.5 cm) average diameter	15 ft (4.5 m) long; 2 inch (5 cm) average diameter	10 to 15 ft (3 to 4.5 m) long; 2 inch (5 cm) average diameter	2 ft (0.6 m) long, 1 inch (2.5 cm) diameter. Size varies with breed	As dog but proportionately smaller in length; 1.0 to 1.5 ft (0.3 to 0.45 m) long
Specific characters	Sacculated with longitudinal bands. Vary in number from 1 to 4 on large colon, to 2 on small colon	Tubular, no bands or sacculations. Part is coiled in two directions (ansa spiralis). No differentiation into large and small colon	As cow	Coiled like cow. Cecum, 3 bands and 3 sacculations. First part of colon, 2 bands and 2 sacculations, extending to coils. Remainder has no bands	Short and like shepherd's crook. In 3 parts: (1) ascending, (2) transverse, and (3) descending. No bands	As dog
Position	Large colon: mainly in ventral abdominal cavity as dorsal and ventral coils. Extends from sternum to pelvic brim. Origin and termination situated dorsally caudal to stomach. Small colon: Lies dorsal to large colon and mingled with small intestines	In dorsal abdominal cavity, to right of median plane with small intestines. Coiled part in lower right flank	As cow	On each side of median plane, mainly to the left caudal to the stomach. Coiled part in ventral part of abdominal cavity, dorsal to umbilicus	Short ascending part lies along right flank, with long descending part on left of median plane extending to the pelvic cavity	As dog

CECUM

	Horse	Cow	Sheep	Pig	Dog	Cat
Capacity	4 to 5 gal (18 to 22 liters)	1 to 1.25 gal (4.5 to 5.5 liters)	1 quart (1 liter)	3 pints to 1 gal (1.5 to 4.5 liters)	Less than 0.5 pint (0.25 liters)	About 2 oz (60 ml)
Size	4 ft long, 8 to 10 inch diameter (1.25 m × 20 to 25 cm)	30 in long, 4 inch diameter (75 × 12 cm)	10 inch long, 2 inch diameter (25 × 5 cm)	8 to 12 inch long, 3 to 4 inch diameter (20 to 30 cm × 7.5 to 10 cm)	5 to 6 inch long, 1 to 1.5 inch diameter (12 to 15 cm × 2.5 to 4 cm)	1 to 2 inch long, 0.75 inch diameter (2.5 to 5 cm × 2 cm)
Shape	Comma-shaped. Sacculated with four longitudinal bands. Two extremities, one rounded (base), other pointed (apex)	Tubular with rounded free extremity	As cow	Tubular and sacculated with three longitudinal bands. Extremity rounded	Tubular and coiled	Tubular or conical and slightly curved
Position	Base extends from 15th rib to tuber coxae on right of median plane. Longitudinal axis extends ventrally over right flank to xiphoid region generally. Cranial border lies parallel with and 5 to 6 inch (12.5 to 15 cm) ventral to costal arch	Extends along right flank from near the ventral end of the last rib to the pelvic inlet	As cow	A vertical position in the left or right flank, reaching the abdominal floor between and umbilicus and the pubis	On the right, midway between flank and median plane, dorsal to the umbilical region	As dog
Openings	The ileum and large colon enter at lesser curvature of the base. Openings are 2 inch (5 cm) apart	Colon and cecum continuous. Ileum joins obliquely	As cow	As cow	Ileum and colon continuous and cecum joins obliquely	As cow

LIVER

	Horse	Cow	Sheep	Pig	Dog	Cat
Weight	10 to 12 lb (about 5 kg); 0.8 to 1.5% body weight	10 to 12 lb (about 5 kg); about 1.2% body weight	20 to 25 oz (about 700 gm); about 1.5% body weight	4 lb (1 to 2 kg); about 1.7% body weight	4 oz to 3 lb (120 gm to 1.4 kg); 1.5 to 5.9% body weight	2 to 4 oz (60 to 120 gm); 2.5% body weight
Shape	Oblique and irregular ellipse	Irregularly rectangular with rounded corners	Rectangular	Irregular	As pig	As pig
Characters	Three lobes: right lateral, left lateral, and central lobes. Right lateral more extensive in foal, left lateral in old animal. Caudate process	Two lobes (dorsal and ventral). Caudate process	As cow. Occasionally papillary process	Four lobes: (1) right lateral, (2) left lateral, (3) right central, (4) left central. Caudate process. Large amount of interlobular tissue producing mottled appearance	Four lobes with caudate and papillary processes. Often caudate process called a lobe. Left lateral lobe largest and left central smallest. Papillary process large	As dog, but right central lobe largest and right lateral lobe smallest
Relationship to right kidney	Renal impression	As horse	As horse	No renal impression	As horse	As horse
Umbilical fissure	Small and shallow on central lobe	Shallow depression on right border between dorsal and ventral lobes	Deep depression in right border and almost completely divides organ into dorsal and ventral lobes	Between right and left central lobes	As pig	As pig
Esophageal notch	Deep	Deep, but not as much as horse	Shallow	Deep and wide	As pig	As pig

LIVER (Continued)

	Horse	Cow	Sheep	Pig	Dog	Cat
Gallbladder	Absent	Pear-shaped, 4 to 6 inch (10 to 15 cm) long	Tubular and narrow, 4 inch (10 cm) long	Pear-shaped. Lies between central lobes. Partly visible	Pear-shaped and hidden in depression in right central lobe. Does not reach ventral border	Tubular and bent. Visible on right central lobe. Cystic duct sinus
Bile duct	Enters duodenum beside pancreatic duct in diverticulum 5 to 6 inch (12 to 15 cm) from pylorus	Enters duodenum 2 ft (60 cm) from pylorus	Enters duodenum with pancreatic duct about 12 inch (30 cm) from pylorus	Opens on papilla 2 inch (5 cm) from pylorus	Enters duodenum 3 inch (7.5 cm) from pylorus	Enters duodenum 1 to 1.5 inch (2.5 to 4 cm) from pylorus
Posterior vena cava	Only small amount embedded along dorsal border	Partially embedded	As cow	Almost entirely embedded	Deeply embedded	As dog
Color	Red brown to purple. Friable	Red brown. Friable	Red brown. Occasionally specimen black. Friable	Red brown. Lobulated and not friable	Dark red. Not friable	Deep red but not as dark as dog. Not friable
Ligaments	1. Coronary 2. Falciform 3. Round 4. Right lateral 5. Left lateral 6. Caudate	1. Coronary 2. Falciform (may be present) 3. Round (in young) 4. Right lateral 5. Caudate	As cow	1. Coronary 2. Falciform (may be present) 3. Round (in young)	1. Coronary 2. Falciform (small in young) 3. Round 4. Right lateral 5. Left lateral 6. Caudate	As dog

PANCREAS

	Horse	Cow	Sheep	Pig	Dog	Cat
Weight	12 oz (350 gm); 0.06% body weight	12 oz (350 gm); 0.06% body weight	3 to 5 oz (100 to 150 gm)	1 to 2 oz (25 to 60 gm)	0.5 to 3.5 oz (15 to 100 gm); 0.13 to 0.35% body weight	0.5 to 1.5 oz (15 to 45 gm)
Shape	Irregularly triangular	Irregularly quadrilateral	Irregularly triangular	Triradiate	V-shaped	V-shaped
Position	Ventral to the 16th, 17th, and 18th thoracic vertebrae	Almost entirely to right of median plane, ventral to 1st, 2nd, and 3rd lumbar transverse process	As cow, but ventral to the upper part of last rib and 1st lumbar transverse process	Across the dorsal wall of the abdomen ventral to the 1st, 2nd, and 3rd lumbar vertebrae	Right arm dorsal to first part of duodenum, ending a short distance caudal to the kidney and the left branch between stomach and colon ending at the left kidney	As dog
Ducts	Two ducts: (1) Pancreatic duct enters beside the bile duct. (2) Accessory pancreatic duct enters the duodenum on the opposite side to the other duct	One duct opening 12 inch (30 cm) caudal to the bile duct	One duct opening in common with the bile duct—ductus choledochus communis	One duct opening near the bile duct, 4 to 5 inch (10 to 12 cm) from pylorus	Two ducts: (1) Opens close to bile duct or may open in company with bile duct. (2) Opens 1 to 2 inch (2.5 to 5 cm) caudal to other duct	One duct opening near bile duct

SPLEEN

	Horse	Cow	Sheep	Pig	Dog	Cat
Weight*	35 to 40 oz (1000 to 1200 gm); 0.16% body weight	32 oz (700 to 1100 gm); 0.17% body weight	3 to 4 oz (90 to 120 gm); 0.17% body weight	10 to 15 oz (280 to 425 gm); 0.12% body weight	0.5 to 5 oz (15 to 150 gm) (Bressou—2 gm per kg); 0.2% body weight	5 to 10 gm; 0.3% body weight
Size*	About 20 inch (50 cm) long and 8 to 10 inch (23 cm) wide	20 inch (50 cm) long and 6 inch (15 cm) wide	5 to 6 inch (13 cm) by 3 to 4 inch (8.5 cm)	12 to 25 inch (30 to 65 cm) by 2 to 4 inch (5 to 10 cm)	7 to 10 inch (18 to 25 cm) long	About 3 inch (7 cm) long
Shape	Comma or triangular shaped	Elongate and elliptical with ends rounded and thin	Approximately triangular with angles rounded	Strap-like and slightly curved	Faliciform (sickle-shaped), long, narrow, and widest ventrally	Generally like dog, less falciform
Color	Dark bluish red	Mulberry	Bluish red	Dark red	Red	Red
Hilus	Longitudinal on visceral surface	On dorsal third of visceral surface near cranial border	As cow	Longitudinal ridge on visceral surface	As pig	As pig

* All measurements highly variable.

KIDNEYS

	Horse	Cow	Sheep	Pig	Dog	Cat
Weight	Right—23 to 24 oz (about 700 gm) Left— 22 to 23 oz (about 680 gm)	Right—20 to 25 oz (about 700 gm) Left—about 1 oz (30 gm) heavier than right	3 to 5 oz (about 90 to 150 gm)	7 to 9 oz (about 235 gm)	2 oz (57 gm) (varies with breed)	0.25 to 0.5 oz (about 7 to 15 gm)
Size	Right—6 × 6 × 2 inch (15 × 15 × 5 cm) Left—7 × 4 to 5 × 2 inch (17.5 × 10 to 12.5 × 5 cm)	8 to 9 × 4 to 5 × 2.5 inch (20 to 22.5 × 10 to 12.5 × 6.25 cm)	3 × 2 × 1 inch (7.5 × 5 × 2.5 cm)	5 × 2.5 × 1 inch (12.5 × 6.25 × 2.5 cm)	2 × 1 × 1 inch (5 × 2.5 × 2.5 cm)	1 × 0.75 inch (2.5 × 1.8 cm)
Shape	Right—like heart of playing card Left—bean-shaped	Lobulated; Right—elliptical with cranial end larger and rounder Left—twisted and pear-shaped with smaller cranial end	Bean-shaped and smooth	Bean-shaped, flattened, and smooth	Bean-shaped, and relatively large. Darker in color and not as regularly bean-shaped as the sheep	Irregularly globular with 3 or 4 superficial veins converging to hilus and producing wrinkled appearance. Paler than dog (yellowish red); otherwise, as dog
Position	Right—ventral to the upper part of 17th and 18th ribs and 1st lumbar transverse process Left—nearer median plane, ventral to 18th rib and 1st and 2nd lumbar transverse process	Right—ventral to last rib and first two or three lumbar transverse processes Left—right of median plane, ventral to 3rd to 5th lumbar vertebra	Right—ventral to first three lumbar transverse processes Left—right of median plane, ventral to 3rd to 5th lumbar vertebrae	Symmetric, ventral to the first four lumbar transverse processes. No contact with the liver	Right—ventral to first three lumbar transverse processes Left—ventral to the 2nd, 3rd, and 4th lumbar transverse processes (variable in position)	Right as dog. Left as dog, but has less variation in position

LARYNX

	Horse	Cow	Sheep	Pig	Dog	Cat
External appearance	Relatively high compared with length. Very oblique rostral opening	Width, length, and height almost equal	As cow, but on smaller scale	Greater length than width or height. Opening more horizontal than cow. Looseness and flexibility of entire structure when compared with other larynges. No articulation with hyoid bone	Like cow in relative dimension but opening is more horizontally placed	As dog
Arytenoid cartilage	Apex of opening formed by union of corniculate cartilages dorsally is narrow and sharp. Inverted V-shape	Apex of union rounded with cartilages more parallel. Edges of cartilages are everted	Apices of cartilages meet more obtusely than cow and thus ventral edges are wider apart. Edges slightly everted	Apices divided and produce an appearance of a second and smaller pair of cartilages between the larger corniculate cartilages	Thickened and rounded folds extending transversely from the lateral borders of the epiglottis. Folds are separated in the median plane by a cleft. Cleft also separates corniculate cartilages more caudally. Opening to larynx is triangular with base caudo-dorsal and the cleft is median in the dorsal border	Corniculate cartilages very small, lying parallel with each other. Borders of cartilages approximated in midline. Aryepiglottic fold does not pass directly between cartilages, but forms deep recess on each side

LARYNX (Continued)

	Horse	Cow	Sheep	Pig	Dog	Cat
Epiglottic cartilage	Elongate and oval with sharp apex and border rounded and irregular	Oval to round. Border thickened, rounded, and regular	More triangular than cow. Border thinner and irregular. Apex pointed and thin	Rounder than cow and larger in comparison. Slight apex present with thinner border than cow. More scoop-like than cow	Regularly triangular, with thickened and rounded border. Apex pointed and thick	Leaf-shaped with pointed and thin apex. Width relatively regular and lateral border thick and round
Thyroid cartilage	Thyroid notch with slight laryngeal prominence rostrally. Articulates with hyoid bone	No notch, and thyroid prominence is caudal. Articulates as horse	As cow. Articulates as horse	No notch or prominence. No articulation with hyoid bone	Small notch. Articulates as horse	Small notch. Articulates as horse
Internal characters	Lateral ventricle leading to saccule between ventricular and vocal folds and muscles. Saccule directed caudally and dorsally. Middle ventricle present	No defined middle or lateral ventricles or saccule. Thyro-arytenoid muscle	As cow	Narrow ventricle opens to saccule between the divisions of the vocal ligament. Saccule directed rostrally. Thyro-arytenoid muscle is undivided. Middle ventricle present	Wide ventricle opens to saccule through vocal fold. Saccule directed dorsally and caudally. Thyro-arytenoid muscle is divided and part attached to epiglottic cartilage	Two ventricles on each side represented by depressions, of which the rostral is the larger. Smaller caudal depression represents ventricle of the dog and occurs between the two parts of the vocal ligament. More rostral depression lies immediately caudal to the lateral parts of the epiglottis
Vocal fold	Vocal fold oblique, with dorsal end more caudal	Vocal fold almost vertical	As cow	Vocal fold oblique, with dorsal end cranial	Vocal fold oblique, with dorsal end slightly caudal	As dog

LUNGS

	Horse	Cow	Sheep	Pig	Dog	Cat
Size	Average weight 13 lb (6 kg)	Average weight 7.5 lb (3.5 kg). Right lung 1.5 times left lung	Weight 8 to 10 oz (250 to 300 gm) As cow	Weight 2 lb (about 1 kg)	Variable	Variable
Lobes	Not divided into lobes	Left lung—3 lobes Right lung—4 or 5 lobes Right apical lobe reaches left costal wall	As cow	Left lung—2 or 3 lobes Right lung—4 lobes	Left lung—3 lobes Right lung—4 lobes	As dog Apical lobes more triangular
Fissures	Absent	Extend two-thirds to dorsal border. Variable fissure between right apical lobes	As cow	Generally as cow but fissure between right apical lobes generally absent	Fissures extend over dorsal border to root	As dog
Cardiac notch	Larger on left side, 2nd intercostal space to 6th rib	Extends to 4th intercostal space on left side and, on right, pericardium may be completely covered	Left side as cow Right side: notch triangular opposite ventral parts of 4th and 5th ribs	Notches triangular and small; left notch larger than right	Notch larger on right side, triangular and from 4th to 6th ribs. On left side, shallow and well defined	As dog
Bronchi	Main bronchus divides internally. No apical bronchus	As horse. Apical bronchus on right side	As cow	As cow	Main bronchus divides outside lung. No apical bronchus	As dog
Dorsal border	Narrow	As horse	As horse	As horse	Wide and rounded	As dog
Lobulation	Indistinct	Very distinct with large lobules	Very distinct with small lobules	As cow	Indistinct	As dog

TESTIS AND EPIDIDYMIS

	Horse	Cow	Sheep	Pig	Dog	Cat
Weight of testis	6 to 10 oz (200 to 300 gm)	7 to 10 oz (250 to 300 gm)	6 to 10 oz (200 to 300 gm)	5 oz (150 gm)	0.05 to 0.75% body weight	
Shape	Oval	Elongate oval	As bull	Elliptical	Round to oval	More rounded than dog
Superficial vascular patterns on testis	Small vessels extending from free border toward body of epididymis	Very large and tortuous vessels extending from tail toward head	Vessels of different sizes extending from epididymal border. Tunica vaginalis and tunica albuginea are thicker than in bull, and superficial vessels are not as visible through tunics	Many small vessels extending from free border toward body of epididymis	Single vessel and branches extending from tail toward head of testis	Less extensive system than dog, but extending in a similar direction
Parenchyma	Reddish gray	Yellow to creamy orange	Creamy white	Grayish to dark red	Reddish	Reddish
Epididymis	Head and body associated with attached border of testis. Tail forms only slight prominence caudally	Epididymis extends one-third distance down cranial border, forming wide V-shape. Tail rounded and molded to distal extremity of testis	Epididymis extends one-half distance down cranial border, forming narrow V-shape. Tail rounded with defined neck. Tail more pronounced than in bull. Readily palpated in live animal	Head and body like horse. Tail prominent caudally, forming blunt conical projection	Head and body like horse. Tail slightly prominent	Epididymis along attached border only. Tail not prominent

OVARIES

	Horse	Cow	Sheep	Pig	Dog	Cat
Shape, size, and weight	Bean-shaped. 3 × 1.5 inch (7.5 × 2.5 × 3.75 cm). About 2.5 to 3 oz (70 to 90 gm)	Oval. 1.5 × 1 × 0.5 inch (3.75 × 2.5 × 1.25 cm). About 0.5 oz or more (about 11 to 18 gm)	Almond or oval. 1 × 0.25 inch (2.5 × 0.5 cm). About 0.1 oz (2 to 3 gm)	Round. 1 × 0.5 inch (2.5 × 1.25 cm). About 0.2 to 0.5 oz (8 to 16 gm)	Elongate, flattened, and oval. Less than 1 inch (2.5 cm) long and 0.5 in (1.5 cm) thick. About 0.1 to 0.4 oz (3 to 12 gm)	Like dog but smaller (8 to 9 mm long)
Position	Ventral to 4th or 5th lumbar vertebra. One larger than other and left usually caudal to right. About 20 to 22 inch (50 to 55 cm) from vulva	Usually on lateral wall of pelvic inlet. Right usually larger than left. About 16 to 18 inch (40 to 45 cm) from vulva. Varies in position with number of parturitions	Usually on lateral wall of pelvic inlet. About 7 inch (17.5 cm) from vulva. Varies in position with number of parturitions	On lateral wall of pelvic inlet. Varies in position with number of parturitions	Near posterior pole of kidney below 3rd or 4th lumbar vertebra	As dog
Ovulation fossa	Ovulation fossa on free border. Ovarian bursa formed by mesosalpinx	No ovulation fossa. Ovarian bursa present	As cow	As cow. Hilus present on ovary	As cow	As cow. Ovarian bursa extremely small
Broad ligament	Broad ligament attached in sublumbar region	Broad ligament attached to flank and lateral pelvic wall	As cow	As cow	Broad ligament attached in sublumbar region	As dog
Surface	Corpora lutea do not project from the surface	Follicles and corpora lutea both project	As cow	As cow	As cow	As cow

UTERUS

	Horse	Cow	Sheep	Pig	Dog	Cat
Length	Body about 10 inch (25 cm). Horns about 7 to 8 inch (18 cm) × 4 inch (10 cm). Cervix about 2 to 3 inch (6 cm)	Body about 1.5 inch (4 cm). Horns about 15 inch (38 cm). Cervix about 4 inch (10 cm)	Body less than 1 inch (2 cm). Horns about 4 to 5 inch (10 to 12 cm). Cervix about 1.5 inch (4 cm)	Body about 2 inch (5 cm). Horns about 4 to 5 inch (12 cm). Cervix about 4 inch (10 cm)	Body about 1 inch (2 to 3 cm). Horns 5 to 6 inch (12 to 15 cm). Cervix about 1 inch (2.5 cm)	Shorter than dog. Body, 1.5 cm
Anterior extremities of cornua	Blunt	Tapered	Tapered	Tapered. Difficult to differentiate from Fallopian tubes	Tapered. As pig	Tapered. As pig
Horns	Large, uniform diameter, and relatively straight	Horns united for 3 to 4 inch (7.5 to 10 cm) near body. Horns coiled	As cow, but 1 to 2 inch (2.5 to 5 cm). Horns coiled	Horns flexuous	Uniform diameter, diverge like a V, and slightly curved	As dog
Round ligament	Short	Reaches internal abdominal ring	As cow	About 6 inch (15 cm) long	Passes through inguinal canal for short distance	As dog
Internal	Mucous membrane smooth and folded	Cotyledons	As cow	Smooth and folded	Folded	As dog
Cervix	Cervix projects into vagina 1 to 2 inch (2.5 to 5 cm)	Does not project as much as mare	Similar to cow usually, but may not project into vagina	Does not project	Projects a short distance into vagina	As dog

HEART

	Horse	Cow	Sheep	Pig	Dog	Cat
Weight	About 9 lb (3.4 kg), great variation; 0.6 to 0.7% body weight	About 5.5 lb (2.23 kg); 0.4 to 0.5% body weight	About 0.5 lb (220 to 240 gm), 0.4% body weight	1 lb or less (450 gm); 0.35% body weight. 2.2 to 6.1 gm per kg body weight	5 to 15 oz (150 to 450 gm), 0.8 to 1.4% body weight. 5.9 to 13 gm/kg body weight	3.9 to 8.54 gm/kg body weight
Shape	Irregularly flattened cone	Relatively longer than horse, with shorter base	Apex more or less pointed than cow	Broad, short, and blunt	Ovoid with round blunt apex	As dog
Vena hemiazygos	Vena hemiazygos does not reach heart	Vena hemiazygos opens into greater cardiac vein below posterior vena cava	As cow	As cow	As horse	As horse
Os cordis	Absent	2 ossa cordis	1 os cordis	Absent	Absent	Absent
Brachiocephalic trunk	Brachiocephalic trunk only from aorta	As horse	As horse	Brachiocephalic and left subclavian arteries arise from aorta independently	As pig, but brachiocephalic artery may be divided into right subclavian artery and bicarotid trunk	As pig
Fat	Soft, yellow, and oily	Soft and yellow	Hard and white	Softer than sheep and white to cream color	Very little fat unless animal in very fat condition. When white, oily fat present	Generally very little fat

BRAIN

	Horse	Cow	Sheep	Pig	Dog	Cat
Weight	23 oz (650 gm); ½ of 1% body weight	16 to 17 oz (450 gm)	4.5 to 5 oz (130 gm)	4 to 4.5 oz (125 gm)	Varies from 1 to 5 oz (150 gm), average 2 to 2.5 oz (60 to 70 gm); 0.3 to 1% body weight	20 to 28 gm; 1.0% body weight
External appearance, cerebral hemisphere	Oval and relatively long. Frontal and occipital poles almost equal in size. Gyri extensive	Short, high, wide, and circular. Frontal poles smaller than occipital. Dorsal prominence—marginal pole. Gyri and sulci simpler pattern than horse	Irregularly ovoid and bean-shaped from side. Flattened rostrally. Frontal and occipital poles more equivalent in size than cow. No dorsal prominence. Gyri and sulci simpler than cow	Elongate, oval, and widest in caudal third. Bean-shaped laterally. Occipital pole larger than frontal. Gyri simple like sheep	Triangular from above and broadest in caudal third. Frontal poles narrow and flattened laterally. Gyri simpler than pig	More circular from above and laterally, widest at temporal poles. Frontal lobes not constricted. Gyri simpler than dog

BRAIN (Continued)

	Horse	Cow	Sheep	Pig	Dog	Cat
External appearance, midbrain and hindbrain	Pons prominent and cerebellum not overlapped to great extent. Axis of brain stem relatively straight	Pons smaller than horse and cerebellum overlapped to a great extent. Cerebellum shorter, smaller, but broader. Medulla short and wide. Axis of brain stem bent	Medulla shorter and wider than cow. Pons smaller, cerebellum relatively long and not overlapped by cerebrum to extent as in cow. Axis of brain stem straighter than cow	Pons very indistinct, medulla short. Cerebellum short, wide, and more overlapped by cerebrum than sheep. Axis of brain stem sharply bent	Medulla broad and thick. Pons small but more distinct than pig. Axis of brain sharply bent	As dog. Cerebellum more exposed
Hypophysis	Ovoid and large	Thicker than horse	Long and large in relation to size of brain	Small and irregularly circular	Small and circular	As dog
Olfactory region	Relatively large bulbs and large striae	Bulbs smaller but lateral stria larger than horse	Bulbs large and ovoid. Lateral stria large	Large bulbs and lateral stria	Bulbs and lateral stria relatively large	Bulbs elongate
Posterior colliculi	Very small in comparison to anterior colliculi	Form large depression in surface of cerebellum	Displaced laterally	Form large depression in cerebellum	Large and displaced laterally	

Bibliography

Adams, O. R.: *Lameness in Horses,* 3rd ed., Philadelphia, Lea & Febiger, 1974.

Alexander, G. and D. G. Alexander: *Biology.* 9th ed., New York, Barnes & Noble, 1969.

American Institute of Biological Sciences: *Biological Science: An Inquiry Into Life.* New York, Harcourt, Brace & World, Inc., 1963.

American Institute of Biological Sciences: *High School Biology* (Biological Sciences Curriculum Study). Chicago, Rand McNally & Co., 1963.

Anthony, C. P., and N. J. Kolthoff: *Textbook of Anatomy and Physiology.* 9th ed. St. Louis, C. V. Mosby Co., 1975.

Arey, L. B.: *Developmental Anatomy.* 7th ed. Philadelphia, W. B. Saunders Co., 1965.

Arey, L. B.: *Human Histology.* 3rd ed. Philadelphia, W. B. Saunders Co., 1968.

Asdell, S. A.: *Patterns of Mammalian Reproduction.* 2nd ed. Ithaca, New York, Comstock Publishing Co., Inc., 1964.

Atkinson, Dickson, Harbaugh, Law, Lowe, Mohler, Murray, Pearson, Ransom and Trumbower: *Diseases of Cattle.* Rev. ed. Washington, D. C., United States Government Printing Office, 1964.

Barclay, A. E., K. J. Franklin, and M. M. L. Prichard: *The Foetal Circulation.* Springfield, Ill., Charles C Thomas, 1945.

Barcroft, J.: *Researches on Pre-Natal Life.* Vol. I, Springfield, Ill., Charles C Thomas, 1947.

Becker, R. B., and P. T. Dix Arnold: Circulatory system of the cow's udder. University of Florida Agricultural Experiment Station Bulletin 379, Nov. 1942.

Becker, R. B., S. P. Marshall, and P. T. Dix Arnold: Omasal function. J. Dairy Sci., *46*:835, 1963.

Bell, G. H., D. Emslie-Smith, and C. R. Paterson: *Textbook of Physiology and Biochemistry.* 9th ed. Baltimore, Williams and Wilkins, 1976.

Belling, T. H., Jr.: Bovine ovarian palpation I: normal ovaries. Veterinary Medicine, *59*:161, 1964.

Belling, T. H., Jr.: Bovine ovarian palpation II: abnormals and therapy. Veterinary Medicine, *59*:289, 1964.

Best, C. H. and N. B. Taylor: *The Living Body.* 5th ed. New York, Holt, Rinehart & Winston, 1973.

Bevelander, G.: *Outline of Histology.* 6th ed. St. Louis, C. V. Mosby, 1967.

Bloom, W. and D. Fawcett: *A Textbook of Histology.* 9th ed. Philadelphia, W. B. Saunders Co., 1968.

Boyd, W.: *A Textbook of Pathology.* 8th ed. Philadelphia, Lea & Febiger, 1970.

Bradley, J. V.: *Elementary Microstudies of Human Tissue.* Springfield, Ill., Charles C Thomas, 1972.

Bradley, O. C., revised by T. Grahame: *The Topographical Anatomy of the Head and Neck of the Horse.* 2nd ed. Edinburgh, W. Green & Son, Ltd., 1947.

Bradley, O. C., revised by T. Grahame: *The Topographical Anatomy of the Limbs of the Horse.* Edinburgh, W. Green & Son Ltd., 1946.

Bradley, O. C., revised by T. Grahame: *The Topographical Anatomy of the Thorax and Abdomen of the Horse.* Edinburgh, W. Green & Son Ltd., 1946.

Cassida, L. E.: Fertilization failure and embryonic death in domestic animals. *In* E. Engle (ed.): *Pregnancy Wastage.* Springfield, Ill., Charles C Thomas, 1953, pp. 27–37.

Cole, H. H., and P. T. Cupps: *Reproduction in Domestic Animals.* 3rd ed. Vol. I. New York, Academic Press, 1977.

Copenhaver, W. M., D. E. Kelley, and R. L. Wood: *Bailey's Textbook of Histology.* 17th ed. Baltimore, Williams & Wilkins, 1978.

Crosby, E., T. Humphrey, and E. W. Lauer: *Correlative Anatomy of the Nervous System.* New York, The Macmillan Co., 1962.

Crouch, J. E.: *Functional Human Anatomy.* 3rd ed. Philadelphia, Lea & Febiger, 1978.

Davenport, H. W.: *Physiology of the Digestive Tract.* 4th ed. Chicago, Year Book Medical Publishers, 1977.

Davenport, H. W.: *The ABC of Acid-Base Chemistry.* 6th ed. Chicago, The University of Chicago Press, 1974.

DeCoursey, R. M.: *The Human Organism.* 3rd ed. New York, McGraw-Hill Book Co., 1968.

DeRobertis, E. D. P., W. W. Nowinski, and F. A. Saez: *General Cytology.* 5th ed. Philadelphia, W. B. Saunders Co., 1970.

DeRobertis, E. D. P., F. A. Saez, and E. M. F. DeRobertis Jr.: *Cell Biology.* 6th ed. Philadelphia, W. B. Saunders Co., 1975.

Dukes's Physiology of Domestic Animals. See Swenson, M. J.

Dyce, K. M., and G. J. G. Wensing: *Essentials of Bovine Anatomy*. Philadelphia, Lea & Febiger, 1971.

Edwards, L. F., and G. R. L. Gaughran: *Concise Anatomy*. 3rd ed. New York, McGraw-Hill Book Co., Inc., 1971.

Elias, H., and J. E. Pauly: *Human Microanatomy*. 3rd ed. Philadelphia, F. A. Davis, 1966.

Ellenberger, W., H. Baum, and H. Dittrich: *An Atlas of Animal Anatomy for Artists*. 2nd ed. New York, Dover Publications, Inc., 1957.

Ellenberger, W., and H. Baum: *Handbuch der vergleichenden Anatomie der Haustiere*. 18th ed. Berlin, Springer, 1943.

Evans, H. E., and G. C. Christensen: Miller's Anatomy of the Dog. 2nd ed., Philadelphia, W. B. Saunders Co., 1979.

Evans, H. M., and H. H. Cole: *An Introduction to the Study of the Oestrous Cycle in the Dog*. Berkeley, University of California Press, 1931.

Finerty, J. C., and E. V. Cowdry: *A Textbook of Histology*. 5th ed. Philadelphia, Lea & Febiger, 1960.

Foust, H. L., and R. Getty: *Atlas and Dissection Guide for the Study of the Anatomy of Domestic Animals*. 3rd ed. Ames, Iowa, the Iowa State College Press, 1954.

Ganong, W. F.: *Review of Medical Physiology*. 8th ed. Los Altos, Lange Medical Publications, 1977.

Getty, R.: *Sisson and Grossman's Anatomy of the Domestic Animals*. 5th ed. Philadelphia. W. B. Saunders Co., 1975.

Getty, R.: The sense organs and integument. *In* Miller, Christensen, and Evans: *Anatomy of the Dog*. Philadelphia, W. B. Saunders Co., 1964, pp. 837–863.

Giese, A. C.: *Cell Physiology*. 4th ed. Philadelphia, W. B. Saunders Co., 1973.

Gilmore, J. P.: *Renal Physiology*, Baltimore, The Williams and Wilkins Co., 1972.

Goss, C. M. (ed.): *Anatomy of the Human Body* by Henry Gray. 29th American ed. Philadelphia, Lea & Febiger, 1973.

Grant, J. C. B.: *An Atlas of Anatomy*. 6th ed. Baltimore, Williams and Wilkins Co., 1972.

Greisheimer, E. M., and M. P. Wiedeman: *Physiology and Anatomy*. 9th ed. Philadelphia, J. B. Lippincott Co., 1972.

Gremmel, F.: Coat colors in horses. J. Heredity, *30*:437, 1939.

Grollman, S.: *The Human Body*. 4th ed. New York, The Macmillan Co., 1978.

Guyton, A. C.: *Physiology of the Human Body*. 5th ed. Philadelphia, W. B. Saunders Co., 1979.

Guyton, A. C.: *Textbook of Medical Physiology*. 5th ed. Philadelphia, W. B. Saunders Co., 1976.

Habel, R. E.: *Guide to the Dissection of Domestic Ruminants*. 2nd ed., Ithaca, Habel, 1970.

Hafez, E. S. E., (ed.): *Reproduction in Farm Animals*. 3rd ed., Philadelphia, Lea & Febiger, 1974.

Ham, A. W.: *Histology*. 7th ed. Philadelphia, J. B. Lippincott Co., 1974.

Herman, H. A., and F. W. Madden: *The Artificial Insemination of Dairy Cattle–A Handbook*. 2nd ed. New York, Lucas Bros., 1964.

Jenkins, T. W.: *Functional Mammalian Neuroanatomy*. 2nd ed. Philadelphia, Lea & Febiger, 1978.

Kitchell, R. L.: Introduction to the nervous system. *In* Miller, Christensen, and Evans: *Anatomy of the Dog*. Philadelphia, W. B. Saunders Co., 1964, pp. 464–479.

Kon, S. K., and A. T. Cowie: *Milk: The Mammary Gland and Its Secretions*. Vols. I. II. New York, Academic Press, 1961.

Langley, L. L.: *Outline of Physiology*. New York, McGraw-Hill Book Co., 1961.

Leach, W. J.: *Functional Anatomy: Mammalian and Comparative*. 3rd ed., New York, McGraw-Hill Book Co., Inc., 1961.

Leaf, A. and R. S. Cotran: *Renal Pathophysiology*. New York, Oxford University Press, 1976.

Mauger, H. M.: *An Introduction to Veterinary Anatomy*. 3rd ed. Columbus, Ohio, 1953.

May N. D. S.: *The Anatomy of the Sheep*. 3rd ed. Brisbane, University of Queensland Press, 1970.

Maynard, L. A., and J. K. Loosli: *Animal Nutrition*. 6th ed. New York, McGraw-Hill Book Co., Inc., 1969.

McGrath, J. T.: *Neurologic Examination of the Dog*. 2nd ed. Philadelphia, Lea & Febiger, 1960.

McLeod, W. M.: *Bovine Anatomy*. 2nd ed. Minneapolis, Burgess Pub. Co., 1958.

McNaught, A. B., and R. C. Callander: *Illustrated Physiology*. 3rd ed. Baltimore, Williams and Wilkins, 1975.

Meyer, H.: The brain. *In* Miller, Christensen, and Evans: *Anatomy of the Dog*, Philadelphia, W. B. Saunders Co., 1964, pp. 480–532.

Miller, M. E., G. C. Christensen, and H. E. Evans: *Anatomy of the dog*. Philadelphia, W. B. Saunders Co., 1964.

Miller, O. L., Jr.: The visualization of genes in action. Scientific American, *228*:34, 1973.

Mountcastle, V. B., (ed.): *Medical Physiology*. 2 vols., 13th ed. St. Louis, C. V. Mosby Co., 1974.

Nalbandov, A. V.: *Reproductive Physiology*. 2nd ed., San Francisco, W. H. Freeman & Co., 1964.

Nelson, O. E.: *Comparative Embryology of the Vertebrates*. New York, The Blakiston Co., 1960.

Netter, F. H.: *The CIBA Collection of Medical Illustrations*. Vol. I, Summit, New Jersey, CIBA-GEIGY, 1958, 1969.

Nickel, R., A. Schummer, and E. Seiferle: *Lehrbuch der Anatomie der Haustiere*. Berlin, Paul Parey, 1954.

Nomina Anatomica Veterinaria. 2nd ed. Vienna, World Association of Veterinary Anatomists, 1973.

Orten, J. M., and O. W. Neuhaus: *Human Biochemistry*. 9th ed. St. Louis, C. V. Mosby Co., 1975.

Patten, B. M.: *Embryology of the Pig*. 3rd ed. New York, McGraw-Hill Book Co., 1948.

Patten, B. M.: *Foundations of Embryology*. 2nd ed., New York, McGraw-Hill Book Co., 1964.

Patton, S.: Milk. Scientific American, *221*:58, 1969.

Perry, E. J., (ed.): *The Artificial Insemination of Farm Animals*. 4th ed. New Brunswick, Rutgers University Press, 1968.

Porter, K. R., and M. A. Bonneville: *Fine Structure of Cells and Tissues*. 4th ed. Philadelphia, Lea & Febiger, 1973.

Prosser, C. L. and F. A. Brown: *Comparative Animal Physiology*. 3rd ed. Philadelphia, W. B. Saunders Co., 1973.

Rasch, P. J., and R. K. Burke: *Kinesiology and Applied Anatomy*. 6th ed. Philadelphia, Lea & Febiger, 1978.

Roberts, S. J.: *Veterinary Obstetrics and Genital Diseases*. Ann Arbor, Edwards Bros., 1956.

Romer, A. S.: *The Vertebrate Body*. 4th ed. Philadelphia, W. B. Saunders Co., 1970.

Rooney, J. R. II, W. O. Sack, and R. E. Habel: *Guide to the Dissection of the Horse*. Ann Arbor, Edwards Brothers, Inc., 1967.

Ruch, T. C., and H. D. Patton (eds.): *Medical Physiology and Biophysics*. 20th ed. Philadelphia, W. B. Saunders Co., 1973 and 1979. (3 vols)

Rushmer, R. F.: *Cardiovascular Dynamics*. 4th ed. Philadelphia, W. B. Saunders Co., 1976.

St. Clair, L. E.: The nerve supply to the bovine mammary gland. American Journal of Veterinary Research, *3*:10, 1942.

Salisbury, G. W., and N. L. VanDemark: *Physiology of Reproduction and Artificial Insemination of Cattle*. San Francisco, W. H. Freeman & Co., 1961.

Sisson, S. and J. D. Grossman: *The Anatomy of the Domestic Animals*. 4th ed. Philadelphia, W. B. Saunders Co., 1953.

Smith, F.: *A Manual of Veterinary Physiology*. 4th ed. London, Balliere, Tindall, and Cox, 1912.

Somers, R. K.: *The Lymph Glands of Cattle, Hogs, and Sheep*. United States Department of Agriculture, Circular No. 866, Revised January, 1951, Washington, D.C.

Spector, W. S.: *Handbook of Biological Data*. Philadelphia, W. B. Saunders Co., 1956.

Steen, E. B., and A. Montague: *Anatomy and Physiology*. Vols. I–II. New York, Barnes & Noble, 1959.

Steindler, A.: *Kinesiology of the Human Body*. Springfield, Ill., Charles C Thomas, 1970.

Swenson, M. J., (ed.): *Dukes Physiology of Domestic Animals*. 9th ed. Ithaca, Cornell University Press, 1977.

Taylor, J. A.: *Regional and Applied Anatomy of the Domestic Animals*. Vol. 2. Philadelphia, J. B. Lippincott Co., 1959.

Thomas, B. A. (ed.): *Cytology*. A scope monograph. The Upjohn Co., 1973.

Trautmann, A. and J. Fiebiger: *Fundamentals of the Histology of Domestic Animals*. 9th ed. Ithaca, Comstock Publishing Associates, 1957.

Trum, B. F.: The estrous cycle of the mare. Cornell Veterinarian, *40*:17, 1950.

Turner, C. D. and J. T. Bagnara: *General Endocrinology*. 6th ed. Philadelphia, W. B. Saunders Co., 1976.

Turner, C. W.: *The Comparative Anatomy of the Mammary Glands*. Columbia, Missouri, Univ. Cooperative Store, 1939.

Turner, C. W.: *The Mammary Gland I: The Anatomy of the Udder of Cattle and Domestic Animals*, Columbia, Missouri, Lucas Bros., 1952.

Tuttle, W. W., and B. A. Schottelius: *Textbook of Physiology*. 16th ed. St. Louis, C. V. Mosby Co., 1969.

Upjohn Company: "On the biological significance of prostaglandins," 1973.

Vander, A. J.: *Renal Physiology*. 2nd ed. New York, McGraw-Hill Book Co., 1980.

Villee, C. A.: *The Placenta and Fetal Membranes*. Baltimore, Williams and Wilkins Co., 1960.

Willis, W. D. Jr. and R. G. Grossman: *Medical Neurobiology*. 2nd ed. St. Louis, C. V. Mosby Co., 1977.

Young, W. C. (ed.): *Sex and Internal Secretions*. 3rd ed. Baltimore, Williams and Wilkins Co., 1961.

Youngmans, W. B.: *Fundamentals of Human Physiology*. 2nd ed. Chicago, Year Book Medical Publishers, Inc., 1962.

Zietzschmann, O., and O. Krölling: *Lehrbuch der Entwicklung geschichte der Haustiere*. 2nd ed. Berlin, Paul Parey, 1955.

Index

Italicized figures indicate illustrations
Italicized words indicate approved form in *Nomina Anatomica Veterinaria*